ORGANOMETALLIC CHEMISTRY

Edited by

H. ZEISS

Research Associate
Monsanto Chemical Company
Dayton, Ohio

American Chemical Society
Monograph Series

REINHOLD PUBLISHING CORPORATION, NEW YORK

CHAPMAN & HALL, LTD., LONDON

Photocomposed by THE SCIENCE PRESS, INC., Lancaster, Pa.

Printed in the United States of America
THE GUINN CO., INC.
New York 14, N. Y.

CONTRIBUTORS

HERBERT C. BROWN, *Department of Chemistry, Purdue University, Lafayette, Indiana*

J. CHATT, *Akers Research Laboratories, Imperial Chemical Industries, Ltd., Welwyn, Herts., England*

G. E. COATES, *Chemistry Department, University of Durham, England*

HENRY GILMAN, *Department of Chemistry, Iowa State University, Ames, Iowa*

F. GLOCKLING, *Chemistry Department, University of Durham, England*

ROLF HUISGEN, *Institut für Organische Chemie, University of Munich, Germany*

H. D. KAESZ, *Department of Chemistry, Harvard University, Cambridge, Massachusetts*

P. L. PAUSON, *Department of Chemistry, Royal College of Science and Technology, Glasgow, Scotland*

JAMES W. RICHARDSON, *Department of Chemistry, Purdue University, Lafayette, Indiana*

F. G. A. STONE, *Department of Chemistry, Harvard University, Cambridge, Massachusetts*

L. M. VENANZI, *Chemistry Department, Oxford University, England*

HANS J. S. WINKLER, *Department of Chemistry, Iowa State University, Ames, Iowa*

H. ZEISS, *Research and Engineering Division, Monsanto Chemical Company, Dayton, Ohio*

KARL ZIEGLER, *Max-Planck-Institut für Kohlenforschung, Mülheim/Ruhr, Germany*

iii

GENERAL INTRODUCTION

American Chemical Society's Series of Chemical Monographs

By arrangement with the Interallied Conference of Pure and Applied Chemistry, which met in London and Brussels in July, 1919, the American Chemical Society was to undertake the production and publication of Scientific and Technologic Monographs on chemical subjects. At the same time it was agreed that the National Research Council, in cooperation with the American Chemical Society and the American Physical Society, should undertake the production and publication of Critical Tables of Chemical and Physical Constants. The American Chemical Society and the National Research Council mutually agreed to care for these two fields of chemical progress. The American Chemical Society named as Trustees, to make the necessary arrangements of the publication of the Monographs, Charles L. Parsons, secretary of the Society, Washington, D. C.; the late John E. Teeple, then treasurer of the Society, New York; and the late Professor Gellert Alleman of Swarthmore College. The Trustees arranged for the publication of the ACS Series of (a) Scientific and (b) Technological Monographs by the Chemical Catalog Company, Inc. (Reinhold Publishing Corporation, successor) of New York

The Council of the American Chemical Society, acting through its Committee on National Policy, appointed editors (the present list of whom appears at the close of this sketch) to select authors of competent authority in their respective fields and to consider critically the manuscripts submitted.

The first Monograph of the Series appeared in 1921. After twenty-three years of experience certain modifications of general policy were indicated. In the beginning there still remained from the preceding five decades a distinct though artibrary differentiation between so-called "pure science" publications and technologic or applied science literature. By 1944 this differentiation was fast becoming nebulous. Research in private enterprise had grown apace and not a little of it was pursued on the frontiers of knowledge. Furthermore, most workers in the sciences were coming to see the artificiality of the separation. The methods of both groups of workers are the same. They employ the same instrumentalities, and frankly recognize that their objectives are common, namely, the search for new knowledge for the service of man. The officers of the Society therefore combined the two editorial Boards in a single Board of twelve representative members.

Also in the beginning of the Series, it seemed expedient to construe rather broadly the definition of a Monograph. Needs of workers had to be recognized. Consequently among the first hundred Monographs appeared works in the form of treatises covering in some instances rather broad areas. Because such necessary works do not now want for publishers, it is considered advisable to hew more strictly to the line of the Monograph character, which means more complete and critical treatment of relatively restricted areas, and, where a broader field needs coverage, to subdivide it into logical subareas. The prodigious expansion of new knowledge makes such a change desirable.

These Monographs are intended to serve two principal purposes: first, to make available to chemists a thorough treatment of a selected area in form usable by persons working in more or less unrelated fields to the end that they may correlate their own work with a larger area of physical science discipline; second, to stimulate further research in the specific field treated. To implement this purpose the authors of Monographs are expected to give extended references to the literature. Where the literature is of such volume that a complete bibliography is impracticable, the authors are expected to append a list of references critically selected on the basis of their relative importance and significance.

PREFACE

The extraordinary convergence of organic and inorganic chemistry in the metallocene and metallarene structures has provided a new area of mutual interest shared by experimental and theoretical chemists alike. Yet this is only one of the truly exciting resurgences occurring in organometallic chemistry. The enthusiasm readily discernible in the communications appearing on this subject is documented by the rapidly increasing numbers of papers and scientists devoted to the study of the carbon-metal compounds. The universality of effort and the increase in scientific intercourse between inorganic and organic chemists permit the optimistic view that the artificial barriers which existed formerly between organic and physical disciplines are being leveled at this border also.

As is true in all fields undergoing rapid expansion, the problem of merely reporting significant advances is difficult enough. To attempt a critical evaluation of the accumulating data and results for inclusion in a permanent reference text is next to impossible at this stage. On the other hand, the chemical literate must be informed of new lines of progress having significance and, one hopes, major scientific merit. This latter consideration led to the present effort.

This monograph, then, is not a comprehensive survey of organometallic chemistry. In fact, it does not contain an exhaustive treatment of any one subject. It does consist of a series of research subjects which are *under active investigation—at the present time—by their respective authors*. Nor can it be claimed that the choice of subjects encompasses the entire reach of organometallic research. It is true, however, that the selection includes some of the chemical lodes currently producing new knowledge in prodigious quantity; and further, the information to be found in these pages is straight from the source. The intent of this monograph, therefore, is to bring to the graduate student and the more advanced chemist a reliable account of contemporary research in organometallic chemistry.

The arrangement of chapters in this volume is arbitrary and the responsibility of the editor. Little justification can be offered for the particular order chosen beyond the choice of the topic of "Carbon-Metal Bonding" for Chapter 1. In this case a consideration of the present state of theory regarding this type of chemical combination will be useful and rewarding when encountering the specific sigma- and pi-bonded compounds and complexes in subsequent chapters.

No attempt has been made to equate styles of presentation, since it is held that each author best knows how to present his own work. Indeed it is hoped that each chapter will delineate the character and personality of its author.

Finally, I wish to acknowledge personally my indebtedness to former students at Yale and to my associates, past and present, who have aided and in many ways stimulated and advanced my own interest in organo-metallic chemistry. I wish also to thank Eva J. Cox, Magdalene B. Peacock and Betty D. Zeiss for their invaluable assistance in preparing manuscript and reading proof.

Sulphur Grove, Ohio   HAROLD H. ZEISS
August, 1960

CONTENTS

1. CARBON-METAL BONDING

JAMES W. RICHARDSON

Purdue University, Lafayette, Indiana

INTRODUCTION

The major objective of this chapter is to collect together some of the more important points in the qualitative theoretical description of chemical bonds, especially as applied to such heteropolar systems as occur in organometallics. These principles are developed mostly in connection with problems associated with carbon compounds of transition elements, with, however, the general applicability of the discussion to other organometallics indicated from time to time.

The language developed in the discussion is mainly qualitative molecular orbital (MO) theory, although appropriate translation is occasionally made into the more familiar valence bond (VB) language. One of the hopes of this effort is that the newer MO viewpoint will enhance and complement present understanding in the area. The theoretical development begins with an analysis of bonding in HeH$^+$, in order to gain a feeling for the application of MO theory to the simplest heteropolar system. Basic principles developed there are applied to some nonorganic derivatives of transition elements and then successively to selected cyanide, carbonyl and cyclopentadienyl derivatives, thus furnishing a background for more specific applications in later chapters. Considerable detail is presented, which on first reading might be omitted. It is included not only to describe the diversity of bonding interactions present in transition metal compounds but also to indicate the way in which MO theory is used in such problems.

Various observations on bonding in those compounds are then collected and used to suggest some reasons why normal alkyl and aryl bonds had rarely been reported and to speculate about the conditions under which they are more stable.

For the sake of being specific, the discussion proceeds in terms of compounds of the first transition series only; but the same general description applies to the later series as well. Furthermore, not all types of transition metal-carbon systems are considered here. The significant omissions—particularly square planar complexes and the unusual bonds to ethylenic and acetylenic molecules—are analyzed, however, in later chapters in conjunc-

1

tion with their chemical properties. They represent direct applications of the bonding pictures presented in this chapter.

SINGLE BONDS, POLAR AND NONPOLAR

The chemistry of metal-carbon bonds is, by and large, the chemistry of heteropolar bonds; so it is well to begin by studying the simplest of them all, the bond in HeH^+.† In VB language the He to H bond is largely ionic, being best represented by the structure He: H^+, though there is some contribution from the covalent structure $(He—H)^+$. Thus the charge distribution in HeH^+ is rather like that in free He, there being only a moderate polarization toward the proton as represented by the covalent structure.

MO Description of HeH^+

An alternative description of the HeH^+ molecule is provided by the Coulson and Duncanson MO wave function (10) (some details of which are given later), from which a theoretical charge density may be calculated and compared with that for free He. The approximate contour maps are given in Fig. 1.1. From this drawing one can qualitatively view the bonding as a deformation of the He atom charge cloud caused by the approach of the proton.

The process of deformation can be described in another way. If the charge on the proton in the molecule were zero, then, of course, the electron distribution would be that of neutral He. As it is increased to 1 (i.e., as the electron affinity of the H center increases from 0) there is a continuous deformation to that indicated in Fig. 1.1 by the dashed line. If the charge at the proton center were to be increased still further to 2, then the electronic charge would become equally distributed between the two ends of the molecule; that is, the bond would become nonpolar (or completely covalent in VB language).

The concept of continuous change from extreme polarity to complete covalency is familiar in much of chemistry; it is to be emphasized that it applies equally to the chemistry of all bonding systems, including alkali halides, metal-carbon bonds and transition-metal complexes. The description of HeH^+ applies qualitatively as well to such a molecule as LiCl, for example. One might say that the Li^+ ion imbeds itself somewhat in the charge distribution of the Cl^- ion and causes some polarization in its

---

†For a similar treatment of the simplest homopolar molecule H_2^+, see the discussion in Coulson's book (9), p. 77. This book affords a more general introduction to the molecular orbital treatment of bonding and its comparison with valence bond theory.

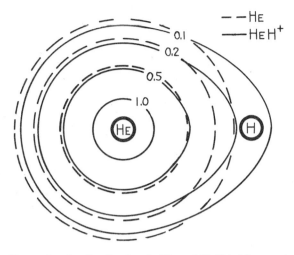

Fig. 1.1. Charge density distribution in He and HeH$^+$. The numbers assigned to the various charge density contour lines are on a relative scale. The internuclear distance is taken to be 0.8 Å, i.e., approximately at the calculated energy minimum.

direction, *or* that there is a small but significant covalent bonding. A similar sort of behavior might be expected in the Li—CH$_3$ bond, although the valence-shell charge density might well be shifted more to the Li in this case.

It is apparent even from Fig. 1.1, that dividing up the bond charge density into contributions from atoms at either end of the bond must be somewhat arbitrary, and, except for finer details, largely a matter of computational or descriptive convenience. In speaking of such division, one must keep firmly in mind the theoretical framework within which the discussion proceeds.

It is instructive to look a little deeper into the nature of the continuous deformation as revealed in the simple MO wave function. The coefficients in the ground state MO $\psi_{\text{HeH}+} = C_{\text{He}}(1s_{\text{He}}) + C_{\text{H}}(1s_{\text{H}})$, calculated by Coulson and Duncanson, give

$$\psi_{\text{HeH}^+} = 0.85(1s_{\text{He}}) + 0.25(1s_{\text{H}}). \tag{1.1}$$

If the molecule were completely polar (ionic) then C_{H} would be 0; if it were completely nonpolar (covalent) then C_{H} would equal C_{He}. The charge distribution corresponding to Eq. 1.1 is given by

$$\psi^2_{\text{HeH}^+} = 0.72(1s_{\text{He}})^2 + 0.22\frac{(1s_{\text{He}})(1s_{\text{H}})}{S} + 0.06(1s_{\text{H}})^2, \tag{1.2}$$

where $S = \int(1s_{\text{He}})(1s_{\text{H}})dv = 0.55$ is the overlap integral. This is to say that

72 per cent of the bonding electron density is "on" He, 6 per cent "on" H, and 22 per cent is "in" the normalized overlap distribution $(1/S)(1s_{He})(1s_H)$. It is this last-mentioned amount of charge which may be thought of as holding the molecule together, and to which the bond energy is roughly proportional.

Aside from the nuclear repulsion, the calculated total energy of the molecule is the sum of the energies of these three charge distributions weighted by the coefficients in Eq. 1.2, which have been so determined as to minimize the calculated total energy. The energy of each charge distribution is composed of (a) its kinetic energy, (b), the potential energy arising from attractions by the two nuclei, and (c) the potential energy arising from repulsions by all other electronic charge distributions. (For systems containing more than two electrons there is a fourth contribution, the exchange energy, which in effect reduces the repulsion between electrons of the same spin. The only time this quantity must be considered explicitly here is in connection with the magnetic properties of the transition metal compounds.) Once the atomic orbitals $(1s_{He})$ and $(1s_H)$ have been chosen, the kinetic energy of each of the three charge distributions is fixed. The net potential energy of each charge distribution is influenced in the following ways:

1. lowered by + charge of He core (nucleus) and raised by other electron density "on" He;
2. lowered by + charge of H core (nucleus) and raised by other electron density "on" H;
3. raised by (other) electron density in the overlap region.

The Antibonding Wave Function

Using the wave function (Eq. 1.1) and after a certain amount of mathematical exercise, the magnitude of each of the energy terms may be evaluated and the coefficients C_{He} and C_H obtained for the energy minimum. In addition to that wave function, however, there is also obtained an approximation to the first excited MO ψ^*, which is described as antibonding, or repulsive, in character; any electron in it would *tend* to cause the molecule to dissociate. These antibonding solutions are of no immediate importance in describing the chemical properties of metal-carbon bond systems, *except* in the very important case of transition metal compounds.

ψ^* has the form $0.83(1s_{He}) - 1.13(1s_H)$; the charge density derived from this function is given in Fig. 1.2 in a manner corresponding to that for ψ in Fig. 1.1. The antibonding character is related to the low charge density in the region between the nuclei, which arises from the overlap contribution being negative in this case. The most striking difference between ψ^2 and ψ^{*2} is that the polarity of one is rather opposite to that of the other; the difference would be much more extreme were the overlap integral S

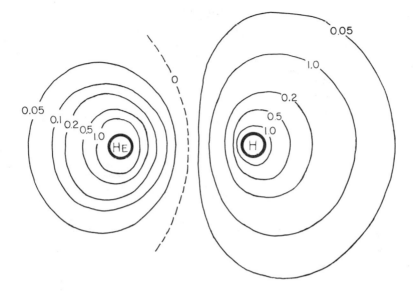

Fig. 1.2. Charge density distribution in the antibonding MO of HeH⁺. The numbers assigned to the various contour lines are on the same relative scale as in Fig. 1.1.

smaller. The wave functions ψ and ψ^* for HeH⁺ may be used to estimate also the charge distribution in HeH. Here the estimated total charge distribution would result from adding twice the distribution of Fig. 1.1 to that of Fig. 1.2, since in the ground state of HeH there would be two electrons in an orbital described by ψ and one electron in an orbital described by ψ^*.

Correlation Diagram

A convenient summary of the relative energy effects can be obtained from the so-called correlation diagram, which for HeH is given in Fig. 1.3. The vertical scale measures energy from an arbitrary zero. Roughly speaking, the line at the left of the diagram represents the energy of one electron in a $1s_H$ orbital in the field of all the other charges in the molecule. The line to the right is the similar quantity for one electron in a $1s_{He}$ orbital. That the energy for $1s_{He}$ [$E(1s_{He})$] lies below that for $1s_H$ [$E(1s_H)$] on the diagram is another way of saying that He⁺ is more electronegative than H⁺. The energy difference Δ is roughly determined by the electronegativity difference, but allowance must be made for the occurrence of formal charge in polar systems. An electron in $1s_{He}$ becomes stabilized by an amount E_B when the small amount of $1s_H$ character is added to it. Calculation of E_B by these approximations reveals that E_B varies directly with S and in-

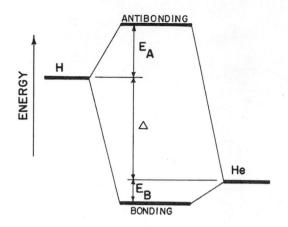

Fig. 1.3. Energy level correlation diagram for HeH molecule.

versely with Δ; i.e., that bond stabilization is favored by greater overlap of the bonding orbitals, but lessened by greater electronegativity difference. It must be emphasized, however, that E_B does not represent the *total* dissociation energy, but—roughly speaking—only that portion which is *not* due to simple electrostatic attraction between ions in the molecule. This conclusion follows from the construction of $E(1s_H)$ and $E(1s_{He})$, by which they already largely contain the "ionic" energy among other terms; E_B mainly represents additional "delocalization" energy.

A similar discussion applies to the quantity E_A of Fig. 1.3. An electron in ψ^* is *destabilized* by an amount E_A proportional to E_B. In a great many cases, like the present, "antibondingness" is a direct reflection of (and, in fact, because of the way in which S enters, a magnification of) "bondingness." This observation is of relevance to the discussion of compounds of transition elements which follows.

OCTAHEDRAL TRANSITION-METAL COMPLEXES

With the basic principles of the last section in mind, it is now possible to gain some qualitative understanding of bonding in the simpler transition-metal complexes and then in various transition metal-carbon bond systems.† Limiting attention to valence-shell AOs in an octahedral prototype

†The most familiar description of the electronic structure of transition metal complexes, of course, follows the original hybrid-orbital valence-bond theory; see Pauling (*32*). More recently the crystal field model of the physicists has been revived and, with some necessary modifications, renamed "ligand field theory." This theory is a specialization of the more general MO theory presented here. It focusses

complex MX_6 of a first row transition element M and making use of the restrictions symmetry places upon the MO wave function, it is quickly found that the *qualitative* discussion of the electronic structure of MX_6 is no more complicated than that of HeH^+. In the discussion immediately following, X may be a halogen or perhaps a group like H_2O, NH_3 or even CH_3.

Orbitals for Octahedral Complexes

Viewing the formation of MOs in MX_6 as the "fusion" of the various $3d$, $4s$ and $4p$ AOs of M onto orbitals of all the ligands, there will arise one bonding and one antibonding MO from every metal and ligand orbital pair. Some notion of the possible wave functions and orbital charge distributions can be gained from Fig. 1.4, wherein the various metal orbitals are shown together with the particular arrangement of ligand orbitals onto which each "fuses." Bonding MOs result from addition, and antibonding MOs from subtraction, of the metal AO from the ligand orbital combination.

Because of the symmetry of the system, certain sets of MOs behave in exactly the same way (that is, are degenerate) and differ *only* by some spatial transformation. Specifically, the MOs derived from the three different metal $4p$ orbitals are related by the interchange of the coördinate axes; the same situation holds also with respect to three of the five $3d$ orbitals, $3d_{xy}$, $3d_{xz}$, and $3d_{yz}$. The other two $3d$ orbitals $3d_{x^2-y^2}$ and $3d_{z^2}$ are also degenerate; the spatial transformation relating this pair is merely a little more involved than with the others.

As can be seen from Fig. 1.4, the σ-type bonding in MX_6 arises from the $3d_{x^2-y^2}$ and $3d_{z^2}$, the $4s$ and the $4p$'s. This set of orbitals is in fact the basis for the d^2sp^2 hybrid orbital combination used in the valence bond description of these complexes. The π-type bonding arises from the remaining $3d$ AOs and from an additional interaction with the $4p$'s. If π-bonding is either neglected or absent, then these last-mentioned MOs are absent, and only a *non-bonding* set of three $3d$ AOs is left.

Complexes with Simple Ligands

The correlation diagram for this latter situation is depicted in Fig. 1.5. It is apparent after a moment's inspection that this diagram simply repre-

attention almost entirely upon the valence-shell *d*-orbitals of the transition metal atom and treats the metal-ligand interaction *as if* it were purely electrostatic in nature, although this restriction is generally relaxed afterwards. For a survey of the details and applications of ligand field theory, reviews by Orgel (*30*) and Griffith and Orgel (*16*) and the text by Basolo and Pearson (*3*) may be consulted.

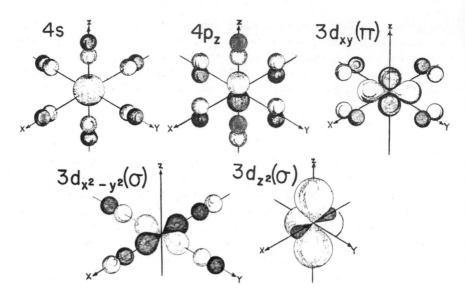

Fig. 1.4. Atomic orbital combinations for MOs in octahedral complexes. Shaded lobes are negative, and unshaded lobes positive, regions of the atomic orbital wave functions. Just one of each of the $4p$ and $3d\pi$ triplets is shown; the others are related to these by a simple rotation of $90°$ about the x or y axes. For example, the MO derived from $4p_x$ is obtained by rotating the *entire* collection of orbitals $90°$ around the y axis. Only the shape of the $3d_{z^2}$ orbital is shown. It interacts with σ orbitals along all six axes, but with double weight to those along the z axis, to compensate for that deficiency in the $3d_{x^2-y^2}$ orbital degenerate with it.

sents the superposition of correlation diagrams for each of the metal-ligand orbital pairs and each one constructed according to the principles laid down in the discussion of HeH$^+$. The relative energy positions of the metal and of the ligand orbitals again is not determined solely by the energy of the electrons (or electronegativity) of each *isolated* part of the molecule, but also by localized charges in other parts. Still, with increasing charge on the metal atom, those energies will go down relative to the ligands and the bonding will become less polar, as in Fig. 1.5a.

Occupation of the various orbitals is indicated by the state of the circles drawn in the lines corresponding to the MO energy levels in the center of each diagram. Filled circles are MOs always occupied, in most cases by the coördination electrons brought up by the ligand groups. Open circles are MOs normally unoccupied in the ground state. Half-filled circles represent MOs—usually rather metallic in character—occupied by whatever valence electrons there were on the metal ion. This last-mentioned set of MOs contains the electrons which give to the transition metal compounds their many intriguing spectral, magnetic and chemical properties.

If some of the ligands were groups like methyl, then in contrast with electron-pair donor ligands such as ammonia, one valence electron on the metal must pair up with the odd electron of the methyl group in one of the bonding MOs. As extreme examples $Co(CH_3)_6^0$ and $Cu(CH_3)_6^{+2}$, if they could be prepared, would not only be isoelectronic with $Cr(NH_3)_6^{+3}$ but also would have parallel magnetic and spectral properties. In like manner, then $Cr(OH_2)_5CH_3^{+2}$ (the benzyl and dichloromethyl analogs of which *have* been reported) should have properties similar to $V(OH_2)_6^{+2}$; both are rather unstable, which is no particular confirmation. However, one might expect $Mn(OH_2)_5CH_3^{+3}$ to have properties and stabilities similar to $Cr(OH_2)_6^{+3}$. In comparing thermodynamic stabilities here it is probably more important for the species to have the same net charge, than for them to have exactly the same number of electrons. Indeed, the presence of somewhat different numbers of electrons in the non-bonding $3d\pi$ AOs should not be too significant in *this* regard.

Usual ligands have π-type electrons as well as σ-type coordination electrons and thus there will be further interaction—beyond those indicated in Fig. 1.5—with the $3d\pi$ orbitals of the metal. If, however, the ligand π orbitals are preoccupied in other bonding (as in the cases of NH_3, CH_3, and one $2p\pi$ AO in H_2O) then to the extent that hyperconjugation is

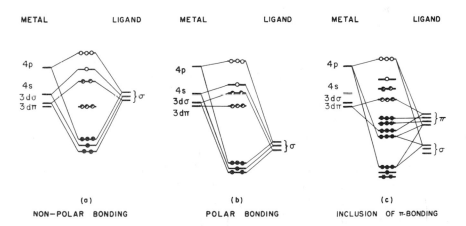

Fig. 1.5. Energy level diagrams for simple MX_6 transition metal complexes. The circles represent electron orbitals. Filled circles are orbitals always occupied by electron pairs; open circles are antibonding orbitals always vacant. Half-filled circles are orbitals which may be vacant, half- or doubly-occupied, depending upon the particular metal ion involved, and upon the magnetic state it is in.

negligible, the $3d\pi$'s remain non-bonding. Otherwise (with ligands like O^{-2}, F^-, OH^- or the other $2p\pi$ AO in H_2O) ligand lone-pair π electrons become somewhat stabilized and the metal $3d\pi$ electrons somewhat more destabilized.

With metals at the end of each transition series there frequently occur complexes with a square planar configuration of ligands. While this case does not contribute to the main line of development in this chapter, it does arise in application of the theory to some specific complexes treated in Chapter 10. Appropriate orbital and correlation diagrams are presented there. The removal of a pair of opposite ligands in an octahedral complex yields the square planar complex, splits up the energies of the various degenerate MOs and also causes a mixing of the interactions of the metal $3d_{z^2}$ and $4s$ AOs.

Unsaturated Ligands—$Fe(CN)_6^{-4}$

The preceding considerations are satisfactory for the first row saturated ligands mentioned. But with heavier analogs of them or with unsaturated ligands there are additional fairly low-lying orbitals which probably influence mainly π-type metal ligand bonding. These additional orbitals may be extravalent d orbitals on a halogen for example or may be a π^* (antibonding) MO of an unsaturated ligand. This further and rather important additional type of interaction will be illustrated by a consideration of the electronic structure of $Fe(CN)_6^{-4}$.

The cyanide ion electrons include a lone pair in something like an s-$p\sigma$ hybrid projecting well out from the carbon toward the metal and two pairs in the bonding π_{CN} MOs between C and N. Explicit interactions with other electrons are neglected. But also to be considered are the next highest *unoccupied antibonding* π_{CN}^* MOs between C and N. These MOs probably lie at least 5 ev above the ground state. The probable relative location of metal and ligand orbitals and the essential features of a reasonable correlation diagram (including occupation of the MOs) are given in Fig. 1.6. Because of strong overlap of the CN lone-pair electrons with the metal $3d\sigma$, $4s$ and $4p\sigma$ AOs there is probably rather strong bonding (and also antibonding with $3d\sigma$) in the sigma system, with the consequent transfer of considerable electron density to the metal. If there were no π^*_{CN} orbitals, then the equal occupation of the bonding and antibonding (dashed level of Fig. 1.6) orbitals produced by the $3d\pi$ interaction would result in a net repulsive contribution to the total energy and no net charge transferred one way or the other. But, the mixing of π^*_{CN} character into the otherwise antibonding π MOs doubtless decreases or even removes the antibonding character between metal and carbon. A likely description of the two occupied π MOs is indicated in Fig. 1.7. The lower diagram represents one of the lowest π MOs which contains some mixing of the $3d\pi$ AO with the π MO of the CN. This may be thought of as the analog of the $^-$Fe—C≡N: valence bond structure. The upper diagram of Fig. 1.7 then represents the next higher π MO, assuming rather extensive interaction with $\pi*_{CN}$ and is the analog of the Fe=C=N̈:$^-$ valence bond structure.

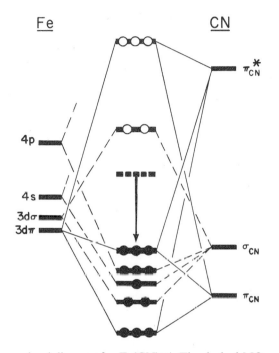

Fig. 1.6. Energy level diagram for Fe(CN)$_6^{-4}$. The dashed MO energy level corresponds to the approximate position of the second highest π-type MO, in the absence of interaction from $\pi*_{CN}$. Quite extensive $\pi*_{CN}$ interaction is assumed, and this particular MO is shown actually as bonding.

The lowest π MO, like all the σ MOs, brings charge to the metal, part of which then is returned to the ligand via interaction with $\pi*_{CN}$ in the next higher occupied π MO. Thus, despite a probable high degree of covalency in *all* the bond orbitals, the metal still can retain a somewhat positive formal charge.

This back donation can occur whenever there are electrons in the $3d\pi$ AOs; Cr(CN)$_6^{-3}$ is an example wherein a single electron, instead of an electron pair, occupies each of the three MOs involved in "back bonding."

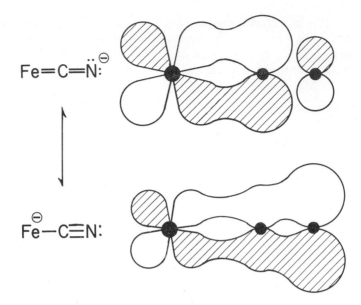

$$Fe = C = \overset{..}{N} \overset{\ominus}{:}$$

$$\overset{\ominus}{Fe} - C \equiv N:$$

Fig. 1.7. π-bonding MOs in octahedral CN complexes. The shape of the MOs along only one metal-CN bond axis is shown. The lower diagram corresponds to the lowest energy π MO; the upper to the middle-energy π MO, assuming rather extensive π^*_{CN} interaction. To the left are drawn the resonance structures most nearly analogous; note that only the distributions of the two pairs of electrons which resonate between the Fe—C and the C—N bond are to be compared.

CARBONYL COMPOUNDS

Since electronically CO is presumably quite similar to CN^-,† many of the same principles of bonding are applicable in the discussion of carbonyl compounds. Among the important differences which do arise, however, are the absence of appreciable localized charge and in some cases altered geometry. The discussion of $Cr(CO)_6$, for example, closely parallels that of the isostructural $Fe(CN)_6^{-4}$; however, since Cr enters the molecule as a neutral atom, it probably "demands" less charge from the CO groups in the bonding orbitals and therefore likewise returns less through "back bonding." Hence, it is reasonable to expect that the metal-carbon bond order is less in $Cr(CO)_6$ than in $Fe(CN)_6^{-4}$.

Correlation Diagram for Ni(CO)₄

The tetrahedral carbonyls present a rather different correlation diagram,

† Additional details regarding the MO description of the CO molecule have been given, e.g., by Coulson (9), p. 211, and Sahni (36).

since the molecular symmetry places entirely different restrictions upon the wave functions. In fact, the orbitals which were π-bonding to octahedral ligands ($3d_{xy}$, $3d_{xz}$, and $3d_{yz}$) become mainly σ bonding in tetrahedral compounds and $3d_{z^2}$ and $3d_{x^2-y^2}$ become entirely π-bonding.

A reasonable correlation diagram for $Ni(CO)_4$ is drawn in Fig. 1.8. Its somewhat more complicated appearance arises from the fact that the various AOs from which the MOs are constructed are resolved into fewer non-interacting groups in the tetrahedral symmetry. Specifically, each of

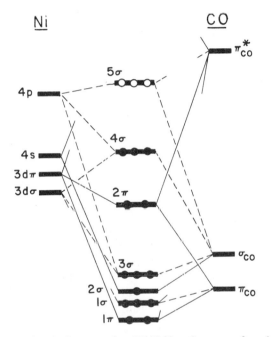

Fig. 1.8. Energy level diagram for $Ni(CO)_4$. See text for the identification scheme for the various MOs.

the $3d\sigma$ AOs now mixes not only with one of the $4p$'s and with the lone pair σ orbitals on the carbons, but also to some extent with both π_{CO} and π^*_{CO} ligand MOs. The relative orientation of these five orbitals along one bond axis is indicated in Fig. 1.9a. It is apparent from this drawing that, from a geometrical standpoint, the bonding is as much π as σ in character and that it is somewhat misleading to call the MOs produced "σ" MOs. Indeed, the terminology has already been strained in application to these nonlinear molecules. For the sake of avoiding the introduction of further terminology and of making clear the distinction from the other π interactions, however, the MOs produced from these interactions will be called

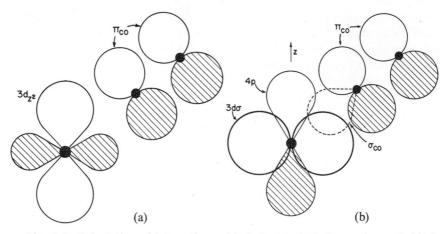

Fig. 1.9. Orientation of interacting orbitals in tetrahedral complexes. Orbitals from only one ligand are shown. Hatched areas are negative parts of the orbitals.

σ in the following discussion. Together with the *bona-fide* σ-type bonding MO resulting from $4s$ interacting with the σ_{CO} orbitals, these σ MOs will for clarity be numbered in order of increasing energy as indicated in Fig. 1.8; the lowest four are occupied.

It seems likely that most of the π_{CO} character is localized in 1σ and that 3σ and 4σ are largely composed of $3d\sigma$, $4p$ and σ_{CO} for the situation depicted in Fig. 1.8 with $4p$ energetically lower than π^*_{CO}. The case of the reverse ordering will be briefly considered later. The $3d\pi$ AOs interact only with π_{CO} and π^*_{CO}. The orientation of $3d_{z^2}$ with respect to one of the ligand π orbitals is shown in Fig. 1.9b; the arrangement with $3d_{x^2-y^2}$ (not shown) appears rather different, though it is exactly equivalent energetically.

In Fig. 1.8 and in the discussion which follows, all non-bonding combinations of ligand π orbitals will be ignored.

Sigma Bonding Systems

The third and fourth lowest MOs of Fig. 1.8 (2σ and 3σ) [which would correspond largely to the sd^3 tetrahedral hybrids of valence bond theory mixed with the ligand σ orbitals] give rise to the basic σ-bonding in the molecule. But also must be considered the 4σ MOs, which are occupied as well. If there were no contribution of π^*_{CO} or of $4p$ AOs, the 4σ MOs would be almost completely antibonding and the return of electron density to the CO groups would cancel the donation of density to the metal in 3σ, just as would have been the case with the π system of $Fe(CN)_6^{-4}$ in the absence of π^*_{CN} acceptor orbitals on the ligand. In the present case, however, additional mixture to 4σ is expected mainly of $4p$ character serving to reduce somewhat the return of σ-electron density to the CO groups. And, what is more important, this admixture probably serves also to decrease considerably the antibonding repulsive character of 4σ. Thus there might well be expected a moderate net bond stabilization and a small accumulation of charge on the metal due to the *combined* effect of 1σ, 3σ and 4σ (which arise from the $3d$ and $4p$ orbitals), added to comparable effects due to the 2σ MO (which arises from the $4s$ orbitals).

Parenthetically, it might be pointed out that a repulsive tendency, inherent here in the 4σ MO, does not arise in an octahedral system such as $Cr(CO)_6$, mentioned earlier. There *all* σ interactions lead to stabilization, and it is reasonable to expect on this basis that $Cr(CO)_6$ would be more stable thermodynamically than $Ni(CO)_4$, even on a *per bond* basis.

Pi Bonding Systems

With respect to π bonding in tetrahedral carbonyls, the situation is exactly analogous to that in octahedral cyanides. Without π^*_{CO} acceptor orbitals, the bonding stabilization in 1π would be overridden by the antibonding destabilization in 2π, with no net transfer of charge one way or the other. But again the π^*_{CO} admixture to 2π very likely serves markedly to lower its energy, probably giving a *net* stabilization from π bonding as indicated in Fig. 1.8 and at the same time effecting a net removal of charge from the metal. Note again that the increase in bond order between metal and carbon occurs simultaneously with a decrease in bond order between carbon and oxygen; in fact one effect is an approximate measure of the other.

The extent of admixture of π^*_{CO} to 4σ and 2π depends on, among other things, the energy separation between the $3d$ AOs of the metal and the π^*_{CO} orbitals. As pointed out in the earlier discussion of bonding in HeH^+, the relative positioning of these orbital energies depends upon a number of factors including the electron attracting ability of the respective groups and the presence of localized charges in the molecule. If, by some means or other, the energies of the metal orbitals are raised with respect to that of π^*_{CO}, (all other factors being constant) then the contribution of π^*_{CO} to 2π and 4σ will increase, the strength of the metal-carbon bond will tend to increase, while that of the carbon-oxygen bond will decrease. Edgell (*12*), in developing a general MO description of the bonding based upon symmetry considerations in $Ni(CO)_4$ and the ions $Co(CO)_4^-$ and $Fe(CO)_4^{-2}$ isoelectronic with it, has pointed out that this particular alteration would likely occur in this sequence if the excess charge were mainly located on the metal. (This conclusion follows from the argument that excess negative charge on the metal would be more effective in repelling, i.e. raising the energy of, electrons "on" the metal than those "on" the more distant CO groups.)

This analysis of the bonding, including the location of the excess charge, is quite compatible with the interpretation of the vibrational spectra of these three molecules by Edgell and co-workers (*12*), who find that in the order $Ni(CO)_4$, $Co(CO)_4^-$ and $Fe(CO)_4^-$ the stretching force constants of the metal-carbon bonds increase and those of the carbon-oxygen bonds decrease. In other words, these data do tend to confirm the hypothesis that as formal charge builds up on the metal atom "back bonding" *via* the π system increasingly tends to remove it; the metal-carbon bond becomes stronger, and the carbon-oxygen bond becomes weaker.

One further point of clarification is necessary, however. As the metal orbitals are raised in energy with respect to those of the ligand then, of course, the probable net strength of the occupied σ MOs ought to decrease. Therefore, to account for the experimental data, it must be assumed also that the σ-bond energy increases at a greater rate than the π-bond energy decreases in passing through the sequence Ni to Fe.

If these last-mentioned rates of bond energy change were assumed reversed, then as an alternate explanation of the data one would have to consider the opposite situation: that the excess charge rests mainly on the CO groups and that *they* are raised in energy with respect to the metal. By hypothesis this would result in increasing σ-bond strength, as the data indicate.

However, this process removes from the CO groups only what are essentially lone pair electrons i.e., essentially *non-bonding* between carbon and oxygen; hence there should not be expected any significant change in the strength of the CO bond—in contrast to the observed weakening.

Thus the more reasonable interpretation would seem to be that the excess charge in the negative ions resides mostly on the metal atom, and so the first explanation of the variation of bonding with excess charge is preferred.

Charge Distribution in $Ni(CO)_4$

With the preceding considerations in hand, then, it becomes possible to shed some light on a problem long recognized in the theory of bonding in this type of system, namely, how the neutral species Ni and CO can interact to form a stable molecule without violating the reasonable assumption that there is not a build-up of considerable charge separation in the molecule. It should be noted that charge transfer itself is not a necessary condition for stable bond formation. It is only suggested in the present case by the presumption of the simple valence bond theory that the important resonance structure is

$$: O\equiv C^+ - \overset{\displaystyle \overset{..}{\underset{|}{O}} \atop \overset{|||}{\underset{|}{C}}}{\underset{\displaystyle \overset{|}{\underset{|||}{C^+}} \atop \underset{..}{O}}{Ni^{-4}}} - C^+\equiv O :, \qquad (I)$$

representing the *coördination* of the CO lone pairs into the vacant tetrahedral $4s4p^3$ hybridized orbitals and thus imparting a –4 formal charge to the Ni. However, since there are only two occupied $3d$ orbitals of the strongly π bonding type, back-bonded structures such as (II)

$$: O\equiv C^+ - \overset{\displaystyle \overset{..}{\underset{|}{O}} \atop \overset{|||}{\underset{|}{C^+}}}{\underset{\displaystyle \overset{||}{C} \atop \underset{..}{O:}}{Ni^{-2}}} = C = \overset{..}{O} :, \qquad (II)$$

may be more important than (I). In these structures, though, Ni carries a –2 formal charge, which is disturbingly large. Of course there are a wide variety of other resonance structures—among them no-bond and other types of π back-bonded structures—which would reduce the formal charge also, but which only an extended calculation would provide the proper mixture.

A second feature of the bonding worth noting at this point is the dissociation energy ΔH^0_{298} of 140 kcal/mole (*13,37*) according to the equation

$$Ni(CO)_{4(g)} \longrightarrow Ni_{(g)} + 4CO_{(g)}.$$

The total energy per Ni—CO bond therefore is 35 kcal, which is a rather small value and which, it may be noted, is less than similar values for the methyl derivatives of metals to the right of Ni in the Periodic Table (*24*). Taken *by itself*, the bond energy hardly implies significant multiple bond character in the carbonyls. The fact remains that the Ni—CO bond is energetically rather weak.

As presently constituted, the MO discussion above lacks sufficient quantitative character, which again can be provided only by quite extensive calculation, to predict the detailed characteristics of the bonding. However, accepting as requirements upon the wave functions the reasonable assumption of approximate electroneutrality and the observation of moderate bond energy, it is possible to show how the MO theory may provide a satisfactory description of the molecule and to use those requirements in making some rough and tentative predictions regarding the bond character.

The preceding MO discussion of $Ni(CO)_4$ will now be summarized in a more specific form with those requirements in mind. The quantitative statements given are quite approximate and have been guided by some *very rough* calculations in addition to the principles already given.

(1) The $4s$ AO partakes in bonding with one particular combination of ligand lone pair orbitals, resulting in the accumulation of about 0.5 unit of electron charge on Ni and a relatively small energy stabilization as usual bond energies go—perhaps the order of 30 kcal. Both quantities are small because of the relatively large energy separation between the $4s$ and the lone-pair electrons of the ligand, as indicated in Fig. 1.8.

(2) The triplets of $3d\sigma$ and of $4p$ interact with the remaining three combinations of CO lone-pair electrons, forming the 3σ and 4σ MOs, with two major results. (a) 3σ is moderately strongly bonding, and 4σ is greatly reduced in antibonding character by the very important mixing in of the $4p$ AOs. The combined contribution of each of these three pairs of MOs to the total energy is thus probably somewhat bonding and even their combined contribution with 1σ may well be about that obtained from the electron pair in 2σ discussed in (1). (b) Estimating the amount of charge transferred to the metal in 1σ, 3σ and 4σ is more hazardous in the absence of detailed calculations, but a contribution of 1 to 1.5 units to an excess of electron density "on Ni" is both reasonable according to the rough computations and compatible with the final result. This acquisition of excess negative charge is the price Ni must pay to reduce the repulsion otherwise present in 4σ.

(3) Because the energy separation between the $3d\pi$ AOs and the π_{CO} orbitals is greater than the separation between the $3d\sigma$ AOs and σ_{CO} orbitals, as indicated in Fig. 8, 1π is probably less bonding than either 2σ or 3σ. But, considering among other things rough estimates of the $3d\pi$ AO overlap with π_{CO} relative to that with π^*_{CO}, it is reasonable to conclude that 2π is also moderately bonding. The net effect of the four electron pairs in 1π and 2π may therefore be supposed to provide the remainder of the bond energy. Furthermore, to the extent that stabilization of 2π is proportional to the charge withdrawn to the CO groups, this π back-bonding would withdraw somewhat more charge from Ni than was deposited there by the action of 3σ and 4σ, and approximately also compensate for the charge deposited on Ni by 1σ, thus preserving reasonable electroneutrality.

Bond Orders in $Ni(CO)_4$

The over-all bond energy by this analysis comes approximately half from the σ bonding and half from the π bonding. One might translate the conclusions regarding charge transfers into the statement that the net bond strength is as if the bond order between Ni and each CO were a trifle less than 1, being composed of nearly equal amounts of σ and π character. The resulting π bond order in each CO group then lies in the neighborhood of 1.7. These conclusions about π bond order agree rather well with the opinion of Cable and Sheline (5), who place the Ni—C and C—O π bond orders at about 0.5 and 1.5, respectively. There is disagreement, however, about the metal-carbon σ bond order. Cable and Sheline regard the σ bond order as 1, and the resulting total bond order of 1.5 as compatible with the observation that the Ni—C bond is 0.1 Å shorter than the sum of the covalent radii. Even neglecting the uncertainty in the appropriate covalent radius for Ni, however, a fair share of the apparent contraction may be due to a decreased "radius" of C in CO with change in hybridization. Just as well, on the other hand, it could be argued (as Cable and Sheline admit) that comparing Edgell's (12) most recent determination of the metal-carbon force constant in $Ni(CO)_4$ (1.98×10^5 dynes/cm) to that in $Ge(CH_3)_4$ (2.72×10^5 dynes/cm) (5) supports the present contention that the *net* Ni—C bond order is more nearly 1 (if not less).

This downgrading of the importance of σ bonding relative to π bonding is in accord, for example, with the observations made by Nyholm and Short (29) who found that replacement of a CO group in $Ni(CO)_4$ occurs only when the substituting group also can form π-type bonds with the metal. Nyholm and Short suggest that this critical influence of π-type bonding is best described by a fully double-bonded structure

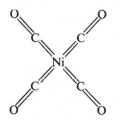

(III)

which implies equal weights for σ and π bonding between metal and carbon. The same *relative* importance of σ- and π-type contributions has been obtained here. Essentially what has been suggested in this regard is that a better estimate of σ and π character is had by *decreasing* the σ-bond character expressed in resonance structure II, rather than *increasing* the π-bond character.

It will be noted from the preceding section that the postulated amount of charge returned to the CO groups by π back bonding is rather close both to the limit imposed by resonance structure II and to the less definite (though perhaps somewhat greater) limit which might reasonably be deduced from the MO correlation diagram. It finally then should be indicated how this analysis of bonding would be extended to $Co(CO)_4^-$ and $Fe(CO)_4^{-2}$. If, as the metal orbital energies rise with respect to the ligands, the level of the $4p$ passes that of π^*_{CO}, it is reasonable to expect a reversal of the roles of $4p$ and π^*_{CO} in influencing the character of 4σ. If so, then a large fraction of the amount of charge which $4p$ formerly retained now passes to the ligand and specifically into the π^*_{CO} orbitals. Thus, in this particular region of relative energies, there might be expected a marked increase in metal-carbon bond order and a corresponding decrease in the carbon-oxygen bond order, accompanying the delocalization of the excess net charge. This variation would, of course, be superimposed upon the other (and probably smaller) changes—involving the lower-energy MOs— already discussed. As a rough guess, it might be supposed that by means of these various processes a third of the net excess charge resides on the CO groups.

It is interesting to observe how diversified the π-type interactions can become in tetrahedral systems. Giacometti (15) had shown earlier that what here are called $3d\sigma$ AOs can be involved in resonance structures encompassing three metal-carbon π bonds, enhancing thereby the return of charge to the CO groups. What has been indicated here is in more detail how and to what extent this additional interaction might be important.

BIS-CYCLOPENTADIENYL COMPOUNDS

The amazing rate at which the area opened by the preparation of ferrocene $Fe(C_5H_5)_2$ by Kealy and Pauson (20) has expanded needs no further comment here. This original discovery has led to the preparation of analogs of ferrocene covering the whole transition series, to their ions, to similar benzene compounds and to mixed derivatives with CO groups. Their various unusual properties begin with their geometry—the now familiar "sandwich" configuration, wherein the metal atom lies symmetrically between the two parallel ring molecules. The orientation apparently involves equal bonding from metal to each of 10 or 12 nearest carbon atoms in the bis-cyclopentadienyl or bis-benzene compounds. But since it is unlikely that the metal could form that many electron-pair bonds, some expression of delocalized bonding is evidently needed in the description of the electronic structure of these materials, whether the MO or the VB language is used. Again, however, the discussion given here will be couched mainly in MO terms, this time with a good deal more precedent. Again, also, the discussion will be limited mainly to bonding in the prototype molecule, ferrocene.

This new and interesting kind of bonding interaction has prompted a variety of theoretical descriptions by Jaffé (18), Dunitz and Orgel (11),

Moffitt (27), Liehr and Ballhausen (22), Yamazaki (40), Ruch (34), Brown (4), Linnett (23), Matsen (25) and Robertson and McConnell (33) among others, using mainly MO theory or at least some of the factors inherent in it.

Despite the fact that it contains conclusions which later considerations deem inadequate, Moffitt's paper deserves special recommendation because of its superb exposition of the way in which symmetry is used in the general MO theory of molecular bonding.

Orbitals for Bis-cyclopentadienyl Compounds

One of the most important observations to be made before analyzing the molecular electronic structure is that the axial symmetry of the C_5H_5 radical (or the C_6H_6 molecule as the case may be) is preserved upon entering the molecule. Consequently, it may be imagined that during the process of bond formation the AOs of the metal simply "fuse onto" the various existing MOs of the two rings, in the language used in the earlier discussion of HeH^+. In this regard the two rings of the sandwich act cooperatively. When the metal AO involved is symmetrical above and below the equatorial plane of the molecule (as for example the $4s$ AO) then the MOs of one ring add (symmetrically) to those of the other. When the metal AO is unsymmetrical (as for example the $4p$ AO which projects toward each ring), then the MO's of one ring subtract (antisymmetrically) from those of the other.

Except with respect to some of the fine details of the interaction, consideration is generally limited to only the π electrons of the rings. In both C_5H_5 and C_6H_6, there are three occupied π MO's, one called a and the other constituting a degenerate pair called e_1. Also both molecules have as next highest (and unoccupied) π MOs a second degenerate pair called e_2. And finally, in benzene only, there is one MO still higher in energy, but which need not be considered here. Each a MO is a symmetrical sum of all the carbon $2p\pi$ AOs of the ring; each e_1 MO is another combination which describes 1 unit of angular momentum about the 5-(or 6-) fold axis; each e_2 MO describes 2 units of angular momentum. In real form the e_1 MOs have one nodal plane perpendicular to the ring and the e_2 MOs have two nodal planes. Compared to a linear molecule, with the z axis along the bonds, the ring and metal orbitals can be classified as follows:

symmetrical	unsymmetrical
σ': a'; $4s$; $3d_{z^2}$	σ'': a''; $4p_z$
π': e_1'; $(3d_{xz}, 3d_{yz})$	π'': e_1''; $(4p_x, 4p_y)$
δ': e_2'; $(3d_{xy}, 3d_{x^2-y^2})$	δ'': e_2''

(The pairs of AOs within each parentheses are degenerate with each other.)

The primed ring orbitals are the symmetrical combinations and the double primed the antisymmetrical combinations; e.g., $a' \approx (a_{\text{ring }1} + a_{\text{ring }2})$ and $a'' \approx (a_{\text{ring }1} - a_{\text{ring }2})$. Actually, one must delve a bit more deeply into the symmetry properties of these wave functions in order to be entirely accurate in this classification. The present resolution, however, is quite sufficient for present purposes and to the extent that it is immaterial whether the two rings are staggered or eclipsed, it is entirely adequate.

As with all the transition elements, the $4s$ and $3d$ AOs are of about the same orbital energy, and also for Fe (according to Moffitt) about the same as the e_1 MOs of C_5H_5, if the rings and the metal are neutral. For other transition elements and for ionic species, the relative positioning of $4s$ and $3d$ with e_1 will be somewhat different.

These various statements of symmetry and relative energy are summarized in the right and left sides of Fig. 1.10. For clarity, the $3d$ and $4p$ AOs are split into their various symmetry components, though not necessarily on the basis of relative energies.

Basically, there are three problems to be faced by the description of the bonding: (a) how bonding arises in this peculiar geometry, (b) how observed magnetic properties of the various $M(C_5H_5)_2$ and $M(C_6H_6)_2$ molecules and ions arise, and (c) how the bonding and charge distribution between metal and rings affects the aromatic character of the rings.

Unfortunately the considerable theoretical attention received by these systems has yet to produce any marked unanimity on many of the details, although there is wide agreement on the general features. As distinguished from the tetrahedral carbonyls, the complexity here arises not from the interaction of a great number of orbitals having the same symmetry properties but rather from the even greater number of individual interactions. Therefore, it becomes harder to assess the relative importance of the various bonding factors. This section will contain a roughly historical development of the theory, with comments on some of the significant points of the major contributions and a synthesis of some conclusions from each, in order to obtain what *at most* may be an improved picture of the bonding, or *at least* one which accommodates some recent paramagnetic resonance results by McConnell, Porterfield and Robertson (*26*). But even so, there will also be indicated some of the uncertainties remaining.

Correlation Diagram and Bond Properties

Approximate locations of the bonding and antibonding MOs produced by the metal-ring interactions are indicated in the central part of the correlation diagram of Fig. 1.10. The relative spacings of the MO energy levels is again only approximate; furthermore, they no doubt change as various other transition metals are substituted. The MOs are identified in Fig. 1.10 according to the properties indicated in the preceding section.

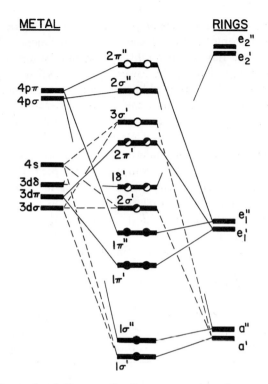

Fig. 1.10. Energy level diagram for ferrocene and analogous compounds. The MOs are classified according to symmetry as if the molecule were linear. See text for further description. The correspondence between the classification terms used here to identify the various MO energy levels and the proper (group theory) symbols used by other authors is easily established upon tracing each MO back to the particular metal and ring orbitals from which it arises.

Occupation of the orbitals again is indicated by the filled, open and half-filled circles.

Dunitz and Orgel (11) were the first to emphasize the importance of the $1\pi'$ MOs to the geometry and stability of the molecules. This degenerate pair of MOs is formed in this arrangement of atoms by the interaction of the $3d\pi$ ($3d_{xz}$ and $3d_{yz}$) AOs equally with all carbon orbitals of both rings. Further, a reasonably large overlap (S being the order of 0.3) between these orbitals may be expected under these conditions. Finally, since the metal $3d\pi$ AOs and these ring (e_1) MOs have approximately equal energy, all factors suggest a fairly large energy stabilization *via* this pair of MOs. It is in fact believed that the greatest contribution of all to the bond energy arises here, and to that extent, the bonding could largely be described as one single bond (but of π-type symmetry) between the metal and *each* of the rings.

It is helpful at this point to refer briefly to the magnetic properties of the series of metal compounds. As the number of valence shell electrons increases beyond the number brought up by the cyclopentadienide (cp) ions (completely filling thereby the lowest four levels) there will be found additional electrons in MOs derived largely from the remaining metal AOs ($3d\sigma$, $3d\delta$ and $4s$). Depending upon the energy separations between these MOs there will be various conditions of electron pairing. For example, in $Ti(cp)_2^{+2}$ there will be no additional electrons; in $V(cp)_2^{+}$ there evidently (as judged from the observed paramagnetism) is one electron in each of $2\sigma'$ and $1\delta'$; in $Fe(cp)_2$ $2\sigma'$ and $1\delta'$ are completely occupied. Coming finally to $Ni(cp)_2$ which is paramagnetic, the question of where those last two electrons are housed then arises. The first explanation was advanced by Moffitt (27), who recognized that here the $3d\sigma$ (i.e., $3d_{z^2}$) and $4s$ orbitals are of the same symmetry and thus under the force-field of the molecule may well be hybridized in some fashion. For example, the two hybrids $h \sim (3d_{z^2} + 4s)$ and $k \sim (3d_{z^2} - 4s)$ could be formed, the first (h) strongly directed *toward* both rings and the other (k) largely localized equatorially around the iron atom *between* the two rings. If one of these orbitals is raised high in energy to the vicinity of the $4p$ AOs, then the observed paramagnetism of $Ni(cp)_2$ is explained by assigning the last two unpaired electrons to some combination of h or k and $4p$ orbitals. Moffitt believed that specifically the h combination would be raised by the concentration of charge density in both rings.

Later, however, Dunitz and Orgel, and along similar lines Ruch (34), re-evaluated all other bonding interactions in addition to those with $3d\pi$ already mentioned. As guides to the several predictions, these authors approximated the appropriate overlap integrals between all metal AOs and their corresponding ring MOs. The numerical results suffer from uncertainties in the forms of the metal orbitals; nonetheless there seems to be agreement that (a) the overlap between $3d_{z^2}$ and the ring orbitals is very small (~ 0.02), probably because the ring orbitals unfavorably straddle the nodal surfaces of the $3d_{z^2}$ orbital, (see shape of $3d_{z^2}$ in Fig. 1.4) and (b) all other overlaps are appreciable, i.e., at least the same magnitude as the $2p\pi$ orbital overlap between adjacent carbon atoms in benzene (0.25), or larger. Thus extensive bonding is favored in all cases except $3d_{z^2}$ by the overlap factor and is limited only by the energy separations between interacting orbitals. Combining those two factors in each case leads to the estimates of energy levels of Fig. 1.10, which is rather similar to the correlation diagram deduced in the second paper of Dunitz and Orgel. Qualitatively, the following interpretation is suggested:

(a) The $1\pi'$ MO (from $3d\pi$ and e_1') retains its fundamental importance in determining net bond energy and molecular geometry. Similarly, then, $2\pi'$ (antibonding to $1\pi'$) lies rather high.

547.4 Z36
c.1

(b) Not because of electrostatics as Moffitt suggested, but because of the strong overlap and thus strong bonding of the $4s$ AO with the a' in the $1\sigma'$ MO, $3\sigma'$ becomes quite strongly antibonding and therefore well removed to the neighborhood of $2\pi'$ or beyond. This conclusion then preserves Dunitz and Orgel's interpretation of the paramagnetism in $Ni(cp)_2$.

In a subsequent MO discussion, using an alternate approach in which the semi-quantitative aspects were evaluated by electrostatic type calculations in which overlaps were ignored, Liehr and Ballhausen (*22*) had occasion to assess the magnitude of the electrostatic coupling (considered so important by Moffitt) of $3d_{z^2}$ to $4s$ by the electric field of the rings. They found this coupling effect negligibly small, just like the overlap between $3d_{z^2}$ and the ring orbitals according to Ruch, and to Dunitz and Orgel. One immediate consequence of combining these two independently calculated results is that the $3d\sigma$ AO is thus predicted to be almost the entire constituent of the $2\sigma'$ MO, which is therefore largely non-bonding in the molecule. This consequence, along with the general arrangement of MOs in the middle energy range, is consistent with the paramagnetic resonance results of McConnell, Porterfield and Robertson for $V(cp)_2$ (*26*). For this compound a very small hyperfine interaction from the V^{51} nuclear spin is observed, which implies slight (no more than 8 per cent) $4s$ character in the 2σ MO.

(c) Because of its (energy) distance from a_1'', the $4p_z$ interaction is very small, and $1\sigma''$ is not much lower in energy than a_1'' was in the free C_5H_5 radical.

(d) The $4p\pi$ orbitals probably contribute more to the total bond energy than the $4p\sigma$ because of their proximity to e_1''. This contribution to the net bond energy may well be even greater than indicated in Fig. 1.10. Indeed, in the case of *ions* of these compounds, wherein most of the net positive charge likely lies on the metal, it may be expected that the metal orbitals will be shifted downward relative to the orbitals of the C_5H_5 radical. Under these conditions, it is reasonable to suppose that the primary $3d\pi$ interactions *via* the $1\pi'$ MOs will *decrease*, but the $4p\pi$ interactions *via* the $1\pi'$ MOs will correspondingly *increase* (along with the other interactions with a' and a'' cp orbitals) still preserving the preference for the sandwich structure.

(e) Finally, there should be some moderately small interaction of the e_2' orbitals with the $3d\delta$ AO, but leaving the charge density in the equatorial region between the rings.

Magnetic Properties

The magnetic properties would follow from the character and energy spacing of the MO's in the middle energy part of the correlation diagram.

But of course all the discussions have been highly qualitative, so that conversely, in actual practice, the observed magnetic susceptibilities have been used to infer the energy spacings and thus to some degree bonding characteristics in the several molecules. This subject will not be pursued further here; for details the more recent theoretical papers may be consulted.

Charge Distributions

The charge distribution in ferrocene is of prime importance in understanding residual chemical properties of the cyclopentadienyl rings in the molecule. Accumulated data regarding the type and nature of ring-substituted ferrocene derivatives strongly suggest that the rings possess typical aromatic properties. This situation evidently arises because of the equivalent bonding from metal to each carbon, the considerable independence of each ring, and the apparent absence of charge separation as judged by the near equality of first ionization constants in $Fe(C_5H_4COOH)_2$ and C_6H_5COOH.

The allocation of charge between metal and rings which would reasonably be deduced from the MO discussion presented is compatible with the data. Of the ten electrons necessary to give the two rings electroneutrality two come from the four shared equally with the metal in the $1\pi'$ MOs; somewhat less than four—say 3.5—come from $1a'$ and $1a''$—and perhaps as much more comes from the e_1 interactions with $4p\pi$ in the $1\pi''$ MO; the difference may well come from the delocalization of the $3d\delta$ electrons (present in ferrocene) into the previously vacant e_2 ring orbitals.

Two qualifying points, however, might be noted. First, aromatic character depends upon the *availability*, but not necessarily the *presence* of electron density at a point in the ring. Even if the metal assumed a net negative charge, it is reasonable to suppose that an attacking positive group would rather easily polarize the metal-ring bond, and draw some of the charge back. Second, even if charge does leave the ring for the metal, it does not go very far away. Also it should be observed that excess charge builds up on the metal at twice the rate it leaves *one* of the rings. Therefore, charge-caused inductive and/or direct field effects should be more nearly cancelled here than if the polarizing group were located at a single position in the ring. Hence it could be that moderate heteropolarity of the over-all metal to ring bonding is allowable.

Representation of Bonding by "Equivalent Orbitals"

Despite the considerable advantages of the MO theory in interpreting magnetic, spectral and internal rotational properties of these molecules, the resulting description of charge distribution does suffer to some extent from "over-dissection." Linnett (*23*) has shown how the molecular wave functions as deduced above in terms of the symmetry MOs can be transformed into a representation in terms of "equivalent orbitals" which leads to an enhanced understanding of the electronic distribution. What is found is that the six occupied bonding σ and π MOs of the earlier discussion can be variously combined to produce six equivalent localized orbitals (each containing an electron pair, three bonding to one ring and three to the other) symmetrically arranged about the molecular axis. The maximum in the charge density in each of these lobes lies close to the ring. Each triplet of equivalent orbitals resembles rather closely in shape the three adjacent lobes of the octahedral or trigonal prism d^2sp^3 hybrid orbitals, which a number of chemists, especially Fischer (*14*), prefer to consider.

To this extent, then, it is justifiable to view the metal-ring bonding as the interaction of the metal ion in octahedral, or better trigonal prismatic, d^2sp^3 hybridization with the pair of cyclopentadienide rings situated on opposite trigonal faces. In this picture, the three pairs of π electrons from each ring coordinate into the vacant d^2sp^3 orbitals of the metal. While this extreme covalency would place a very large negative formal charge on the metal, sufficient ionic character can be added to the bond so as to reduce it to reasonable size. Both pictures omit (although this factor could be added) the "back bonding" from the $3d\delta$ orbitals which assists in removing excess charge from the metal.

It should be emphasized that despite the appearance of three-fold symmetry in the metal to benzene bond which is offered by the d^2sp^3 hybrid orbital or the equivalent orbital picture, the metal interaction in MO theory (which underlies the equivalent orbital description) retains cylindrical symmetry as in ferrocene. Indeed, as Linnett points out, the location of the maxima of the lobes of the equivalent orbitals with respect to the position of the ring carbon atoms is perfectly arbitrary. Thus there should be expected no impairment of the six-fold symmetry of the benzene rings.

The relative merits of the hybrid orbital picture and the MO picture (or the equivalent orbital representation derived from it) have been, and will continue to be, long argued. From the standpoint of keeping track of electrons and counting bonds, there is advantage in the valence bond, hybrid orbital scheme compared to the delocalization features of the MO theory. On the other hand, when it is desired to relate physical measurements—such as magnetic susceptibility or optical and magnetic resonance spectra —to details of the bonding and thence to chemical properties of these molecules, the MO description possesses many advantages.

However, one feature of the hybrid orbital picture which has been repeatedly stressed by Fischer and which merits much further discussion here is its emphasis on the attainment of a rare gas configuration by the metal. This point serves as the basis for the final section of this chapter.

STABILITY OF ALKYL AND ARYL TRANSITION-METAL COMPOUNDS

The final topic of this chapter may be stated in the form of a question which has long frustrated many chemists: "Why are the transition metals so reluctant to form normal bonds to alkyl and aryl carbon atoms?" In attempting to shed some light on that problem, however, what actually will be considered are two other related questions: "Why should they?" and "When might they?"

Review

If the only purpose of the preceding discussion in this chapter were to give a reasonably general description of the transition metal-to-carbon bond, then much of the detail might have been sacrificed in the interest of including a broader range of compounds. As indicated in the **Introduction**, however, this specialization has been done in order to demonstrate and catalog the variety of interactions present in the metal-carbon bonds of a few known prototype molecules. Many of these intereactions are either absent or are manifested in a different way in molecules formed only from elements other than transition metals.

It is, perhaps, appropriate to recapitulate briefly for the types of molecules considered, the various ways in which the transition metal valence shell orbitals participate in bonding. (a) In the simplest octahedral complex ions, like those of H_2O, NH_3 or the halides, the major contribution to the total bond energy undeniably arises from electrostatic forces. Nevertheless, refined considerations based upon spectra and magnetics (*31*) and Pauling's electroneutrality principle (*32*) (among others) point strongly toward participation of the $4s$, $4p$ and at least two of the $3d$ (here called $3d\sigma$) AOs in bonding. The three remaining $3d$ ($3d\pi$) AOs probably remain rather non-bonding in the H_2O and NH_3 cases, although, if they are unoccupied, there is evidence to indicate they may be used in stabilizing intermediate species during some chemical reactions of these ions. In the oxides and halides, and even more so in the phosphorous and arsenic ligands (i.e., those with extravalent d-orbitals) the metal $3d\pi$ orbitals appear to participate directly by giving some multiple-bond character to the metal-ligand interaction. (b) This $3d\pi$ bonding appears to make especially significant contribution to the bond stabilization when the ligand is some unsaturated group, of which CN^- is an extreme example. (c) When the coordination number becomes reduced to four, it is still found that every metal orbital can function in some manner or other, not only with unsaturated ligands but also with other attached atoms like Cl, P or As with extravalent d-orbitals. (d) Despite the apparent predominance of the $d\pi$-type bonding in the bis-cyclopentadienyl compounds, it seems quite reasonable that chemically significant contributions arise from the participation of all the other metal AOs except possibly one of the $4p$ orbitals and probably in some cases the $3d_{z^2}$.

In short, the metal in its choice of ligand apparently strives to make profitable use of as many of its valence orbitals as possible (35). This would account, for example, for the great predisposition for the octahedral configuration. Even complexes of Ni, Cu, or Pt which formally are four-coördinate frequently crystallize or in solution solvate in such a way as partially to expand their coördination sphere to six. More to the present interest, this desire is also exhibited by the occurrence of certain derivatives of those bis-cyclopentadienyl compounds which have unoccupied low energy MOs (such as $2\sigma'$ or $1\delta'$ of Fig. 1.10). Other groups apparently coördinate electrons into those orbitals if they are vacant, or pair up with electrons there if they are half occupied. Thus there have been isolated compounds like $Ti(cp)_2 (C_6H_5)_2$ by Summers and Uloth (38), which achieve a fuller utilization of the metal AOs than in the parent bis-cyclopentadienyl molecule.

Of course all this is in large part a restatement of Sidgwick's Effective Atomic Number rule of attainment of the next inert gas structure by the metal. This correspondence becomes more clear when it is recalled that the number of bonding MOs formed is, in most cases, equal to the number of metal valence-shell AOs, and when the bonding MOs are completely occupied, there are 18 valence electrons associated with the metal. Most, but by no means all, of the exceptions occur when there is an unsufficient number of electrons to completely fill the nonbonding orbitals present. The principle given, though, is somewhat more general than Sidgwick's rule in suggesting not so much that the "right" number of electrons be present, but more that each one is as far as possible helping to stabilize the molecule.

Clearly then this represents the adaptation of bonding principles familiar in the chemistry of elements in other parts of the Periodic Table, as exemplified forcefully by electron deficient molecules like diborane or trimethylaluminum dimer discussed by Lewis and Rundle (21).

It is relevant to comment here that this principle can apply to both types of stability—thermodynamic and kinetic. Ordinarily, attention is directed to total molecular bond energy which is maximized by full orbital utilization. But if unused valence-shell orbitals are present, they can provide (unless geometry interferes) a lower energy path for an attacking group—leading to kinetic instability or liability.

Comparison of Methyl and Halogen Bonding

The problem of why normal transition metal-alkyl and -aryl bonds are uncommon evidently requires simultaneous consideration of other possible molecular species in the reaction mixture. For purposes of illustration, one such comparison between $FeCl_3$ and the hypothetical $Fe(CH_3)_4$ will be presented here. Only in the gas phase at very high temperatures does $FeCl_3$ exist in monomeric form. At lower temperatures or dissolved in nonpolar solvents like benzene the dimeric form

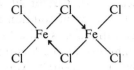

is stable. This local tetrahedral environment of the metal also occurs in moderately polar solvents which coordinate an electron pair into the vacant tetrahedral position, as in the etherate

In the solid state, $FeCl_3$ crystallizes in such a way that each iron ion subtends an octahedron of chloride ions. And finally, in solutions of very polar solvents like water, the compound is completely hydrolyzed to give the $Fe(H_2O)_6^{+3}$ complex ion.

The $Fe(CH_3)_4$ molecule is suggested for comparative purposes here because it would likely be tetrahedral and because there are just enough electrons to fully utilize the $3d$ and $4s$ AOs of the iron, without leaving any unpaired electrons.

In any form wherein the iron atom in $FeCl_3$ is in a tetrahedral environment, the localized electronic structure about it may be described in much the same language as used with $Ni(CO)_4$, with adjustments, of course, for a change of ligand orbitals and number of electrons. Specifically, the σ_{CO}, π_{CO} and π^*_{CO} ligand orbitals are replaced by chlorine $3p\sigma$, $3p\pi$ and $3d\pi$ AOs, respectively, but with relative orbital energy spacings somewhat changed.

The correlation diagram would then be quite similar to Fig. 1.8, except that five electrons must be removed from the 2π and 4σ MOs. An MO discussion of tetrahedral $FeCl_4^-$ ion has been given by Zaslow and Rundle (41). The correlation diagram for $Fe(CH_3)_4$ would be obtained simply by eliminating all contributions from ligand π orbitals and removing six σ electrons. This would leave as the only occupied MOs in Fig. 1.8 2σ, 3σ and 2π (which would be pure nonbonding $3d$ AOs in character).

An analysis (like that given for $Ni(CO)_4$, though much less detail is required) of bonding in $Fe(CH_3)_4$ and, for example, in $FeCl_3 \cdot OEt_2$ yields conclusions which in part are schematically presented in Fig. 1.11. Obviously the much more limited bonding interactions in $Fe(CH_3)_4$ make more understandable the reluctance of $Fe(CH_3)_4$ to form from $FeCl_3$ in a reaction with a Grignard reagent, or perhaps even from a reagent like $LiCH_3$. Of course, greater diversity of bonding interaction does not necessarily prove greater total bond energy. Indeed it is quite another problem to prove by computation alone that one bond is stronger than another.

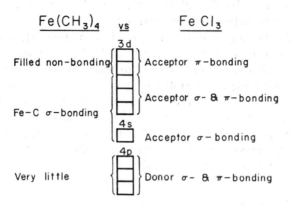

Fig. 1.11. Bonding comparisons between $Fe(CH_3)_4$ and $FeCl_3$. The $FeCl_3$ is presumed to occur in such form as to provide (approximate) tetrahedral coördination. Classification of donor and acceptor character is according to the discussion of $Ni(CO)_4$.

Assuming a wide variety of simplifications, including those contained in "Mulliken's Magic Formula," (*28*) Jaffé and Doak (*19*) have suggested reasons why alkyl and aryl bonds to transition metals are weaker than those to all other elements. Their calculations indicate that bonds to transition metals have (a) only a third or so of the ionic resonance energy which makes stable the bonds to alkali and alkaline earth metals and (b) about half the "covalent" energy which makes stable the known bonds to all the other elements. Their predictions regarding the instability of alkyl transition-metal bonds may be unduly pessimistic however. If their calculated "ionic" and "covalent" contributions are combined in the proportions suggested by Mulliken in his "Magic Formula," the $Fe-CH_3$ bond turns out to have $\sim$75 per cent of the energy of the $Al-CH_3$ or $P-CH_3$ bonds, for example. In view of all the uncertainties and assumptions implicit in these calculated results, at least moderate stability in the $Fe-CH_3$ (and other transition-metal alkyl) bonds perhaps ought not to be ruled out.

If there is attached to the metal an aryl carbon instead of an alkyl carbon, there would be possibility of multiple bonding interactions. In the hypothetical molecule $Fe(C_6H_5)_4$, the occupied $3d\pi$ AOs (non-bonding in $Fe(CH_3)_4$) could donate charge to a limited extent into acceptor π orbitals of the phenyl rings and there could also be in addition some involvement of the $4p$ AOs. Furthermore, Jaffé has suggested that the overlap and relative electronegativity factors are such as to indicate stronger σ bonding to the metal in aryl derivatives. Thus, on both counts, aryl derivatives are expected to be more stable than alkyl derivatives. This conclusion agrees with what experimental data have been accumulated.

It might also be supposed that the $Fe(CH_3)_4$ or $Fe(C_6H_5)_4$ molecules, if formed, would also be susceptible to attack by basic groups *via* the little-used valence-shell orbitals, and to be more readily decomposed.

Assuming that these considerations apply in similar fashion to various other possible "normal" transition metal to carbon bond systems, it can be concluded that in general these molecules will be unstable in any environment containing "more useful" ligands. But it still may be, as Cotton has pointed out in his review of the chemistry of these molecules (8), that they could be important as reaction intermediates.

Conditions for Stability

What is clearly suggested, both by the preceding discussion and perhaps to a greater extent by the array of presently known compounds, is that a better chance for stability in normal alkyl or aryl bonds to transition metals should be expected in mixed complexes. For example, $Ti(Cp)_2 (C_6H_5)_2$ has been prepared by Summers and Uloth (38); $(CO)_5MnCH_3$ by Coffield, Kozikowski and Closson (7); $Cr(Tetrahydrofuran)_3(C_6H_5)_3$ by Herwig and Zeiss (17); $[Cr(H_2O)_5(CH_2C_6H_5)]^{+2}$ by Anet and Leblanc (2) and $[Cr(H_2O)_5CHCl_2]^{+2}$ by Anet (1); and a variety of platinum compounds of the type $(PR_3)_2PtXCH_3$ and $(PR_3)_2Pt(CH_3)_2$, where X = halogen or halogenide, by Chatt and co-workers (6).

Chatt and Shaw, in fact, have already noted the relevance of "conditioning" the metal for carbon bond formation, by complexing it with other groups as well. They have suggested that somehow the proximity of the valence-shell d-orbitals to the s- and p-orbitals must be involved, perhaps because that proximity allows promotion of electrons from nonbonding into antibonding MOs, or from bonding into nonbonding MOs, in either event weakening the metal-carbon bond. This weakening, they reason, should be least when the energy separation between highest occupied and lowest unoccupied orbitals is greatest.

Referring back to Figs. 1.5 and 1.6 and the accompanying discussion for octahedral complexes, it may readily be seen how occupation of the nonbonding and antibonding MOs, metal-ligand electronegativity differences and the presence of extravalent acceptor orbitals on the ligand are related to the criterion of Chatt and Shaw for stability of the normal transition metal to carbon bond.

The details of this proposed bond weakening process and the reasons for the special susceptibility of the metal-carbon bond over others in the molecule are presented more fully in Chapter 9. This hypothesis has led to successful attempts at attaching alkyl and aryl groups to Group VIII metals to which PR_3 groups were already bound. Previous experimentation had indicated that PR_3 groups are very effective in creating the desired energy separation, especially in the later transition series. Thus there were prepared compounds of the type mentioned above.

In many respects the bonding principles already presented in this chapter are consistent with the basic requirements of Chatt and Shaw, although they are approached by a different path. The use of π-bonding ligands is compatible with the principle of full utilization of all available orbitals. The large energy splitting listed as a requirement is an indication of vigorous covalent bonding by both the σ- and the π-type MOs and of an approach to saturation of the bonding desires of the metal. The difference centers around the assumption that the energy splitting requirement is *fundamentally* necessary and that the metal-carbon bond dissociation process is as described. There perhaps is not yet available any unequivocal experimental data to settle this particular point directly. But on a qualitative basis it may be that the conditions required by Chatt and Shaw are too stringent when applied to transition elements which have vacant $3d$ nonbonding AOs or antibonding MOs derived from them. For example, the necessary conditions of electronic configuration and energy splitting they postulate likely occur in $Ti(OR)_3(C_6H_5)$ as they note (R = isopropyl group) but not so likely in $Ti(cp)_2(C_6H_5)_2$, both of which are known.

As already mentioned, throughout the whole consideration of transition metal aryls and alkyls there is uncertainty about which type of stability is more important—thermodynamic or kinetic. So far as storing a compound in a bottle is concerned, either one is adequate; but with respect to designing a sequence of preparative reactions, the decision, of course, becomes all-important. In this connection, Chatt and Shaw make the very relevant observation that "those electronic configurations which occur in stable organo-transition-metal complexes are just those which Taube (*39*) has pointed out as occurring in nonlabile complexes with the common ligands."

A good example of the importance of the kinetic factor is afforded by the formation of $Cr(H_2O)_5CHCl_2^{+2}$ in solution. In postulating a mechanism for the formation of this molecule, Anet suggests that in the final step a Cr^{+2} ion reacts with a $CHCl_2$ radical previously produced to give the complex $Cr(H_2O)_5CHCl_2^{+2}$. In this complex, the electronic structure about the Cr is very similar to that about the chromic ion in $Cr(H_2O)_6^{+3}$, say. On this basis, Anet makes the reasonable suggestion that the stability of this system is due to the familiar inertness of Cr(III) complexes to substitution.

Conclusion

The position taken regarding the further preparation and isolation of normal alkyl and aryl transition metal compounds may be summarized in the following way. The present direction of synthesizing "mixed" derivatives would seem most profitable. In choosing ligands to "condition" the metal, π bonding effects should be carefully considered. If the metal has nearly filled $d\pi$ orbitals, then ligands with predominately π *acceptor* properties should be considered; if the $d\pi$ orbitals are nearly vacant then π *donor* ligands should be preferable. This π bonding effect should be greatest for π acceptor ligands if the metal is neutral (or partially negatively charged) and for π donor ligands if the metal is positively charged. Evidence cited, for example, by Chatt and Shaw indicates furthermore that stability is greater in the second and third transition series. Finally, and very importantly, careful attention must be paid to the kinetic aspect of stability, by proper adjustment of electronic and steric factors so as to minimize further decomposition reaction of the organometallic compound formed.

References

(1) Anet, F. A. L., *Can. J. Chem.,* **37,** 58 (1959).
(2) Anet, F. A. L., and Leblanc, E., *J. Am. Chem. Soc.,* **79,** 2649 (1957).
(3) Basolo, F., and Pearson, R. G., "Mechanisms of Inorganic Reactions," New York, John Wiley & Sons, Inc., 1958.
(4) Brown, D. A., *J. Chem. Phys.,* **29,** 1086 (1958).
(5) Cable, J. W., and Sheline, R. K., *Chem. Reviews,* **56,** 1 (1956).
(6) Chatt, J., and Shaw, B. L., *J. Chem. Soc.,* 705, 4020 (1959).
(7) Coffield, T. H., Kozikowski, J., and Closson, R. D., *J. Org. Chem.,* **22,** 598 (1957).
(8) Cotton, F. A., *Chem. Reviews,* **55,** 551 (1955).
(9) Coulson, C. A., "Valence," Oxford, Clarendon Press, 1952.
(10) Coulson, C. A., and Duncanson, W. E., *Proc. Roy. Soc. (London),* **165,** 90 (1938).
(11) Dunitz, J. D., and Orgel, L. E., *J. Chem. Phys.,* **23,** 954 (1955); *Nature,* **171,** 121 (1953).
(12) Edgell, W. F., Abstracts, 134th Meeting, Am. Chem. Soc., Chicago, Sept., 1958; talks before various Am. Chem. Soc. local sections, 1958–59; and subsequent personal communication. *Cf.* also Edgell, W. F., Huff, J., Thomas, J., Lehman, H., Angell, C., and Asato, G., *J. Am. Chem. Soc.,* **82,** 1254 (1960).

(13) Fischer, A. K., Cotton, F. A., and Wilkinson, G., *J. Am. Chem. Soc.,* **79,** 2044 (1957).

(14) Fischer, E. O., Special Publ. No. 13, London, The Chemical Society, 1959, and earlier references cited therein. (Int. Conf. Coörd. Chem.).

(15) Giacometti, G., *J. Chem. Phys.,* **23,** 2068 (1955).

(16) Griffith, J. S., and Orgel, L. E., *Quart. Reviews,* **11,** 381 (1957).

(17) Herwig, W., and Zeiss, H., *J. Am. Chem. Soc.,* **79,** 6561 (1957).

(18) Jaffé, H. H., *J. Chem. Phys.,* **21,** 156 (1953).

(19) Jaffé, H. H., and Doak, G. O., *J. Chem. Phys.,* **21,** 196, 1118 (1953); **22,** 1462 (1954).

(20) Kealy, T. J., and Pauson, P. L., *Nature,* **168,** 1039 (1951).

(21) Lewis, P. H., and Rundle, R. E., *J. Chem. Phys.,* **21,** 986 (1953).

(22) Liehr, A. D., and Ballhausen, C. J., *Acta Chem. Scand.* **11,** 207 (1957).

(23) Linnett, J. W., *Trans. Faraday Soc.,* **52,** 904 (1956).

(24) Long, L. H., and Sachman, J. F., *Trans. Faraday Soc.,* **53,** 1606 (1957); **54,** 1797 (1958).

(25) Matsen, F. A., *J. Am. Chem. Soc.,* **81,** 2023 (1959).

(26) McConnell, H. M., Porterfield, W. W. and Robertson, R. E., *J. Chem. Phys.,* **30,** 442 (1959).

(27) Moffitt, W., *J. Am. Chem. Soc.,* **76,** 3386 (1954).

(28) Mulliken, R. S., *J. Phys. Chem.,* **56,** 295 (1952).

(29) Nyholm, R. S., and Short, L. N., *J. Chem. Soc.,* 2670 (1953).

(30) Orgel, L. E., "Tenth Solvay Conference in Chemistry," p. 320, Brussels, 1956.

(31) Owen, J., *Proc. Roy. Soc., (London)* **A227,** 183 (1955); *Discuss. Faraday Soc.,* No. 19, 127 (1955).

(32) Pauling, L., "The Nature of The Chemical Bond," 3rd. Ed., Ithaca, N. Y., Cornell University Press, 1960.

(33) Robertson, R. E., and McConnell, H. M., *J. Phys. Chem.,* **64,** 70 (1960).

(34) Ruch, E., *Rec. trav. chim.,* **75,** 638 (1956).

(35) Rundle, R. E., *J. Phys. Chem.,* **61,** 45 (1957).

(36) Sahni, R. C., *Trans. Faraday Soc.,* **49,** 1246 (1953).

(37) Stull, D. R., and Sinke, G. C., "Thermodynamic Properties of the Elements," American Chemical Society, 1956.

(38) Summers, L., and Uloth, R. H., *J. Am. Chem. Soc.,* **76,** 2278 (1954).

(39) Taube, H., *Chem. Reviews,* **50,** 69 (1952).

(40) Yamazaki, M., *J. Chem. Phys.,* **24,** 1260 (1956).

(41) Zaslow, B., and Rundle, R. E., *J. Phys. Chem.,* **61,** 490 (1957).

2. BENZYNE CHEMISTRY

ROLF HUISGEN

University of Munich, Germany

BENZYNE TYPE INTERMEDIATES IN NUCLEOPHILIC AROMATIC SUBSTITUTIONS

The most exciting news of the last decade in the field of nucleophilic aromatic substitution is the experimental proof of a mechanism with primary elimination. On treating, for instance, fluorobenzene with n-butyllithium, hydrogen fluoride is eliminated. In the second step the intermediate, designated as benzyne, adds another molecule of n-butyllithium and thus the n-butylbenzene which results on hydrolysis is formally a substitution product.

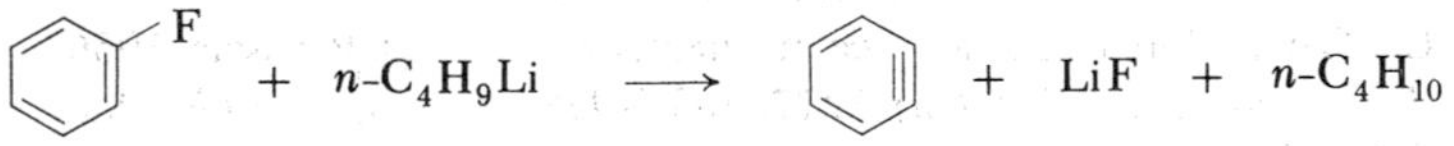

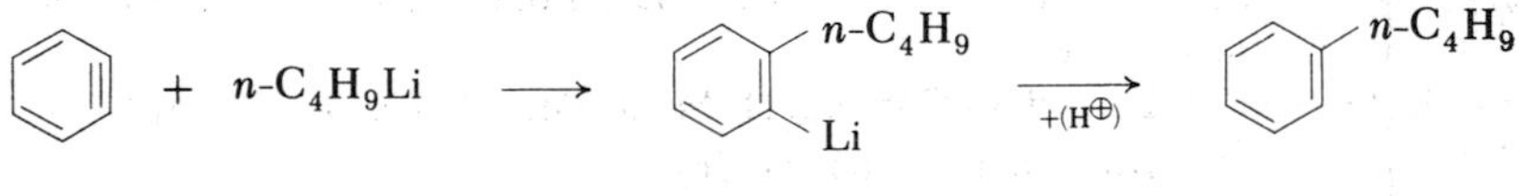

As shown below, the addition of the nucleophilic reagent to arynes which lack the high symmetry of benzyne can follow two different orientations. In one of the isomeric products the new substituent does not appear in the position from which the old one left. An apparent rearrangement during the substitution is the result of the sequence of elimination and addition steps. These characteristic rearrangements offer excellent diagnostic help in elucidating the mechanistic path involving primary elimination.

Usually it is one and the same basic agent which is responsible for the HX-elimination from ArX and which afterwards adds to the extra bond of the aryne. On the other hand, arynes as true intermediates are not limited to reacting only with the liberating basic reagent, but may also unite with other suitable partners present. Formally the products need not be related to the starting components as in a normal substitution. Thus, the reactions of arynes are not restricted to a special group of nucleophilic aromatic substitutions, but justify discussion as "benzyne chemistry."

26

History and Formulation of Benzyne

The observation of rearrangements in nucleophilic aromatic substitution is not at all new but can be traced back for 85 years. Kekulé (*64*) and Wurtz (*124*) discovered the transformation of sodium benzenesulfonate to phenol by molten alkali in the sixties of the last century. As early as the seventies the preferred formation of resorcinol in the alkaline fusion of benzene-1,4-disulfonate (*2*) or 4-bromobenzenesulfonate (*70*) became known.

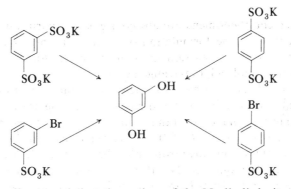

Also it was discovered that the action of the N-alkali-derivatives of ammonia or amines upon aryl halides leads to substitution with rearrangement (*26, 27, 28, 35, 36*).

The first interpretation of a nucleophilic aromatic substitution *via* a primary elimination appears to stem from Stoermer and Kahlert (*97*). In 1902, these authors proposed the intermediate I to explain the formation of 2-ethoxycoumarone in the reaction of 3-bromocoumarone with sodium ethoxide. Surprisingly enough, they accounted for their unsuccessful endeavours to isolate I in terms of a pronounced Baeyer strain in the intermediate. The explanation was not generalized and, therefore, sank into oblivion.

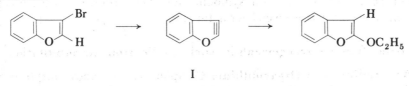

I

The small amount of triphenylene formed on treating chlorobenzene with sodium was ascribed by Bachmann and Clarke (*1*) in 1927 to a trimerization of "phenylene radicals," C_6H_4. Wittig (*108, 111*) postulated the "dipolar phenylene" (II) as intermediate in the formation of *o*-lithiobiphenyl from fluorobenzene and phenyllithium. Also, the formula of "dehydrobenzene" (III) was once mentioned in this connection; II and III were

not regarded as being identical. The same dipolar phenylene was used by
Morton *et al.* (*78*) to interpret the reaction of chlorobenzene with amylsodium.

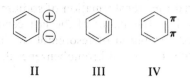

II   III   IV

Rearrangement phenomena are always signs for alarm and require the
greatest attention in the formulation of reaction paths. One can almost
state that the history of reaction mechanisms is the history of successful
interpretations of molecular rearrangements.

The most significant argument for the elimination mechanism in nucleophilic aromatic substitutions is based on these rearrangements. In 1953/54,
two research groups made use of this argument and proposed benzyne type
intermediates. Roberts *et al.* (*82*) in Pasadena investigated the isotope
distribution in aniline obtained from chlorobenzene-(1-^{14}C) with potassium
amide in liquid ammonia (p. 44); these authors coined the name "benzyne." Huisgen and Rist (*43*) in Munich treated *o*- and *m*-fluoroanisole
with phenyllithium and isolated, after carbonation, practically identical
mixtures of isomeric methoxybiphenylcarboxylic acids (p. 40).

Roberts as well as Wittig formulated in their publications benzyne as
shown in III. The inclusion of a linear acetylenic bond in an aromatic
nucleus is somewhat frightening to the conservative chemist. In fact, the
bond hybridization of benzyne does not correspond with that of a normal
triple bond. The symbol IV with the two π's for extra electrons of benzyne, although not completely correct either, stresses the nearly undisturbed benzene resonance of this intermediate. However, formula IV, used
by the author for many years, (*43–55*) should be abandoned in favor of
III in the interest of a uniform symbolization. The discussion of the bond
system in arynes will be given later in this chapter.

Evidence from Rearrangements in Nucleophilic Aromatic Substitutions

Aryl Halides and Organolithium Compounds. The above mentioned
action of metallic sodium upon halobenzenes turned out to be rather
useless from the mechanistic viewpoint compared with the homogeneous
reaction of aromatic substances with organolithium compounds.

The capability of the latter to replace by lithium the hydrogen bound
to the aromatic nucleus, was discovered independently by Gilman (*23,24*)
and by Wittig (*104,107*). In this recently reviewed (*30*) reaction the position
ortho to an acidifying substituent is "metalated." Such exchanges, exempli-

fied by the metalation of trifluoromethylbenzene, are often regarded as modified Brönsted acid-base reactions.

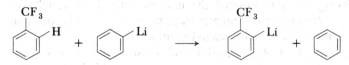

However, these interactions are not simple proton transitions, but involve the organolithium compound rather than the carbanion in the role of the base. The rising rates of metalation in the series

N,N-dimethylaniline < benzotrifluoride < anisole

< chlorobenzene < fluorobenzene

reflect the increasing acidification of hydrogen by the substituent.

Fluorobenzene, the most acidic benzene derivative, reacts very fast with phenyllithium. As Wittig *et al.* (*105*) found, the *o*-lithiofluorobenzene, V, undergoes a remarkable substitution by a second molecule of phenyllithium in which the fluorine is exchanged by the anionoid phenyl of the lithium reagent. Carbonation then leads to biphenyl-*o*-carboxylic acid. The notorious inertness of halogen attached to an aromatic nucleus makes this type of substitution highly problematic within the classic additive scheme of nucleophilic substitution.

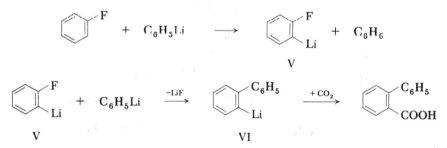

In this well known mechanism the nucleophile Y^- adds in the introductory step to the aromatic site (*13,89*). The inherent disinclination of the aromatic nucleus to assume a negative charge is overcome by activating substituents such as A which can take over the anionic charge in the additive intermediate VII by way of electron attracting inductive and resonance effects. The latter is limited to activating groups *ortho* or *para* to the point of substitution.

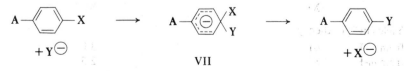

Obviously the neighboring C—Li bond in V reduces the readiness of the C—F carbon to open an electron sextet to accept the entering nucleophile. Wittig (*108*) postulated the intermediate II, although Wittig and Fuhrmann (*106*) described no rearrangements in the analogous reactions of the twelve haloanisoles with phenyllithium.

Huisgen and Rist (*43*) treated *o*- and *m*-fluoroanisole with 4 equivalents of phenyllithium. Subsequent carbonation yielded the two isomeric methoxybiphenylcarboxylic acids XI and XII in almost identical relative proportions. It is evident from experience with metalations (*30*) that VIII and IX are the primary products. If this pair of isomeric lithiofluoroaromatic compounds yields the same products, then 3-methoxybenzyne (X) is an attractive intermediate for the mechanistic solution.

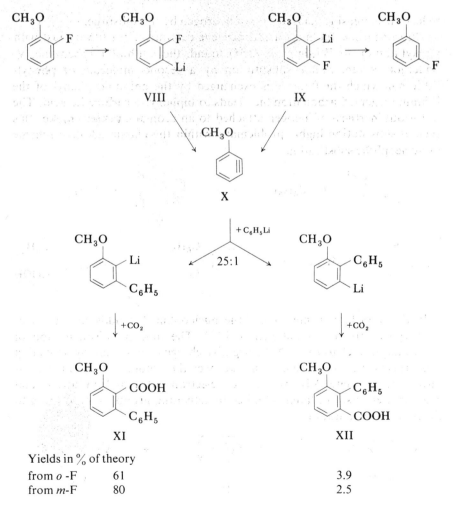

Yields in % of theory

from *o*-F	61	3.9
from *m*-F	80	2.5

The methoxy function in anisyne (X) exerts a great influence on the ratio of the two phenyllithium adducts formed. The direction leading finally to the most hindered carboxylic acid XI is favored by a factor of 25.

The behavior of the fluoronaphthalenes towards excess phenyllithium is also consistent with a quantitative primary elimination to the naphthynes (*43,47*). 1,2-Naphthyne, formed from 1-fluoronaphthalene *via* the 2-lithium derivative, accepts the anionic phenyl of phenyllithium in the positions 1 and 2 in the proportion 37:63 as shown by the yields of phenylnaphthoic acids in subsequent reaction with carbon dioxide. 2-Fluoronaphthalene is metalated at the 1-position 3.7 times faster than at position 3. The 3-lithium derivative yields *via* 2,3-naphthyne only 2,3-phenylnaphthoic acid. However, the fraction metalated at 1 gives rise to the two isomeric 1,2-phenylnaphthoic acids in the same relative ratio as the reaction sequence starting from 1-fluoronaphthalene.

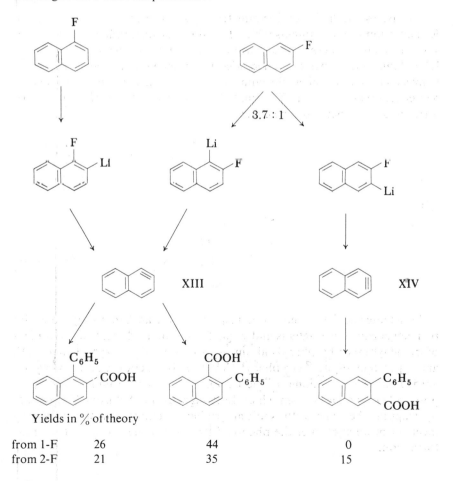

Yields in % of theory		
from 1-F	26	44	0
from 2-F	21	35	15

The elimination-addition mechanism is by no means limited to conversions by phenyllithium. The analogous reactions of other organolithium compounds are illustrated by *tert*-butyllithium which adds to 1,2-naphthyne in the proportion 34:66 giving 1- and 2-*tert*-butylnaphthalene after hydrolysis (*47*).

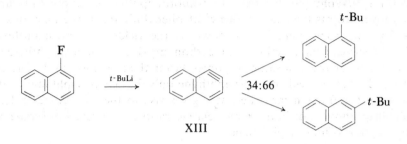

XIII

Because of the high bond symmetry of benzyne the two directions of RLi addition are indistinguishable. The slightest disturbance of the bond system which will permit observation of the rearrangement is an isotopic label. Jenny and Roberts (*63*) degraded the biphenyl obtained from fluorobenzene-(1-^{14}C) and phenyllithium and interpreted their data to mean a 53 per cent rearrangement. The small deviation from the 50:50 ratio can be attributed to a kinetic isotope effect.

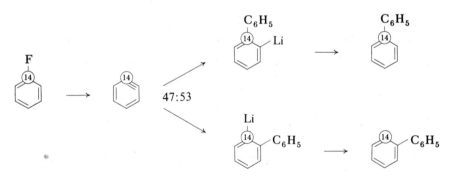

Aryne intermediates seem to be responsible for an interesting molecular rearrangement. Lüttringhaus and v. Sääf (*71*) obtained from the treatment of diphenyl ether by phenylsodium 46 per cent *o*-hydroxybiphenyl (XV) and 9 per cent *o*-phenoxybiphenyl (XVI). This reaction was formerly regarded as an intra-anionic isomerization. Wittig and Pohmer (*114*) proposed a benzyne mechanism which Lüttringhaus and Schuster (*73*) proved by trapping benzyne with sodium triphenylmethide. In the following mechanism we encounter the phenoxide ion as leaving group in the aryne formation.

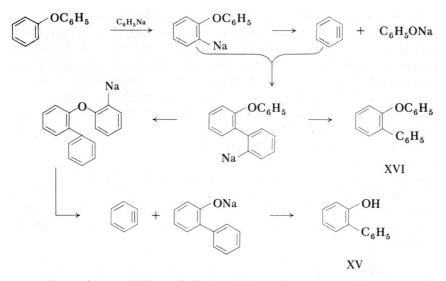

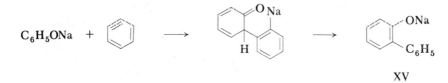

An alternative possibility offers the addition of the phenoxide anion with the nucleophilic *o*-position to benzyne:

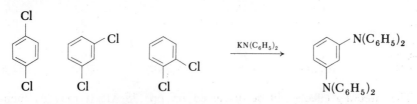

Aryl Halides and Alkali Amides. The preferred formation of tetraphenyl-*m*-phenylenediamine from all the isomeric dichlorobenzenes and potassium diphenylamide at high temperature offers an early example of the mentioned *o*-rearrangements (*35,36*).

The amination of halobenzenes by potassium amide in liquid ammonia was worked out by Bergstrom *et al.*(*5*). On treating 1- or 2-chloro-, -bromo- and -iodonaphthalene under the same conditions Urner and Bergstrom (*100*) obtained nearly identical mixtures consisting of 43–53 per cent of 2-naphthylamine and 2–3 per cent of the 1-isomer. Astoundingly enough, the fluoronaphthalenes reacted slowly but without rearrangement.

The illustrious researches of Roberts *et al.* (*82,84*) proved the benzyne type mechanism of such aminations by the extent of rearrangement. Chlorobenzene-(1-^{14}C) gave 43 per cent of an isotopically mixed aniline which contained 48 per cent of the label in position 1 and 52 per cent in 2. It was concluded from this ratio approaching 1:1 that an intermediate with two equivalent neighboring positions is responsible for product formation.

Substituents in the benzyne skeleton influence the addition of nucleophilic reagents by steric and electronic effects. As one would expect, 3-substituents in benzyne exert a stronger orientational power than 4-substituents. In extreme cases, one of the two routes of addition is totally suppressed (Table 2.1) (*83*). On superficial inspection of Table 2.1 it seems puzzling that electron attracting and releasing substituents in 3-position such as CF_3— or CH_3O— lead to exclusive entering of the amino group in position 1. Analogous aminations of aromatic polyhalides are also described (*122*).

TABLE 2.1. AMINATION OF ARYL HALIDES BY SODIUM OR
POTASSIUM AMIDE IN LIQUID AMMONIA (*83*).

R	Hal	% Total	Yields of Substituted Anilines Percentage ratio		
			o-	*m-*	*p-*
o-OCH$_3$	Br	33	–	100	–
o-CF$_3$	Cl	28	–	100	–
o-CH$_3$	Br(Cl)	64	49(45)	51(55)	–
p-OCH$_3$	Br	31	–	49	51
p-CF$_3$	Cl	25	–	50	50
p-CH$_3$	Cl	35	–	62	38
p-F	Br	30	–	20	80
m-OCH$_3$	Br	59	–	100	–
m-CF$_3$	Cl	16	–	100	–
m-CH$_3$	Br(Cl)	64(61)	22(40)	56(52)	22(8)

The directing effects will be discussed on pp. 78–81. It may be mentioned here that Roberts' mechanism of benzyne formation from bromobenzene and potassium amide does not include metallorganic intermediates. However, the mechanistic scheme proposed on pp. 54–58 justifies the discussion of all these reactions in a review of organometallic compounds.

In *m*-substituted halobenzenes the hydrogen halide elimination by KNH_2 can take two different courses yielding 3- and 4-substituted benzynes. The remarkable fluctuations in the ratios of the products obtained from o- or m-tolyl halides (Table 2.1) may be taken as a warning in theoretical interpretations. The occasional poor yields of arylamines point to side and successive reactions, and thus, the preferential selection of single isomers in subsequent conversions can change the isomer ratio.

The arylation of ammonia by benzyne indeed does not stop at the stage of aniline. Bergstrom (5) isolated from a typical experiment with bromo-benzene and KNH_2 in liquid ammonia 22 per cent aniline, 18 per cent di-phenylamine and 1 per cent p-aminobiphenyl. In a separate experiment aniline was subjected to the same phenylating agent. Despite the excess ammonia a preferential reaction of the aniline was noted (123):

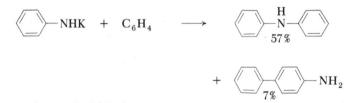

The rate of amination of halobenzenes by potassium amide is highly de-pendent on the nature of the halogen. Bromobenzene reacts fastest while fluorobenzene turns out to be inert (5). Sodamide is less soluble in liquid ammonia, but displays the same activity as KNH_2; the solubility of $LiNH_2$ is too low to permit its use (93).

Lithium dialkylamides in ether, for solubility reasons, make an ideal model system for mechanistic studies. Aminolysis of organolithium com-pounds (C_6H_5Li, n-BuLi) by HNR_2 gives ethereal solutions of known titer. Larger quantities are conveniently prepared from equivalent amounts of secondary amines and metallic lithium in the presence of half an equivalent of styrene or naphthalene (125); the dilithium adduct is aminolyzed to ethylbenzene or dihydronaphthalene respectively and the N-lithium compound.

Substitutions by $LiNR_2$ in ether were studied mainly by Gilman et al. (4,26,27,28,29), who frequently observed a concomitant rearrangement:

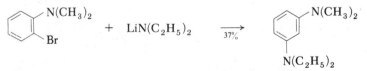

Insight into the mechanism led to a great increase in the yields which had been modest. The same reagent which brings about the elimination of hydrogen halide, adds afterwards to the aryne as shown for chlorobenzene and lithium piperidide. The thus-formed o-lithiophenylpiperidine XVII as organolithium compound will now compete with lithium piperidide for benzyne. This undesired secondary reaction, leading to products of higher molecular weight, can be suppressed by the presence of free piperidine which quickly protolyzes XVII (48). A low stationary concentration of benzyne offers additional help.

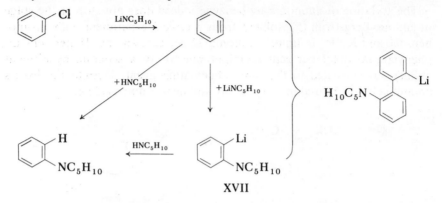

XVII

The 1:1 reaction of chlorobenzene and lithium piperidide gives a meager 18 per cent yield of N-phenylpiperidine (114). Huisgen and Sauer (48) observed that the addition of four equivalents of piperidine increased the amount of product formed to 54 per cent. The tertiary amine can be obtained easily in 85–94 per cent of theory from any of the four halobenzenes if the lithium piperidide is prepared *in situ* by the slow addition of phenyllithium to the ether solution containing four equivalents of piperidine.

The rearrangements become noticeable in the *p*-halotoluene (F, Cl, Br) series. With lithium piperidide and piperidine in ether 74–88 per cent of a mixture of N-tolylpiperidines results, which consists of the *m*-tolyl and the *p*-tolyl isomers in the ratio 56:44. A complete reaction *via* 4-methylbenzyne accounts for the independence of this ratio from the nature of the halogen (48).

Unlike the reaction of 2-halonaphthalene (F, Cl) with phenyllithium (p. 41), lithium piperidide induces only the elimination to 1,2-naphthyne

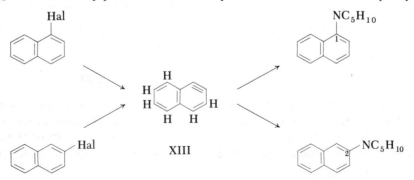

XIII

(XIII). All 1- and 2-halonaphthalenes (Cl, Br, I) are converted to N-naphthylpiperidines in a constant isomer ratio (*88*) (Table 2.2).

TABLE 2.2. REACTIONS OF HALONAPHTHALENES WITH LITHIUM PIPERIDIDE AND PIPERIDINE IN BOILING ETHER. IR-ANALYSIS OF ISOMERIC N-NAPHTHYL-PIPERIDINES (*88*).

Halo-naphthalene	Ratio of isomers 1-		2-	% Total yield of pure isomers
1-Cl	31.5	:	68.5	91
2-Cl	31		69	92
1-Br	30		70	93
2-Br	31		69	79
1-I	34		66	77
2-I	31.5		68.5	54

Huisgen and Sauer (*46*) encountered in the treatment of fluoronaphthalenes with lithium piperidide the same anomalous behaviour as described with potassium amide (*100*) on p. 43. The ratio of isomeric naphthylpiperidines shifts dramatically with the concentration, pointing to competing substitution mechanisms. High lithium piperidide and low piperidine concentrations yield the isomeric amines in the "1,2-naphthyne ratio" of Table 2.2. On the other hand, up to 84 per cent of N-[1-naphthyl]-piperidine results from the reaction of 1-fluoronaphthalene with piperidine in large excess and small concentration of lithium piperidide.

The competing substitution without rearrangement seems to follow the classic pattern of addition-elimination. A different course of the primary elimination, leading from the 1-fluoro isomer to 1,4-naphthyne (XVIII), can be excluded: 1- and 2-fluoro-4-methylnaphthalene show the same competing reaction paths (*88*).

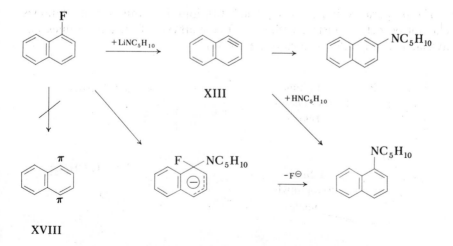

The dependence of the isomer ratio on the concentrations should throw light on the quotient of the rate equations of the competing processes. In a large number of experiments Huisgen, Sauer, Mack and Ziegler (52) found that a square function fit the data best (Fig. 2.1):

$$\frac{d(\text{Elimination mechanism})}{d(\text{Addition mechanism})} = K\frac{[\text{Lithium piperidide}]^2}{[\text{Piperidine}]^2}$$

The factors influencing the reactivity are so numerous that only a partial solution will be offered on p. 57.

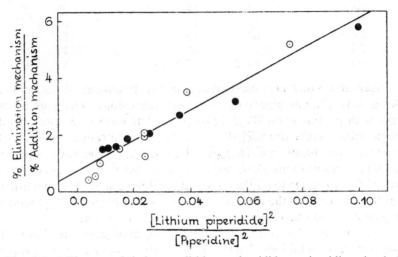

Fig. 2.1. 1-Fluoronaphthalene + lithium piperidide + piperidine in boiling ether. In the experiments represented by ● a larger excess of $LiNC_5H_{10}$ and HNC_5H_{10} was used. In these cases the average concentrations can be more precisely stated.

The preparative importance of substitutions by lithium dialkylamides can not be better illustrated than by the synthesis of tertiary amines not available by any other known route (49,56):

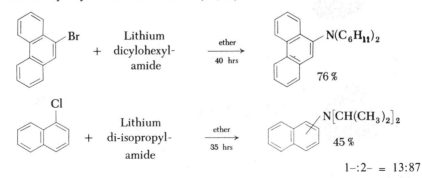

The treatment of aryl halides with sodamide in an excess of boiling dialkylamine (*93*) offers the most simple and convenient variant. Thus Bunnett and Brotherton (*14*) obtained with piperidine as basic component very good yields of N-arylpiperidines while sterically hindered amines gave lower yields. That secondary amines do not react noticeably with sodamide hints at a slightly mysterious phenomenon. An aryne formation by sodamide followed by addition of the dialkylamine does not offer an unambiguous explanation because additive substitutions with the reagent sodamide + piperidine are known. The system is always heterogenous; a surface reaction seems to be involved.

Interestingly enough, Bunnett and Brotherton (*14*) found that halonaphthalenes with sodamide and piperidine suffer a dual elimination; besides 1,2-naphthyne 19 per cent of the 2,3-isomer is formed (*cf.* Table 2.2). We suppose that not the heterogeneity but the higher temperature is responsible for this deviation because the solution of lithium piperidide in boiling piperidine gives the same result (*88*).

Normal aryl halides are resistant towards the alkali derivatives of aryl- or diarylamines in liquid ammonia or in boiling ether. The substitution requires temperatures of 150 300° (*39,67,76*) and the rearrangements (*35,36,92*) testify for benzyne type intermediates.

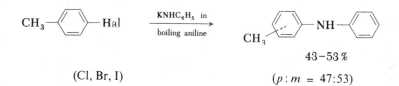

$$CH_3\text{—}\underset{(Cl,\ Br,\ I)}{\langle\ \rangle}\text{—Hal} \quad \xrightarrow[\text{boiling aniline}]{KNHC_6H_5\ \text{in}} \quad CH_3\text{—}\langle\ \rangle\text{—NH—}\langle\ \rangle$$

43–53 %

(*p* : *m* = 47:53)

Distinctly different, the Ullmann procedure—arylation of aromatic amines by aryl bromides or iodides in the presence of copper—takes place without rearrangement (*33,34,99,103*). The mechanism still has to be elucidated.

Free amines, even at high temperature, are not able to abstract HHal from non-activated aryl halides. The lack of rearrangement leaves no doubt that the substitutions with free piperidine above 250° belong to the additive mechanism (*69*).

Aryl halides or sulfonates and alkali hydroxide. Even to-day the hydrolysis of chlorobenzene by 3 *N* NaOH at 370° offers one of the important industrial paths to phenol. The phenoxide ion can again be involved in the reaction, and when it is, gives rise to diphenyl ether and *o*- and *p*-hydroxybiphenyl as side products (*37,77*).

Under the same conditions *o*-chlorobiphenyl gives a mixture of *o*- and *m*-hydroxybiphenyl (*9*). All three isomeric chlorotoluenes yield a cresol

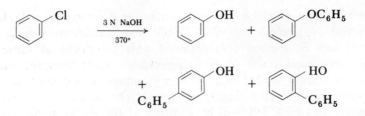

with the *m*-isomer predominating (*94*). Experiments of Bottini and Roberts (*8*) prove conclusively that the halotoluene hydrolysis is due to the concomitant action of mechanisms with and without rearrangement. The data in Table 2.3 are convincing evidence that the elimination-addition mechanism is favored by raising the temperature, by increasing the strength of the base and by the nature of the halogen in the series I < Br < Cl. Also the position of the halogen plays a role. In the reaction of *o*-, *m*- and *p*-bromotoluenes with 4 *N* NaOH at 240°, the addition-elimination mechanism (without rearrangement) participates to the extent of 15, 49 and 53 per cent respectively.

TABLE 2.3. ORIENTATIONS IN HYDROLYSIS
OF HALOTOLUENES (*8*).

Halotoluene	Temperature	Base	Cresol Composition in %		
			o-	*m*-	*p*-
o-Cl	340°	4N NaOH	48	52	
m-Cl	340°	4N NaOH	21	64	15
p-Cl	340°	4N NaOH		50	50
p-Cl	300°	4N NaOH		48	52
p-Cl	250°	4N NaOH		14	86
p-Cl	340°	4N NaOAc		10	90
p-Br	340°	4N NaOH		50	50
p-Br	340°	4N NaOAc		0	100
p-I	340°	4N NaOH		49	51
p-I	250°	4N NaOH		3	97

Again the results with chlorobenzene-[1-^{14}C] point to competing mechanisms (*8*). 4 *N* NaOH transforms this substance to 58 per cent phenol-[1-^{14}C] and 42 per cent phenol-[2-^{14}C]. The conditions of the Dow process mentioned above are favorable for the elimination-addition path. Thus, 1000 ton quantities of benzyne were handled in the industrial autoclaves without anybody's suspecting it. The analysis of the less volatile by-products of the industrial chlorobenzene hydrolysis confirmed this conclusion. Lüttringhaus and Ambros (*72*) isolated 2- and 4-phenoxybiphenyl as well as 2,6-diphenylphenol.

The conversions of halophenols, halobenzenesulfonic acids, phenol-sulfonic acids and benzenedisulfonic acids to diphenols by molten alkali at temperatures above 300° have been the subjects of numerous older investigations. The sometimes fragmentary results, the lack of standardized conditions and unsatisfactory analytical methods make a renewed study highly desirable.

Conspicuously enough, hydroquinone was never isolated from the *p*-disubstituted compounds. Hydroquinone is stable towards molten alkali, but some results suggest a loss by redox reactions during the conversion (*58*). Resorcinol was obtained in usually unspecified yield from the alkali-melt of benzene-*p*-disulfonate (*2*), phenol-*p*-sulfonate (*22*) and *p*-bromobenzene-sulfonate (*70*).

Noelting and Stricker (*80*) reported only the formation of catechol from *o*-iodophenol. *o*-Chlorophenol appears to react by another mechanism; the NaOH-melt at 350° yields 70 per cent diphenols which consist of catechol and resorcinol in the ratio of 42:58 (*58*). The same product ratio was observed with sodium *m*-chlorophenoxide as starting material. This agreement suggests that this ratio is due to the NaOH addition to sodium benzyne-3-oxide (Huisgen and Jung (*58*)). It is astonishing that the HCl elimination from *m*-chlorophenoxide results only in 3-substituted benzyne. The conclusions need further confirmation.

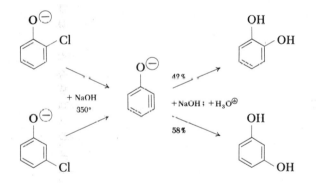

Both sodium benzene-1,2-disulfonate, chlorobenzene-2-sulfonate and phenol-2-sulfonate give in molten NaOH a mixture of roughly 80 per cent catechol and 20 per cent resorcinol. In the KOH-melt the two diphenols are formed in the ratio 90:10 (*58*); the cation appears to have some influence. Sodium phenol-2-sulfonate can be isolated as the intermediate in the conversion of chlorobenzene-2-sulfonate.

More experiments are needed in order to arrive at a consistent mechanistic scheme.

THE MECHANISM OF ARYNE FORMATION

The unsuccessful attempts to isolate benzyne type intermediates provide convincing evidence that arynes are short-lived; nucleophilic addition to an aryne is much faster than its generation.

Aliphatic halides display in S_N reactions an unambiguous sequence of halogen reactivity: F << Cl < Br < I. In the elimination-addition mechanism of nucleophilic aromatic substitution, the reactivity series of halobenzenes shows an amazing dependence on the nature of the basic reagent which brings about the HHal elimination. Bergstrom *et al.* (5) discovered in competition aminations with potassium amide in liquid ammonia the sequence Br > I > Cl; fluorobenzene is inert. In contrast, the reaction of organolithium compounds with fluorobenzene forms benzyne with the highest rate. This discrepancy seemingly indicates different mechanisms of benzyne formation. Nevertheless, it is possible to rationalize all facts by merely varying parameters within a common mechanism as shown below. It seems most appropriate to start the discussion with clear-cut aryne formation by organolithium compounds which is not confused by reversibility phenomena.

Two-step Reaction in Liberation of Benzyne with Organolithium Compounds

The action of phenyl- or *n*-butyllithium on anisole, benzotrifluoride and many suitable benzene derivatives stops with the formation of the *o*-lithio compound which can undergo normal metallorganic reactions. An analogous *o*-lithiohalobenzene intermediate in the system halobenzene and phenyllithium should not be regarded as too speculative a hypothesis. Experimental data warrant the conclusion that the *o*-metalation is the rate determining step with the LiHal elimination as a fast subsequent reaction.

Potentiometric titration of the halide anion, set free from halobenzene, allows kinetic measurements of benzyne formation. Huisgen and Sauer (50) obtained the following rate constants for the reaction with two equivalents of phenyllithium in ether at 20°:

Halobenzene	F	Cl	Br	I
$10^6 k_2 (1/\text{mole} \cdot \text{sec})$	40.8	4.0	4.9	2.8

Apart from the small inversion for chloro- and bromobenzene, the sequence is the one expected for the metalation step. The correlation between metalation rate and acidity was mentioned on p. 39. The covalent fluorine exerts an extreme electronegativity while the other halogens show

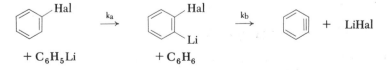

smaller difference (*41,87*). Thus, we encounter a decrease in the inductive acidification of the *o*-hydrogen in the series from fluoro- to iodobenzene.

There remains the possibility of an immeasurably fast LiHal elimination which would not justify assumption of the *o*-lithiohalobenzene as the intermediate. Such a concerted elimination which would result in abandoning the intermediate, can be rigorously excluded. Gilman and Gorsich (*31*) characterized *o*-lithiohalobenzenes as entities of definite life time. They prepared these compounds from *o*-halobromobenzene with *n*-butyllithium by halogen-metal interconversion at low temperatures and trapped them with CO_2 as *o*-halobenzoic acids. Experiments at different temperatures revealed an increasing ease of LiHal elimination from LiF to LiBr. This sequence corresponds to the heterolysis of C-Hal in aliphatic substitutions. While *o*-lithiofluorobenzene was handled at –50°, the presence of *o*-lithiobromobenzene could be demonstrated only at –100° by carbonation. At higher temperatures benzyne formation took place as the products suggested.

Gilman and Soddy (*32*) succeeded in trapping *o*-lithiofluorobenzene at –50° even in the direct metalation of fluorobenzene with *n*-butyllithium. This fact argues for a higher temperature dependence of the metalation compared with LiHal elimination.

The opposite sequence of halide reactivity in the two steps of benzyne formation finds a graphic illustration in the energy profiles of the reactions (Fig. 2.2). The metalation step with phenyllithium is exothermic because

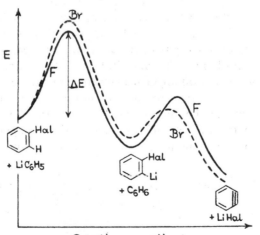

Reaction coordinate

Fig. 2.2. Energy profiles of benzyne formation from fluoro- and bromobenzene with phenyllithium.

halobenzenes are more acidic than benzene. The first determining activation barrier is higher for bromobenzene than for the fluoro compound. The reverse relation for the second barrier, due to the LiHal elimination, leads to a crossing of the energy profiles.

Can it be taken for granted that the second step is a LiHal elimination with liberation of C_6H_4? Whereas the benzyne intermediate offers the simplest rationalization for the equivalence of the neighboring positions, it is not possible to rule out completely an alternative hypothesis. Thus, a very fast equilibrium of the o-lithioaryl halides, formulated for lithiofluoroanisole, would be in accordance with the observed products.

Admittedly, this is not an attractive hypothesis because no reasonable mechanism for the simultaneous exchange of the two substituents can be conceived. Moreover, the mechanistic problem of the substitution by the metallorganic compound (p. 39) is not solved but only side-stepped.

The results on the amination mechanism, discussed in the next section, permit the abandoning of the highly improbable equilibrium above.

The Reaction of Halobenzenes with Alkali Amide in Liquid Ammonia

A limited number of ingenious experiments using deuterium labels allowed Roberts to outline a mechanistic scheme, which explains Bergstrom's halobenzene reactivity series F << Cl < Br > I by a reversibility of the primary proton removal. Despite its resistance towards potassium amide in liquid ammonia, Hall, Piccolini and Roberts (38) observed a very fast D,H-exchange of o-deuterofluorobenzene in the mentioned system. Thus, the proton or deuteron abstraction is quite normal; indeed it is the fastest D,H-exchange in the halobenzene series. However, the reprotonation is so much faster than the LiF elimination that nothing happens except an equilibration involving a minute concentration of the anion.

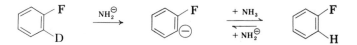

In the amination of o-deuterobromobenzene Roberts, Semenow, Simmons and Carlsmith (84) found a kinetic isotope effect $k_H/k_D = 5.5$ which is in the correct range for the breaking of the C—H bond in an activation process. Probably it is the rate-determining step, though an intramolecular isotope effect does not allow an unqualified conclusion.

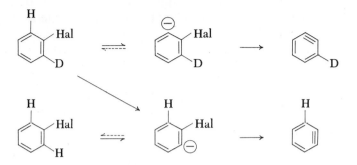

It is easy to see that any reprotonation of the carbanion (dotted arrow) should result in an apparent decrease of the H-D isotope effect. The inference that the loss of the bromide ion is very fast compared with the reprotonation, was pictured by Roberts as a concerted one-step HBr elimination:

The lower kinetic isotope effect in the amination of *o*-deuterochlorobenzene $(k_H/k_D = 2.1)$ suggests some reprotonation. Roberts' interpretation foresees here the stepwise process sketched above.

The equilibrium hypothesis of p. 54 can be refuted. Starting with chlorobenzene-[1-^{14}C], the equilibration and reprotonation should lead to some chlorobenzene-[2-^{14}C] and finally to some aniline-[3-^{14}C]. The degradation showed the label to be restricted to position 1 and 2 (*84*).

Roberts' mechanistic deductions include some arbitrary assumptions. It is questionable if free carbanions instead of metallorganic compounds are involved in the proton abstraction from halobenzenes by alkali amides in liquid ammonia. The high kinetic isotope effect in the case of *o*-deuterobromobenzene proves only that the deprotonation is irreversible, but not that the loss of H and Br is simultaneous.

Kinetics of the Reaction of Halobenzenes with Lithium Piperidide in Ether

The kinetic studies of Huisgen *et al.* in this section and on pp. 58–62 offer not a mere confirmation of the mechanistic concepts described, but indicate extensions and modifications. The gross accordance of all data, independently arrived at, provides some confidence for the general mechanistic conclusions.

The main difference between the systems lithium dialkylamide in ether and alkali amide in liquid ammonia might be found in the inferior aptitude of ether for ion solvation. Therefore, it seems very probable that only covalent Li—N and Li—C bonds are involved rather than free anionic functions.

The kinetics of the reaction of halobenzenes with two equivalents of lithium piperidide in ether can be evaluated by the second order law. Free piperidine influences the rate of aryne formation by lithium piperidide to a surprising extent without appearing in the stoichiometric equation (50). Some rate constants of the four halobenzenes are plotted in Table 2.4 versus the concentration of free piperidine. The constants of the system, fluorobenzene and lithium piperidide, are greatly decreased with rising piperidine concentration. Those of chlorobenzene do not change appreciably. Bromo- and iodobenzene show a positive dependence on the amine to a different degree.

TABLE 2.4. RATE CONSTANTS OF BENZYNE FORMATION FROM HALOBENZENES WITH LITHIUM PIPERIDIDE IN ETHER AT 20° ($10^5 k_2$ 1/mole-sec): INFLUENCE OF FREE PIPERIDINE (50).

(Slowest halobenzenes in italics)

Piperidine (Mole/l)	Halobenzenes			
	F	Cl	Br	I
0.0	110	27.5	44	*16.8*
0.1	67	26	68	*23*
0.2	43	*25*	90	31
0.3	30	*24*	110	38
0.4	*20*	23	129	46
0.6	*11*	21	160	60

With a suitable choice of piperidine concentration nearly all possible halogen reactivity sequences can be realized (Table 2.4). In the absence of free amine, that is, on working only with lithium piperidide in ether, fluorobenzene is fastest, followed by the other halobenzenes at small intervals. The order in this series is qualitatively the same as that found with phenyllithium as the benzyne generating base (Table 2.5).

TABLE 2.5. RATE CONSTANTS OF BENZYNE FORMATION FROM HALOBENZENES BY LITHIUM BASE IN ETHER AT 20° (50); $10^6 k_2$ (1/mole-sec)

LiB	C_6H_5 F	C_6H_5 Cl	C_6H_5 Br	C_6H_5 I
Phenyllithium	40.8	4.0	4.9	2.8
Lithium piperidide	860	275	440	168

The reduction of the overall rate for fluorobenzene with excess secondary amine in Table 2.4 offers direct kinetic proof for the demetalation of *o*-lithiofluorobenzene by piperidine. The metalation equilibrium of fluorobenzene which lies far on the side of the reactants never becomes fully established because it is constantly disturbed by the LiF elimination. The kinetic and energetic situation is illustrated by the energy profiles in Fig. 2.3. The endothermic metalation by lithium piperidide is slow for all halobenzenes and more or less rate-determining (k_a). The *o*-lithiohalobenzene enters two competing fast reactions: The LiHal elimination (k_b) and the protolysis by piperidine (k_a'), giving back the starting material.

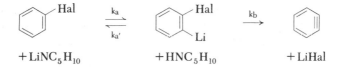

The k_a values of the halobenzenes decrease from the fluoro to the iodo compound (*cf.* p. 52). Furthermore, they show increasing ratios of k_b/k_a' due to the rising elimination rate of the LiHal. For *o*-lithiofluorobenzene the activation barriers of the two competing reactions are of comparable height. Therefore, an excess of piperidine enforces the "back-reaction," the demetalation. Here we face the reason for the suppression of the naphthyne formation from fluoronaphthalene in the presence of excess secondary amine (pp. 47–48).

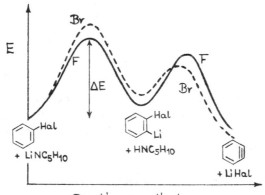

Fig. 2.3. Energy profiles of benzyne formation from fluoro- and bromobenzene with lithium piperidide.

The high value of k_b/k_a' for bromo- and iodobenzene results in a practically irreversible metalation. There is no necessity to postulate a different mechanism. The continuous variation of the parameters within the two-step process formulated above gives a satisfactory answer.

However, the validity of the differential equation

$$\frac{d[\text{Benzyne}]}{dt} = \frac{k_a k_b}{k_a'} \frac{[C_6H_5\text{Hal}]}{[\text{HNC}_5H_{10}]} [\text{LiNC}_5H_{10}]$$

is limited because an accelerating influence of the free piperidine is superimposed. Probably all halobenzenes are subject to this positive rate effect, the nature of which will be discussed in the next section. This effect is overcome in the case of fluorobenzene by the rate-retarding demetalation; the deviation from the expected linear function in Table 2.4 can possibly be attributed to it. For chlorobenzene the two opposing effects seem to balance each other, while for bromo- and iodobenzene the rate-enhancing one predominates (Table 2.4).

The tendency of lithium amides and organolithium compounds toward complex formation is more widespread than previously suspected. The rate constants of Tables 2.4 and 2.5 are only apparent constants. The reaction of bromobenzene with one equivalent of lithium piperidide in ether displays the typical kinetics of self-retardation caused by complexing of the product LiBr with lithium piperidide (54). The quantitative evaluation of experiments with different initial lithium bromide concentrations gives the true k_2 values and discloses an ether soluble 1:1 complex which is inactive in aryne formation. Huisgen and Mack (54) measured dissociation constants of 0.025 and 0.030 mole/l for the complexes of lithium piperidide with LiBr or LiI, respectively. They can be formulated as salt-like (XIX) or anion bonded (XX).

As further examples analogous complexes of phenyllithium and LiHal as well as the autocomplexes of organolithium compounds in ether are cited (110,112). The kinetics of ring closure reactions suggested similar autocomplexes of lithium dialkylamides (51).

Rate and Nature of the Metalating Agent

The variation in ability of several lithium dialkylamides to liberate benzyne from bromobenzene is reasonably accounted for by steric factors (Table 2.6). The rate constants of the N-lithium derivatives of the cyclic

TABLE 2.6. RATE CONSTANTS OF BENZYNE FORMATION FROM
BROMOBENZENE WITH $LiNR_2$ AND ONE EQUIVALENT OF HNR_2
IN ETHER AT 20° (50); $10^5 k_2$ (1/mole·sec).

Lithium pyrrolidide	141
Lithium piperidide	113
Lithium diethylamide	12.0
Lithium di-isobutylamide	8.9
Lithium dicyclohexylamide	3.2

bases exceed that of lithium diethylamide by a factor of ten while branching of the N-bound alkyl further diminishes the rate.

A comparison of the activity of phenyllithium and lithium piperidide in benzyne formation discloses another remarkable fact. Phenyllithium converts piperidine in an exothermic reaction quantitatively into lithium piperidide and benzene. That leaves no doubt that phenyllithium is a much stronger base than lithium piperidide. Nevertheless, the latter is the more efficient agent in abstracting HHal from halobenzenes as the 30–90 times higher rate constants in Table 2.5 (p. 56) convincingly show. This dramatic violation of the basicity sequence—the steric requirements of the two lithium bases probably are not grossly different—suggests that the interaction of base and halobenzene in benzyne formation is not a simple proton transfer. Otherwise, Brönsted's catalysis law would demand a linear relationship between the logarithm of the relative rate and the p_K value of the base. This violation may also be taken as a sign not to simplify reactions of metallorganic compounds and metal amides by invoking free anions.

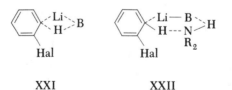

XXI   XXII

An interpretation of the metalation as including a lithium-hydrogen exchange *via* a four-membered cyclic transition state XXI appears reasonable (50). During this concerted bond-breaking and -making the base B appears with a coordination number higher by one than in the ground state. In contrast to phenyllithium, lithium piperidide still owns an unshared electron pair at the basic center. Supposedly this facilitates energetically the formation of the transition state XXI of which the stereochemistry is unsettled yet. The relation to the metalation mechanism proposed by Bryce-Smith (11,12) should be mentioned.

A six-membered ring would result if a molecule of free amine is inserted into the cyclic transition state XXI. The formation of XXII needs a higher activation entropy but the energy requirements are lower than for XXI. Possibly such a third order metalation is responsible for the rate enhancement by free piperidine (p. 58).

Rate and Nature of the Aryl Group

In the mechanism depicted above for the aryne formation from aryl bromides, the *o*-metalation dictates the over-all rate. As a consequence the specific rate, on varying the aryl group, should be a simple function of the acidity of the C—H bond adjacent to the C—Br. The readiness of several aryl bromides for aryne formation is compared in Table 2.7. The partial rate factors are based on 1.0 for an *o*-position of bromobenzene. *m*-Substituted bromobenzenes form two isomeric arynes, the ratio of which is revealed by product analyses (*53*).

The expectation that the electron releasing alkyl groups diminish C—H acidity, and therefore the rate factor, is confirmed. The overall influence of phenyl as a substituent is electron-attracting and, therefore, acidity-increasing. Also the importance of steric effects can be recognized from the alkyl derivatives in Table 2.7.

Since the dipole moment of anisole is directed from oxygen to the aromatic nucleus, why do the bromoanisoles show partial rate factors > 1?

TABLE 2.7. PARTIAL RATE FACTORS OF ARYNE FORMATION FROM BROMOBENZENE DERIVATIVES WITH 2 EQUIVALENTS OF LITHIUM PIPERIDIDE IN THE PRESENCE OF 2 EQUIVALENTS OF PIPERIDINE IN ETHER AT 20° (*53*) (UPPER LIMITS SET IN ITALICS).

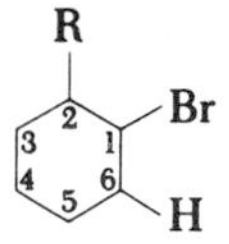

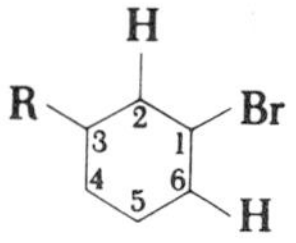

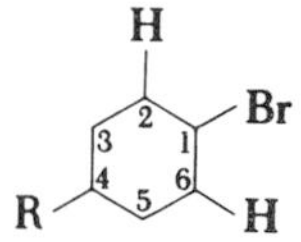

R-	H at C-6	C-2	C-6	C-2
H-	1.0	1.0	1.0	1.0
CH_3-	0.50	0.35	0.38	0.45
$(CH_3)_2CH$-	0.37	0.19	0.44	0.53
C_6H_5-	1.9	1.8	0.91	2.0
Br-	140	940	< 40	83
F-	34	1700	< 40	25
CH_3O-	1.4	600	< 30	1.2
$(CH_3)_2N$-	0.58	7.3	< 0.3	0.23
CF_3-	4.6	58	< 12	3.4

Stabilization of the anion plays an important part in determining acidity. This is a major factor in our case even though only a fractional negative charge is involved in a transition state such as XXI (p. 59). The methoxy group promotes metalation by way of the inductive effect which disperses the mentioned negative charge. Noteworthy is the extreme partial rate factor of 600 for *m*-bromoanisole where the C—H acidity is enhanced by two flanking substituents.

The inductive and resonance effects of the methoxy group exert antagonistic influences on the C—H acidity. This is best demonstrated by 2-methoxynaphthalene which is metalated in position 3 exclusively (*96*). The acidity-weakening resonance effect is active in position 1, but reaches 3 for known reasons (*42,102*) only to a minor extent. 3-Lithio-2-methoxynaphthalene opens a path to rare naphthalene-2.3-derivatives (*43*).

The partial rate factors of bromo-*N.N*-dimethylanilines in Table 2.7 point to the dominating acidity-decreasing resonance effect. Again the position 2 of the *m*-bromo isomer with a factor of 7.3 is exceptional. Perhaps a primary coordination of the metalating reagent at the unshared pair of the amine nitrogen facilitates the process. The comparison with the data for bromoanisoles, bromofluorobenzenes and dibromobenzenes suggests a similar coordination as a promoting effect in *m*-bromoanisole.

No numerical values of aromatic C—H acidities are known. The acidities of substituted pyridinium ions (*10*) offer a useful correlation (*53*). The linearity of the plot between the logarithms of the partial rate factors of Table 2.7 and the p_{K_a} values of pyridinium salts is better than expected considering the different nature of the proton abstractions (Fig. 2.4).

Naphthalene is more acidic than benzene as its metalation by phenylsodium (*25*) shows. Therefore, the formation of 1,2-naphthyne is faster than that of benzyne, especially if the hydrogen in position 1 is reacting (Table 2.8). 9-Bromophenanthrene shows, with a partial factor of 39, a further increase of acidity (*53*).

The reaction of aryl fluorides with phenyllithium shows a similar rate gradation (*61*) to the one in the system aryl bromide and lithium piperidide (Table 2.8). This supports again a common mechanism of aryne formation. To the best of our knowledge this is the two-step process with primary metalation. The evidence for a concerted mechanism (*84*) seems inconclusive.

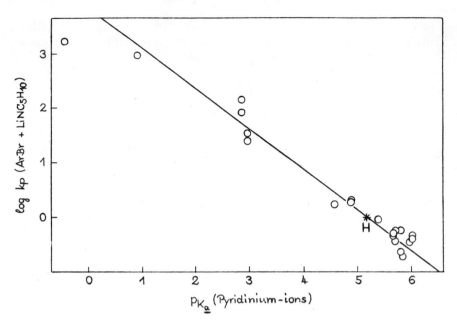

Fig. 2.4. Correlation of the logarithms of partial rate factors of aryne formation from subst. bromobenzenes with the pK_a values of subst. pyridinium ions (53).
Substituents: CH_3, $(CH_3)_2CH$, C_6H_5, Br and $(CH_3)_2N$ (NH_2).

TABLE 2.8. PARTIAL RATE FACTORS OF ARYNE FORMATION
IN ETHER AT 20° (53,61)

Aryl halide	Aryl bromide +2 $LiNC_5H_{10}$	Aryl fluoride +4 C_6H_5Li
Halobenzene	1.0	1.0
1-Halonaphthalene	6.8	2.5
2-Halonaphthalene	11.6	10.6
2-Halo-1-methylnaphthalene	1.2	
9-Halophenanthrene	39	16.4
3-Halopyrene	6.8	

Other Routes to Arynes

The o-metalation of halobenzenes needs a relatively high concentration
of organolithium compounds or lithium amides. In the desire to avoid the
subsequent addition of these lithium bases to benzyne, Wittig and Pohmer
(114) developed new paths to o-metalhalobenzenes. Shaking o-fluoro-
bromobenzene in ether with lithium-amalgam gives benzyne via o-lithio-
fluorobenzene. The isolated products are 24 per cent biphenylene, 3 per

cent triphenylene and 2 per cent *o*-phenylenemercury; the latter was characterized by Wittig and Bickelhaupt (*117*) as the hexamer containing an 18-
membered ring.

Biphenylene arises perhaps from a dimerization of benzyne. Without
doubt the formation of triphenylene is better explained by the successive
addition of two benzynes to *o*-lithiofluorobenzene with a final cyclization
by the additive mechanism.

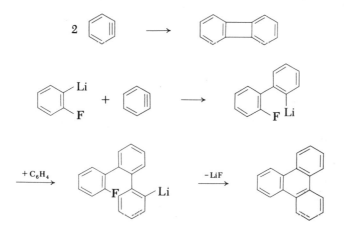

Still more attractive as a preparative method is the treatment of *o*-fluoro-
bromobenzene with magnesium in ether. Benzyne and magnesium fluoro-
bromide are formed *via* the Grignard compound (*114*).

The halogen-lithium exchange usually takes place much faster than the
hydrogen-lithium replacement. Gilman and Gorsich (*31*) carried out the
conversion of *o*-fluorobromobenzene by *n*-butyllithium to *o*-lithiofluoro-
benzene at –50° (p. 53).

All endeavors to prepare benzyne type intermediates from other than
metallorganic compounds have so far been unsuccessful. The pyrolysis of
silver *o*-chlorobenzoate by Köbrich (*65*) shows some promise:

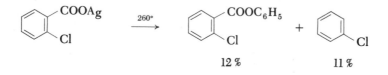

Relation to Other Eliminations

Olefinic substitutions following an elimination-addition mechanism are
well known. Reppe's industrially important conversion of vinyl chloride to

vinyl ethyl ether passes through acetylene (*81*). Of course, the deeper
saddle in the energy profile here marks a rather long-lived intermediate. A
close mechanistic relation of the primary *trans*-elimination of vinyl halides
to the one leading to benzyne seems doubtful.

This connection between elimination in aromatic and olefinic series is
better established in the transformation of 1-chlorocyclohexene to 1-
phenylcyclohexene with phenyllithium, observed by Wittig and Harborth
(*109*). Scardiglia and Roberts (*90*) used ^{14}C-labeled 1-chlorocyclohexene
and found the label distribution in accordance with cyclohexyne as a
highly strained intermediate. Cyclooctyne is the smallest isolable cyclic
alkyne (*7*).

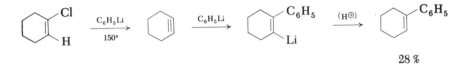

In 1912 Favorsky and Boshovsky (*20*) obtained dodecahydrotriphenyl-
ene (XXIII) from 1,2-dibromocyclohexene and sodium at room temperature in low yield. They entertained the idea of a trimerization of an
elimination product and extended the studies later to other ring sizes (*21*).

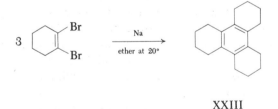

XXIII

However, the mechanism is not unequivocal. Treatment of dibromocyclo-
hexene by phenyllithium gives none of XXIII. Instead, two substances of
probable structures XXIV and XXV are isolated, the formation of which
fits an addition-elimination scheme better (*60*).

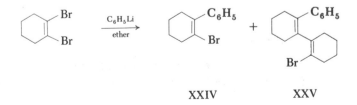

XXIV   XXV

The base-catalyzed concerted HBr-abstraction from bromo-olefins seems to follow the same *trans*-course as the olefin-forming elimination, Ingold's E_2 reaction (*62*). *cis*-Bromostyrene undergoes this elimination with NaOH in isopropanol 10^5 times faster than the *trans*-isomer (*17*). On the other hand, Cristol and Helmreich (*18*) found for the conversion of bromostyrenes to phenylacetylene by phenyllithium in ether only a ratio k_{trans}/k_{cis} of 2. A still lower ratio of k_{trans}/k_{cis} of 1.3 was established with a competition method using lithium piperidide as base by Huisgen and Herbig (*57*); no stereoisomerization takes place prior to the HBr elimination. The interpretation favored by Cristol (*18*), a primary α-elimination of bromostyrene, seems improbable. In the bromostilbene series the structure forbids an α-elimination, but the same phenomenon, lack of steric discrimination, appears. On treatment with lithium piperidide in ether, the geometric isomers are transformed with a rate ratio of only 1.7 in favor of *trans*-elimination (*57,60*).

The hypothesis of a two-step elimination, initiated by a hydrogen-lithium exchange, is deduced from studies on benzyne formation. Under the conditions of Tables 2.7 and 2.8, the partial rate factors would amount to 1500 for bromo-*trans*- and 2100 for bromo-*cis*-stilbene (*57*).

This mechanism can be regarded as the reversal of a recently proposed (*98*) two-step nucleophilic addition to the triple bond if one replaces the carbanion by the metallorganic compound. However, the addition is completely stereoselective. Similar eliminations to triply bonded products, also lacking stereoselectivity, were described recently (*85,86,101*).

TYPICAL REACTIONS OF ARYNES

Benzyne acts as an electron deficient species. Numerous additions of metallorganic substances and metal amides, mentioned above, testify to this tendency of benzyne to unite with nucleophilic agents. So far, the reactions of benzyne with the generating reagents have been in the forefront. It is appropriate for a high-energy intermediate also to accept agents which themselves are not capable of setting arynes free.

Phenylation of Carbanions

Benzyne adds not only the potential carbanions of normal alkali metallorganic compounds, but also ones with higher resonance stabilization.

Extensive studies have been made by Bergstrom *et al.* using the system bromobenzene and potassium amide in liquid ammonia. The reaction between potassium triphenylmethide and bromobenzene does not start before a further equivalent of potassium amide is added; 46 per cent tetraphenylmethane is obtained (*123*). The catalytic role of the potassium amide was recognized by Wright and Bergstrom (*123*), but its function remained in the dark. The criterion of rearrangement was not evident because only halobenzenes were used. A straightforward explanation follows from the foregoing. The amide liberates benzyne from bromobenzene. The interaction of potassium triphenylmethide and benzyne corresponds to a phenylation.

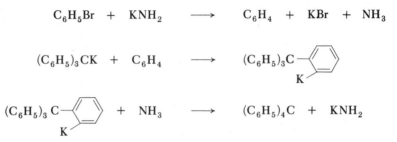

$$C_6H_5Br \ + \ KNH_2 \ \longrightarrow \ C_6H_4 \ + \ KBr \ + \ NH_3$$

If the substrate contains more than one acidic C—H, successive phenylations are observed. Treatment of acetonitrile with 2 equivalents of chlorobenzene and 3 equivalents of KNH_2 in liquid ammonia yields 31 per cent phenyl- and 28 per cent diphenylacetonitrile (*6*). Under the same conditions, 2-picoline is phenylated to 24 per cent 2-benzyl-, 18 per cent 2-benzhydryl- and 18 per cent 2-tritylpyridine (*19*). It is noteworthy that even the acidity of *o*-tolunitrile is sufficient to give 32 per cent 2-benzyl- and 9 per cent 2-benzhydrylbenzonitrile (*19*). *p*-Bromotoluene reacts with sodium phenylacetylide and sodamide to give 16 per cent tolylphenylacetylene containing the *p*-, and the *m*-isomers in the ratio 43:57 (*91*). Leake and Levine (*68*) recently described analogous phenylations of ketones and esters. Table 2.9 (p. 67) summarizes the literature on carbanion phenylations. Surprisingly enough, sodium cyanide is unreactive (*15*).

Benzyne as Dienophile

The electron deficiency of benzyne is not only removed by the addition of nucleophiles, but also by Diels-Alder synthesis. This new domain of aryne chemistry was discovered and developed by Wittig in a series of brilliant papers. In the first example the yield profited from a neat trick—the use of furan both as solvent for the preparation of the metallorganic intermediate and as the active diene. *o*-Fluorbromobenzene and lithium amalgam give, in furan, 76 per cent 1,4-dihydronaphthalene-1,4-endoxide

TABLE 2.9. PHENYLATIONS OF CH-ACIDIC COMPOUNDS BY
HALOBENZENE AND ALKALI AMIDE IN LIQUID AMMONIA

	Ref.
Triphenylmethane	*93,123*
Diphenylmethane	*93,123*
Fluorene	*91*
9-Phenyl-1,2-benzofluorene	*93*
Phenylacetylene	*91*
2-Picoline	*19*
Quinaldine	*19,123*
4-Methylquinoline	*19*
Acetonitrile	*6*
Isobutyronitrile	*15*
o-Tolunitrile	*6*
Acetophenone	*68*
Acetone	*68*
Methyl ethyl ketone	*68*
Diethyl ketone	*68*
Ethyl acetate and propionate	*68*
Ethyl phenylacetate	*68*
Diethyl malonate	*68*
Indene	*56*
2-Methylindazole	*56*

(XXVI) (*114*). Some further transformations of XXVI are formulated below. This diene synthesis can be extended to substituted benzynes (*120*).

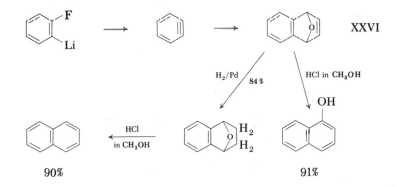

The interaction of anthracene and benzyne in tetrahydrofuran leads to
triptycene (*113*). The yield amounts to 28 per cent using o-fluorobromo-
benzene and magnesium as the generator and 10 per cent with the system
fluorobenzene and n-butyllithium (*115*).

Even N-methylpyrrole as a very weak diene reacts with benzyne analogously. The 1:1 adduct, XXVII, can be isolated only in meager yield because

it undergoes an interesting reaction with a second molecule of benzyne. The presumed ylide intermediate rearranges to XXVIII (*119*).

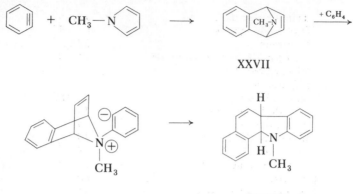

XXVII

XXVIII

Other successful Diels-Alder syntheses are listed below (*116,118*).

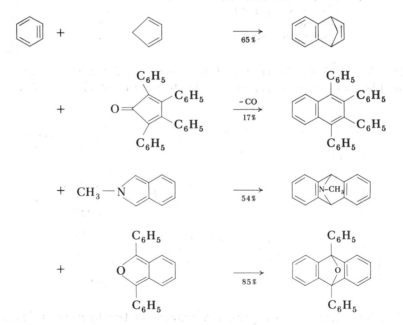

Ring Closure Reactions

The intermolecular base addition to the extra bond of arynes opens new paths to a variety of heterocyclic systems.

Treatment of methyl-[2-(*m*-chlorophenyl)-ethyl]-amine with phenyl-lithium in ether gives the *N*-lithio derivative **XXIX** from which an intra-molecular aryne formation was expected. The subsequent, intramolecular addition of the secondary amino group renders the tertiary cyclic base **XXX**. A quantitative rearrangement is concomitant with the nucleophilic substitution. In the presence of 1.5 equivalents of lithium diethylamide the yield of *N*-methylindoline (**XXX**) reaches 88 per cent of theory (*45*).

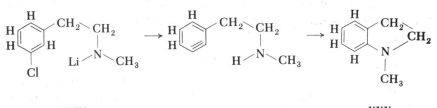

          XXIX   **XXX**

The cyclization of the corresponding *o*-chloro compound **XXXI** to the same product **XXX** takes place without rearrangement, but is slower and slightly less productive. Huisgen and König (*45*) observed the same phe-nomenon in closing the ring of *N*-methyltetrahydroquinoline (**XXXIII**) from the two isomers of the higher homolog **XXXII** with phenyllithium; under standard conditions the *m*-chloro compound is superior.

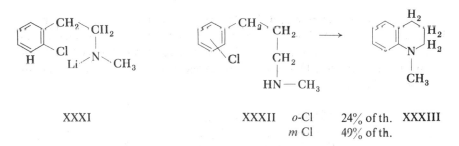

      XXXI   **XXXII** *o*-Cl   24% of th. **XXXIII**
                                              m Cl   49% of th.

In the *o*-chloro compounds **XXXI** and **XXXII** the basic N—Li group cannot reach the hydrogen in the *m*-position for the HCl elimination. Here the aryne formation cannot but take an intermolecular course. An obvious explanation is to ascribe the faster ring closure of the *m*-chloro compounds to the intramolecular liberation of the aryne, but this does not present the full truth. Kinetic studies provided some interesting details (see ref. *51*).

On treating methyl-[2-(2,5-dichlorophenyl)-ethyl]-amine with phenyl-lithium the elimination can involve *o*- or *m*-chlorine. The product analysis discloses again the preference for the latter (*59*):

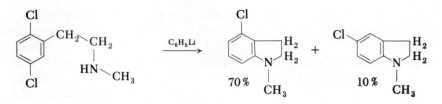

Some further examples of König and Huisgen's work (*66*) underscore the generalization of this new synthetic principle. Sodamide or sodium hydride in ether or potassium amide in liquid ammonia are also suitable condensing reagents.

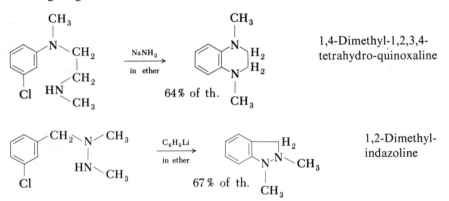

1,4-Dimethyl-1,2,3,4-tetrahydro-quinoxaline

1,2-Dimethyl-indazoline

The intramolecular base addition to arynes belongs to the limited number of cyclizations which give medium-sized and large rings in satisfactory yields (*59,66*). In the closure of the 16-membered *meta*- (XXXIV) and the 17-membered *para*-ring (XXXV) the heterogenous reaction with sodamide in ether is efficient.

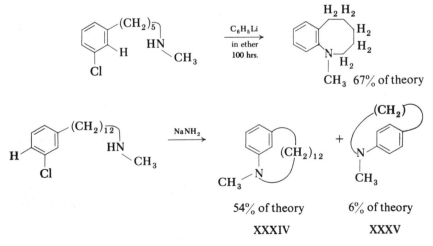

Alkoxides are added by arynes only reluctantly. Even in the intramolecular course the yields of coumarane and chromane from XXXVI, n = 2,3 are poor (*59*). The intermolecular addition of lithium diethylamide which liberates the aryne, appears as a powerful competitor.

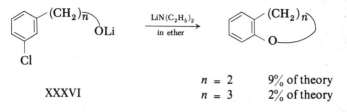

n = 2	9% of theory
n = 3	2% of theory

XXXVI

Hrutfiord and Bunnett (*40*) reported recently on the cyclization of *N*-acylated *o*- and *m*-haloanilines by potassium amide in liquid ammonia. Here, not only anionic sulfur and carbon but also oxygen is successful in closing the ring. Supposedly, the transition state of the O-addition would profit from the aromatic oxazole resonance. The reactants were *o*-halo-anilides with one exception. Though probable, the aryne mechanism has to be proved for the majority of these examples.

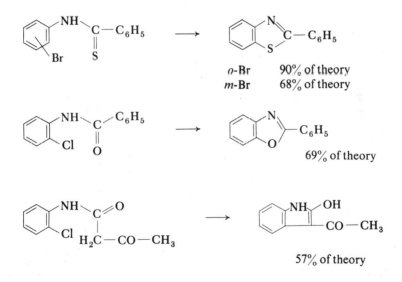

o-Br	90% of theory
m-Br	68% of theory

69% of theory

57% of theory

Catalytic Arylation of Aryl Chlorides

The discrepancy between basicity and rate of HHal elimination from halobenzenes, described on p. 59, led Huisgen, Sauer and Hauser (*44*) to an application of preparative interest. The normally sluggish biphenyl formation from chlorobenzene and phenyllithium is considerably accelerated by catalytic quantities of secondary amines, for instance piperidine. The immediately formed lithium piperidide liberates benzyne from chlorobenzene with a rate constant which is 70 times higher than the one of phenyllithium, (Table 2.5, p. 56). Subsequently, both lithium bases compete in the addition to benzyne; and the phenyllithium, because of its higher concentration, is the more successful. On summing up the following three equations, the function of lithium piperidide as the catalyst becomes obvious.

$$C_6H_5Cl \ + \ LiNC_5H_{10} \ \longrightarrow \ C_6H_4 \ + \ LiCl \ + \ HNC_5H_{10}$$

$$C_6H_5Cl \ + \ LiC_6H_5 \ \longrightarrow \ C_6H_5{-}C_6H_5 \ + \ LiCl$$

A biphenyl synthesis is not very exciting but within this scheme of "catalytic arylation" the aryl chloride as well as the organolithium compound can be varied over a wide range to produce mixed biaryls. The reaction of 1-chloronaphthalene and phenyllithium yields, under standard conditions in ether after a limited time of 2 hours, only 4 per cent of phenylnaphthalenes (isomer ratio 33:67). The same experiment, with 13 mole per cent of piperidine added, achieves 29 per cent of phenylnaphthalenes. In a 60 min-

TABLE 2.10. REACTIONS OF ARYL CHLORIDES WITH 2-2.5
EQUIVALENTS OF ARYLLITHIUM WITHOUT AND WITH
0.3-0.5 EQUIVALENTS OF PIPERIDINE IN
BOILING ETHER (44).

Aryl Chloride	RLi	Time in hrs.	Ar-R in % of Theory Without	With Piperidine
Chlorobenzene	Phenyl-	9	17	61
Chlorobenzene	o-Tolyl-	2	6	23
1-Chloronaphthalene	Phenyl-	2	4	29
2-Chloronaphthalene	Phenyl-	2	10	50
4-Chlorobiphenyl	Phenyl-	6	18	65
9-Chlorophenanthrene	Phenyl-	1	13	58
9-Chlorophenanthrene	o-Tolyl-	1	14	60
9-Chlorophenanthrene	Mesityl-	40	9	36

ute treatment of 9-chlorophenanthrene with phenyllithium, addition of 12 mole per cent of piperidine increases the yield from 13 to 58 per cent of 9-phenylphenanthrene. Table 2.10 includes additional data.

The amine catalysis of arylation offers, moreover, a convincing argument in favor of the elimination-addition mechanism of substitution. In the case of 9-chlorophenanthrene, for instance, the symmetry of XXXVII means that rearrangement products will be unobservable; the amine catalysis offers a clue to the mechanism. Also, 9-chloroanthracene is converted by phenyllithium to 9-phenylanthracene. The lack of piperidine catalysis favors the mechanism with primary addition and argues against a 9,10-anthracyne as the intermediate (Hauser and Huisgen (*56*)).

XXXVII

QUANTITATIVE DATA FROM COMPETITION EXPERIMENTS AND THE NATURE OF ARYNES

The experimental facts described in the preceding section are easily accounted for by the assumption of arynes as true intermediates. It is pretty awkward to interpret the KNH_2-catalysis discussed on p. 66, for instance, as a polymolecular reaction merely passing through a transition state which contains benzyne only as a resonance structure. Wittig and Härle (*120*) considered the proof for the intermediate to be equivocal and discussed recently a possible bimolecular reaction of *o*-lithiofluorobenzene and a diene leading directly to the diene adduct.

Characterization of Benzyne as Intermediate

How is a rigorous proof of a dip in the energy profile of a reaction demonstrated? One possible way is to search for a suitably substituted model system with an energy valley deep enough to permit isolation of the intermediate. In this fashion Meisenheimer (*75*) established the additive intermediate in the activated nucleophilic aromatic substitution (p. 39). The direct detection of arynes by physical methods seems worth discussing only after a new access to arynes is found which avoids metallorganic intermediates.

Another criterion is that based on the capability of a true intermediate to select freely a partner for further reaction in a competitive experiment. In a conversion *via* a transition state only all compounds which appear in the product have to enter the activated complex as reactants. However, the energy saddle of an intermediate can be the starting point of branching reactions. Measurements of overall rate and product composition in competitive experiments proved, for example, the carbonium intermediate in aliphatic S_N1 reactions (3).

Huisgen, Mack and Möbius (55) developed the clear competition phenomenon of the "catalytic phenylation" (pp. 71–73) into a rigid quantitative test. Lithium piperidide and phenyllithium compete in the formation of and in the addition to the aryne. Chloro- or fluorobenzene were treated with a 10- to 12-fold excess of lithium piperidide and phenyllithium in varying proportions. The ratio of biphenyl to N-phenylpiperidine in the product turned out to be a linear function of the proportion of the two lithium reagents (Fig. 2.5). Based on a free competition of the two nucleophiles for benzyne, the following equation should be fulfilled. The large excess of the lithium bases allows substitution of the differentials by the total product yields.

$$d[\text{Biphenyl}]/dt = k_2 [\text{Benzyne}] [\text{LiC}_6\text{H}_5]$$

$$d[\text{N-Phenylpiperidine}]/dt = k_2'[\text{Benzyne}] [\text{LiNC}_5\text{H}_{10}]$$

$$\frac{d[\text{Biphenyl}]}{d[\text{N-Phenylpiperidine}]} = \frac{k_2}{k_2'} \cdot \frac{[\text{LiC}_6\text{H}_5]}{[\text{LiNC}_5\text{H}_{10}]} \sim \frac{[\text{C}_6\text{H}_5-\text{C}_6\text{H}_5]}{[\text{C}_6\text{H}_5-\text{NC}_5\text{H}_{10}]}$$

The slope of the straight line (k_2/k_2') brings to light the fact that benzyne prefers the addition of phenyllithium 4.4-fold over that of lithium piperidide. On the other hand, lithium piperidide liberates benzyne 27 times faster from fluorobenzene and 70 times faster from chlorobenzene than phenyllithium does. Thus, the divergence of total rate and product composition makes a discriminating intermediate evident.

The collective arguments on pp. 52–53 and 55–58 pointed to o-lithio-halobenzene as the first intermediate in benzyne formation. However, the idea that this is the selective intermediate, responsible for product composition, can be rejected. Apart from the difficulty of reconciling them with the rearrangements (pp. 38–51), fluoro- and chlorobenzene show in Fig. 2.5 identical competition constants. The isomer mixtures, resulting from lithium piperidide additions to arynes (pp. 46–47), are independent of the nature of the halogen in the aryl halide. Therefore, it seems justified to assume that a halogen-free intermediate is responsible for product formation. The conversion of o-lithiohalobenzene to benzyne offers the most simple and straightforward rationalization.

Selectivity Differences of Arynes

A reagent is the more discriminating the higher the activation barriers to its reactions are. Thus, competition constants offer a key to the estimation of the "hotness" of a reagent.

1-Fluoronaphthalene and 9-chlorophenanthrene were subjected to the

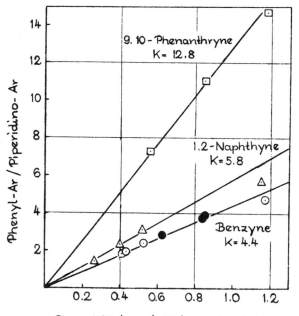

Fig. 2.5. Competition of phenyllithium and lithium piperidide in the addition to arynes in boiling ether (55). Reactants. ○ Fluorobenzene, ● Chlorobenzene, △ 1-Fluoronaphthalene, □ 9-chlorophenanthrene.

same treatment with excess of phenyllithium and lithium piperidide as described for halobenzenes (p. 74). The arylbenzenes and the *N*-arylpiperidines were submitted to quantitative infrared analysis. Plotting of the product ratio *versus* the ratio of lithium bases resulted in straight but steeper lines than those found for benzyne (Fig. 2.5). The calculated competition constants of 5.8 for 1,2-naphthyne (XIII) and 12.8 for 9,10-phenanthryne (XXXVII) unveil a rising selectivity (benzyne 4.4) (55). Undoubtedly phenanthryne is a "cooler" intermediate than benzyne. That the stability of benzyne is increased by the fusing on of other rings, is a touchstone for any structural theory of arynes.

TABLE 2.11. COMPETITION CONSTANTS OF ARYNES IN THE
SYSTEM PHENYLLITHIUM AND LITHIUM PIPERIDIDE
IN ETHER (*55,61*)

3-Dimethylaminobenzyne	3.0
3-Methoxybenzyne	3.1
3-Trifluoromethylbenzyne	3.7
Benzyne	4.4
1,2-Naphthyne	5.8
9,10-Phenanthryne	12.8

In view of the strong influence of substituents on the orientation of nucleophilic additions to arynes, the interaction of the extra bond of benzyne with substituents in position 3 is of special interest. The data of Table 2.11, which in part need confirmation by further experiments, disclose that electron attracting as well as releasing substituents decrease slightly the selectivity of benzyne.

The Nucleophilicity Scale towards Aryne as Reference Acid

The lack of an absolute scale of nucleophilic strength may be looked upon as commonplace in theoretical organic chemistry. A new scale has to be defined for every new electrophilic agent (Lewis acid). The knowledge of such scales is not only of intriguing theoretical interest, but also its practical importance can hardly be overestimated. Such a scale brings to light the scope of application of a reagent.

Arynes readily add nucleophilic reagents and therefore are to be classified as electrophiles. Competition experiments allow one to establish the specific nucleophilic scale.

In phenylations by benzyne in liquid ammonia (pp. 44 and 66) the nucleophilic substrate B faces the basic solvent which is present in high concentration as competitor. Its success is reflected in the relative yields of arylation products Ar—B and Ar—NH_2 or, less reliably, in the absolute yield of Ar—B. That the second and third phenylations of ammonia to di- and triphenylamine are favored and that the reaction with B often does not stop with monophenylation, are complicating factors. Moreover, the development of meaningful numerical values of addition rates is prevented by the unknown acid-base equilibria and, finally, by the uncertainty as to whether ammonia, potassium amide or both adds to benzyne. Thus, the modest result cannot be more than a qualitative sequence. The ability of BH compounds to act as benzyne acceptors decreases in the series,

> thiophenol, fluorene, α-picoline, γ-picoline,
> indene, triphenylmethan, phenylacetylene,
> diphenylamine, phenol, pyrrol,

and are based on experiments of Scardiglia and Roberts (*91*) and of Hauser and Huisgen (*56*).

More conclusive are competition experiments of the type described in the foregoing sections. Though the solubility in ether makes a careful choice of nucleophilic reactants necessary, the competition is limited to pairs of lithium bases. As the results are not disturbed by acid-base equilibria, a numerical evaluation is possible. The high selectivity makes 9,10-phenanthryne a suitable reference Lewis acid. Table 2.12 offers some

TABLE 2.12. RELATIVE ADDITION RATES OF NUCLEOPHILIC
REAGENTS TO 9,10-PHENANTHRYNE (XXXVII) IN
BOILING ETHER (*60,61*).

Nucleophile	k_2 rel. (Addition)	HHal Elimination from 9-Halo- phenanthrene
Lithium thiophenoxide	1700	−
Phenyllithium	1280	+
Lithium piperidide	100	+
Piperidine	100	−
Lithium N-methylanilide	38	−
Lithium diethylamide	26	+
Lithium dicyclohexylamide	5	+
Lithium phenoxide	0–3	−

data, elaborated by Huisgen, Mack and Möbius (*60,61*), on relative addition rates of nucleophilic reagents to 9,10-phenanthryne. The value of 100 for lithium piperidide was chosen as an arbitrary base.

One of the peculiarities of the special scale is the top position of anionic sulfur. Lithium thiophenoxide excels even phenyllithium despite the fact that the basicities of the two reagents differ by some 30 p_K units in the opposite direction. Scardiglia and Roberts (*91*) as well as Bunnett and Brotherton (*15*) have also remarked on the high affinity of thiophenoxide for benzyne. Of course it is well known that anionic sulfur functions are very good nucleophiles in aliphatic S_N? and additive aromatic substitution too.

A particularly vexing problem is offered by the identical addition rates of lithium piperidide and free piperidine, elucidated in a three-component competition with lithium N-methylanilide as the third nucleophilic reagent (Mack and Huisgen (*74*)). The tendency to share the electron pair at the nitrogen atom with an electrophilic partner is doubtlessly much more pronounced for lithium piperidide than for the free secondary amine, since the basicity difference may amount to about 25 units on the p_K scale. Nevertheless, the identical addition rates become a bit less strange on looking at the products. In the case of lithium piperidide an energy-rich lithium-organic compound results while piperidine addition leads to the tertiary amine (N-[9-phenanthryl[-piperidine). Supposedly, the reaction of phenanthryne with piperidine is more exothermic than the one with lithium piperidide, because in the latter a lithium amide is transformed into a more basic organolithium compound. The influence of product stability on the activation barrier of the addition seems to compensate for the higher electron sharing tendency of lithium piperidide.

Table 2.12 includes also the capabilities of the nucleophilic reagents to set free phenanthryne from the 9-halophenanthrene. The perplexing lack of parallelism in the two functions, HHal elimination from aryl halide and addition to aryne, stresses again the absence of a common nucleophilicity sequence.

Orientation in Addition to Arynes

The two directions of base addition to arynes which are lacking the high symmetry of benzyne or 9,10-phenanthryne, offer another type of competition phenomenon. That the two orientations are not used to an equal extent has been shown frequently throughout this chapter. Table 2.1 (p. 44) offers quantitative data on the ammonia addition to arynes. The piperidine addition in ether is free of the disadvantages pointed out on p. 45. Here the high yields and the inertness of the products assure reliable addition ratios. The data of Table 2.13 are based mainly on the researches of Huisgen and Herbig (*57*). Under the conditions used the addition of free piperidine prevails over that of the N-lithium derivative.

TABLE 2.13. REACTIONS OF ARYL BROMIDES WITH LITHIUM
PIPERIDIDE AND PIPERIDINE IN ETHER (*57*).

(The pairs of numbers are the addition ratios of the piperidine-nitrogen to the 3- and 4-substituted benzynes.)

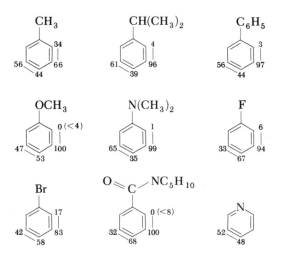

Table 2.13 presents in condensed form data of one year's research and is best illustrated by a detailed example. Cumene, as written in the table, expresses the following facts:

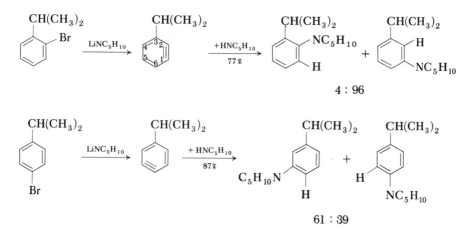

4 : 96

61 : 39

The interpretation (p. 77) of the identical addition rates of piperidine and lithium piperidide suggests a concerted addition mechanism which avoids an ammonium zwitterion as an intermediate. Formula **XXXVIII** depicts the transition state of piperidine addition to 3-methoxybenzyne. In agreement with the pronounced electrophilic character of arynes it is assumed that bond-making between N and C is progressed further in the transition state than the closing of the CH-bond. The result is partial charge separation as shown in **XXXVIII**. The accomodation of the nega-

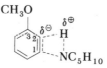

XXXVIII

tive charge by the inductive effect of the 3-substituent seems to be the major orienting factor. In the instance chosen it leads to the exclusive formation of N-[*m*-methoxy-phenyl]-piperidine.

Admittedly, the quantitative aspects of Table 2.13 are not fully understood at present. That the ratios 34:66 and 4:96 for methyl and isopropyl in position 3 reflect a steric hindrance seems to be a safe assumption. Also, the 1:99 ratio of 3-dimethylaminobenzyne may in part be due to the steric effect. The orientational influence of 4-substituents is much smaller. Provided activation entropies are constant, the ratios of Table 2.13 correspond only to $\Delta\Delta H\ddagger$ values between 0.14 and 0.46 kcal. Attempts to disentangle the effects have not been made.

The addition ratios are surprisingly constant and independent of the nature of the nucleophilic addend as demonstrated by the following examples.

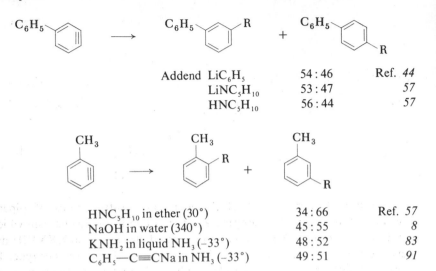

Addend	LiC_6H_5	54 : 46	Ref. 44
	$LiNC_5H_{10}$	53 : 47	57
	HNC_5H_{10}	56 : 44	57

HNC_5H_{10} in ether (30°)	34 : 66	Ref. 57
NaOH in water (340°)	45 : 55	8
KNH_2 in liquid NH_3 (–33°)	48 : 52	83
C_6H_5—C≡CNa in NH_3 (–33°)	49 : 51	91

This small variation of the addition ratios may be of preparative importance; the orientation in the addition of new nucleophilic agents is predictable once the characteristic ratio has been measured.

More quantitative data are needed to attain a consistent picture of the steric and electronic effects which control the orientation. The addition ratios of several lithium bases to 1,2-naphthyne, measured by Huisgen and Zirngibl (47,49), caution one not to overemphasize steric factors. In correspondence with past experience in the naphthalene series one might expect the addition of a bulky anion R at position 1 to be hampered by the hydrogen in the peri-position. This hindrance should make the proportion in which the anionoid R becomes attached to position 1 or 2, a measure of the steric requirements of the nucleophile. Table 2.14 reveals instead of a dramatic shift with changing steric demands, an amazingly constant ratio of about one to two. A deviation of this ratio in the expected direction is only observed with the bulky groups of lithium diisopropylamide and dicyclohexylamide; here, the fraction of 1-addition falls to 13 and 7 per cent, respectively. Thus, the normal addition ratios seem to be dominated mainly by electronic effects.

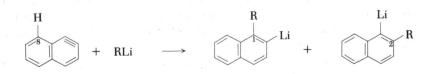

TABLE 2.14. SUBSTITUTIONS OF 1-HALONAPHTHALENE WITH NUCLEOPHILIC REAGENTS. RATIOS OF THE TWO ADDITION DIRECTIONS TO 1,2-NAPHTHYNE (47,49).

1-Halo-naphthalene	System	% Addition of R at C-1	C-2
F	LiC_6H_5 in ether; $+ CO_2$	37	63
Cl	LiC_6H_5 in ether; $+ H_2O$	34	66
F	Li-n-butyl in ether; $+ CO_2$	33	67
F	Li-$tert$-butyl in ether; $+ H_2O$	34	66
Br	Na-thiophenoxide in liquid NH_3 (15)	34	66
Cl,Br	Li-piperidide + piperidine in ether	31	69
F,Cl	Li-piperidide in boiling piperidine	31	69
Cl	Li-diethylamide + HNR_2 in ether	39	61
Cl	Li-di-isobutylamide + HNR_2 in ether	36	64
Cl	Li-di-isopropylamide + HNR_2 in ether	13	87
Cl	Li-dicyclohexylamide + HNR_2 in ether	7	93

Structure of Benzyne

A benzyne type intermediate has never been isolated or detected directly. The mass of indirect experimental evidence for this new kind of intermediate may be summarized as follows.

(a) The typical rearrangements indicate that two neighboring carbon atoms of the aromatic nucleus are equally involved in the anomalous valence state of the intermediate. Isomeric aryl halides can yield identical products via one and the same aryne (pp. 40–41, 46–47).

(b) The nature of the aryne-liberating agents and the reactivity sequences obtained with halogen variation and aryl variation allow the conclusion that the o-hydrogen of the aryl halide is removed as a proton. A hydrogen-metal exchange is the introductory step of most aryne formations (pp. 52–62).

(c) Quantitative competition experiments prove, in connection with rate measurements, the appearance of a selective intermediate, called aryne, responsible for product formation. It is highly probable that this intermediate is halogen-free (p. 74).

(d) Additions of a multitude of nucleophiles characterize the aryne as an electron deficient compound. The nucleophilicity sequence towards the aryne as a reference electrophile is a special one and does not correspond with any other series known (pp. 76–78).

(e) The selectivity of the aryne depends on the structure and shows an increase in the series benzyne, 1,2-naphthyne and 9,10-phenanthryne (pp. 74–75).

The formulation of arynes as Ar-X minus HX, used in this chapter, is in accordance with the requirements above. All other structures of the intermediate can be excluded but one: a complex of the "naked" aryne with a metal cation or a metal halide. It was emphasized that all known formations of arynes pass through metallorganic intermediates. A coördination of benzyne with metal which has been discussed in all research groups concerned with the problem (*cf.* Wittig and Bickelhaupt (*117*)) is still open to experimental proof or rejection. Both benzyne and metal cations are electron seeking so that their combination would demand a new bond type. That not only lithium and magnesium but also sodium and potassium could participate in such a complex, looks a bit strange. However, this lack of full understanding is a weak argument in view of the recent revolutions in metallorganic chemistry.

Simmons and Smith (*95*) discovered the transformation of olefins with methylene iodide and zinc-copper-couple to cyclopropanes. The proposed intermediate is a complex of CH_2 with the zinc iodide. In contrast to the hot methylene, resulting from the photolysis of diazomethane or ketene, the "mitigated" methylene of the mentioned reaction can add to olefinic double bonds but is unable to insert itself between C—H bonds. Wittig and Schwarzenbach (*121*) found possibly the same species involved in the photolysis of diazomethane in the presence of zinc iodide. On the other hand, Schmeisser and Schroeter (*92a*) recently have isolated a metal-free methylene, the dichlorocarbene.

It is a principle of rationalism to confine any discussion to the simplest possible solution which is in accordance with the facts. This would mean a metal-free benzyne. One always finds *neighboring* positions of the aromatic nucleus included in the aryne formation. All endeavours to demonstrate other than 1,2-eliminations have been in vain. Therefore, it is felt that the two extra electrons of benzyne form a bond. Without the assistance of this supposedly weak bond the elimination is not promoted.

The structure of benzyne can be described by two extreme formulations. In the first one the benzene ring retains its σ-bond skeleton with sp^2 hybridization and the geometry of a regular hexagon. The two electrons, forming the special bond of benzyne, occupy two sp^2 orbitals within the plane of the carbon atoms. The binding overlap of these orbitals has to be very weak because they are not parallel as in normal π-type overlap, but include an angle of 60°. This bond does not to a first approximation interact with the aromatic π-cloud which is displayed above and beneath the σ-plane.

We reach the second extreme by a terrible distortion of the benzene nucleus to a structure with sp hybridized bonds on the two carbon atoms involved in the elimination (XXXIX). Of the disposable p-orbitals one pair would enter the weakened aromatic π-cloud. The second pair would form

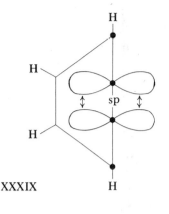

H

H

H

sp

H

H

XXXIX

a more or less normal π-bond in the plane of the carbon skeleton. The enormous Baeyer strain would, of course, be a high price to pay for a better third bond.

The principles of bond hybridization allow a continuum of intermediate structures between the two extremes mentioned. It seems a sound assumption to ascribe to the extra orbitals of benzyne mainly an sp^2 nature with a slight increase of the p-character. Here we face a new bond type which does not correspond to the usual hybridizations. Jenny and Roberts (*63*) have tried to rationalize this unusual bond by relating the ring strain in benzyne to the one in cyclopropene. Dipolar structures like II (p. 38) may be regarded as less important resonance forms.

The 1,2-bond of naphthalene and the 9,10- of phenanthrene show increasing bond orders compared with benzene and, therefore, diminished bond lengths. These smaller carbon-carbon distances have been confirmed by X-ray analyses. It is easy to imagine that the special bond of benzyne with its weak orbital overlap would profit from the shrinking bond distance in the series benzyne, 1,2-naphthyne and 9,10-phenanthryne. Considerable satisfaction can be taken in the observed selectivity order (pp. 74–75) which fits nicely with the expected bond stabilities (*55*).

A benzyne structure with a triplet state, discussed by Müller and Röschcisen (*79*), later considered by Wittig and Härle (*120*), seems very unlikely. Only with coupled spins can the extra electrons of benzyne contribute to the bond energy. The compromise between the two extreme structures of benzyne discussed above certainly involves a distortion in the hexagonal symmetry of the carbon system. Quantum mechanical calculations (*16*) point to a higher contribution of *one* Kekulé structure in the aromatic resonance.

The pictures devised for reaction mechanisms are never absolute but reflect the contemporary state of development in theoretical chemistry. The expression "elucidation of a mechanism" has lost its original meaning. It concerns a directed process aiming at an ever increasing refinement in our comprehension of reaction drama.

No doubt, the interpretation of a large group of nucleophilic aromatic substitutions with primary elimination has developed in less than a decade into a full-fledged mechanistic scheme. In the author's opinion the potential of arynes in theory and laboratory practice is far from being exhausted. Where will the next breakthrough in benzyne chemistry occur?

Acknowledgment. I am very grateful to Professor C. Hansch for his help in preparing the English text.

References

(1) Bachmann, W. E., and Clarke, H. T., *J. Am. Chem. Soc.*, **49,** 2089 (1927).
(2) Barth, L., and Senhofer, C., *Ber.*, **8,** 1477 (1875); **9,** 969 (1876).
(3) Bateman, L. C., Hughes, E. D., and Ingold, C. K., *J. Chem. Soc.*, 960, 774 (1940).
(4) Benkeser, R. A., and DeBoer, C. E., *J. Org. Chem.*, **21,** 281 (1956).
(5) Bergstrom, F. W., Wright, R. E., Chandler, C., and Gilkey, W. A., *J. Org. Chem.*, **1,** 170 (1936).
(6) Bergstrom, F. W., and Agostinho, R., *J. Am. Chem. Soc.*, **67,** 2152 (1945).
(7) Blomquist, A. T., and Liu, L. H., *J. Am. Chem. Soc.*, **75,** 2153 (1953).
(8) Bottini, A. T., and Roberts, J. D., *J. Am. Chem. Soc.*, **79,** 1458 (1957).
(9) Britton, E. C. (to Dow Chemical Co.), U. S. Patents 1,959,283 and 1,996,744 (May 15, 1934 and April 9, 1935).
(10) Brown, H. C., and McDaniel, D. H., *J. Am. Chem. Soc.*, **77,** 3752, 3756 (1955).
(11) Bryce-Smith, D., *J. Chem. Soc.*, 1079 (1954).
(12) Bryce-Smith, D., Gold, V., and Satchell, D. P. N., *J. Chem. Soc.*, 2743 (1954).
(13) Bunnett, J. F., and Zahler, R. F., *Chem. Reviews*, **49,** 273 (1951).
(14) Bunnett, J. F., and Brotherton, T. K., *J. Am. Chem. Soc.*, **78,** 155, 6265 (1956); *J. Org. Chem.*, **22,** 832 (1957).
(15) Bunnett, J. F., and Brotherton, T. K., *J. Org. Chem.*, **23,** 904 (1958).
(16) Coulson, C. A., Special Publ. No. 12, p. 85, London, The Chemical Society, 1958.
(17) Cristol, S. J., and Norris, W. P., *J. Am. Chem. Soc.*, **76,** 3005 (1954).
(18) Cristol, S. J., and Helmreich, R. F., *J. Am. Chem. Soc.*, **77,** 5034 (1955).
(19) Dirstine, P. H., and Bergstrom, F. W., *J. Org. Chem.*, **11,** 55 (1946).
(20) Favorsky, A. J., and Boshovsky, W., *Ann.*, **390,** 122 (1912).
(21) Favorsky, A. J., Schostakovsky, M. F., and Domnin, N. A., *J. Gen. Chem.* (U.S.S.R.), **6,** 720 (1936).
(22) Fierz-David, H. E., and Stamm, G., *Helv. Chim. Acta*, **25,** 364 (1942).
(23) Gilman, H., and Young, R. V., *J. Am. Chem. Soc.*, **56,** 1415 (1934); **57,** 1121 (1935).
(24) Gilman, H., Langham, W., and Jacoby, A. L., *J. Am. Chem. Soc.*, **61,** 106 (1939).
(25) Gilman, H., and Bebb, R. L., *J. Am. Chem. Soc.*, **61,** 109 (1939).
(26) Gilman, H., Crounse, N. N., Massie, S. P., Benkeser, R. A., and Spatz, S. M., *J. Am. Chem. Soc.*, **67,** 2106 (1945).
(27) Gilman, H., Kyle, R. H., and Benkeser, R. A., *J. Am. Chem. Soc.*, **68,** 143 (1946).

(28) Gilman, H., and Kyle, R. H., *J. Am. Chem. Soc.*, **70**, 3945 (1948).

(29) Gilman, H., and Melvin, H. W., *J. Am. Chem. Soc.*, **72**, 995 (1950).

(30) Gilman, H., and Morton, J. W., *Org. Reactions*, **8**, 258 (1954).

(31) Gilman, H., and Gorsich, R. D., *J. Am. Chem. Soc.*, **78**, 2217 (1956); **79**, 2625 (1957).

(32) Gilman, H., and Soddy, T. S., *J. Org. Chem.*, **22**, 1715 (1957).

(33) Goldberg, I., *Ber.*, **39**, 1691 (1906).

(34) Goldberg, I., and Nimerovsky, M., *Ber.*, **40**, 2448 (1907).

(35) Haeussermann, C., and Bauer, E., *Ber.*, **32**, 1912 (1899).

(36) Haeussermann, C., *Ber.*, **33**, 939 (1900); **34**, 38 (1901).

(37) Hale, W. J., and Britton, E. C., *Ind. Eng. Chem.*, **20**, 114 (1928).

(38) Hall, C. E., Piccolini, R., and Roberts, J. D., *J. Am. Chem. Soc.*, **77**, 4540 (1955).

(39) Heydrich, C., *Ber.*, **18**, 2156 (1885).

(40) Hrutfiord, B. F., and Bunnett, J. F., *J. Am. Chem. Soc.*, **80**, 2021, 4745 (1958).

(41) Huggins, M. L., *J. Am. Chem. Soc.*, **75**, 4123 (1953).

(42) Huisgen, R., *Ann.*, **559**, 101 (1948); **564**, 16 (1949).

(43) Huisgen, R., and Rist, H., *Naturwissenschaften*, **41**, 358 (1954); *Ann.*, **594**, 137 (1955).

(44) Huisgen, R., Sauer, J., and Hauser, A., *Angew. Chem.*, **69**, 267 (1957); *Chem. Ber.*, **91**, 2366 (1958).

(45) Huisgen, R., and König, H., *Angew. Chem.*, **69**, 268 (1957); *Chem. Ber.*, **92**, 203 (1959).

(46) Huisgen, R., and Sauer, J., *Angew. Chem.*, **69**, 390 (1957).

(47) Huisgen, R., and Zirngibl, L., *Chem. Ber.*, **91**, 1438 (1958).

(48) Huisgen, R., and Sauer, J., *Chem. Ber.*, **91**, 1453 (1958).

(49) Huisgen, R., and Zirngibl, L., *Chem. Ber.*, **91**, 2375 (1958).

(50) Huisgen, R., and Sauer, J., *Chem. Ber.*, **92**, 192 (1959).

(51) Huisgen, R., König, H., and Bleeker, N., *Chem. Ber.*, **92**, 424 (1959).

(52) Huisgen, R., Sauer, J., Mack, W., and Ziegler, I., *Chem. Ber.*, **92**, 441 (1959).

(53) Huisgen, R., Mack, W., Herbig, K., Ott, N., and Anneser, E., *Chem. Ber.*, **93**, 412 (1960).

(54) Huisgen, R., and Mack, W., *Chem. Ber.*, **93**, 332 (1960).

(55) Huisgen, R., Mack, W., and Möbius, L., *Tetrahedron*, **9**, 29 (1960).

(56) Huisgen, R., and Hauser, A., unpublished; Ph.D. thesis of Hauser, A., University of Munich, 1959.

(57) Huisgen, R., and Herbig, K., unpublished results, (1958/59).

(58) Huisgen, R., and Jung, D., unpublished results, (1959).

(59) Huisgen, R., König, H., and Lepley, A. R., *Chem. Ber.*, **93**, 1496 (1960).

(60) Huisgen, R., and Mack, W., unpublished results; Ph.D. thesis of Mack, W., University of Munich, (1959).

(61) Huisgen, R., and Möbius, L., unpublished results, (1959).

(62) Ingold, C. K., "Structure and Mechanism," p. 419, London, G. Bell and Sons, Ltd., 1953.

(63) Jenny, E. F., and Roberts, J. D., *Helv. Chim. Acta*, **38**, 1248 (1955).

(64) Kekulé, A., *Zeitschr. f. Chem.*, **1867**, 300; *Compt. rend.*, **64**, 753 (1864).

(65) Köbrich, G., *Chem. Ber.*, **92**, 2985 (1959).

(66) König, H., and Huisgen, R., *Chem. Ber.*, **92**, 429 (1959).
(67) Kym, O., *J. prakt. Chem.* [2], **51**, 325 (1895).
(68) Leake, W. W., and Levine, R., *J. Am. Chem. Soc.*, **81**, 1169, 1627 (1959).
(69) Lellmann, E., and Büttner, M., *Ber.*, **23**, 1383 (1890).
(70) Limpricht, H., *Ber.*, **7**, 1349 (1874).
(71) Lüttringhaus, A., and Sääf, G., *Ann.*, **542**, 241 (1939); **557**, 25 (1947).
(72) Lüttringhaus, A., and Ambros, D., *Chem. Ber.*, **89**, 463 (1956).
(73) Lüttringhaus, A., and Schuster, H., *Angew. Chem.*, **70**, 438 (1958).
(74) Mack, W., and Huisgen, R., *Chem. Ber.*, **93**, 608 (1960).
(75) Meisenheimer, J., *Ann.*, **323**, 205 (1902).
(76) Merz, V., and Weith, W., *Ber.*, **6**, 1511 (1873).
(77) Meyer, K. H., and Bergius, F., *Ber.*, **47**, 3155 (1914).
(78) Morton, A. A., Davidson, J. B., and Hakan, B. L., *J. Am. Chem. Soc.*, **64**, 2242 (1942).
(79) Müller, E., and Röscheisen, G., *Chem. Ztg.*, **80**, 101 (1956).
(80) Nölting, E., and Stricker, T., *Ber.*, **20**, 3018 (1887).
(81) Reppe, W. (to I. G. Farbenind. A.-G.), German Patents 550,403 and 584,840 (Dec. 25, 1928 and Sept. 25, 1933); "Neue Entwicklungen auf dem Gebiet der Chemie des Acetylens und Kohlenoxyds," p. 4, Berlin, W. Springer-Verlag, 1949.
(82) Roberts, J. D., Simmons, H. E., Carlsmith, L. A., and Vaughan, C. W., *J. Am. Chem. Soc.*, **75**, 3290 (1953).
(83) Roberts, J. D., Vaughan, C. W., Carlsmith, L. A., and Semenow, D. A., *J. Am. Chem. Soc.*, **78**, 611 (1956).
(84) Roberts, J. D., Semenow, D. A., Simmons, H. E., and Carlsmith, L. A., *J. Am. Chem. Soc.*, **78**, 601 (1956).
(85) Parham, W. E., and Stright, P. L., *J. Am. Chem. Soc.*, **78**, 4783 (1956).
(86) Parham, W. E., Motter, R. F., and Mayo, G. L. O., *J. Am. Chem. Soc.*, **81**, 3386 (1959).
(87) Pauling, L., "The Nature of the Chemical Bond," 2nd Ed., p. 60, Ithaca, N. Y., Cornell Univ. Press, 1940.
(88) Sauer, J., Huisgen, R., and Hauser, A., *Chem. Ber.*, **91**, 1461 (1958).
(89) Sauer, J., and Huisgen, R., *Angew. Chem.*, **72**, 294 (1960).
(90) Scardiglia, F., and Roberts, J. D., *Tetrahedron*, **1**, 343 (1957).
(91) Scardiglia, F., and Roberts, J. D., *Tetrahedron*, **3**, 197 (1958).
(92) Scardiglia, F., and Roberts, J. D., *J. Org. Chem.*, **23**, 629 (1958).
(92a) Schmeisser, M., and Schröter, H., *Angew. Chem.*, **72**, 349 (1960).
(93) Seibert, R. A., and Bergstrom, F. W., *J. Org. Chem.*, **10**, 544 (1945).
(94) Shreve, R. N., and Marsel, C. J., *Ind. Eng. Chem.*, **38**, 254 (1946).
(95) Simmons, H. E., and Smith, R. D., *J. Am. Chem. Soc.*, **80**, 5323 (1958); **81**, 4256 (1959).
(96) Sunthankar, S. V., and Gilman, H., *J. Org. Chem.*, **16**, 8 (1951).
(97) Stoermer, R., and Kahlert, B., *Ber.*, **35**, 1633 (1902).
(98) Truce, W. E., Simms, J. A., and Boudakian, M. M., *J. Am. Chem. Soc.*, **78**, 695 (1956).
(99) Ullmann, F., *Ber.*, **36**, 2382 (1903).

(100) Urner, R. S., and Bergstrom, F. W., *J. Am. Chem. Soc.*, **67,** 2108 (1945).

(101) Viehe, H. G., *Chem. Ber.*, **92,** 1950 (1959).

(102) Waters, W. A., *J. Chem. Soc.*, 727 (1948).

(103) Weston, P. E., and Adkins, H., *J. Am. Chem. Soc.*, **50,** 859 (1928).

(104) Wittig, G., Pockels, U., and Dröge, H., *Ber.*, **71,** 1903 (1938).

(105) Wittig, G., Pieper, G., and Fuhrmann, G., *Ber.*, **73,** 1193 (1940).

(106) Wittig, G., and Fuhrmann, G., *Ber.*, **73,** 1197 (1940).

(107) Wittig, G., and Merkle, W., *Ber.*, **75,** 1491 (1942).

(108) Wittig, G., *Naturwissenschaften*, **30,** 696 (1942).

(109) Wittig, G., and Harborth, G., *Ber.*, **77,** 306 (1944).

(110) Wittig, G., Meyer, F. J., and Lange, G., *Ann.*, **571,** 167 (1951).

(111) Wittig, G., *Angew. Chem.*, **66,** 10 (1954).

(112) Wittig, G., Ludwig, R., and Polster, R., *Chem. Ber.*, **88,** 294 (1955).

(113) Wittig, G., and Ludwig, R., *Angew. Chem.*, **68,** 40 (1956).

(114) Wittig, G., and Pohmer, L., *Chem. Ber.*, **89,** 1334 (1956).

(115) Wittig, G., and Benz, E., *Angew. Chem.*, **70,** 166 (1958).

(116) Wittig, G., Stilz, W., and Knauss, E., *Angew. Chem.*, **70,** 166 (1958).

(117) Wittig, G., and Bickelhaupt, F., *Chem. Ber.*, **91,** 883 (1958).

(118) Wittig, G., and Knauss, E., *Chem. Ber.*, **91,** 895 (1958).

(119) Wittig, G., and Behnisch, W., *Chem. Ber.*, **91,** 2358 (1958).

(120) Wittig, G., and Härle, H., *Ann.*, **623,** 17 (1959).

(121) Wittig, G., and Schwarzenbach, K., *Angew. Chem.*, **71,** 652 (1959).

(122) Wotiz, J. H., and Huba, F., *J. Org. Chem.*, **24,** 595 (1959).

(123) Wright, R. E., and Bergstrom, F. W., *J. Org. Chem.*, **1,** 179 (1936).

(124) Wurtz, A., *Compt. rend.*, **64,** 749 (1864); *Ann. Chem. Pharm.*, **144,** 121 (1867).

(125) Ziegler, K., Jakob, L., Wollthan, H., and Wenz, A., *Ann.*, **511,** 64 (1934),

3. VINYLMETALLICS

H. D. KAESZ and F. G. A. STONE

Harvard University, Cambridge, Massachusetts

INTRODUCTION

During the latter half of the nineteenth century alkyl and aryl derivatives of metals and metalloids were made in increasing numbers principally from diorganozinc or -mercury compounds. This work represents the birth of organometallic chemistry, a field which received strong impetus in 1900 with Victor Grignard's description of a direct reaction between organo-halides and magnesium metal in ether. For over half a century following Grignard's discovery, chemists too numerous to mention have used the highly reactive organomagnesium halides to make alkyl and aryl deriva-tives of metals and metalloids. Many hundreds of compounds of this nature are now described in the chemical literature. Although all of these substances were not obtained through the use of Grignard reagents, alkyl-and arylmagnesium halides have played a dominant part in developing this branch of chemistry.

The existence of so many alkyl and aryl compounds has for several years stood in marked contrast to the paucity of information on compounds in which a vinyl* group is bonded to a metal or metalloid. This situation arose through the lack of availability of suitable reagents for making such compounds, rather than through an inherent thermal instability of the de-sired substances. Only during the last decade have increasing numbers of vinylmetallic and -metalloidal compounds been described, partially remov-ing the discrepancy between the wide knowledge of alkyl- and arylmetal and -metalloid compounds on the one hand and the much less extensive knowledge of vinylmetal and -metalloid chemistry on the other. Studies showing that compounds RMgX, RLi and R_2Hg, where $R = CH_2:CH$, $CH_3CH:CH$, $C_6H_5CH:CH$, etc., can be formed under the appropriate re-action conditions have opened the way for preparation of many new com-pounds with vinyl groups bonded to a metal or metalloid. It must not be

---

*Henceforth, for the sake of brevity, the groups $CH_2:CH$ —, $ClCH:CH$—, $CH_3CH:CH$—, $C_6H_5CH:CH$—, etc., will be referred to collectively as vinyl, un-less there is a possibility of ambiguity, in which case the terms β-chlorovinyl, propenyl, styryl, perfluorovinyl, etc., will be used.

thought from this, however, that all known vinylmetal and -metalloidal compounds were recently discovered. The dehydrohalogenation of 2-bromoethylphosphonium and -arsonium salts to form vinyl derivatives of phosphorus and arsenic was observed in 1860 (*49*), while the interesting substance $(CH_3)_3SnCH{=}CHSn(CH_3)_3$ was described in 1930 (*76*). The ability of certain metal halides to add to acetylene has been known for years. Indeed, this type of reaction, which affords β-chlorovinyl compounds, has been studied more or less continuously since 1898, when it was observed that acetylene was absorbed by acidic solutions of mercury(II) chloride to give a precipitate of composition $C_2H_2Cl_2Hg$ (*12*).

It is the purpose of this chapter to review the chemistry of vinylmetallics with emphasis on recent developments. Also presented is a brief survey of vinylsilicon and vinylphosphorus compounds, included because silicon and phosphorus represent somewhat of a transition between metals and non-metals. Thus the study of these vinyl compounds enables a better understanding of the chemistry of the vinyl group when it is bonded to metals.

The most important entry into the field of vinyl chemistry has been through the use of vinyl compounds of lithium, sodium and magnesium. These compounds will, therefore, be considered first, followed by a review of vinyl derivatives of other elements according to the positions of the elements in the Periodic Classification.

VINYL COMPOUNDS OF ALKALI METALS AND MAGNESIUM

Alkali Metals

Before discovery of the various vinyl Grignard reagents, described in the next section, compounds containing the vinyllithium grouping $C{=}C{-}Li$ were of special importance because they helped to fill a gap in the spectrum of synthetically useful organometallic reagents. Now that vinyl Grignard reagents can be readily made, the vinyllithium compounds are somewhat less important. Quite apart from synthetic considerations, however, the chemistry of certain vinyllithium compounds has raised the interesting question as to whether their reactions occur with retention of geometrical configuration. This aspect of vinylmetal chemistry is considered in more detail in a later section in which the chemistry of vinylmercury compounds is discussed.

In the attempted formation of vinyllithium compounds chemists encountered the same difficulties as in the preparation of vinyl Grignards, namely, inertness of the vinylic halides, and dehydrohalogenation or coupling of the desired product if formed. As the result of extensive studies in this field, particularly by Braude and his co-workers (*15*), these difficulties have been largely overcome. A series of vinyllithium compounds was prepared *in solution* by direct metallation. The successful formation of ethereal solutions of these compounds required the use of very pure halides. Since the subject of vinyllithium chemistry has been reviewed (*15*) fairly recently, no purpose is served by considering the subject in detail here. However, solutions of the simplest vinyllithium, $CH_2:CHLi$, have only recently been prepared, this being of interest in that vinyl chloride and bromide were found to be inert to lithium in diethyl ether, while vinyl iodide underwent dehydroiodination and coupling (*15*). The first reported successful formation of a diethyl ether solution of $CH_2:CHLi$ appears to be that of Nesmeyanov and his co-workers (*96*), who found that if divinylmercury was treated with lithium in diethyl ether and this mixture subsequently treated with carbon dioxide, acrylic acid was formed. More recently other workers (*7*), apparently unaware of the work of the Russian chemists, have reported that divinylmercury reacts with lithium according to the equation.

$$2\,Li + (CH_2:CH)_2Hg \xrightarrow[\text{ether}]{\text{pentane or}} 2\,CH_2:CHLi + Hg$$

It was also reported that sodium- and potassium-vinyl can be made in a similar manner (*7*). For reasons which are discussed later there are certain disadvantages in using divinylmercury as a synthetic reagent. Therefore, the report that vinyl chloride reacts directly with lithium, provided tetrahydrofuran is used as solvent, undoubtedly suggests a more convenient route to $CH_2:CHLi$ even though no definite proof of formation of the reagent was given (*1*). More recently it has been shown that vinyllithium can definitely be obtained from the readily prepared vinyltin compounds by an exchange reaction (*130*).

$$(CH_2:CH)_4Sn + 4\,C_6H_5Li \xrightarrow[\substack{\text{hydrocarbon}\\\text{solvent}}]{(C_2H_5)_2O\text{ or}} 4\,CH_2:CHLi + (C_6H_5)_4Sn \downarrow$$

Since vinyllithium can be made in hydrocarbon solvents, unlike vinylmagnesium chloride or bromide, it is just possible that the lithium compound will find some use as a vinylating agent on occasions when it is advantageous to avoid using cyclic ethers as solvents.

Vinylsodium was first produced by treating ethylene with amylsodium in pentane in the presence of sodium *iso*propoxide (*89*). With propene and the butenes, however, the reaction with amylsodium led to monometallation, but principally in the allyl position (*88*). This exchange reaction as a method for obtaining α-alkenylsodium derivatives is thus evidently rather limited. However, following the discovery (*vide infra*) that vinyl Grignards can be made in good yield if cyclic ethers are used as solvent, it was found that vinyl chloride reacts directly with alkali metals in tetrahydrofuran (*1*). A detailed description for making vinylpotassium in this manner has been given.

Magnesium

Following the discovery of the reaction between alkyl halides and magnesium, research workers quickly began attacking the problem of forming Grignard reagents from vinylic halides. A Grignard reagent from 2-bromostyrene was reported in 1902, but the yield was poor due to formation of phenylacetylene and to a coupling reaction giving 1,4-diphenylbutadiene (*142*). Later workers (*120*) using magnesium activated with iodine succeeded in increasing the yield of styrylmagnesium bromide to 55 per cent, with only a 19 per cent yield of 1,4-diphenylbutadiene. In 1923 Ziegler (*153*) formed β,β-diphenylvinylmagnesium bromide, and after treatment with acetophenone obtained a 75 per cent yield of the desired alcohol. However, as late as 1953 formation of the parent Grignard $CH_2:CHMgBr$ had not been described in the literature, and it was thought that unsubstituted vinyl halides were too inert to react with magnesium (*35*). In contrast to this failure Grignard reagents of several substituted vinyl halides had been made, albeit often in very poor yield due to coupling and acetylene formation, e.g., $(CH_3)_2C:CHBr$ (*77*), $C_5H_{11}CH:CHBr$ (*68*), $(Aryl)_2C:-C(Aryl)Br$ (*73*), and $C_6H_5(t\text{-}C_4H_9)C:CHBr$ (*143*).

In 1950 interest was renewed in the reaction between 3-bromocoumarone and metals (*9*) first described by Reichstein and Baud (*114*).

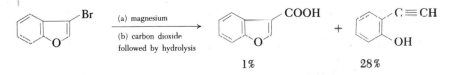

1% 28%

In an analogous manner it was observed that when β-bromodihydropyran was treated with magnesium, sodium, potassium, butylsodium or butyllithium and the reaction mixture hydrolyzed, an acetylenic alcohol $HO(CH_2)_3C\equiv CH$ was obtained (*141*). It was suggested (*141*) that this reaction and that involving 3-bromocoumarone proceed *via* a vinyl-metal intermediate. Departing from the study of heterocyclic compounds, Normant (*103*) became interested in reactions of this kind, and investigated the effect of magnesium, butyllithium, *etc.*, on non-cyclic β-halogenated vinyl ethers, using a variety of ethers as solvent. It was found that reaction proceeded well only when cyclic ethers like tetrahydrofuran were used as solvents. It thus became evident that those reactions involving 3-bromocoumarone or β-bromodihydropyran and leading to acetylene formation occurred because the reactant itself was a cyclic ether, and thus promoted reaction. This suggested that cyclic ethers like tetrahydrofuran* would be excellent media for formation of vinyl Grignards, an idea which was confirmed when the halides $CH_3CH:CHBr$, $C_5H_{11}CH:CHBr$ and $C_6H_5CBr:CH_2$ were shown to form Grignards in the then unheard-of yields of 70–95 per cent (100). Subsequently formation of the most elusive vinyl Grignard, $CH_2:CHMgBr$, was reported (101,102).

It is fitting that the first publication to describe the successful formation of $CH_2:CHMgBr$ came from the same country in which the reaction between magnesium and alkyl halides had been discovered. It must be mentioned in passing that, independently but concurrently with Normant's work, vinylmagnesium chloride and several of its homologues were prepared by other workers (113) using cyclic ethers like tetrahydrofuran as solvent.

Related to the preparation of the simple vinyl Grignards $CH_2:CHMgX$ (X = Br, Cl) has been the formation of Grignards from the perfluorovinyl halides, $CF_2:CFI$ and $CF_2:CFBr$. Perfluorovinyl iodide reacts directly in diethyl ether with magnesium activated with iodine (104) or ethyl bromide (71). To form $CF_2:CFMgBr$, however, tetrahydrofuran must be used as solvent (60,71). Use of these perfluorovinyl Grignards to make perfluorovinyl compounds of other elements is mentioned elsewhere in this chapter.

VINYL COMPOUNDS OF THE GROUP IIb METALS

Several different classes of vinyl compounds of mercury are known; divinylzinc has been prepared; and although divinylcadmium has not been reported at present, there appears to be no reason why this vinylmetallic should not exist.

Divinylzinc (b.p. 32°/22 mm), prepared by the following reaction (9),

$$ZnCl_2 + 2\,CH_2:CHMgBr \xrightarrow{\;(CH_2)_4O\;} (CH_2:CH)_2Zn + 2\,MgBrCl$$

is less stable than diethylzinc, but otherwise its properties are those to be expected for a relatively low molecular weight organo-zinc derivative. It is spontaneously flammable in air, and on treatment with water affords ethylene quantitatively (9). With boron halides it undergoes reactions of the type (17),

$$(CH_2:CH)_2Zn + BX_3 \longrightarrow CH_2:CHBX_2 + CH_2:CHZnX$$

In view of the flammability and thermal instability of divinylzinc, however,

---

*Reports in the literature that $CH_2:CHMgBr$ will form in diethyl ether are probably the result of workers using vinyl bromide seriously contaminated with ethyl bromide (62). In a recent review (102a), concerning applications of vinyl Grignard to organic chemistry, Normant has also made this point.

the vinylhaloboranes are best prepared from vinyltin compounds as described in a later section.

Divinylmercury has been prepared from the reaction between mercury(II) halides and excess of vinylmagnesium bromide (*6,10,115*). Treatment of mercury(II) halides with vinyl Grignard in a 1:1 ratio yields the vinyl-mercury halides, $CH_2:CHHgX$ (X = Cl, Br, I) (*10*), which may also be prepared from vinyltin compounds. Indeed they were first prepared by this method (*123*).

$$R_3SnCH:CH_2 + HgX_2 \xrightarrow{(C_2H_5)_2O} R_3SnX + CH_2:CHHgX$$

Divinylmercury (b.p. 59.5°/20 mm) is thermally comparatively stable. At ambient temperatures samples sealed *in vacuo* show no decomposition over periods of months. However, at its normal boiling point, about 156°, it decomposes rapidly. The mercury compound is highly toxic, but unlike diethylmercury it has an easily detectable and very objectionable odor. Mineral acids cleave the vinyl group from divinylmercury. A very interesting study has been made of the rate of reaction of a series of symmetrical diorganomercury compounds with hydrogen chloride in dimethyl sulfoxide (*31*). Rate of reaction is in the sequence.

$$\Delta_2Hg > (CH_2:CH)_2Hg > (C_6H_5)_2Hg >> (C_2H_5)_2Hg >$$

$$(i\text{-}C_3H_7)_2Hg > (n\text{-}C_3H_7)_2Hg > (CH_3)_2Hg.$$

The observed second-order kinetics of these reactions, as well as the effect of adding dioxane, water and various inorganic salts, indicate that cleavage proceeds *via* a four-center mechanism involving attack of hydrogen chloride on the Hg—C bonds. It will be noted that divinylmercury is cleaved much more easily than diethylmercury, being similar in this respect to dicyclopropyl- and diphenylmercury. The faster rates of reaction shown by these unsaturated organometallics may be due to an increased electropositivity of the mercury, due to the greater electronegativity of the attached carbon atom, or to the ability of the unsaturated groups to form a stable bond with the incoming hydrogen atom (*31*).

Divinylmercury was first prepared (*6*) in order to use the compound in the synthesis of other vinyl derivatives. In this respect it has proven useful, e.g.,

$$BF_3 + (CH_2:CH)_2Hg \longrightarrow CH_2:CHBF_2 + CH_2:CHHgF$$

$$PCl_3 + (CH_2:CH)_2Hg \longrightarrow CH_2:CHPCl_2 + CH_2:CHHgCl$$

However, since a vinyl group on tin is also very labile, sometimes vinyltin compounds can be used instead of divinylmercury for synthetic work. In

view of the toxicity of the mercury compound, use of tin compounds whenever possible is greatly to be preferred.

The vinylmercury halides, CH_2:CHHgX, appear to have little synthetic
value. They do not react with boron halides, at least in the absence of a
solvent. They may be used, however, to make CH_2:CHHgR compounds
(R = phenyl, or alkyl) by treatment with the appropriate Grignard reagent
(*10*). It is interesting that CH_2:CHHgC$_2$H$_5$ reacts with boron trifluoride
to yield vinyldifluoroborane, the vinyl group being cleaved preferentially
(*17*). Treatment of vinylmercury halides with tin(II) chloride and sodium
hydroxide at 58–87° using acetone as solvent affords divinylmercury (*96*).
It has long been known that alkyl- and arylmercury halides may also be
reduced in this manner (*25*).

Very recently *bis*(perfluorovinyl)mercury, $(CF_2:CF)_2Hg$ (b.p.
65°/17 mm), has been prepared by treating perfluorovinylmagnesium
iodide in diethyl ether with mercury(II) chloride at –5° (*134*). The per-
fluorovinylmercury compound reacts with iodine to give perfluorovinyl
iodide.

A great variety of substituted vinyl compounds of mercury are known as
a consequence of the work of Nesmeyanov and his co-workers (*90,93*). As
is not the case for the simple CH_2:CH derivatives, the possibility of *cis*-
and *trans*-isomerism exists in β-substituted vinyl compounds. This possibility raises the question of retention of configuration during chemical reactions, and, therefore, the chemistry of substituted vinylmercury compounds
has been studied more thoroughly than that of the simple derivatives.*

Substituted vinyl compounds of mercury have been prepared principally
by two routes: the addition of mercury(II) halides across an acetylenic
bond, a process not recognized as such but reported in 1898; and by the
action of substituted-vinyl compounds of other metals on mercury(II)
halides. The second route has become increasingly important as more substituted vinylmetallic compounds have become known, e.g., *tris*-(β-chlorovinyl)stibine (1945), vinyllithium compounds (1950), and the many
Grignards of vinylic halides (1954).

Around the turn of the century a well known commercial process for
converting acetylene into acetaldehyde, which was eventually oxidized to
acetic acid, involved bubbling acetylene through an acid solution of mercury salts, the salts acting as a catalyst. In 1898, in an attempt to capture

---

*The problems of *cis*- and *trans*-isomerism and of retention of configuration
also apply to the β-substituted vinyl derivatives of other elements (e.g., Li, Mg, B,
Tl, Sn, Pb and Sb). Substituted vinyl derivatives of zinc and cadmium have not
been made, most likely because they would supply no radically new chemical facts,
especially since the mercury compounds have been characterized.

possible intermediates in the process, Biginelli (*12*) bubbled acetylene through a strong hydrochloric acid solution of mercury(II) chloride and obtained, besides much acetaldehyde, a solid (m.p. 124°) which analyzed as $C_2H_2HgCl_2$. This same compound, obtained in improved yield, was treated by Jenkins (*55*) with ammonia in chloroform solution and under these conditions gave a precipitate of mercury (II) chloride and a soluble compound formulated as $(C_2H_2)_2HgCl_2$ (m.p. 70°).

These compounds were not studied in detail until the Russian school of chemists under Nesmeyanov became interested in their nature. It was reported in 1940 that when either Biginelli's compound, the *mono*-derivative, or Jenkins' compound, the *bis*-derivative, was treated with certain Lewis bases, "adducts" were formed (*38*).

$$C_2H_2 \cdot HgCl_2 + C_5H_5N \longrightarrow (C_5H_5N)(C_2H_2)HgCl_2$$
$$\text{m.p. } 76° \text{ (dec.)}$$

On the other hand, when the mercury compounds were treated with ligands known to form strong complexes with mercury(II) chloride, acetylene was released (*98*), viz.,

$$(C_2H_2)_2HgCl_2 + (C_6H_5)_3P \longrightarrow [(C_6H_5)_3P]_2HgCl_2 + 2\ CH{\equiv}CH$$

The mercury compounds also afforded acetylene on heating to 100°, or, if higher melting, to their melting points. Treatment with diazomethane also liberated acetylene (*39*).

$$(C_2H_2)_2HgCl_2 + CH_2N_2 \longrightarrow ClCH_2HgCl + N_2 + 2\ C_2H_2$$

These reactions made it seem likely that the compounds of Biginelli and Jenkins were of the Werner type with acetylene occupying a coordination position or positions around mercury(II), as does, for example, ethylene in Zeise's salt, $K(C_2H_4PtCl_3)$. Since strong bases were able to displace acetylene, it seemed reasonable to assume that the molecule was held by relatively weak interaction with the central Hg^{+2} ion. Further work of the Russian chemists, however, quickly demonstrated that certain properties of "$CH{\equiv}CH \cdot HgCl_2$" and "$(CH{\equiv}CH)_2HgCl_2$" were inconsistent with formulation as complex salts. Treatment with bromine or iodine yielded 1-bromo-2-chloroethylene and 1-chloro-2-iodoethylene respectively. With hydrogen bromide or hydrogen chloride the two mercury compounds gave vinyl chloride (*39,149*). These cleavage reactions indicated that the mercury derivatives were organometallic compounds containing a covalent carbon-mercury bond, and should be regarded as ClCH:CHHgCl and $(ClCH:CH)_2Hg$. Formulation of the compounds as chlorovinyl derivatives implies the existence of *cis*- and *trans*-isomers. It was highly significant, therefore, when two distinct isomers of (ClCH:CH)$_3$Sb were isolated from the reaction between acetylene and antimony pentachloride, as described in a later section of this chapter. When the higher-melting, less-soluble isomer of (ClCH:CH)$_3$Sb was treated with mercury(II) chloride Biginelli's compound could be isolated, and this could be disproportionated into Jenkins' compound (ClCH:CH)$_2$Hg. However, when the other (ClCH:CH)$_3$Sb isomer was treated with mercury(II) chloride, it also yielded a compound ClCH:CHHgCl, but this compound was more soluble and lower melting than the original compound of the same composition isolated by Biginelli. Furthermore, when the new compound ClCH:CHHgCl was caused to disproportionate with ammonia the product was a *bis*-mercury derivative, (ClCH:CH)$_2$Hg, but unlike Jenkins' compound the new substance was a liquid at room temperature. When either Jenkins' or Biginelli's compound was treated with chlorine, it yielded the *trans*-isomer of 1,2-dichloroethylene, ClCH:CHCl. However, when the two analogous mercury compounds synthesized by the Russian group, starting from the lower melting isomer of (ClCH:CH)$_3$Sb, were treated with chlorine, they yielded only *cis*-1,2-dichloroethylene. The above behavior is of course in agreement with the expected occurrence of isomerism in β-chlorovinyl-mercury compounds.

Assignment of absolute configurations for the four mercury compounds was very important because the compounds were used by the Russian chemists to test whether configuration is retained in metal exchange reactions. The isomer of ClCH:CHHgCl first prepared by Biginelli was shown by an X-ray diffraction study to be *trans*-β-chlorovinylmercury chloride (*69,70*). Clearly the other isomer of ClCH:CHHgCl first prepared by the Russian chemists must be *cis*-β-chlorovinylmercury chloride, and a dipole moment study (*98*) further confirmed this fact. Furthermore, it was established by partial chlorination that the *bis*(β-chlorovinyl)mer-cury compounds are *trans-trans* and *cis-cis* compounds, and not a mixture of *cis-trans* groups. By this treatment in each case the expected single isomer of 1,2-dichloroethylene was obtained, as well as the expected single isomer of β-chlorovinylmercury chloride. Similarly, the reactions

$$\textit{cis-}(\text{ClCH:CH})_2\text{Hg} + \text{HgCl}_2 \longrightarrow \textit{cis-}\text{ClCH:CHHgCl}$$

$$\textit{trans-}(\text{ClCH:CH})_2\text{Hg} + \text{HgCl}_2 \longrightarrow \textit{trans-}\text{ClCH:CHHgCl}$$

occurred with retention of configuration. Melting points and solubility relationships also serve to show whether a particular β-substituted vinyl-metal isomer is a *cis*- or a *trans*-compound, since they are in accord with a rule first formulated by Werner, namely, that the higher melting and less soluble isomer has the *trans* configuration.

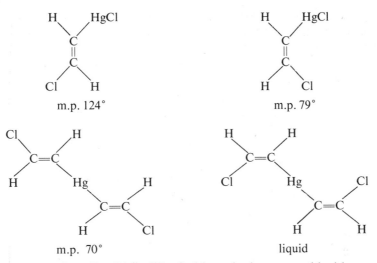

m.p. 124°   m.p. 79°

m.p. 70°   liquid

As was stated earlier Biginelli's β-chlorovinylmercury chloride was the *trans*- isomer, and it was work on the chlorovinyl derivatives of antimony that led to the discovery of the *cis*-isomer series. Besides being synthesized starting from *cis*-antimony derivatives, the *cis*-isomers of the β-chlorovinylmercury compounds were later prepared directly by carrying out the original reaction of mercury(II) chloride with acetylene, not in strong aqueous hydrochloric acid solution, but rather in the vapor phase without solvent (*40*). This reaction yielded almost exclusively the lower melting Biginelli compound, and subsequently all other *cis*-derivatives of the series when treated with the proper reagents. It is interesting to note that even traces of water present in the gas-phase reaction caused the product to be a mixture of *cis* and *trans* isomers. It is necessary to exclude rigorously all traces of moisture in order to obtain pure *cis*-product.

While configuration is strictly retained in the pure stereoisomers themselves, and in metal interconversion reactions (*93*), conditions have been found for the isomerization reaction from *trans*-isomer to *cis*-isomer. In a manner analogous to that found for other organic *cis-trans*-isomers, the β-chlorovinylmercury derivatives can be converted from the *trans*-isomer to the *cis*-isomer by the action of ultraviolet light (*94*) or peroxides (*97*). Thus, when pure *trans-trans*-(ClCH : CH)$_2$Hg (m.p. 70°) is irradiated in the fused state by a quartz vapor lamp for 17 hours, a 45 per cent yield of the *cis-cis*-(ClCH : CH)$_2$Hg, a liquid, is obtained (*94*). The yield increases with length of exposure, for a 76 hour irradiation affords a 66 per cent yield of the *cis-cis*-compound. When ultraviolet irradiation is carried out in solvents like ethanol or benzene, the interconversion is much less, no doubt due to the solvents' themselves absorbing the radiation. A much faster and more complete isomerization of *trans*- into *cis*-isomers ensues on the use of peroxide catalysts in solvent media (*97*). Thus a 90 per cent conversion is obtained at about 90–100° in about 8 hours using a variety of solvents such as xylene, toluene, dioxane, and carbon tetrachloride, and any of the following peroxides as catalysts: benzoyl peroxide, acetyl peroxide or sodium peroxide.

It is interesting to summarize briefly at this point the development of ideas concerning the nature of the bond from mercury to the β-chlorovinyl group. When the "dual" reactivity of the β-chlorovinylmercury compounds was first discovered, i.e., that they would react on the one hand like Werner complexes or on the other as typical organometallic compounds, it was postulated that a labile tautomeric equilibrium existed (*90*).

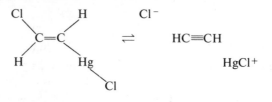

However, when it became clear that the β-chlorovinylmercury compounds firmly retained their stereoisomeric configurations during metal-exchange reactions, tautomerism became an unreasonable postulate. This in turn led to a use of the resonance concept, with a description of the bonding in terms of two resonance hybrids.

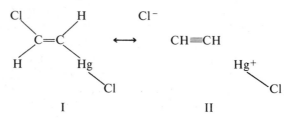

This idea implies that the carbon-carbon linkage has partial triple-bond character. The results of an early Raman spectrum study (*90*) were interpreted as supporting this concept, since a band was observed lying between the region normally ascribed to the double bond and that ascribed to the triple bond. In a later paper (*91*), however, the band originally thought to be highly significant was assigned as an overtone band. Furthermore, bands at the normal frequencies for double bonds were observed in the Raman spectra of the isomers of $(ClCH:CH)_2Hg$ and $(ClCH:CH)_3Sb$. This seemed to obviate the necessity for attributing too much importance to contributions from the canonical form II. Moreover, it was recognized (*91*) that it was unnecessary to postulate triple-bonded contributions to the ground state structure of β-chlorovinyl compounds in order to account for the elimination of acetylene in certain reactions. Release of acetylene in the presence of a strong base is to be expected from what is now known about elimination reactions in organic chemistry.

The reaction between mercury salts and acetylene is quite general, since the Russian chemists have been able to synthesize many substituted vinylmercury compounds by treating a variety of acetylenes, $RC\equiv CR$ ($R = H$, CH_3, C_6H_5, CH_3COO, etc.) with mercury(II) salts, HgX_2 ($X = Cl$, Br, CH_3COO-). Some of these vinylmercury compounds have been used to prepare the corresponding thallium compounds.

The various β-substituted vinylmercury compounds have been used to make β-substituted vinyl derivatives of other elements, e.g.,

$$(CH_3CH:CH)_2Hg + SnBr_2 \longrightarrow (CH_3CH:CH)_2SnBr_2 + Hg$$

$$(ClCH:CH)_2Hg + SnCl_2 \longrightarrow (ClCH:CH)_2SnCl_2 + Hg$$

$$(ClCH:CH)_2Hg + Pb(OAc)_4 \longrightarrow (ClCH:CH)_2Pb(OAc)_2 + Hg(OAc)_2$$

Indeed, transmetallation reactions such as these, as well as similar reactions involving the formation of substituted vinylmercury compounds, e.g.,

$$CH_3CH:CHLi + HgBr_2 \longrightarrow CH_3CH:CHHgBr + LiBr$$

$$(ClCH:CH)_2SnCl_2 + 2HgCl_2 \longrightarrow 2ClCH:CHHgCl + SnCl_4$$

$$(ClCH:CH)_2PbCl_2 + 2Hg \longrightarrow 2ClCH:CHHgCl + Pb$$

all proceed with strict retention of geometrical configuration. These reactions were studied by Nesmeyanov and his co-workers (*90,93*) in order to establish definitely that configuration is retained in electrophilic and homolytic substitutions at the olefinic carbon atom. This fact had already been indicated by work of Braude and his co-workers (*15*), Dreiding and Pratt (*34*), and Curtin *et al.* (*30*), who found that if, under suitable reaction conditions, an alkenylbromide was treated with lithium metal or butyllithium so as to make an alkenyllithium compound, on treatment of the mixture with suitable reagents, e.g., carbon dioxide, methanol, etc., the product had the same geometrical configuration as the starting alkenylbromide, e.g.,

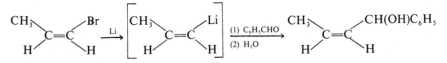

This behavior implies that metallation and reaction of the vinyllithium compound proceed with retention of geometrical configuration, or alternatively, that both reactions involve inversion. It has been pointed out that

the latter possibility is unlikely (*15*). However, since all that is unambiguously demonstrated by reactions of the type (*16*)

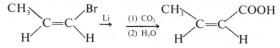

is an *overall* retention of configuration, Nesmeyanov and his co-workers, starting from *trans-β*-chlorovinylmercury chloride, effected a series of reactions involving both "odd and even cycles" and showed that the final product was always the same *trans-β*-chlorovinylmercury chloride, e.g.,

(1) *trans*-CHCl : CHHgCl $\xrightarrow{NH_3}$ *trans*-(CHCl : CH)$_2$Hg $\xrightarrow{PbX_4}$

$\qquad$ *trans*-(CHCl : CH)$_2$PbX$_2$ $\xrightarrow{Hg}$ *trans*-CHCl : CHHgCl

(2) *trans*-CHCl : CHHgCl $\xrightarrow{NH_3}$ *trans*-(CHCl : CH)$_2$Hg $\xrightarrow{TlCl_3}$

$\qquad$ *trans*-(CHCl : CH)$_2$TlCl $\xrightarrow{SnCl_2}$

$\qquad$ *trans*-(CHCl : CH)$_2$SnCl$_2$ $\xrightarrow{HgCl_2}$ *trans*-CHCl : CHHgCl.

It is inconceivable that, in different cycles involving both odd and even numbers of reactions, inversions of configuration of the chlorovinyl group occur just the necessary number of times for it to regain its original form. It should be noted that Nesmeyanov et al. isolated and characterized various intermediates in the cycles, establishing geometrical configuration both on the basis of melting point and on other studies, e.g., the Raman spectrum of *bis-(trans-β*-chlorovinyl)mercury, or conversion of *bis-(trans-β*-chlorovinyl)tin dichloride into the *cis*-isomer by ultraviolet irradiation. The establishment of the structure of *trans*-ClCH : CHHgCl by X-ray diffraction has been mentioned previously.

After it was shown that vinyllithium compounds could be easily made (*15*), these compounds were used to make analogous mercury compounds, and then the latter were used to make analogous derivatives of thallium and tin. Again each vinylic bromide gave rise to two series of isomeric mercury compounds with configurations the same as the starting bromide.

$\qquad$ *cis*-CH$_3$CH : CHBr $\xrightarrow[-5°]{Li/(C_2H_5)_2O}$ $\xrightarrow{HgBr_2}$ *cis*-CH$_3$CH : CHHgBr $\qquad$ m.p. 60–2°

or

$\qquad$ *trans*-CH$_3$CH : CHBr $\longrightarrow \longrightarrow$ *trans*-CH$_3$CH : CHHgBr $\qquad$ m.p. 120°

$\qquad$ *cis*-CH$_3$CH : CHHgBr $\xrightarrow{Na_2SnO_2}$ *cis*-(CH$_3$CH : CH)$_2$Hg $\qquad$ b.p. 79°/14 mm.

or

$\qquad$ *trans*-CH$_3$CH : CHHgBr $\longrightarrow$ *trans*-(CH$_3$CH : CH)$_2$Hg $\qquad$ b.p. 87°/14.5 mm.

$$cis\text{-}(CH_3CH:CH)_2Hg \xrightarrow{HgCl_2/CH_3OH} cis\text{-}CH_3CH:CHHgCl \quad \text{m.p. } 89\text{–}92^\circ$$

or

$$trans\text{-}(CH_3CH:CH)_2Hg \longrightarrow trans\text{-}CH_3CH:CHHgCl \quad \text{m.p. } 124\text{–}5^\circ$$

Although *cis*- and *trans*-propenyllithium are configurationally stable for moderately long periods in boiling diethyl ether, this is not true of the stereoisomers of dipropenylmercury of di- and triarylvinyllithium reagents. Thus, *cis*-α,β-diphenylvinyllithium isomerizes to the *trans*-isomer at temperatures above -40° in benzene-ether solution. Therefore, in transmetallation reactions involving stilbenyllithium compounds it is necessary to form the lithium compound at -40°, and then subject it immediately to treatment with other reagents in order to observe retention of configuration.

It is worth noting that although in the various series of transmetallation reactions there is an overall retention of configuration, there is no definite proof of the absolute configuration of the vinyllithium reagents used in some of the cycles. Thus, in the conversion of a vinylic halide into a mercury derivative *via* a vinyllithium reagent overall retentivity could be due to the reaction scheme,

$$cis\text{-}RBr \xrightarrow{Li} trans\text{-}RLi \xrightarrow{HgX_2} cis\text{-}R_2Hg$$

or to

$$cis\text{-}RBr \xrightarrow{Li} cis\text{-}RLi \xrightarrow{HgX_2} cis\text{-}R_2Hg$$

where R is a β-substituted vinyl group. This kind of difficulty is similar to that mentioned above concerning the reactions of β-substituted vinyllithium compounds with carbon dioxide, benzaldehyde etc. Although it seems most likely that the overall reaction of the lithium compounds does not proceed *via* two inversion steps, unfortunately this problem of the configuration of the lithium reagents has led to questioning (*29*) of the method of odd and even cycles used by Nesmeyanov *et al.* Thus the following cycles,

$$RBr \longrightarrow RLi \longrightarrow R_2Hg \xrightarrow{Br_2} RBr$$

$$RBr \longrightarrow RLi \longrightarrow R_2Hg \longrightarrow RHgBr \xrightarrow{Br_2} RBr$$

$$RBr \longrightarrow RLi \longrightarrow R_2Hg \longrightarrow RHgCl \longrightarrow RSnCl_3 \xrightarrow{Br_2} RBr$$

where R is the bromostilbene group, have been shown to proceed with retention of configuration both when R is *cis*-stilbenyl and when R is *trans*-stilbenyl (*93*). It has been suggested (*29*) that this can be explained if conversion of the bromide to the lithium reagent and the reactions of the organometallics with bromine to complete the cycle involve inversion, while all other reactions in the cycles occur with retention. However, this cannot be a valid explanation, since it is clear from the work of Nesmeyanov *et al.* that intermediates in the cycle involving the stilbenyl group have been isolated, and that physical properties are in accordance with expectations. Thus, starting from *cis*-bromostilbene, a chloromercurystilbene is obtained melting at 131° whereas from *trans*-bromostilbene the chloromercurystilbene melts at 142°. Furthermore, the suggestion that bromination of an organometallic proceeds with inversion appears to have little validity since when *trans*-β-chlorovinylmercury chloride, a compound whose absolute configuration has been settled by X-ray diffraction, is chlorinated, pure *trans*-1,2-dichloroethylene is obtained.

One interesting point which may be mentioned in connection with the stilbene derivatives is that ultraviolet radiation converts the *bis,cis*-mercury isomer into the *bis,trans*-mercury isomer. In all other known conversion reactions of this kind it is the *trans*-isomer which is converted into the *cis*-isomer.

Nesmeyanov and his co-workers have also investigated mercury compounds of the type $CH_2:C(CH_3)HgX$. It is hardly necessary to point out that with these compounds *cis-trans*-isomerism does not occur, and there exists only one series of derivatives.

$$CH_2:C(CH_3)Br \xrightarrow[-5°]{Li/(C_2H_5)_2O} \xrightarrow[(X=Cl,Br)]{HgX_2} \begin{array}{ll} CH_2:C(CH_3)HgCl & \text{m.p. } 154\text{-}5° \\ CH_2:C(CH_3)HgBr & \text{m.p. } 167° \end{array}$$

$$\downarrow Na_2SnO_2$$

$$[CH_2:C(CH_3)]_2Hg$$
$$\text{b.p. } 69°/13\text{ mm}$$

Some thallium and tin compounds have been made from $[CH_2:C(CH_3)]_2$-Hg.

VINYL COMPOUNDS OF THE GROUP III ELEMENTS

Vinyl derivatives of the Group III elements have been studied extensively. Many vinylboron compounds have been characterized. Some vinylaluminum compounds have been reported, as well as vinylthallium halides, while evidence exists for the occurrence of vinylgallium compounds (*19*).

Boron

Initial interest in vinylboron compounds stemmed from the possibility that when a vinyl group is bonded to a boron atom linked to two other atoms, i.e., sp^2-hybridized boron, the boron p_z-orbital might participate in the vinyl group's π-electron system (*105*). Such a process, involving partial double-bond character in the bond from boron to the α-carbon atom of the vinyl group, would be similar to that believed responsible for the existence of alkoxy- and aminoboranes as monomers rather than as dimers (e.g., diborane (*136*)), viz.,

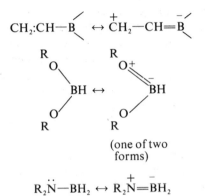

(one of two
forms)

$$R_2\ddot{N}-BH_2 \leftrightarrow R_2\overset{+}{N}=\overset{-}{B}H_2$$

In a vinylboron compound partial shift of unsaturation from the carbon-carbon bond of the vinyl group to an adjacent boron-carbon bond might well affect the properties of the molecule. To understand this it is necessary to recall that species like $(CH_3)_2BC_2H_5$ have only a transient existence at ambient temperatures, disproportionating into the corresponding symmetrical triorganoboranes. Such behavior is fairly general in boron chemistry, other examples being the ready disproportionation of alkyldiboranes into trialkylboranes and diborane, and the rapid transformation of mixed halides into symmetrical trihalides, e.g.,

$$3\ BCl_2F \longrightarrow 2\ BCl_3 + BF_3$$

These disproportionation reactions undoubtedly proceed *via* a four-center mechanism involving the p_z-orbital of boron. Clearly, if this p_z-orbital is involved in internal dative bonding, as is believed to occur in the alkoxy- and aminoboranes mentioned above, the tendency of the boron compound to disproportionate will be greatly reduced. With this in mind Ritter and co-workers (*105*) made some vinyl- and propenylalkylboranes to determine whether the presence of a vinyl or propenyl group would stabilize the molecule, permitting the isolation of unsymmetrical compounds like $(CH_3)_2BCH{:}CH_2$.

Treatment of dimethylbromoborane with vinylsodium or propenyl-lithium afforded a mixture of dimethylalkenylboranes, methyldialkenyl-boranes and the trialkenylboranes. Separation of these mixtures was some-times effected by fractional condensation in a high-vacuum system, or alternatively by gas-phase chromatography. In this manner dimethylvinyl-, methyldivinyl- and trivinylborane, dimethylpropenyl- and methyldipro-penylborane were obtained (Table 3.1). The constitution of these com-pounds was demonstrated by treating them with silver ammonium hydrox-ide solution, with which reagent the organoboranes afforded hydrocarbons, e.g., methane, ethylene, butadiene etc.

It was found that on storage at room temperature for about five days dimethylvinylborane decomposes only to the extent of about 33 per cent. Methyldivinylborane could be heated at 100° for one hour with 98.5 per cent recovery of the original sample, and on subsequent heating at 100° for 70 hours little further decomposition occurred. The stability of these unsymmetrical boranes is in striking contrast to the transient existence of species like $CH_3B(C_2H_5)_2$. This behavior supports the idea that meso-merism in the alkenylboranes restricts the boron atoms to a planar con-figuration and, therefore, inhibits disproportionation.

Trivinylborane slowly decomposes at 0°, as is evidenced by a slow drop in vapor pressure, but the mode of decomposition is not clear. One prod-uct of decomposition has been referred to as a "daughter compound" (105). Later workers (20) have obtained a compound with vapor pressures similar to those reported for this daughter compound and with a molecular weight (by vapor density) close to that expected for trivinylborane and, moreover, also containing three vinyl groups per boron atom. It may be that trivinylborane is monomeric as a gas but slowly changes from monomer to dimer, or even to more highly polymerized species in the liquid phase.* A less likely alternative is that rotation about the B—C bonds in trivinylborane is restricted enough to cause isomerism. Further-more, it is unlikely that isomers of this kind would have such large differ-ences in vapor pressure as are found between what appear to be different forms of trivinylborane. The vapor pressure of trivinylborane at 0° is re-ported to be 63 mm (105), while that of the "daughter" compound after chromatography is about 40 mm at the same temperature (20,105).

Unlike trimethylborane or triethylborane, trivinylborane can be mixed with dry air at 25° without being oxidized. Methyldivinylborane is inter-

---

*Such behavior is not unknown in the chemistry of the Group III elements. When dimethylaminodichloroborane $[(CH_3)_2NBCl_2]$ is initially formed it is monomeric, but in one or two days it is completely transformed to a dimer. On sublimation the dimer reverts to the monomer. Similarly, as a solid $(CH_3)_2BNH_2$ is dimeric, but as a gas at 30° it is monomeric (78).

mediate between trivinylborane and the very easily oxidized trialkylboranes in its behavior towards air. The relative inertness of the vinylboranes towards oxidation has been ascribed to a lowering of the acidity
of the boron atom brought about by mesomerism involving the vinyl
groups' π-electrons and the boron p_π-orbital (*105*).

In order to extend this field still further a number of vinylboron halides
have been prepared (Table 3.1), and some of their physical properties and
chemical reactions have been investigated (*20,27*).

The reaction between divinylmercury and boron trihalides to give vinyldihaloboranes was mentioned earlier in this chapter. Subsequently, it was
found that the reaction between boron trihalides and vinyltin compounds
yields vinyldihaloboranes, divinylhaloboranes, or trivinylborane depending
on the ratio of reactants and especially on the boron halide taken for reaction (*18,20*). Since boron halides cleave vinyl groups from tin in preference to alkyl groups, compounds like di-*n*-butyldivinyltin may be used to
make vinylboron compounds.

Vinyldifluoroborane can be made in 50–60 per cent yield *via* the reaction,

$$(CH_2:CH)_4Sn + 2\ BF_3 \xrightarrow[\substack{\text{about} \\ \text{24 hours}}]{60°} 2\ CH_2:CHBF_2 + (CH_2:CH)_2SnF_2$$

No divinylfluoroborane is produced in this reaction even in the presence of
a large excess of the vinyltin compound and using temperatures up to
150°. The resistance of vinyldifluoroborane to further vinylation is in
distinct contrast to the behavior, discussed below, of vinyldichloro- and
vinyldibromoborane, and is further demonstrated by the fact that vinyldifluoroborane has been 95 per cent recovered after several hours' treatment
with divinylmercury at 110°, at which temperature the mercury compound
is appreciably decomposed.

When vinyldifluoroborane is treated with diethylzinc or trimethylaluminum, reaction takes place with partial conversion of the vinylboron
compound to triethylborane or trimethylborane respectively.

In the absence of other compounds vinyldifluoroborane is relatively
stable. Indeed it has the same order of thermal stability as ethyldifluoroborane. In the gas phase both organoboron compounds will withstand temperatures of 200° for at least 20 hours with only one or two per cent
decomposition. As mentioned later, other vinylboron halides are much less
stable than vinyldifluoroborane.

By treating boron trichloride with tetravinyltin, or di-*n*-butyldivinyltin,
the compounds vinyldichloro- and divinylchloroborane may be obtained.
Vinylation of boron trichloride in this manner is essentially complete after
one to two hours at 60°. By adjusting the proportions of reactants it is
possible to convert boron trichloride mainly to vinyldichloro- or to divinyl-

chloroborane, although mixtures are always obtained. For example, in a typical vinylation of boron trichloride in which divinylchloroborane was desired, using a molar ratio of $(CH_2:CH)_4Sn:BCl_3$ of 1 : 1 the product distribution was found by chromatography to be $CH_2:CHBCl_2$ (5.2 per cent), $(CH_2:CH)_2BCl$ (91.7 per cent), and $(CH_2:CH)_3B$ (3.1 per cent). The compound here listed as trivinylborane analyzed correctly, but the vapor pressures observed for this substance did not agree with those reported earlier (*105*); more than one form of trivinylborane appears to exist, as mentioned above.

Treatment of boron tribromide with tetravinyltin affords mixtures of vinylbromoboranes and trivinylborane. The boiling points of these compounds are apparently fairly close since they cannot be separated by distillation in a high-vacuum system. The boron-bromine bond is very reactive and an attempt to separate the vinylbromoboranes by gas chromatography led to decomposition. Vinyldichloroborane and divinylchloroborane, on the other hand, are readily separable either by distillation in a vacuum system or by normal fractional distillation in an inert atmosphere at atmospheric pressure. Vinyldichloroborane is sufficiently thermally stable to be distilled at normal pressures, provided the still-pot does not exceed a temperature of about 80°. Pure samples of vinyldichloroborane stored in sealed ampules as liquid undergo slight decomposition over a period of months with formation of a white solid.

The resistance of vinyldifluoroborane to further vinylation has already been mentioned. For this reason divinylfluoroborane was made by treating the readily accessible divinylchloroborane with antimony trifluoride well below room temperature. Divinylfluoroborane is thermally much less stable than vinyldifluoroborane, being about five per cent decomposed after storage in the gas phase at room temperature for 24 hours. At 80° it quickly decomposes, principally to trivinylborane and vinyldifluoroborane. Divinylchloroborane is less stable thermally than vinyldichloroborane but is more stable than divinylfluoroborane. It is of interest that whereas the slow decomposition of vinylchloroboranes appears to involve polymerization, the decomposition of divinylfluoroborane involves disproportionation, a phenomenon observed with the alkylhaloboranes.

On treatment of vinyldihaloboranes with ammoniacal silver oxide the vinyl group is cleaved as ethylene. When the divinylhaloboranes are treated with ammoniacal silver oxide, butadiene is formed as well as ethylene. It appears that at least two vinyl groups must be attached to each boron atom before butadiene appears as a reaction product.

Although ethyldifluoroborane does not afford ethane when heated with water, but instead yields an ethylboronic acid, vinyldifluoroborane reacts with water at 100° to give ethylene. Vinyldichloroborane also reacts with water at elevated temperatures to afford ethylene essentially quantitatively. Divinylchloroborane on the other hand releases only about 30 per cent of its vinyl groups as ethylene on treatment with water at 100° for approximately fifteen hours. Butadiene is not a product of the hydrolysis of divinylchloroborane. With water at lower temperatures the vinylhaloboranes would undoubtedly yield mainly vinylboronic acids. It is clear from this work, however, that water cleaves the vinyl groups from the vinylboron halides much more easily than it cleaves ethyl groups from ethylboron halides.

The vinyldihaloboranes are similar to the alkyldihaloboranes in undergoing exchange reactions with boron trihalides (*18*). Thus if vinyldichloroborane is mixed with boron trifluoride, the equilibrium

$$3\ CH_2:CHBCl_2 + 2\ BF_3 \rightleftharpoons 3\ CH_2:CHBF_2 + 2\ BCl_3$$

is quickly established. In an equilibrium of this type involving a series of Lewis acids addition of a Lewis base leads to removal of the strongest acid as an adduct. Therefore, since boron trichloride is a stronger Lewis acid than boron trifluoride (*135*), it is not surprising that the reaction,

$$3\ (CH_3)_3N \cdot BCl_2CH:CH_2 + 3\ BF_3 \longrightarrow 3\ CH_2:CHBF_2 +$$
$$2\ (CH_3)_3N \cdot BCl_3 + (CH_3)_3N \cdot BF_3$$

occurs. In these reactions it is possible that halogen atoms only are exchanged, or alternatively, that vinyl groups are exchanged followed by halogen atom transfer. In order to determine which of these mechanisms is operative, experiments were carried out using $B^{10}F_3$ and vinyldichloroborane having a normal boron isotopic distribution. Mass spectrometry showed that the boron content of the boron trifluoride recovered at the end of the reaction had not been isotopically diluted, proving conclusively that only halogen exchange is involved and that no vinyl groups are transferred from one boron atom to another in these reactions (*18*).

Very recently vinylboron halide chemistry has been extended by the preparation of perfluorovinylhaloboranes (*60*). These substances may be made from perfluorovinyltin compounds,

$$(CH_3)_2Sn(CF:CF_2)_2 \xrightarrow[(X\ =\ F,\ Cl)]{BX_3} CF_2:CFBX_2$$

These reactions proceed slowly at room temperature or more satisfactorily on mild heating. Perfluorovinyldifluoroborane may also be prepared by the reaction:

$$CF_2:CFBCl_2 \xrightarrow[-78°]{SbF_3} CF_2:CFBF_2$$

It is also formed by the reaction,

$$(CH_3)_3N \cdot BCl_2CF:CF_2 \xrightarrow[100]{BF_3} CF_2:CFBF_2$$

The existence of these perfluorovinylboron compounds (Table 3.1) is very interesting, since it might be argued that if a highly fluorinated organo-group is bonded to boron, there would be a tendency for a transfer of fluorine from the perfluoro-group to boron to form the thermodynamically very stable boron trifluoride. Indeed, although perfluorovinyldichloroborane may be heated for a few hours at 100° without decomposition, on standing for a few weeks at room temperature it affords small amounts of boron trifluoride. The fluoride $CF_2:CFBF_2$ and the chloride $(CF_2:CF)_2BCl$ are much less stable. In the gas phase at room temperature *bis*(perfluorovinyl)chloroborane is extensively decomposed within one day.

Perfluorovinyldifluoroborane reacts slowly with water at ambient temperatures and more rapidly at 100° to form trifluoroethylene quantitatively. Perfluorovinyldichloroborane, on the other hand, first forms hydrogen chloride with water, and only on heating of the solution is trifluoroethylene produced quantitatively.

Mention has been made earlier in this section of the properties of the alkylvinylboranes which make it seem likely that in these compounds there is a mesomeric effect involving the vinyl group's π-electron system and the boron p_π-orbital. One possible method of detecting the operation of such an effect in vinylboron compounds is by a gas-phase dissociation study of suitable molecular addition compounds formed by pairing analogous ethylboron and vinylboron compounds with the same Lewis base. The reader is referred elsewhere (*21,135*) for a more detailed discussion of how a study of this type can provide information on steric, inductive, mesomeric and other effects. Here it is only necessary to point out that usually the more electronegative an atom or group, the more it will increase the acceptor power of an atom to which it is bonded. Therefore, on the basis of an inductive effect, since the vinyl group is more electronegative than the ethyl, vinylboranes should be stronger Lewis acids than ethylboranes thus forming more stable addition compounds. However, a mesomeric effect in a vinylborane would have the reverse effect, reducing Lewis acidity by increasing the reorganizational energy required of the acid in addition compound formation (*135*). In an ethylborane in which a similar mesomeric effect would not occur, the reorganizational energy required for the boron atom to acquire tetrahedral configuration would be less. Thus an appreciable mesomeric effect in vinylboranes might so counteract the inductive effect of the vinyl group that vinylboranes might be weaker Lewis acids than

TABLE 3.1. VINYLBORON COMPOUNDS

Compound	M.p. °C	B.p.[a] °C	$\log p(mm) = B-AT^{-1}$ B	A	$\Delta H[a]$ (vapor) kcal/mole^{-1}	Trouton Constant[a] e.u.	Ref.
$(CH_2:CH)_3B$	–	55°[b]	8.570	1848	8.00	24.4	105
$(CH_2:CH)_2BCH_3$	–	–	7.816	1574	–	–	105
$CH_2:CHB(CH_3)_2$	–	0°/126 mm	–	–	–	–	105
$CH_2:CHBF_2$	–133.4	–38.8	7.915	1180	5.40	23	20
$(CH_2:CH)_2BF$	–164 to –157[c]	23.8	7.416	1347	6.16	20.7	20
$CH_2:CHBCl_2$	–111.1	45.1	7.434	1449	6.63	20.8	20
$(CH_2:CH)_2BCl$	–109.6	71.1	7.885	1723	7.88	22.9	20
$CHCl:CHBCl_2$	–	98–100°	–	–	–	–	14
$(CHCl:CH)_2BCl$	–	80°/25 mm	–	–	–	–	14
$CF_2:CFBF_2$	–96	–14	8.247	1389	6.39	24.6	60
$CF_2:CFBCl_2$	–108	38.5	8.008	1645	7.53	24.2	60
$(CF_2:CF)_2BCl$	–57.5	100.5	7.861	1861	8.52	22.8	60
$(CF_2:CF)_3B$	–107	104.9	8.559	2147	9.83	26.0	60
$ClCH:CHB(OH)_2$	129	–	–	–	–	–	14
$(ClCH:CH)_2BOH$	–	66°/3 mm	–	–	–	–	14
$(ClCH:CH)_2BOC_2H_5$	–	74°/3 mm	–	–	–	–	14
$(ClCH:CH)_2BNC_5H_{10}$	–	95°/2 mm	–	–	–	–	14

[a] Except for the chlorovinyl compounds, obtained by extrapolation of the vapor pressure equation.
[b] Recently, a normal boiling point of 79.5° has been reported for this compound (142a).
[c] Forms a glass.

ethylboranes. This change would appear as a lower enthalpy of dissociation for the vinylboron adduct than for the ethylboron adduct. Unfortunately, as mentioned earlier, unsymmetrical trialkylboranes have only a transient existence, and even compounds like methyldivinylborane are too unstable to use in gas-phase dissociation studies in which the presence of base would serve only to increase even more the tendency of the acid to decompose irreversibly. Thus it might be thought that since vinyldifluoroborane is highly stable and can be used in gas-phase dissociation measurements, examination of two addition compounds such as $(CH_3)_3N \cdot BF_2C_2H_5$ and $(CH_3)_3N \cdot BF_2CH:CH_2$ would give a clear answer as to whether a vinyl group does interact with the vacant orbital of an adjacent boron atom. If the vinyldifluoroborane adduct were to show a lower enthalpy of dissociation than the ethyldifluoroborane adduct a mesomeric effect in the vinyl-boron compound would be clearly demonstrated. On the other hand, if the vinyldifluoroborane adduct had a measurably higher enthalpy of dissociation than the ethyldifluoroborane complex it would be clear that the inductive effect of the vinyl group predominates. In order to answer questions of this nature the acceptor power of the boron atoms in the series CH_3BF_2, $C_2H_5BF_2$, $CH_2:CHBF_2$, and $n\text{-}C_3H_7BF_2$ has been compared (27) using trimethylamine as the reference base with the results summarized in Table 3.2. The most striking aspect of these results is the closeness of the enthalpy values for all the compounds measured. In terms of enthalpy changes one may say unequivocally only that the vinyldifluoroborane adduct appears to be stronger than the propyldifluoroborane adduct, while all other comparisons lie within the limits of experimental error.*

The gas-phase dissociation data do not permit any clear decision as to the importance of mesomeric interactions between the vinyl group and the boron atom in $CH_2:CHBF_2$. It is possible that the enthalpy of dissociation of trimethylamine-vinyldifluoroborane is low as compared to the value which would be expected if the vinyl group were acting purely inductively, although prediction of a hypothetical "inductive only" value is difficult.

One approach, admittedly speculative, is to predict the inductive effect of the vinyl group from data involving polar substituent constants, σ^* (140). These constants, derived from studies of the rates of ester hydrolysis, are considered to reflect the electron withdrawing power of various substituent groups. It has been found that the effects of a wide variety of groups on rates and equilibria of several different types can be correlated

---

*Enthalpy changes reported here are good to $\pm$ 0.2 kcal. From the *dissociation constants* reported in Table 3.2 an order of stability $CH_2:CH-$, CH_3, C_2H_5, C_3H_7 is apparent. However, equilibrium constants are determined in part by entropy terms, and need not follow the order of ΔH. Most authors seem to feel that ΔH is a better measure of zero-point potential energy effects than ΔF.

with some degree of accuracy with σ^* values. In particular, the results of Brown and his co-workers on the gas-phase dissociation of the trimethylborane addition compounds of some primary aliphatic amines RNH_2 have been found (*140*) to follow the relation $\Delta H = -7.26\ \Sigma\sigma^* + 24.54$, where ΔH is the enthalpy of dissociation and $\Sigma\sigma^*$ is the sum of the σ^* values for the substituents, in this instance two hydrogen atoms and an alkyl group, on the nitrogen atom. If it is assumed that polar effects are governing in dissociation of the type,

$$(CH_3)_3N \cdot BF_2R_{(g)} \rightleftharpoons (CH_3)_3N_{(g)} + BF_2R_{(g)}$$

an equation $\Delta H = a\Sigma\sigma^* + b$ might be applicable, where $\Sigma\sigma^*$ is now the sum of the values of the substituents on boron. Using the σ^* values for the methyl group and for fluorine (*140*) one may evaluate the constants "a" and "b" by using the measured ΔH value for $(CH_3)_3N \cdot BF_2CH_3$ (Table 3.2) and the best available estimates for ΔH of $(CH_3)_3N \cdot BF_3$ (26.6 – 30.9 kcal mole^{-1}) (*135*). Such a procedure suggests that the ΔH values for the trimethylamine adducts of ethyldifluoro- and propyldifluoroborane should be 19.8 to 20.0 kcal/mole^{-1}. These values are close to the observed values (Table 3.2).

TABLE 3.2. GAS PHASE DISSOCIATION OF (CH$_3$)$_3$N · BF$_2$R COMPOUNDS*

R	Δ_H° kcal/mole^{-1}	Δ_S° e.u.	K_p at 150° atm.
CH$_3$-	20.1	40.8	0.0323
CH$_3$CH$_2$-	20.2	41.8	0.0494
CH$_3$CH$_2$CH$_2$-	20.1	41.8	0.0614
CH$_2$: CH	20.4	38.5	0.00793

*The results presented are for the dissociation, $(CH_3)_3N \cdot BF_2R_{(g)} \rightarrow (CH_3)_3N_{(g)} + RBF_{2(g)}$.

Unfortunately no σ^* value is available for the vinyl group. However, application of this same procedure to phenyldifluoroborane (σ^* for phenyl, 0.60) and propenyldifluoroborane (σ^* for propenyl, 0.36) suggests enthalpies of dissociation for the hypothetical trimethylamine adducts of these acids of 21.5–22.3 kcal and 20.9–21.4 kcal respectively. Granting the questionable assumptions, it appears that if the vinyl group in vinyldifluoroborane were acting only on an inductive basis, the enthalpy of dissociation of $(CH_3)_3N \cdot BF_2CH:CH_2$ should be about 21.0 kcal. It thus appears that an unmoderated inductive effect of the vinyl group in vinyldifluoroborane might be detectable by the gas-phase dissociation technique.

It is evident, however, that polar effects need not be the only ones operating in the RBF$_2$ series, and evidence for this is provided by a nuclear

magnetic resonance study (*27*) of the F^{19} chemical shifts in these compounds (Table 3.3). The possibility of partial double bond character in
boron trifluoride has long been recognized (*26,106,135*) and has been in-
voked to explain the apparent weakness of boron trifluoride as an acid
compared to boron trichloride, with pyridine or nitrobenzene as reference
bases (*22*). Partial double bonding probably also occurs in the B—F linkages in RBF_2 compounds. The effect may even be greater per B—F bond,
since in the organodifluoroboranes one of the fluorine atoms of boron trifluoride has been replaced by an organogroup which would be less effective in filling the boron p_π-orbital than a fluorine atom, with its available
p_π-electrons. This behavior is indicated by the relative chemical shifts of

TABLE 3.3. F^{19} CHEMICAL SHIFTS IN RBF_2

Compound	Chemical Shift (δ)*		Pure liquid (ppm)
	In solution (ppm)	Infinite dilution (ppm)	
CH_3BF_2	69.3	68.8	73.6
$C_2H_5BF_2$	74.9	74.6	78.4
n-$C_3H_7BF_2$	73.2	72.8	75.8
$CH_2:CHBF_2$	88.9	88.6	92.7
BF_3	126.8	–	–

*Relative to CCl_3F at infinite dilution.

the F^{19} resonances in organodifluoroboranes and boron trifluoride given in
Table 3.3. It should be noted that the F^{19} resonances are not directly related to Lewis acidity of the molecule since they provide no information
about the total electron density at the boron atom, which is determined in
part by the inductive effect of the R group acting in the σ-bonds. However, it would be expected that the more effective an R group in RBF_2
is in filling the boron p_π-orbital, the more ionic will be the fluorine,
which should show resonance at higher field on the basis of the usual qualitative interpretations of F^{19} chemical shifts. The results in Table 3.3 show
that the vinyl group is much more effective in moving the F^{19} resonance up-
field than are the alkyl groups despite the lower electronegativity of the latter. Since RBF_2 compounds are weaker Lewis acids than boron trifluoride,
there must be more electron density around boron in RBF_2 than in BF_3.
However, within the RBF_2 series the nuclear magnetic resonance studies
indicate that the amount of B—F π-bonding is a function of the ability
of the R group to fill the boron p_π-orbital.

This section on vinylboron compounds will be concluded by mentioning
some β-substituted vinylboron compounds. β-Chlorovinylboron compounds have been prepared from the β-chlorovinylmercury compounds
(*14*) or from acetylene and boron trichloride (*3*). The following reactions illustrate work done in this area.

$$\text{ClCH:CHHgCl} + \text{BCl}_3 \xrightarrow[\substack{\text{sealed tube} \\ \text{2 hrs. at } 50°}]{\text{petroleum ether}} \text{ClCH:CHBCl}_2 \xrightarrow{\text{water}} \text{ClCH:CHB(OH)}_2$$

$$(\text{ClCH:CH})_2\text{Hg} + \text{BCl}_3 \xrightarrow[\text{heat}]{\text{C}_6\text{H}_6} (\text{ClCH:CH})_2\text{BCl} \xrightarrow{\text{water}} (\text{ClCH:CH})_2\text{BOH}$$

$$(\text{ClCH:CH})_2\text{BCl} \xrightarrow{\text{C}_2\text{H}_5\text{OH}} (\text{ClCH:CH})_2\text{BOC}_2\text{H}_5$$

$$(\text{ClCH:CH})_2\text{BCl} \xrightarrow{\text{piperidine}} (\text{ClCH:CH})_2\text{BNC}_5\text{H}_{10}$$

$$\text{ClCH:CHB(OH)}_2 \xrightarrow{\text{aqueous HgCl}_2} \text{ClCH:CHHgCl}$$

$$\text{CH}{\equiv}\text{CH} + \text{BCl}_3 \xrightarrow[150°]{\text{Hg}_2\text{Cl}_2} \text{ClCH:CHBCl}_2$$

All the β-chlorovinylboron compounds release acetylene on basic hydrolysis.

Organolithium reagents have also been used to make β-substituted boron compounds (79).

$$(\text{CH}_3)_2\text{C}{=}\text{CHLi} + (\text{CH}_3\text{O})_3\text{B} \longrightarrow (\text{CH}_3)_2\text{C}{=}\text{CHB(OH)}_2$$
$$\text{m.p. } 84\text{--}6°$$

Aluminum

Since aluminum alkyls are known to bring about the polymerization of ethylene, it is to be expected that vinylaluminum compounds would tend to polymerize, although it is probable that some of the monomers would be sufficiently stable to permit characterization. It is, therefore, interesting that a number of vinylaluminum compounds have very recently been reported (5). Very little information is at present available on the properties of these compounds. Trivinylaluminum (b.p. 50–60°/1 mm) polymerizes slowly on standing at room temperature, while the vinylaluminum halides polymerize very readily. Reactions reported in the preliminary communication include the following (5):

$$(\text{CH}_2\text{:CH})_2\text{Hg} + \text{Al} \xrightarrow[50°]{\text{pentane}} (\text{CH}_2\text{:CH})_3\text{Al} \xrightarrow{(\text{CH}_3)_3\text{N}} (\text{CH}_3)_3\text{N}\cdot\text{Al(CH:CH}_2)_3$$
$$\Big\downarrow (\text{CH}_2)_4\text{O}$$

$$\text{AlX}_3 + \text{CH}_2\text{:CHMgX} \xrightarrow{(\text{CH}_2)_4\text{O}} (\text{CH}_2)_4\text{O}\cdot\text{Al(CH:CH}_2)_3$$

$$(\text{CH}_2\text{:CH})_2\text{Hg} + \text{AlCl}_3 \xrightarrow{\text{benzene}} \text{CH}_2\text{:CHAlCl}_2 + \text{CH}_2\text{:CHHgCl}$$

$$(\text{CH}_2\text{:CH})_4\text{Pb} + 2\,\text{AlCl}_3 \xrightarrow{\text{benzene}} 2\,\text{CH}_2\text{:CHAlCl}_2 + (\text{CH}_2\text{:CH})_2\text{PbCl}_2$$

$$(\text{CH}_3)_3\text{N}\cdot\text{AlX}_3 + \text{CH}_2\text{:CHNa} \xrightarrow{\text{pentane}} (\text{CH}_3)_3\text{N}\cdot\text{Al(CH:CH}_2)_3$$

$$(CH_3)_3N \cdot AlH_3 + (CH_2:CH)_2Hg \xrightarrow{(C_2H_5)_2O} (CH_3)_3N \cdot Al(CH:CH_2)_3$$

$$2\ (CH_2:CH)_2Hg + LiAlH_4 \longrightarrow LiAl(CH:CH_2)_4 + 2\ Hg + 2\ H_2$$

$$\downarrow {\scriptstyle (CH_3)_3NHCl}$$

$$(CH_3)_3N \cdot Al(CH:CH_2)_3$$

Treatment of the vinylaluminum halides with lithium or sodium hydrides yields polymers, formed presumably by addition of the Al—H linkage in one molecule to the vinyl group in another. This observation is related to some of the work of Ziegler and his co-workers (*154*). Dialkylaluminum hydrides react with diphenylacetylene to form an adduct which on treatment with water affords *cis*-stilbene. This is a convenient path for the preparation of *cis*-olefins since it may be applied to other doubly substituted acetylenes besides diphenylacetylene. For purposes of this review, however, the importance of the reaction lies in the fact that the intermediate adduct before hydrolysis must be an alkenylaluminum compound. Such substances are also produced when triethylaluminum or dialkylaluminum hydrides are treated in the correct proportions with acetylene or monosubstituted acetylenes. On addition of excess of acetylene polymerization occurs. This process has been shown to proceed through addition of the aluminum-alkenyl linkage to acetylene so that conjugated dienes are produced. It is interesting that the alkyl-aluminum linkages in the mixed alkylalkenylaluminum compounds do not add to the excess of acetylene. The process has been clarified by a study of the reaction between dibutylaluminum hydride and diethylacetylene. Hydrolysis affords 1,2,3,4-tetraethylbutadiene. Alkenylaluminum compounds also add to ethylene or to themselves at elevated temperatures. The reader is referred to Chapter 5 of this monograph for a detailed discussion of processes of this type.

Thallium

Treatment of thallium(III) halides with vinyl Grignard in a tetrahydrofuran-diethyl ether solvent mixture affords divinylthallium chloride or bromide, crystallized from pyridine as solids, decomposing above 300° without melting (*96*). These compounds have also been obtained from the reaction between thallium(III) halides and divinylmercury. The divinylthallium halides undergo the following reactions, where X represents Cl or Br (*96*),

$$(CH_2:CH)_2TlX \xrightarrow[Hg]{(CH_2)_4O} (CH_2:CH)_2Hg + TlX$$

$$(CH_2:CH)_2TlX \xrightarrow{TlX_3} CH_2:CHTlX_2$$

$$(CH_2 : CH)_2TlX \xrightarrow[SnX_2]{CH_3COCH_3} (CH_2 : CH)_2SnX_2 + TlX$$

The reaction between divinylthallium halides and mercury should be compared with the analogous reaction (43),

$$(C_6H_5)_2TlBr + Hg \longrightarrow (C_6H_5)_2Hg + TlBr$$

A number of β-chlorovinylthallium compounds have been prepared from β-chlorovinylmercury compounds. These compounds were made as part of the program (93) for investigating exchange reactions at the olefinic carbon atom. The preparation of *cis-* and *trans-*β-chlorovinylmercury compounds was described in a previous section. As mentioned previously, exchange of β-chlorovinyl groups proceeds with strict retention of configuration, e.g.,

$$2 \ cis\text{-}(ClCH : CH)_2Hg + TlCl_3 \xrightarrow[\text{10 hrs. room temp.}]{(C_2H_5)_2O}$$

$$cis\text{-}(ClCH : CH)_2TlCl + 2 \ (CHCl : CH)HgCl$$
$$\text{m.p. } 145\text{-}6°$$

$$2 \ trans\text{-}(ClCH : CH)_2Hg + TlCl_3 \longrightarrow$$

$$trans\text{-}(ClCH : CH)_2TlCl + 2 \ (CHCl : CH)HgCl$$
$$\text{m.p. } 166\text{-}7°$$

Other reactions involving β-substituted vinylthallium compounds include,

$$cis\text{-}(ClCH : CH)_2TlCl + SnCl_2 \xrightarrow[\text{4 hrs. room temp.}]{C_2H_5OH} cis\text{-}(ClCH : CH)_2SnCl_2 + TlCl$$

$$trans\text{-}(ClCH : CH)_2BCl + TlCl_3 \xrightarrow[\text{hydrochloric acid} \atop \text{at 50°}]{\text{dilute}} trans\text{-}(ClCH : CH)_2TlCl$$

$$2 \ cis\text{-}CH_3CH : CHLi + TlBr_3 \xrightarrow[6 \ 8°]{(C_2H_5)_2O} cis\text{-}(CH_3CH : CH)_2TlBr + 2 \ LiBr$$

VINYL COMPOUNDS OF THE GROUP IV ELEMENTS

Silicon

A large number of vinylsilicon compounds have been described in the literature most of them known long before vinylating reagents like the Grignard $CH_2 : CHMgBr$ were obtained. The existence of a wide spectrum of vinylsilicon compounds, whereas until recently few vinyl derivatives of other Group IV elements were known, is the result of the extensive studies made in organosilicon chemistry since the discovery of the importance of the silicones. Although most of the effort in organosilicon chemistry was not directed towards making vinylsilicon compounds, work in this area did lead to the discovery of methods not involving the use of vinylmetallics for preparing vinylsilicon compounds. These methods involved direct synthesis from vinyl halides and silicon, dehydrohalogenation reactions, and addition of silanes to acetylenes. Thus, vinyltrichlorosilane has been obtained by the following reactions:

$$CH_2 : CHCl + Si \xrightarrow[300°]{Cu} CH_2 : CHSiCl_3 \qquad (51,138)$$

$$CH_3CH_2SiCl_3 \xrightarrow[(C_6H_5CO_2)_2]{SO_2Cl_2} CH_2ClCH_2SiCl_3 \xrightarrow{quinoline} CH_2 : CHSiCl_3 \quad (51,52)$$

$$+$$

$$CH_3CHClSiCl_3$$

$$HC{\equiv}CH + HSiCl_3 \xrightarrow[Pt/charcoal]{heat} CH_2 : CHSiCl_3 \qquad (147)$$

Since chlorine atoms bonded to silicon may be replaced readily by hydrogen, alkyl, aryl, or alkoxy groups, it is readily seen that numerous vinylsilicon compounds can be obtained from vinyltrichlorosilane. Furthermore, reactions of the type indicated above are fairly general and so have been used to make other vinylsilicon compounds than vinyltrichlorosilane. As this aspect of silicon chemistry has been thoroughly reviewed recently (2,41,44) because of limitations in space it will not be considered again in detail here. In this section mention will only be made of some more recent work on vinylsilicon compounds, and the reader's attention will be drawn to those properties of vinylsilicon compounds which contrast with those of the vinyl derivatives of the heavier Group IVb atoms.

Following the development of vinylmagnesium chloride and bromide (101,113) a number of vinylsilanes were prepared by treating the vinyl Grignard with the appropriate silicon halide, e.g.,

$$4 CH_2 : CHMgCl + SiCl_4 \xrightarrow{reflux} (CH_2 : CH)_4Si + 4 MgCl_2 \qquad (119)$$
$$\text{(in tetrahydrofuran)} \quad \text{(in pentane)} \quad 87\% \text{ yield}$$

$$3 CH_2 : CHMgCl + HSiCl_3 \xrightarrow{reflux} (CH_2 : CH)_3SiH + 3 MgCl_2 \quad (119)$$
$$\text{(in tetrahydrofuran)} \quad \text{(in pentane)} \quad 55\% \text{ yield}$$

$$2 CH_2 : CHMgBr + (C_2H_5)HSiCl_2 \xrightarrow{reflux}$$
$$\text{(in tetrahydrofuran)}$$

$$C_2H_5(CH_2 : CH)_2SiH + MgBr_2 + MgCl_2 \qquad (108)$$
$$22\% \text{ yield}$$

Thus by using the vinyl Grignard reagent organosilanes containing more than one vinyl group can easily be prepared. Prior to these investigations a patent (*112*) described the formation of some vinylsilanes from vinyl bromide, magnesium, and silicon tetrachloride using diethyl ether as solvent.

A process related to this is the condensation reaction (*64,110*),

$$R_nSiCl_{4-n} + (4 - n)CH_2:CHCl \xrightarrow{Na/(C_2H_5)_2O} R_nSi(CH:CH_2)_{4-n}$$

The yield of desired vinylsilane, however, is low.

Vinylsilanes of the type $R_nSi(CH:CH_2)_{4-n}$ (R = alkyl, aryl or hydrogen) polymerize when held at their boiling points for prolonged periods (*119*). This is particularly true when R is hydrogen, as discussed in the next two sections of this chapter, but even compounds like diphenyldivinylsilane must be distilled at reduced pressure in order to avoid heat-induced polymerization.

The olefinic bond in vinylsilicon compounds undergoes many reactions typical of the unsaturated linkage, in general without cleavage of the silicon-carbon bond. Addition reactions occur with halogens, and hydrogen halides add to vinylsilanes to form halogenoalkylsilanes (*41,65*). It is interesting that in the latter reaction Markownikoff's rule is not obeyed, e.g.,

$$CH_2:CHSiMe_3 + HI \longrightarrow CH_2ICH_2Si(CH_3)_3$$

Since the trimethylsilyl group is considered to be electron releasing, this mode of addition is surprising. It has been suggested that silicon-carbon d_π-p_π bonding reverses the polarity of the carbon atoms of the vinyl group so that an anti-Markownikoff addition is observed (*65,137*). Another olefinic reaction sensitive to directive effects is oxymercuration. Trimethylvinylsilane reacts in good yield according to the following scheme (*128*),

$$(CH_3)_3SiCH:CH_2 \xrightarrow[\text{NaOH}]{Hg(OAc)_2} (CH_3)_3SiC_2H_3(OH)HgOAc \xrightarrow{NaCl}$$
$$(CH_3)_3SiC_2H_3(OH)HgCl$$

Treatment of the crystalline product with sodium amalgam afforded a single organosilicon alcohol shown to be $(CH_3)_3SiCH_2CH_2OH$. This established that in the oxymercuration of trimethylvinylsilane the positive portion of the adding reagent becomes bonded to the α-carbon atom of the vinylsilane (*128*). The direction of addition is thus the same as in the addition of hydrogen chloride to vinyltrichlorosilane (*148*), and hydrogen iodide to trimethylvinylsilane (*132*). The formation of a single isomer in the oxymercuration of trimethylvinylsilane is in contrast to the formation of two isomers in its hydroboration. When trimethylvinylsilane is treated with the sodium borohydride-aluminum chloride reagent or with trimethylamine-borane, a borane $[(CH_3)_3SiC_2H_4]_3B$ is formed in which the group-ings $(CH_3)_3SiCH_2CH_2B$ and $(CH_3)_3SiCH(CH_3)B$ are present in about a 2:1 molar ratio (127). Oxidation affords the alcohols $(CH_3)_3SiCH(CH_3)OH$ and $(CH_3)_3SiCH_2CH_2OH$. The hydroboration of trimethylvinylsilane is in contrast to the reaction between vinyltrichlorosilane and sodium borohy-dride, in which case vinyl-silicon bond cleavage occurs with formation of silane (150).

A number of nucleophilic cleavages of certain vinylsilanes are known. When vinylsilane is heated with 30 per cent aqueous sodium hydroxide, ethylene forms almost quantitatively, and halogenovinyl groups are also cleaved from silicon by alcoholic base. On the other hand, propenyltri-chlorosilane (4) and trimethylvinylsilane (65) do not form propylene and ethylene respectively on treatment with base.

The recent preparation of $(CF_2:CF)_4Si$ from silicon tetrachloride and perfluorovinylmagnesium bromide (133) suggests that many other per-fluorovinylsilanes can be prepared. It will be of interest to determine in what manner the chemistry of the new $CF_2:CF—Si$ group contrasts with the chemistry of the long-known $CH_2:CH—Si$ group.

Germanium

Tetravinylgermane may be obtained in about 35 per cent yield by adding germanium(IV) chloride to vinylmagnesium bromide in tetrahydrofuran solution. Hexavinyldigermane is also formed in this reaction in about 26 per cent yield (126). It is interesting that in an ether-toluene solvent system hexaphenyldigermane is a product of the reaction between ger-manium(IV) chloride and phenylmagnesium bromide (56,57). Aliphatic Grignard reagents, on the other hand, do not bring about reductive alkyla-tion of germanium(IV) chloride. Furthermore, tetrachlorosilane and tin(IV) chloride do not undergo reductive coupling when treated with the vinyl or the phenyl Grignard reagent. These observations provide a further example of the frequently demonstrated anomalous nature of germanium chemistry compared with that of silicon or tin. It has been suggested (126) that formation of hexavinyldigermane from germanium(IV) chloride and vinyl Grignard proceeds via the following reaction scheme:

$$GeCl_4 + 2CH_2:CHMgBr \longrightarrow GeCl_2 + CH_2:CHCH:CH_2 + MgCl_2 + MgBr_2$$

$$GeCl_2 + 2CH_2:CHMgBr \longrightarrow (CH_2:CH)_2Ge + MgCl_2 + MgBr_2$$

$$(CH_2:CH)_2Ge + CH_2:CHMgBr \longrightarrow (CH_2:CH)_3GeMgBr$$

$$(CH_2:CH)_3GeMgBr + (CH_2:CH)_3GeCl \longrightarrow$$

$$(CH_2:CH)_3GeGe(CH:CH_2)_3 + 1/2 MgCl_2 + 1/2 MgBr_2$$

This suggestion is attractive in view of the fact that reduction of metal halides to a lower oxidation state by Grignards is well established, and that addition of organometallic reagents to diorganogermane(II) compounds has been reported (*53,139*).

Diethyldivinylgermane and ethyltrivinylgermane have been prepared by the action of vinylmagnesium bromide in tetrahydrofuran on diethylgermanium dichloride and ethylgermanium trichloride respectively (*108,126*). Tri-*n*-butylvinylgermane and triethylvinylgermane have been similarly prepared (*86*).

TABLE 3.4. VINYLGERMANIUM COMPOUNDS

Compound	B.p. °C/mm	n_D^t	d_4^t	Ref.
$(CH_2 : CH)_4 Ge$	52–54/27	1.4676 (25°)	1.040 (25°)	*126*
$(CH_2 : CH)_6 Ge_2$	55/0.35	1.5217 (25°)	1.171 (25°)	*126*
$(C_2H_5)_2Ge(CH : CH_2)_2$	59–60/28.5	1.4540 (25°)	–	*126*
	149.8/760	1.4575 (20°)	1.0193 (20°)	*108*
$C_2H_5Ge(CH : CH_2)_3$	55–57/28	1.4605 (25°)	–	*126,108*
$(C_2H_5)_3GeCH : CH_2$	61/28	1.4501 (20°)	1.0048 (20°)	*86*
$(n\text{-}C_4H_9)_3GeCH : CH_2$	108–109/2	1.4598 (20°)	0.9479 (20°)	*86*
$(CH_2 : CH)_3 GeI$	71–74/12	–	–	*126*
$(CH_2 : CH)_3 GeBr$	58/10	1.5057 (25°)	–	*126*
$CH_2 : CHGeCl_3$	128.6/760	–	–	*19,109*
	128.8/765			
$CH_2 : CHGeH_3$	– 3.5/760[a]	–	–	*19*

[a] Obtained by extrapolation of the equation. $Log_{10}p_{mm} = 7.564 - 1263T^{-1}$.

Vinylgermanium compounds are much more resistant to cleavage of their vinyl groups than are vinyltin compounds. Mercury(II) chloride causes no cleavage of the vinylgermanium bond (*126*). Iodine, bromine, hydrogen bromide and mercaptans add to the double bond in vinylgermanes (*86*), viz.,

$$(n\text{-}C_4H_9)_3GeCH : CH_2 + Br_2 \longrightarrow (n\text{-}C_4H_9)_3GeCHBrCH_2Br$$

$$(n\text{-}C_4H_9)_3GeCH : CH_2 + HBr \longrightarrow (n\text{-}C_4H_9)_3GeCH_2CH_2Br$$

$$(C_2H_5)_3GeCH : CH_2 + HSCH_2COOH \longrightarrow (C_2H_5)_3GeCH_2CH_2SCH_2COOH$$

As described in the next section, with these reagents the vinyl group is cleaved from vinyltin compounds. Furthermore, although mercaptans add to allylgermanes, the latter are cleaved by halogens and halogen acids, and the reaction,

$$(n\text{-}C_4H_9)_3GeCH_2CH : CH_2 + CCl_3COOH \longrightarrow$$

$$(n\text{-}C_4H_9)_3Ge(OCOCCl_3) + CH_3CH : CH_2$$

proceeds much more rapidly than does the reaction.

$$(n\text{-}C_4H_9)_3GeCH:CH_2 + CCl_3COOH \longrightarrow (n\text{-}C_4H_9)_3Ge(OCOCCl_3) + C_2H_4$$

Allylgermanes are also cleaved at 20° by mercury(II) chloride in ethanol (86).

Allyl compounds of metals and metalloids are generally less stable towards cleavage and polymerization than their vinyl analogues. Thus, whereas vinyldifluoroborane is indefinitely stable at ambient temperatures, allyldifluoroborane slowly decomposes (20), and although tetravinyltin can be distilled at atmospheric pressure in the absence of a polymerization inhibitor, allyltin compounds must be distilled at reduced pressure in an inert atmosphere (129). Tetra-allylgermane polymerizes into an insoluble polymer in presence of traces of peroxide (86).

The compound hexavinyldigermane reacts with iodine and bromine (126).

$$(CH_2:CH)_3GeGe(CH:CH_2)_3 + X_2 \longrightarrow 2(CH_2:CH)_3GeX.$$

Since tetravinylgermane does not react with germanium(IV) chloride to give vinylhalogermanes (126), these substances are more difficult to obtain than are their tin analogues. Trivinylgermanium halides are best obtained from hexavinyldigermane as indicated above. One approach to synthesis of the vinyltrihalogermanes is through the ethyl compounds. Since the Ge—C mean bond energy is greater than that of the Sn—C bond in analogous organotin compounds, ethyltrihalogermanes can be chlorinated without cleavage of the organo-group (109).

$$Ge/Cu \xrightarrow[C_2H_5Cl]{heat} C_2H_5GeCl_3 \xrightarrow{SOCl_2} CH_3CHClGeCl_3 + ClCH_2CH_2GeCl_3$$
$$\phantom{Ge/Cu \xrightarrow[C_2H_5Cl]{heat}} 65\% \phantom{C_2H_5GeCl_3 \xrightarrow{SOCl_2}} 4.3\% 37.8\%$$

The 2-chloroethyltrichlorogermane obtained in this way can be dehydrohalogenated with quinoline to afford vinyltrichlorogermane in 26 per cent yield. Vinyltrichlorogermane, however, is much more simply prepared in 70 per cent yield by the reaction (19)

$$GeCl_4 + (CH_2:CH)_2Hg \xrightarrow{80°} CH_2:CHGeCl_3 + CH_2:CHHgCl$$

The compound vinylgermane (Table 3.4) may be prepared by reducing vinyltrichlorogermane with lithium aluminum hydride (19). Vinylgermane was prepared in order to compare its stability with that of vinylsilane. The ability of the Si—H linkage to add to carbon-carbon double and triple bonds under free radical conditions has been known for over a decade (41). It is, therefore, not surprising that molecules containing both Si—H linkages and carbon-carbon double bonds can readily be polymerized. Vinylsilane polymerizes rapidly when irradiated with ultraviolet light (151). Since the Ge—H (36,42,116) and the Sn—H (144,145) linkages also add to unsaturated carbon-carbon bonds, it was of interest to determine whether vinylgermane and vinylstannane had greater or lesser tendencies to poly-merize than vinylsilane. It was found that vinylgermane is less stable than vinylsilane (*19*). Vinylgermane polymerizes to a white solid in daylight, especially in the presence of mercury. The infrared spectrum of polyvinyl-germane is similar to that of polyvinylsilane, and the two polymers prob-ably have similar structures, —$(CH_2CH_2MH_2)_x$—, where M = Si or Ge. Vinylstannane, obtained by reduction of vinyltin trichloride with lithium aluminum hydride, is much less stable than vinylgermane, and must be stored at $-78°$ to avoid decomposition, a process which proceeds by more than one route.

Tin

Prior to the discovery of the vinyl Grignard reagent only a few vinyltin compounds were known. The following studies are illustrative of early work in vinyltin chemistry.

In 1930 Kraus and Neal (*76*) reported studies indicating that they had formed trimethylvinyltin, albeit contaminated with tetramethyltin, by the following postulated reactions.

$$3(CH_3)_3SnNa + CHCl_3 \xrightarrow{\text{liq. NH}_3} [(CH_3)_3Sn]_3CH + 3\,NaCl$$

$$\xrightarrow{\text{decomposes}}$$

$$[(CH_3)_3Sn]_2 + (CH_3)_3SnCH:CHSn(CH_3)_3 \quad \text{(b.p. } 194°/760 \text{ mm)}$$

bis(trimethyl)stannyl ethylene

$$(CH_3)_3SnCH:CHSn(CH_3)_3 + 2\,Na + NH_3 \xrightarrow{\text{liq. NH}_3}$$

$$(CH_3)_3SnNa + CH_2:CHSn(CH_3)_3 + NaNH_2$$

$$CH_2:CHSn(CH_3)_3 + 2\,Na + NH_3 \xrightarrow{\text{liq. NH}_3}$$

$$CH_2:CHSn(CH_3)_2Na + CH_4 + NaNH_2$$

$$CH_2:CHSn(CH_3)_2Na + CH_3I \xrightarrow{\text{liq. NH}_3} (CH_3)_3SnCH:CH_2 + NaI$$

These interesting reactions are worthy of further study.

As mentioned in a previous section, some β-chlorovinyltin compounds have been known for several years as a result of the work of Nesmeyanov and his co-workers (*90,93*).

The compound vinyltin tribromide was obtained by treating a dilute alcoholic solution of sodium stannite with vinyl bromide at $0°$, followed by treatment of the mixture with hydrogen bromide (*131*).

Following the discovery that the vinyl Grignard reagent $CH_2:CHMgX$ can be easily formed, provided tetrahydrofuran is used as solvent

(*101,113*), three groups of workers (*108,118,129*) independently used the Grignard to make vinyltin compounds (Table 3.6), e.g.,

$$4\,CH_2:CHMgBr + SnCl_4 \longrightarrow (CH_2:CH)_4Sn + 2\,MgCl_2 + 2\,MgBr_2 \qquad (129)$$

$$2\,CH_2:CHMgCl + (n\text{-}C_4H_9)_2SnO \longrightarrow$$
$$(n\text{-}C_4H_9)_2Sn(CH:CH_2)_2 + (MgCl)_2O \qquad (118)$$

$$CH_2:CHMgBr + (C_2H_5)_3SnCl \longrightarrow (C_2H_5)_3SnCH:CH_2 + MgBrCl \qquad (108)$$

The replacement of the halogen of organotin halides by vinyl Grignard is a stepwise process which may be controlled to some extent so as to afford alkylvinyltin halides (*118*).

$$CH_2:CHMgCl + n\text{-}C_4H_9SnCl_3 \longrightarrow (n\text{-}C_4H_9)(CH_2:CH)SnCl_2 + MgCl_2$$

Vinyltin compounds of the type, $(CH_2:CH)_nSnCl_{4-n}$ (where $n = 1\text{--}3$), can be made by a method (*117,129*) analogous to that used by Kocheshkov (*72*) for the synthesis of alkyltin chlorides, e.g.,

$$(CH_2:CH)_4Sn + 3\,SnCl_4 \longrightarrow 4\,CH_2:CHSnCl_3$$

Of the vinyltin chlorides only the divinyl compound is a crystalline solid (Table 3.6). Like dialkyltin dihalides, divinyltin dichloride undergoes a number of metathetical reactions (*129*).

$$(CH_2:CH)_2SnCl_2 + 2\,NaSCN \xrightarrow{\text{ethanol}} 2\,NaCl + (CH_2:CH)_2Sn(SCN)_2$$
$$\text{m.p. } 163.6\text{--}165°$$

With the exception of triphenylvinyltin, tetraorganotin compounds containing the $CH_2:CH$—Sn grouping are colorless liquids with high thermal stability. Tetravinyltin can be distilled at atmospheric pressure in the absence of any polymerization inhibitor, only beginning to decompose appreciably near 200° (*129*). The group $CH_2:CH$—Sn is also stable to air and to moisture. This property is in marked contrast to the recently discovered perfluorovinyltin compounds which have been prepared by reactions such as,

$$(CH_3)_2SnCl_2 + 2\,CF_2:CFMgBr \xrightarrow{(CH_2)_2O} (CH_3)_2Sn(CF:CF_2)_2 + MgBr_2 + MgCl_2$$

$$(CH_2:CH)_2SnCl_2 + 2\,CF_2:CFMgBr \xrightarrow{(CH_2)_2O}$$
$$(CH_2:CH)_2Sn(CF:CF_2)_2 + MgBr_2 + MgCl_2$$

and which in the presence of moist air slowly decompose (*60*). A comparison of the effect of various reagents on $(CH_2:CH)_4Sn$ and $(CF_2:CF)_4Sn$ is made below in Table 3.5.

TABLE 3.5.

DECOMPOSITION STUDIES ON $(CF_2:CF)_4Sn$ AND $(CH_2:CH)_4Sn$

Reagent	Conditions		% Decomposition measured in terms of:	
	Time (hr.)	Temp. (°C)	$CF_2:CFH$[a] from $(CF_2:CF)_4Sn$	$CH_2:CH_2$[a] from $(CH_2:CH)_4Sn$
Hydrogen chloride gas	60	100	96	82
Trifluoroacetic acid	15	100	–	74.8
	60	100	94	74.8[b]
Sodium hydroxide solution (20%)	60	100	96.5	6.5
Water	50	25	3	0
	60	100	66	7

[a] A high vacuum system was used for these studies. Gases were manipulated quantitatively and identified by their infrared spectra, after having been purified by fractional condensation.
[b] Only three vinyl groups cleaved even over a long period.

In the complete absence of air, moisture, acid or base, perfluorovinyltin compounds appear to be as thermally stable as their vinyl analogues. A sample of *tetrakis*(perfluorovinyl)tin was heated in a small bulb at 150° for 6 hrs. and was then recovered unchanged.

When bonded to tin both the $CH_2:CH$—group and the $CF_2:CF$—group are very labile. This is of theoretical interest, and is also very useful from the point of view of synthesizing $CH_2:CH$— and $CF_2:CF$—derivatives of other elements.

A qualitative electronegativity scale for organo-groups has been based on the fission of organometallic compounds (*111*). In a reaction of the type,

$$R_2SnR_2' + 2HCl \longrightarrow 2RH + R_2'SnCl_2$$

the more electronegative of the two radicals appears as the hydrocarbon RH, while the less electronegative group remains bonded to the metal. This procedure, developed by Kharasch *et al.* (*66*), has been applied by Seyferth (*125*) to the $CH_2:CH$-group. A number of $R_2Sn(CH:CH_2)_2$ compounds were treated with halogens, hydrogen halides, organic acids and mercaptans. These studies (*125*) showed that the vinyl group is cleaved by these reagents from dimethyl- and di-*n*-butyldivinyltin, whereas the phenyl group is cleaved from diphenyldivinyltin. The position of the vinyl group in the cleavage series is thus.

$$C_6H_5 > CH_2:CH > CH_3 > C_2H_5 > n\text{-}C_3H_7 > n\text{-}C_4H_9$$

This series has recently been extended to include the groups $CF_2:CF-$ and C_2F_5- (60).

$$CF_2:CF \simeq C_6H_5 > CH_2:CH > alkyl > C_2F_5$$

The reaction between bromine and trimethylvinyltin has been studied thermochemically (107). For the process

$$(CH_3)_3SnCH:CH_{2(l)} + Br_{2(g)} \longrightarrow (CH_3)_3SnBr_{(l)} + CH_2:CHBr_{(l)}$$

the enthalpy change is –45.75 kcal/mole^{-1}. From this result the heat of formation of trimethylvinyltin has been calculated to be 4.35 kcal/mole^{-1}. As yet very few physico-chemical studies have been made on vinylmetallic compounds, and this work appears to represent the only thermochemical study.

The cleavage of the vinyl group from alkylvinyltin compounds by halogens and by protonic acids is in distinct contrast to the addition reactions which these reagents undergo with vinylsilicon compounds. This behavior of the vinyltin compounds has been attributed to the relatively low tin-carbon bond energy (125).

The lability of the vinyl group on tin was first recognized by Seyferth (122) who, as mentioned elsewhere in this chapter, used vinyltin compounds to make vinylhaloarsines (83) and vinylmercuric halides (123). In later studies (121) a number of organotin esters were prepared by making use of the preferential cleavage from tin of vinyl groups relative to alkyl groups.

$$(n\text{-}C_3H_7)_3SnCH:CH_2 + RCO_2H \longrightarrow (n\text{-}C_3H_7)_3SnO_2CR + C_2H_4$$

$$(CH_3)_2Sn(CH:CH_2)_2 + 2RCO_2H \longrightarrow (CH_3)_2Sn(O_2CR)_2 + 2C_2H_4$$

In these reactions the stronger the acid the faster is the rate of cleavage. Trifluoroacetic acid reacts vigorously at ambient temperatures, whereas it is necessary to heat a vinyltin compound with acetic acid to insure complete reaction.

Finally, concerning the lability of the $CH_2:CH-$ and $CF_2:CF-$ groupings on tin, the reader is reminded of the important reactions, described previously, that take place between vinyl- and perfluorovinyltin compounds and boron halides, which yield vinyl- and perfluorovinylboron compounds.

Although vinyl groups of various types are cleaved easily from tin, it is possible to add certain reagents to the double bond of vinyltin compounds. Polyhalomethanes in the presence of benzoyl peroxide add to triethylvinyltin at about 90° (124).

$$(C_2H_5)_3SnCH:CH_2 + CCl_3Z \xrightarrow{Bz_2O_2} (C_2H_5)_3SnCHZCH_2CCl_3$$

$$(Z = H, Cl \text{ or } Br)$$

TABLE 3.6. SOME VINYLTIN COMPOUNDS*

Compound	B.p. ($^{\circ}$C/mm) or m.p. ($^{\circ}$C)	n_D^{25}	d_4^{25}	Ref.
$(CH_2:CH)_4Sn$	55–57/17	1.4993	1.267	*118*
	67–70/28	1.4914	1.246	*129*
	160–163/766			*129*
$(CH_3)_3SnCH:CH_2$	99–100/760	1.4544	1.265	*129*
$(CH_3)_2Sn(CH:CH_2)_2$	118.5–120/759	1.4701	1.265	*129*
	120–121/760	1.4720	1.284	*118*
$CH_3(C_2H_5)_2SnCH:CH_2$	56–59/26	1.4697	1.222	*129*
$(C_2H_5)_3SnCH:CH_2$	174/760	1.4780 (20°)	1.2133 (20°)	*108*
	60–62/13	1.4738	1.198	*129*
$(n\text{-}C_3H_7)_3SnCH:CH_2$	90/8	1.4776	1.131	*121*
$(n\text{-}C_4H_9)_3SnCH:CH_2$	95/1.5	1.4751	1.081	*129*
	114/3	1.4761	1.085	*118*
$(n\text{-}C_4H_9)_2Sn(CH:CH_2)_2$	54–55/0.35	1.4797	1.122	*129*
	78–80/2	1.4824	1.127	*118*
$n\text{-}C_4H_9Sn(CH:CH_2)_3$	77–78/8.6	1.4851	1.174	*129*
$(C_6H_5)_3SnCH:CH_2$	m.p. 39–46	–	–	*118*
	" 45.2–45.4	–	–	*129*
$(C_6H_5)_2Sn(CH:CH_2)_2$	153–154/5	1.5949	1.3195	*118*
	121.5/0.4	1.5929	1.334	*125*
$C_6H_5Sn(CH:CH_2)_3$	73–75/0.45	1.5478	1.282	*129*
$(CH_2:CH)_3SnCl$	90–96/26	1.5237	–	*129*
$(CH_2:CH)_2SnCl_2$	m.p. 74.5–75.5	–	–	*129*
$CH_2:CHSnCl_3$	48–50/5.2	–	–	*129*
$n\text{-}C_4H_9(CH_2:CH)SnCl_2$	99–101/3 m.p. 27–28	1.5254	1.533	*118*
$n\text{-}C_4H_9(CH_2:CH)_2SnCl$	82–84/3	1.4970	1.370	*118*
$(n\text{-}C_4H_9)_2(CH_2:CH)SnCl$	112–114/4	1.4987 (20°)	1.266 (20°)	*118*
	82–83/0.6	1.4973	1.273	*125*
$(CH_3)_2(CH_2:CH)SnCl$	73–75/27	1.5105	1.575	*125*
$(CH_3)_2(CH_2:CH)SnBr$	59–61/9.5	1.5350	1.838	*125*
$(n\text{-}C_4H_9)_2(CH_2:CH)SnBr$	96/0.65	1.5102	1.416	*125*
$(n\text{-}C_4H_9)_2(CH_2:CH)SnI$	108.5–109.8/1.75	1.5384	1.556	*125*
$(CH_3)_2(CH_2:CH)SnI$	57.5–59/5.2	1.5762	2.033	*125*
$(CH_2:CH)_3SnI$	60/1.8	1.5828	1.898	*125*
$(CH_2:CH)_3SnF$	m.p. > 300°	–	–	*125*
$(C_6H_5)(CH_2:CH)_2SnF$	m.p. > 300°	–	–	*125*
$(C_6H_5)_2(CH_2:CH)SnF$	m.p. > 300°	–	–	*125*
$(CF_2:CF)_4Sn$	52–54/19	–	–	*60*
$(CH_3)_2Sn(CF:CF_2)_2$	59–61/40	–	–	*60*
$(n\text{-}C_4H_9)_2Sn(CF:CF_2)_2$	60–63/0.4	–	–	*60*
$(n\text{-}C_4H_9)_3SnCF:CF_2$	81–82/0.4	–	–	*60*
$(CH_2:CH)_2Sn(CF:CF_2)_2$	51–53/10	–	–	*60*
$(C_6H_5)_2Sn(CF:CF_2)_2$	75–80/0.02	–	–	*60*

*In addition to the compounds listed in this table, other substances containing vinyltin groups include salts of the divinyltin cation, divinyltin oxide (*118*), 2-chlorovinyltin compounds (*93*), and *iso*propenyltin compounds (*95*).

Reactions similar to these take place with vinylsilicon (*11,45*), and vinyl-germanium compounds (*86*).

$$R_3SiCH:CH_2 \xrightarrow[\text{peroxide}]{CCl_4} R_3SiCHClCH_2CCl_3$$

$$(n\text{-}C_4H_9)_3GeCH:CH_2 + CHCl_3 \longrightarrow (n\text{-}C_4H_9)_3Ge(CH_2)_2CCl_3$$

$$(n\text{-}C_4H_9)_3GeCH:CH_2 + BrCH_2COOC_2H_5 \longrightarrow$$
$$(n\text{-}C_4H_9)_3GeCHBrCH_2CH_2COOC_2H_5$$

Recently it has been found that tin-hydrogen bonds add to carbon-carbon unsaturated linkages (*144,145*). One consequence of this discovery has been the preparation of organotin compounds containing a substituted vinyl group by reactions of the type,

$$R_3SnH + CH\equiv CR' \longrightarrow R_3SnCH:CHR'$$

For addition reactions of this type no catalyst is needed, but mild heating is often necessary. A reaction related to this is that which occurs between organotin hydrides and vinyl compounds of silicon, germanium, tin and lead (*47*), e.g.,

$$(C_6H_5)_3SnH + CH_2:CHSi(C_6H_5)_3 \longrightarrow (C_6H_5)_3SnCH_2CH_2Si(C_6H_5)_3$$

$$(C_6H_5)_2SnH_2 + (CH_2:CH)_2Ge(C_6H_5)_2 \longrightarrow (C_6H_5)_2Sn\underset{CH_2CH_2}{\overset{CH_2CH_2}{<}}Ge\underset{C_6H_5}{\overset{C_6H_5}{<}}$$

It is surprising that the last reaction given proceeds with ring formation rather than with extensive polymer formation. However, prior to this discovery a similar reaction had been observed in silicon chemistry. Organosilanes containing vinyl and hydrogen joined to the same silicon atom afford principally polymeric products when heated with a platinum catalyst; however, some cyclic silicon compounds are formed simultaneously in lesser amounts (*28*), e.g.,

$$(CH_3)_2Si(H)CH:CH_2 \xrightarrow[\text{heat}]{\text{Pt catalyst}} (CH_3)_2Si\underset{CH_2CH_2}{\overset{CH_2CH_2}{<}}Si(CH_3)_2$$

Alkylvinyltin compounds undergo an unusual reaction with iron carbonyls (*67*).

$$R_2Sn(CH:CH_2)_2 \xrightarrow[\text{heat}]{Fe(CO)_5} [R_2SnFe(CO)_4]_2$$

It is interesting that tetra-alkyltin compounds undergo this reaction only to a very slight extent. Thus tetra-*n*-butyltin and iron pentacarbonyl heated together in refluxing ethyl cyclohexane for 8–10 hours afford dibutyltin-iron tetracarbonyl in less than 1 per cent yield. Dialkyldiphenyltin compounds, on the other hand, react with iron pentacarbonyl to give dialkyltin-iron tetracarbonyl compounds in yields (about 30 per cent) comparable to those obtained from the dialkyldivinyltin compounds.

Lead

Tetravinyllead was reported independently by three groups of workers, being obtained by addition of ammonium (*80*) or potassium (*8*) hexachloro-plumbate to vinylmagnesium bromide or chloride, or by addition of lead(II) chloride or acetate to vinyl Grignard (*58*). Yields of the lead compound as high as 75 per cent have been claimed in some of these reactions.

If kept below room temperature tetravinyllead is stable for months, but at higher temperatures it slowly deposits a yellow solid. It is not affected by water, being in this respect similar to tetraethyllead. The vinyl compound is, however, more susceptible to cleavage than its ethyl analog (*58*). The reaction,

$$(CH_2:CH)_4Pb + CH_3COOH \xrightarrow[\text{silica gel}]{\text{room temperature}}$$

$$(CH_2:CH)_3PbOCOCH_3 + CH_2:CH_2$$

proceeds fairly rapidly at room temperature, whereas under the same conditions tetraethyllead and acetic acid do not react. The reaction between tetravinyllead and trichloracetic acid can be explosive, but under controlled conditions trivinyllead trichloracetate can be isolated. With chlorine, tetra-vinyllead affords divinyllead dichloride. During combustion analysis vinyl-lead compounds can react explosively (*58*).

TABLE 3.7. VINYLLEAD COMPOUNDS

Compound	M.p. °C	B.p. °C/mm	Ref.
$(CH_2:CH)_4Pb$	–	69–70/11	*80*[a]
	–	34/0.6	*58*[b]
	–	50/4	*8*
$(CH_2:CH)_2Pb(C_2H_5)_2$	–	30/1	*8*
$(C_6H_5)_3PbCH:CH_2$	33–34	–	*58*
$(C_6H_5)_2Pb(CH:CH_2)_2$	–	yellow liquid	*58*
$(CH_2:CH)_3PbCl$	119–121	–	*58*
$(CH_2:CH)_2PbCl_2$	>300	–	*58*
$(CH_2:CH)_3PbOCOCH_3$	168–170	–	*58*
$(CH_2:CH)_3PbOCOCCl_3$	>300	–	*58*

[a] n_D^{20}, 1.5462; d_4^{20}, 1.7882.

[b] n_D^{26}, 1.5430.

Tetravinyllead can be used to prepare monovinylhalophosphines, -arsines and -stibines (*81*),

$$(CH_2:CH)_4Pb + 2\ MX_3 \xrightarrow{CCl_4} (CH_2:CH)_2PbX_2 + 2\ CH_2:CHMX_2$$

$$M = P, As, Sb, Bi$$

$$X = Cl, Br$$

Several vinyllead compounds are listed in Table 3.7.

VINYL COMPOUNDS OF THE GROUP V ELEMENTS

Although vinylphosphines were not characterized until 1957, three years after the first reference to the vinyl Grignard reagent $CH_2:CHMgX$ had been made, the first vinyl derivatives of phosphorus and arsenic were reported one hundred years ago, being obtained by dehydrohalogenation of 2-bromoethylphosphonium and -arsonium salts (*49,50*). More recently compounds of the type $CH_2:CHP(O)(OR)_2$ have been described (*37,59, 74*), e.g.,

$$(C_2H_5O)_3P + BrCH_2CH_2Br \xrightarrow{160°} (C_2H_5O)_2P(O)CH_2CH_2Br + C_2H_5Br$$

$$\downarrow \text{alcoholic KOH}$$

$$(C_2H_5O)_2P(O)CH:CH_2 + KBr$$

(b.p. $50°/1$ mm; n_D^{25} 1.4260 (*74*))

as well as a series of substituted vinylphosphonic acids and esters. For a discussion of these compounds the reader is referred elsewhere (*75*).

Certain vinylphosphorus compounds have been made by adding phosphorus pentachloride to olefins. β-Chloroalkylphosphorus tetrachlorides are initially formed which are thermally unstable and eliminate hydrogen chloride. After reduction with elemental phosphorus in the presence of iodine, dichlorophosphines are isolated (*148a*). This type of reaction sequence, involving addition followed by an elimination, has also been used to make perfluoroalkenylphosphinic esters (*70a*), e.g., $(CF_3)_2C:CF—P(O)(OEt)_2$.

Trivinyl derivatives of the Group V elements (Table 3.9) have been prepared by treating the appropriate halide with vinylmagnesium bromide in tetrahydrofuran (*83*).

$$3\ CH_2:CHMgBr + X_3M^V \longrightarrow (CH_2:CH)_3M^V + 3\ MgBrX$$

Phenyldivinylphosphine has been similarly prepared by Grignard vinylation of phenyldichlorophosphine (*83*). The two vinylphosphines were, however, obtained in poor yield. Furthermore, in this study the vinyl bromide used to make the Grignard contained appreciable amounts of ethyl bromide so that the vinyl compounds were somewhat contaminated with the ethyl derivatives (*62*). Subsequently, pure trivinylphosphine was obtained by treating phosphorus trichloride well below room temperature with a large excess of vinylmagnesium chloride (*61*). By using the Grignard based on vinyl chloride rather than on vinyl bromide the yield, about 50 per cent, was greatly improved over the original procedure (*83*).

Trivinylphosphine is an air-sensitive liquid. Like trivinylphosphine, trivinylarsine is easily oxidized in air, but in the absence of air both compounds are thermally relatively stable (*83*). Trivinylarsine may be refluxed under nitrogen at its normal boiling point without decomposition. As expected, trivinylstibine and trivinylbismuth are thermally less stable. They are also spontaneously inflammable in air (*83*).

A number of chemical reactions of the $(CH_2:CH)_3M^V$ compounds have been investigated (*83*). As with the trialkyl compounds ability to form "onium" type compounds decreases in passing from the phosphorus to the bismuth derivative, viz.,

	$(CH_2:CH)_3P$	$(CH_2:CH)_3As$	$(CH_2:CH)_3Sb$	$(CH_2:CH)_3Bi$
CH_3I	+	+	+	+
C_2H_5I	+	+	−	−
$CH_2:CHBr$	+	−	−	−

where the plus signs indicate formation of solid adducts.

With iodine, trivinylarsine and trivinylstibine afford di-iodides which undergo thermal decomposition to give the corresponding divinyliodo derivatives, e.g.,

$$(CH_2:CH)_3Sb + I_2 \longrightarrow (CH_2:CH)_3SbI_2 \longrightarrow (CH_2:CH)_2SbI + CH_2:CHI$$

Although trivinylphosphine and phosphorus trihalides react vigorously at room temperature giving only black solids, trivinylarsine and trivinylstibine undergo useful redistribution reactions when mixed with the trichlorides or tribromides of the respective elements, e.g.,

$$(CH_2:CH)_3As + 2\ AsBr_3 \longrightarrow 3\ CH_2:CHAsBr_2$$

$$2\ (CH_2:CH)_3Sb + SbCl_3 \longrightarrow 3\ (CH_2:CH)_2SbCl$$

Good yields of either the monovinyl or divinyl derivatives can be obtained from these exothermic reactions by mixing the reactants in the correct proportions (*83*). Subsequent treatment of the reaction mixtures with alkyl Grignard reagents can lead to the formation of vinylalkylarsines or vinylalkylstibines, e.g.,

$$CH_2:CHSbBr_2 + 2\ n\text{-}C_4H_9MgBr \longrightarrow CH_2:CHSb(C_4H_9)_2 + 2\ MgBr_2$$

Redistribution reactions similar to those described above are fairly general for R_3M^V compounds since they also occur with trialkyl- and triarylarsines, with triarylstibines, and with trimethylbismuth.

Vinyl- and divinylhaloarsines can also be made by a direct process involving passage of vinyl chloride or vinyl bromide over a mixture of arsenic, copper and zinc at about 450° *(82)*.

Another approach to the synthesis of vinyl halides of arsenic is to make use of the lability of vinyl groups bonded to tin. Divinylbromoarsine can be obtained in 80 per cent yield by treating arsenic tribromide with di-*n*-butyl-divinyltin.

$$n\text{-}(C_4H_9)_2Sn(CH:CH_2)_2 + AsBr_3 \xrightarrow{95°} n\text{-}(C_4H_9)_2SnBr_2 + (CH_2:CH)_2AsBr$$

Vinyldibromoarsine may be obtained by changing the proportions of the reactants *(83)*. Unfortunately, extension of this reaction to the preparation of vinylbromostibines and vinylbromophosphines did not lead to pure products. However, as mentioned in earlier sections of this chapter, vinyldihalophosphines can be obtained by treating phosphorus trihalides with divinylmercury *(61)* or tetravinyllead *(81)*. One compound prepared in this manner is the air- and exceedingly moisture-sensitive vinyldichlorophosphine *(61)*. This compound is synthetically useful since on treatment with methylmagnesium chloride it affords vinyldimethylphosphine, thereby permitting an entry into the field of vinylalkylphosphines.

It is worth noting that the volatilities of vinyl derivatives of the Group Vb elements (Table 3.9) are very similar to those of their ethyl analogs, the slight differences being in the expected direction for the molecular weight change. Thus for $(CH_3)_2PC_2H_5$ the extrapolated boiling point is 71.2°, and the entropy of vaporization is 22.4 e.u. For $(CH_3)_2PCH:CH_2$ these constants are 67.9° and 22.7 e.u., respectively.

As far as the phosphorus atom is concerned the vinylphosphines have chemical properties similar to those of the ethylphosphines. They form molecular addition compounds with Lewis acids, "onium" compounds, and solid adducts on treatment with carbon disulfide. Vinylphosphines, however, possess these properties to a different degree from their ethyl analogs, the vinyl group having a demonstrable effect on donor characteristics of the phosphorus atom to which it is bonded. A tetrahydrofuran solution of trivinylphosphine, unlike a tetrahydrofuran solution of trimethylphosphine, does not give an immediate red precipitate with carbon disulfide. It is interesting to note that vinyldimethylphosphine is intermediate between trivinyl- and trimethylphosphine in its behavior toward carbon disulfide, and that triphenylphosphine gives no precipitate with carbon disulfide.

In order to place the electron-pair donor power of vinylphosphines on a quantitative basis, an investigation has been made of variation in relative Lewis base strength in the series $(CH_2:CH)_3P$, $(C_2H_5)_3P$, $CH_2:CHP(CH_3)_2$, $C_2H_5P(CH_3)_2$ and $(CH_3)_3P$, using trimethylboron as the reference acid (63). Before reviewing the results of this study it is worth pointing out that without experimentation it is not possible to predict with certainty how a vinyl group would affect the base strength of a phosphorus atom to which it is bonded.

The tendency for trivalent derivatives of the Group Vb atoms to combine with electron-pair acceptors is markedly affected by the kind of atoms or groups bonded to the Group Vb atoms. Electronegative substituents decrease Lewis base strength, whereas electron-releasing groups increase base strength. For example, trimethylphosphine combines with boron trifluoride to produce $(CH_3)_3P \cdot BF_3$, but phosphorus trifluoride does not form $F_3P \cdot BF_3$. In organic chemistry the vinyl group has long been known as a more electronegative species than the ethyl or the methyl groups (111). Valence theory relates this to changes in atomic electronegativity produced by changes in hybridization, an sp^2-hybridized carbon atom being more electron-attracting than an sp^3-carbon atom. From the foregoing remarks concerning the inductive factor it would be expected that vinylphosphines would be weaker bases than their alkyl analogs, and so form weaker bonds than alkylphosphines with a reference Lewis acid such as trimethylboron. However, other evidence recorded in the chemical literature suggests that the reverse of this might be true.

Phosphorus belongs to the second short period of the Periodic Classification, and there is evidence that under certain favorable conditions the heavier elements of this period can expand their valence shells. In the case of phosphorus this question has been discussed by Van Wazer (146). Relevant to the problem of the base strength of vinylphosphines is the observation that tetramethylphosphonium salts exchange protons readily, whereas tetramethylammonium hydroxide in alkaline deuterium oxide solution only slowly exchanges (32). To account for this it has been suggested (32) that the tetramethylphosphonium ion is stabilized by resonance, viz.,

Furthermore, hydroxide ion rapidly brings about elimination of hydrogen bromide from $[BrCH_2CH_2S(CH_3)_2]^+$ forming $[CH_2:CHS(CH_3)_2]^+$, whereas $[BrCH_2CH_2N(CH_3)_3]^+$ reacts only slowly with hydroxide giving $[HOCH_2-CH_2N(CH_3)_3]^+$ rather than neurine, $[CH_2:CHN(CH_3)_3]^+$ (33). This behavior suggests that vinyldimethylsulfonium ion is also stabilized by resonance, again made possible through the ability of the second row atom to expand its valence shell,

$$[\overset{+}{C}H_2-CH=S(CH_3)_2] \leftrightarrow [CH_2=CH-\overset{+}{S}(CH_3)_2]$$

Neurine cannot be stabilized in a similar way because nitrogen has no vacant orbitals of low enough energy to partake in chemical bonding. In an addition compound of a vinylphosphine it is possible that resonance similar to that suggested for the vinyldimethylsulfonium and tetramethylphosphonium ions might occur, viz.,

$$[\overset{+}{C}H_2-CH=\overset{\overset{R}{|}}{\underset{\underset{R}{|}}{P}}-\bar{B}(CH_3)_3] \leftrightarrow [CH_2=CH-\overset{\overset{R}{|}}{\underset{\underset{R}{|}}{P}}+-\bar{B}(CH_3)_3]$$

If the effect were significant enough, base strength might be increased because of the added stabilization of the final complex.

The results of the relative base strength study for the phosphines, with trimethylboron as the reference acid, are summarized in Table 3.8 (*63*). The trimethylboron adducts of triethylphosphine and trivinylphosphine are so highly dissociated in the gas phase that a meaningful study of the variation of degree of dissociation with temperature proved impossible. Both trivinyl- and triethylphosphine are, therefore, very weak bases towards trimethylboron. However, because of the high volatility of $(CH_2:CH)_3P \cdot B(CH_3)_3$ compared with $(C_2H_5)_3P \cdot B(CH_3)_3$ (it will be noted that the trivinylphosphine adduct is more volatile than the base from which it is derived (Table 3.8)) it is possible to state qualitatively that trivinylphosphine is a poorer donor than triethylphosphine. For complexes of low

TABLE 3.8. GAS-PHASE DISSOCIATION DATA FOR TRIMETHYLBORON ADDUCTS OF PHOSPHINES

Compound	B.p. Ligand[a]	B.p. Complex[a]	$\Delta H^{o[b]}$ kcal/mole^{-1}	$\Delta S^{o[b]}$ e.u.
$(CH_2:CH)_3P \cdot BMe_3$	116.6	84.4	highly dissociated as gas	
$Et_3P \cdot BMe_3$	127.5	147.6	highly dissociated as gas	
$(CH_2:CH)(Me)_2P \cdot BMe_3$	67.9	113.1	14.87	40.82
$(Et)(Me)_2P \cdot BMe_3$	71.2	141.0	17.58	44.42
$Me_3P \cdot BMe_3$	37.8	—	16.53	40.23
	—	—	16.49[c]	40.0[c]

[a]Obtained by extrapolation of the vapor pressure equation.
[b]These constants refer to the reaction, $R_3P \cdot BMe_{3(g)} \rightarrow R_3P_{(g)} + BMe_{3(g)}$.
[c]Values obtained by Sujishi (Thesis, Purdue University, 1949) who also studied trimethylphosphine-trimethylboron.

stability it has long been customary to infer relative stabilities from relative volatilities. If two addition compounds have closely similar structure and molecular weight, the less stable exhibits the higher saturation pressure (*23*). The other molecular addition compounds studied were sufficiently stable to permit determination of thermodynamic functions, and it will be seen from the enthalpies of dissociation of the donor-acceptor bonds that the order of Lewis base strength is $C_2H_5P(CH_3)_2 > (CH_3)_3P > CH_2:CHP(CH_3)_2$. The donor power of phosphorus is weakened by the vinyl group as compared to the ethyl group. In the case of the two phosphines $CH_2:CHP(CH_3)_2$ and $C_2H_5P(CH_3)_2$ this weakening in donor power results in a 2.7 kcal stability difference between their respective trimethylboron adducts. This is a large difference for measurements of this kind. There is thus no evidence for phosphorus in vinylphosphines making significant use of vacant *d*-orbitals in a manner similar to that postulated for phosphorus in $[(CH_3)_4P]^+$ or sulfur in $[CH_2:CHS(CH_3)_2]^+$. An important distinction between the two cases is worth noting. In the tetramethylphosphonium and vinyldimethylsulfonium *ions* the second row atoms bear a positive charge, whereas in an adduct $R_3P \cdot B(CH_3)_3$, although there must be charge transfer in the dative bond, it may not be sufficient to place a positive charge on phosphorus.* Because of this the phosphorus *d*-orbitals may be too diffuse to be effective in π-bonding with the vinyl group in, for example, $CH_2:CH(CH_3)_2P \cdot B(CH_3)_3$, even though in the adduct, in which phosphorus is presumably tetrahedral, some *d* orbitals of phosphorus have the right symmetry for interaction with the vinyl group's π-electrons.

As mentioned previously, the now demonstrated weakening effect of the vinyl group on the donor power of phosphorus is not unexpected if reliance is placed on an inductive argument. However, an alternative explanation for the weakening effect of vinyl groups, as opposed to ethyl, on the Lewis base strength of phosphorus can be sought in terms of a more sophisticated suggestion involving delocalization of the phosphorus lone-pair electrons in the vinyl groups' π-molecular orbitals. In this connection Jaffé's (*54*) work on the ultraviolet spectra of triphenyl derivatives of

---

*A considerable amount of work has been done on the ultraviolet spectra of substances in which a benzene ring is bonded to sulfur. From this it is generally agreed (*13,84,85*), with one exception (*24*), that no resonance of the type Aromatic⁀S—R involving sulfur *d*-orbitals occurs in the *neutral* aromatic sulfides. An electron shift $CH_2:CH\rightharpoonup P$: should serve to increase the donor power of a vinylphosphine, provided the phosphine retains essentially tetrahedral symmetry. In view of the analogy with the neutral sulfur compounds such an effect is unlikely and is, in fact, not supported by the base strength study described here.

the Group Vb elements is of interest. The spectra of $(C_6H_5)_3M$ (M = N, P, As or Sb) compounds have been interpreted by Jaffé (*54*) as evidence that very likely there is resonance interaction among the phenyl groups through the lone-pair on M. This interaction would, of course, make the lone-pair less available for dative bond formation. Lone-pair delocalization in the vinylphosphines, if it occurs, must of necessity be less effective than in triphenylphosphine. In the latter instance delocalization of charge among many more atoms is possible.

In concluding this survey of vinyl compounds of the Group Vb elements, mention must be made of the β-chlorovinyl derivatives of arsenic and antimony.

Acetylene and arsenic trichloride react in the presence of aluminum chloride to give a mixture known as "lewisite" (*46*). It has long been known that this material is a strong vesicant, and that its activity in this respect is due to the presence of β-chlorovinyldichloroarsine. The possibility that the β-chlorovinylarsenic compound would display isomerism was not recognized for many years. This occurrence seemed very probable, however, when it was found that the β-chlorovinyldichloroarsine obtained from acetylene and arsenic trichloride using mercury(II) chloride or copper(I) chloride as catalyst was somewhat less active as a vesicant than the material obtained when aluminum chloride was the catalyst (*48*). This led to a careful study of these mixtures with a consequent separation of two compounds of composition $C_2H_2AsCl_3$ (*48*). Dipole moment studies showed which of the isomers was *trans*-β-chlorovinyldichloroarsine and which was *cis*-β-chlorovinyldichloroarsine (*87*). Several physical constants for these two isomers were then determined (*152*). From these studies it was established that the isomer present in "lewisite" in largest amount is *trans*-β-chlorovinyldichloroarsine, and the more volatile isomer produced in slightly greater quantity when mercury(II) or copper(I) chloride is used as catalyst is *cis*-β-chlorovinyldichloroarsine. Even when mercury(II) or copper(I) chloride is used as catalyst, however, the *trans*-isomer predominates in the product.

Pure *cis*-β-chlorovinyldichloroarsine (m.p. $-44.7°$) dissolves in cold sodium hydroxide solution without evolution of gas, but on warming to 40° vinyl chloride is released. In contrast to this behavior *trans*-β-chlorovinyldichloroarsine (m.p. $-1.2°$) affords acetylene on treatment with sodium hydroxide solution.

During discussion of β-chlorovinylmercury compounds in a previous section brief mention was made of analogous compounds of antimony prepared and characterized by Nesmeyanov and his co-workers.

If a 50 per cent alkaline solution of antimony pentachloride containing a little mercury(II) chloride is maintained under acetylene first at 80–100° and then at 150–175°, the gas is absorbed. The principal product is *tris*-

TABLE 3.9. VINYL COMPOUNDS OF THE GROUP Vb ELEMENTS

Compound	B.p. °C/mm	Ref.	Compound	B.p. °C/mm	Ref.
$(CH_2:CH)_3P$	116.6/760[a]	61	$(CH_2:CH)_3Sb$	149.9/760	83
$(CH_2:CH)_3As$	129.8/760	83	$(CH_2:CH)_3Bi$	158.1/760	83
$(CH_3)_2PCH:CH_2$	67.9/760[b]	61	$n\text{-}C_4H_9As(CH:CH_2)_2$	56/12	83
$C_6H_5P(CH:CH_2)_2$	55/0.5	83	$(n\text{-}C_4H_9)_2AsCH:CH_2$	52/1.5	83
			$(n\text{-}C_4H_9)_2SbCH:CH_2$	73/2.5	83
$CH_2:CHPCl_2$	104/760	61	$CH_2:CHAsCl_2$	63–64/38	81
$CH_2:CHPBr_2$	163–165/760	81	$CH_2:CHAsBr_2$	76/14	81
			$CH_2:CHSbCl_2$	58–63/2	81
$(CH_2:CH)_2AsBr$	59/19	83	$(CH_2:CH)_2SbCl$	60/4.5	83
			$(CH_2:CH)_2SbBr$	42.5/0.7	83
$(CF_2:CF)_3As$	57.5/83	60			
$(cis\text{-}CHCl:CH)_2AsCl$	169.8,/760[c]	152	$(trans\text{-}ClCH:CH)_3SbCl_2$	solid, m.p. 93°	98
$(trans\text{-}CHCl:CH)_2AsCl$	196.6,/760[d]	152	$(cis\text{-}ClCH:CH)_3SbCl_2$	solid, m.p. 61°	98
$(trans\text{-}CHCl:CH)SbCl_2$	102/1.5	98	$(trans\text{-}ClCH:CH)_3Sb$	solid, m.p. 49°	98
$(trans\text{-}CHCl:CH)_2SbCl$	113/2	98	$(cis\text{-}ClCH:CH)_3Sb$	121/3	98

[a] Vapor pressures of this compound conform to the equation, $\log_{10}P_{mm} = 7.868 - 1944T^{-1}$ (61).
[b] Vapor pressures of this compound conform to the equation, $\log_{10}P_{mm} = 7.846 - 1693T^{-1}$ (61).
[c] Vapor pressures of this compound conform to the equation, $\log_{10}P_{mm} = 8.413 - 2450T^{-1}$ (152).
[d] Vapor pressures of this compound conform to the equation, $\log_{10}P_{mm} = 48.66 - 13.297 \log T - 4815T^{-1}$ (152).

(*trans-β*-chlorovinyl)antimony dichloride (Table 3.9). The only other isomer produced is the lower-melting *tris-cis* form in small amounts. Reduction of these isomers with sodium bisulfite in water-alcohol solution affords the corresponding *tris-β*-chlorovinylstibines.

If the temperature is maintained below 50° in the reaction between acetylene and antimony pentachloride, the compound *bis*-(*trans*-chlorovinyl)antimony trichloride may be obtained. Other reactions of these compounds include.

$$(trans\text{-}ClCH:CH)_2SbCl_3 \xrightarrow{\text{aqueous alkali}} CH\equiv CH$$

$$(trans\text{-}ClCH:CH)_2SbCl_3 \xrightarrow{SO_2} (ClCH:CH)_2SO_2$$

$$(trans\text{-}ClCH:CH)_2SbCl_3 \xrightarrow{Sb/(C_2H_5)_2O}$$
$$(trans\text{-}ClCH:CH)_2SbCl + (trans\text{-}ClCH:CH)SbCl_2$$

$$(trans\text{-}ClCH:CH)_3Sb \xrightarrow[\text{(b) hydrolysis}]{\text{(a) } BCl_3 \text{ in } C_6H_6} ClCH:CHB(OH)_2$$

$$(cis\text{-}ClCH:CH)_3Sb \xrightarrow{HgCl_2} cis\text{-}CHCl:CHHgCl$$

THE INFRARED SPECTRA OF SOME VINYL COMPOUNDS

As in many other areas of chemistry infrared spectroscopy has been useful for identification purposes in the field of vinylmetal and -metalloidal compounds. For this reason a few representative spectra of vinyl compounds are given here.*

In the region from about 3000 cm^{-1} to about 1100 cm^{-1} the bands are due to vibrations of individual groups or specific bonds in the molecule. In the case of heavy atoms the band frequencies are more or less independent of the nature of the metal or metalloid to which the $CH_2:CH-$ group is bonded. The spectra of $(CH_2:CH)_2Hg$, $(CH_2:CH)_2Zn$, $(CH_2:CH)_4Sn$ and $(CH_2:CH)_3P$ are all very similar between 3 and 9 microns, just as are the spectra of $(C_2H_5)_2Hg$, $(C_2H_5)_2Zn$, $(C_2H_5)_4Sn$ and $(C_2H_5)_3P$ in this region.* The group-characteristic band patterns of ethyl and vinyl derivatives of the heavier atoms are reproduced in the following spectra.

*Except for the spectrum of divinyltin dichloride,[5] the spectra are taken from the following sources as indicated: (1) H. D. Kaesz and F. G. A. Stone, *Spectrochimica Acta*, 360 (1959). (2) F. E. Brinckman, Ph.D. Thesis, Harvard University. (3) S. L. Stafford, Ph.D. Thesis, Harvard University. (4) F. E. Brinckman and F. G. A. Stone, *J. Inorg. Nucl. Chem.*, **11**, 24 (1959). (5) H. D. Kaesz, unpublished. (6) H. D. Kaesz, S. L. Stafford, and F. G. A. Stone, Abstracts of Papers, 137th Meeting, Amer. Chem. Soc., Cleveland, Ohio, April 1960. (7) H. D. Kaesz, Ph.D. Thesis, Harvard University. See also *J. Org. Chem.*, **24**, 635 (1959).

Summary of the group-characteristic band patterns of ethyl- and vinyl- substituted compounds. (Reproduced from *Spectrochimica Acta*, 360 (1959), by per-
mission of the publishers.)

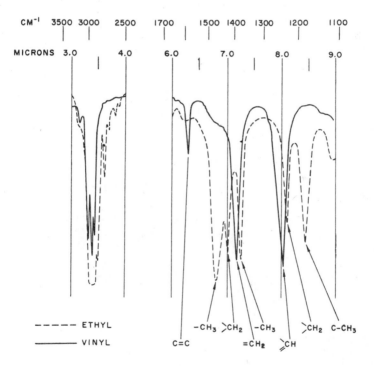

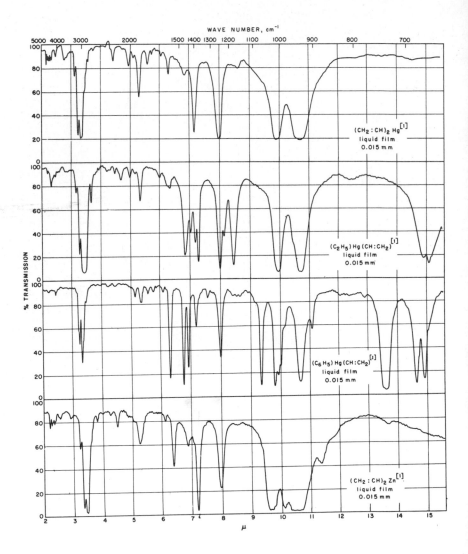

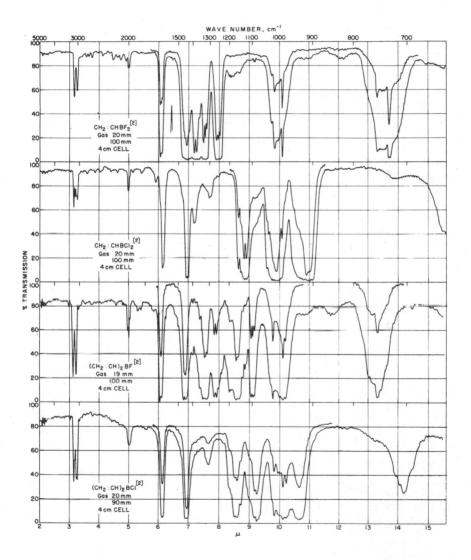

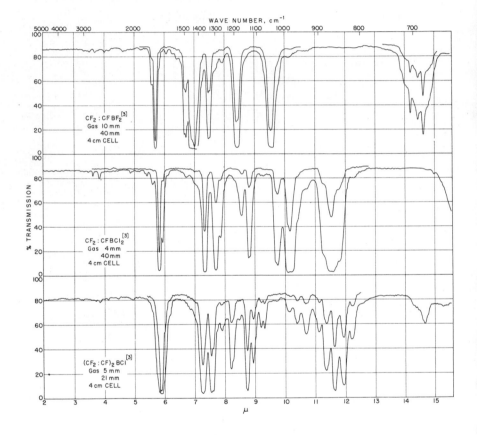

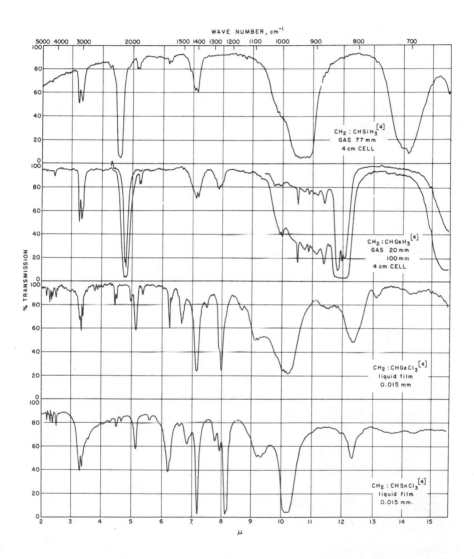

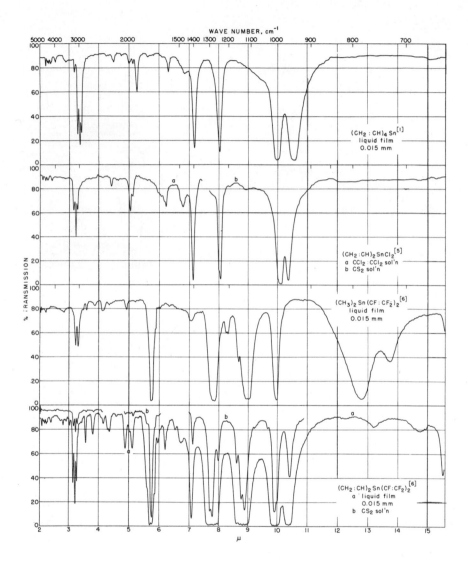

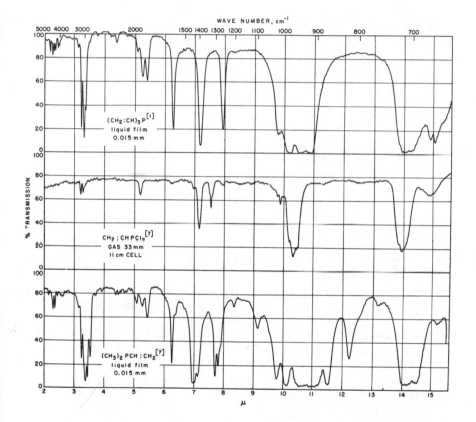

References

(1) Anderson, R. G., Silverman, M. B., and Ritter, D. M., *J. Org. Chem.*, **23**, 750 (1958).

(2) Andrianov, K. A., "Organic Silicon Compounds," Moscow, State Scientific Technical Publishing House for Chemical Literature, 1955. Translated by Technical Information Center, W.A.D.C., Ohio, and distributed by U. S. Department of Commerce.

(3) Arnold, H. R., U. S. Patent 2,402,589 (1946); *C.A.*, **40**, 5769 (1947).

(4) Bailey, D. L., and Pines, A. N., *Ind. Eng. Chem.*, **46**, 2363 (1954).

(5) Bartocha, B., Bilbo, A. J., and Gray, M. Y., Abstracts of Papers, XVII International Congress I.U.P.A.C., Munich, August, 1959.

(6) Bartocha, B., Brinckman, F. E. Kaesz, H. D., and Stone, F. G. A., *Proc. Chem. Soc.*, 116, (1958).

(7) Bartocha, B., Douglas, C. M., and Gray, M. Y., *Z. Naturforsch.*, **14b**, 809 (1959).

(8) Bartocha, B., and Gray, M. Y., *Z. Naturforsch.*, **14b**, 350 (1959).

(9) Bartocha, B., Kaesz, H. D., and Stone, F. G. A., *Z. Naturforsch.*, **14b**, 352 (1959).

(10) Bartocha, B., and Stone, F. G. A., *Z. Naturforsch.*, **13b**, 347 (1958).

(11) Benkeser, R. A., Bennett, E. W., and Hickner, R. A., *J. Am. Chem. Soc.*, **79**, 6253 (1957).

(12) Biginelli, P., *Ann. Farm. Chim.* (*Milan, Italy*), 16 (1898).

(13) Bordwell, F. G., and Boutan, P. J., *J. Am. Chem. Soc.*, **78**, 854 (1956).

(14) Borisov, A. E., *Izvest. Akad. Nauk S.S.S.R., Otdel khim. Nauk,* 402 (1951); *C.A.*, **46**, 2995 (1952).

(15) Braude, E. A., "Progress in Organic Chemistry," (Ed.: J. W. Cook), Vol. 3, p. 172, London, Butterworths, 1955.

(16) Braude, E. A., and Coles, J. A., *J. Chem. Soc.*, 2078 (1951).

(17) Brinckman, F. E., and Stone, F. G. A., Abstracts of Papers, 135th Meeting, Amer. Chem. Soc., Boston, April, 1959, p. 26M.

(18) Brinckman, F. E., and Stone, F. G. A., *Chemistry and Industry*, 254 (1959).

(19) Brinckman, F. E., and Stone, F. G. A., *J. Inorg. and Nuclear Chem.*, **11**, 24 (1959).

(20) Brinckman, F. E., and Stone, F. G. A., *J. Am. Chem. Soc.*, **82**, in press (1960).

(21) Brown, H. C., *J. Chem. Soc.*, 1248 (1956).

(22) Brown, H. C., and Holmes, R. R., *J. Am. Chem. Soc.*, **78**, 2173 (1956).

(23) Brown, H. C., and Pearsall, H., *J. Am. Chem. Soc.*, **67**, 1765 (1945).

(24) Cilento, C., *J. Org. Chem.*, **24**, 413 (1959).

(25) Coates, G. E., "Organometallic Compounds," London, Methuen, 1956.

(26) Cotton, F. A., and Leto, J. R., *J. Chem. Phys.*, **30**, 993 (1959).

(27) Coyle, T. D., and Stone, F. G. A., *J. Am. Chem. Soc.*, **82**, in press (1960).

(28) Curry, J. W., *J. Am. Chem. Soc.*, **78**, 1686 (1956).

(29) Curtin, D. Y., and Crump, J. W., *J. Am. Chem. Soc.*, **80**, 1922 (1958).

(30) Curtin, D. Y., and Harris, E. E., *J. Am. Chem. Soc.*, **73**, 2716, 4519 (1951).

(31) Dessy, R. E., Reynolds, G. F., and Kim, Jin-Young, *J. Am. Chem. Soc.*, **81**, 2683 (1959).

(32) Doering, W. E., and Hoffmann, A. K., *J. Am. Chem. Soc.,* **77,** 521 (1955).

(33) Doering, W. E., and Schreiber, K. C., *J. Am. Chem. Soc.,* **77,** 514 (1955).

(34) Dreiding, A. S., and Pratt, R. J., *J. Am. Chem. Soc.,* **76,** 1902 (1954).

(35) Fieser, L. F., and Fieser, M., "Organic Chemistry," 3rd Ed., New York, Reinhold, 1956.

(36) Fischer, A. K., West, R. C., and Rochow, E. G., *J. Am. Chem. Soc.,* **76,** 5878 (1954).

(37) Ford-Moore, A. H., and Williams, J. H., *J. Chem. Soc.,* 1465 (1947).

(38) Freidlina, R. K., and Kochetkova, N. S., *Izvest. Akad. Nauk S.S.S.R., Otdel. khim. Nauk,* 128 (1945); *C.A.,* **40,** 3450 (1946).

(39) Freidlina, R. K., and Nesmeyanov, A. N., *Doklady Akad. Nauk S.S.S.R.,* **26,** 59 (1940); *C.A.,* **34,** 6567 (1940).

(40) Freidlina, R. K., and Nogina, O. V., *Izvest. Akad. Nauk S.S.S.R., Otdel. khim. Nauk,* 105 (1947); *C.A.,* **42,** 4149 (1948).

(41) George, P. D., Prober, M., and Elliott, J. R., *Chem. Reviews,* **56,** 1065 (1956); and references cited therein.

(42) Gilman, H., and Gerow, C. W., *J. Am. Chem. Soc.,* **79,** 342 (1957).

(43) Gilman, H., and Jones, R. G., *J. Am. Chem. Soc.,* **61,** 1513 (1939); **62,** 2357 (1940).

(44) Gmelins Handbuch der Anorganischen Chemie, "Organische Silicium-verbindungen," System No. 15, Part C, 1958.

(45) Gordon, A. F. (to Dow Corning Corp.), U. S. Patent 2,715,113 (Aug. 9, 1955); *C.A.,* **50,** 7131 (1956).

(46) Green, S. J., and Price, T. S., *J. Chem. Soc.,* 448 (1921).

(47) Henry, M. C., and Noltes, J. G., *J. Am. Chem. Soc.,* **82,** 555, 558, 561 (1960).

(48) Hewett, C. L., *J. Chem, Soc.,* 1203 (1948).

(49) Hofmann, A. W., *Ann. Suppl.,* **1,** 145, 275 (1860); *Phil. Trans.,* **150,** 409 (1860).

(50) Hunt, R., and Renshaw, R. R., *J. Pharmacol. Exp. Therap.,* **25,** 315 (1925).

(51) Hurd, D. T., *J. Am. Chem. Soc.,* **67,** 1813 (1945); (to General Electric Co.), U. S. Patent 2,420,912 (May 20, 1947).

(52) Hurd, D. T., "Inorganic Syntheses," **3,** 58 (1950).

(53) Jacobs, G., *Compt. rend.,* **238,** 1825 (1954).

(54) Jaffé, H. H., *J. Chem. Phys.,* **22,** 1430 (1954).

(55) Jenkins, W. J., *J. Chem. Soc. Transactions,* **119,** 747 (1921).

(56) Johnson, O. H., "Inorganic Syntheses," **5,** 64 (1957).

(57) Johnson, O. H., and Harris, D. M., *J. Am. Chem. Soc.,* **72,** 5564 (1950).

(58) Juenge, E. C., and Cook, S. E., *J. Am. Chem. Soc.,* **81,** 3578 (1959).

(59) Kabachnik, M. I., *Izvest. Akad. Nauk S.S.S.R., Otdel. khim. Nauk,* 233 (1947); *C.A.,* **42,** 4132 (1948).

(60) Kaesz, H. D., Stafford, S. L., and Stone, F. G. A., *J. Am. Chem. Soc.,* **81,** 6336 (1959); *ibid.,* **82,** in press (1960).

(61) Kaesz, H. D., and Stone, F. G. A., *J. Org. Chem.,* **24,** 635 (1959).

(62) Kaesz, H. D., and Stone, F. G. A., *Spectrochimica Acta,* 360 (1959).

(63) Kaesz, H. D., and Stone, F. G. A., *J. Am. Chem. Soc.,* in press.

(64) Kanazashi, M., *Bull. Chem. Soc. Japan,* **26,** 493 (1953).

(65) Kanazashi, M., *Bull. Chem. Soc. Japan,* **28,** 44 (1955).

(66) Kharasch, M. S., and Marker, R., *J. Am. Chem. Soc.*, **48**, 3130 (1926).
(67) King, R. B., and Stone, F. G. A., *J. Am. Chem. Soc.*, in press.
(68) Kirrman, A., *Compt. rend.*, **184**, 1178 (1927).
(69) Kitaigorodsky, A. I., *Izvest. Akad. Nauk S.S.S.R., Otdel. khim. Nauk*, 170 (1945); *C.A.*, **40**, 3451 (1946).
(70) Kitaigorodsky, A. I., *Izvest. Akad. Nauk S.S.S.R., Otdel. khim. Nauk*, 259 (1947); *C.A.*, **42**, 5846 (1948).
(70a) Knunyants, I. L., Pervova, E. J. and Tuleneva, V. V., *Doklady Akad. Nauk S.S.S.R.*, **129**, 576 (1959).
(71) Knunyants, I. L., Sterlin, R. N., Yatsensko, R. D., and Pinkina, L. N., *Izvest. Akad. Nauk S.S.S.R., Otdel. khim. Nauk*, 1345 (1958); *C.A.*, **53**, 6987 (1959).
(72) Kocheshkov, K. A., *Ber.*, **66**, 1661 (1933).
(73) Koelsch, C. F., *J. Am. Chem. Soc.*, **54**, 2045, 3384 (1932).
(74) Kosolapoff, G. M., *J. Am. Chem. Soc.*, **70**, 1971 (1948).
(75) Kosolapoff, G. M., "Organophosphorus Compounds," New York, Wiley, 1950.
(76) Kraus, C. A., and Neal, A. M., *J. Am. Chem. Soc.*, **52**, 4426 (1930).
(77) Krestinsky, W., *Ber.*, **55**, 2754 (1922).
(78) Lappert, M. F., *Chem. Reviews*, **56**, 959 (1956).
(79) Letsinger, R. L., and Skoog, I. H., *J. Org. Chem.*, **18**, 895 (1953).
(80) Maier, L., *Angew. Chemie*, **71**, 161 (1959).
(81) Maier, L., *Tetrahedron Letters*, No. 6, 1 (1959).
(82) Maier, L., Abstracts of Papers Presented at the XVII Congress of the I.U.P.A.C., held in Munich, August, 1959.
(83) Maier, L., Seyferth, D., Stone, F. G. A., and Rochow, E. G., *J. Am. Chem. Soc.*, **79**, 5884 (1957).
(84) Mangini, A., *J. Chim. Phys.*, 240 (1959).
(85) Mangini, A., and Passerini, R., *J. Chem. Soc.*, 4954 (1956).
(86) Mazerolles, P., and Lesbre, M., *Compt. rend.*, **248**, 2018 (1959).
(87) McDowell, C. A., Emblem, H. G., and Moelwyn-Hughes, E. A., *J. Chem. Soc.*, 1206 (1948).
(88) Morton, A. A., and Holden, E. T., *J. Am. Chem. Soc.*, **69**, 1675 (1947).
(89) Morton, A. A., Marsh, F. D., Coombs, R. D., Lyons, A. L., Penner, S. E., Ramsden, H. E., Baker, V. B., Little, E. L., and Letsinger, R. L., *J. Am. Chem. Soc.*, **72**, 3785 (1950).
(90) Nesmeyanov, A. N., *Bull. Soc. Chim.*, 569 (1946).
(91) Nesmeyanov, A. N., Batuev, M. I., and Borisov, A. E., *Izvest. Akad. Nauk S.S.S.R., Otdel. khim. Nauk*, 567 (1949); *C.A.*, **44**, 2374 (1950).
(92) Nesmeyanov, A. N., and Borisov, A. E., *Izvest. Akad. Nauk S.S.S.R., Otdel. khim. Nauk*, 251 (1945); *C.A.*, **40**, 2123 (1946).
(93) Nesmeyanov, A. N., and Borisov, A. E., *Tetrahedron*, **1**, 158 (1957).
(94) Nesmeyanov, A. N., Borisov, A. E., and Abramova, A. N., *Izvest. Akad. Nauk S.S.S.R., Otdel. khim. Nauk*, 289 (1947); *C.A.*, **42**, 4847 (1948).
(95) Nesmeyanov, A. N., Borisov, A. E., and Novikova, N. V., *Izvest. Akad. Nauk S.S.S.R., Otdel. khim. Nauk*, 259 (1959); *C.A.*, **53**, 17890 (1959).

(96) Nesmeyanov, A. N., Borisov, A. E., Savel'eva, I. S., and Golubeva, E. I., *Izvest. Akad. Nauk S.S.S.R., Otdel. khim. Nauk,* 1490 (1958); *C.A.,* **53,** 7973 (1959).

(97) Nesmeyanov, A. N., Borisov, A. E., and Vil'chevskaya, V. D., *Izvest. Akad. Naul S.S.S.R., Otdel. khim. Nauk,* 578 (1949); *C.A.,* **44,** 3881 (1950).

(98) Nesmeyanov, A. N., Freidlina, R. K., and Borisov, A. E., *Izvest. Akad. Nauk S.S.S.R., Otdel. khim. Nauk,* 137 (1945); *C.A.,* **40,** 3451 (1946).

(99) Nesmeyanov, A. N., Kotchetkov, A., and Freidlina, R. K., *Izvest. Akad. Nauk S.S.S.R., Otdel. khim. Nauk,* 657 (1947); *C.A.,* **42,** 5847 (1948).

(100) Normant, H., *Compt. rend.,* **239,** 1510 (1954).

(101) Normant, H., *Compt. rend.,* **239,** 1811 (1954).

(102) Normant, H., *Bull. Soc. Chim.,* 728 (1957).

(102a) Normant, H., *Bull. Soc. Chim.,* 1764 (1959).

(103) Normant, H., and Ficini, J., *Compt. rend.,* **237,** 731 (1953).

(104) Park, J. D., Seffl, R. J., and Lacher, J. R., *J. Am. Chem. Soc.,* **78,** 59 (1956).

(105) Parsons, T. D., Silverman, M. B., and Ritter, D. M., *J. Am. Chem. Soc.,* **79,** 5091 (1957).

(106) Pauling, L., "Nature of the Chemical Bond," 2nd Ed., Ithaca, N. Y., Cornell Univ. Press, 1940.

(107) Pedley, J. B., and Skinner, H. A., *Trans. Faraday Soc.,* **55,** 1 (1959).

(108) Petrov, A. D., and Mironov, V. F., *Izvest. Akad. Nauk S.S.S.R., Otdel. khim. Nauk,* 1491 (1957); *C.A.,* **52,** 7136 (1958).

(109) Petrov, A. D., Mironov, V. F., and .Dolgii, I. E., *Izvest. Akad. Nauk S.S.S.R , Otdel. khim. Nauk,* 1146 (1956); *C.A.,* **51,** 4938 (1957).

(110) Petrov, A. D., Mironov, V. F., and Glukhovtsev, V. G., *Izvest. Akad. Nauk S.S.S.R., Otdel. khim Nauk,* 451 (1956); *C.A.,* **51,** 3440 (1957).

(111) Pritchard, H. O., and Skinner, H. A., *Chem. Reviews,* **55,** 745 (1955).

(112) Pyle, J. (to General Electric Co.), U. S. Patent 2,448,391 (Aug. 31, 1948); *C.A.,* **43,** 1223 (1949); **45,** 391 (1951).

(113) Ramsden, H. E., Leebrick, J. R., Rosenberg, S. D., Miller, E. H., Walburn, J. J., Balint, A. E., and Cserr, R., *J. Org. Chem.,* **22,** 1602 (1957).

(114) Reichstein, T., and Baud, J., *Helv. chim. Acta,* **20,** 892 (1937).

(115) Reynolds, G. F. Dessy, R. E., and Jaffé, H. H., *J. Org. Chem.,* **23,** 1217 (1958).

(116) Riemschneider, R., Menge, K., and Klang, P., *Z. Naturforsch.,* **11b,** 115 (1956).

(117) Rosenberg, S. D., and Gibbons, A. J. (to Metal & Thermit Corp.), U. S. Patent 2,873,288 (Feb. 10, 1959); *C.A.,* **53,** 13054 (1959).

(118) Rosenberg, S. D., Gibbons, A. J., and Ramsden, H. E., *J. Am. Chem. Soc.,* **79,** 2137 (1957).

(119) Rosenberg, S. D., Walburn, J. J., Stankovich, T. D., Balint, A. E., and Ramsden, H. E., *J. Org. Chem.,* **22,** 1200 (1957).

(120) Rupe, H., and Proske, H., *Ber.,* **43,** 1231 (1910).

(121) Saitow, A., Rochow, E. G., and Seyferth, D., *J. Org. Chem.,* **23,** 116 (1958).

(122) Seyferth, D., *Technical Report, Office of Naval Research Contract No. Nonr-1866(13),* February, 1957.

(123) Seyferth, D., *J. Org. Chem.,* **22,** 478 (1957).
(124) Seyferth, D., *J. Org. Chem.,* **22,** 1252 (1957).
(125) Seyferth, D., *J. Am. Chem. Soc.,* **79,** 2133 (1957).
(126) Seyferth, D., *J. Am. Chem. Soc.,* **79,** 2738 (1957).
(127) Seyferth, D., *J. Am. Chem. Soc.,* **81,** 1844 (1959).
(128) Seyferth, D., and Kahlen, N., *Z. Naturforsch.,* **14b,** 137 (1959).
(129) Seyferth, D., and Stone, F. G. A., *J. Am. Chem. Soc.,* **79,** 515 (1957).
(130) Seyferth, D., and Weiner, M. A., *Chemistry and Industry,* 402 (1959).
(131) Solerio, A., *Gazz. chim. ital.,* **85,** 61 (1955).
(132) Sommer, L. H., Bailey, D. L., Goldberg, G. M., Buck, C. E., Bye, T. S., Evans, F. J., and Whitmore, F. C., *J. Am. Chem. Soc.,* **76,** 1613 (1954).
(133) Sterlin, R. N., Knunyants, I. L., Pinkina, L. N., and Yatsenko, R. D., *Izvest. Akad. Nauk S.S.S.R., Otdel. khim. Nauk,* 1492 (1959); *C.A.,* **54,** 1270 (1960).
(134) Sterlin, R. N., Li-Vei-Gan, Knunyants, I. L., *Izvest. Akad. Nauk S.S.S.R., Otdel., khim. Nauk,* 1506 (1959); *C.A.,* **54,** 1273 (1960).
(135) Stone, F. G. A., *Chem. Reviews,* **58,** 101 (1958).
(136) Stone, F. G. A., "Chemical Reactivity of the Boron Hydrides and Related Compounds," "Advances in Inorganic Chemistry and Radiochemistry" (Eds.: H. J. Eméleus and A. G. Sharpe), Vol. II, New York, Academic Press, 1960.
(137) Stone, F. G. A., and Seyferth, D., *J. Inorg. and Nuclear Chem.,* **1,** 112 (1955); see also reference (65).
(138) Strother, C. O., and Wagner, G. H. (to Linde Air Products Co.), U. S. Patent 2,532,430 (Dec. 5, 1950); *C.A.,* **45,** 2968 (1951).
(139) Summers, L., *Iowa State Coll. J. Sci.,* **26,** 292 (1952).
(140) Taft, R. W., "Steric Effects in Organic Chemistry," (Ed.: M. S. Newman), New York, Wiley, 1956.
(141) Tchelitcheff, R., and Paul, S., *Compt. rend.,* **230,** 1473 (1950); **232,** 2230 (1951).
(142) Tiffeneau, M., *Compt. rend.,* **135,** 1346 (1902).
(142a) Topchiev, A. V., Payshkin, A. M., and Prokorova, A. A., *Doklady Akad. Nauk S.S.S.R.,* **129,** 598 (1959).
(143) Tsatsas, G., *Compt. rend.,* **220,** 662 (1945).
(144) van der Kerk, G. J. M., and Noltes, J. G., *J. Appl. Chem.,* **9,** 106 (1959).
(145) van der Kerk, G. J. M., Noltes, J. G., and Luitjen, J. G. A., *J. Appl. Chem.,* **7,** 356 (1957).
(146) Van Wazer, J. R., "Phosphorus and its Compounds," Vol. 1, New York, Interscience, 1958.
(147) Wagner, G. H. (to Union Carbide & Carbon Corp.), U. S. Patent 2,637,738 (May 5, 1953); *C.A.,* **48,** 8254 (1954).
(148) Wagner, G. H., Bailey, D. L., Pines, A. N., Dunham, M. L., and McIntire, D. B., *Ind. Eng. Chem.,* **45,** 367 (1953).
(148a) Walsh, E. N., Beck, T. M., and Woodstock, W. H., *J. Am. Chem. Soc.,* **77,** 929 (1955).
(149) Warchavsky, S. L., *Doklady Akdd. Nauk S.S.S.R.,* **29,** 315 (1940).

(150) Wartik, T., and Pearson, R. K., *J. Inorg. Nucl. Chem.*, **5,** 250 (1958).

(151) White, D. G., and Rochow, E. G., *J. Am. Chem. Soc.*, **76,** 3897 (1954).

(152) Whiting, G. H., *J. Chem. Soc.*, 1209 (1948).

(153) Ziegler, K., *Ann.*, **434,** 75 (1923).

(154) Ziegler, K., "Metal-organic Syntheses," "Perspectives in Organic Chemistry" (Ed.: A. Todd), New York, Interscience, 1956.

4. ORGANOBORANES

HERBERT C. BROWN

Purdue University, Lafayette, Indiana

INTRODUCTION

Frankland, the father of organometallic chemistry, synthesized the first organoboranes in 1859. He obtained both trimethylborane and triethylborane by the reaction of the corresponding dialkylzinc on triethylborate (*48*).

$$3 \ R_2Zn + 2 \ B(OC_2H_5)_3 \longrightarrow 2 \ R_3B + 3 \ Zn(OC_2H_5)_2$$

For many years the synthesis of organoboranes by the action of an organometallic derivative on a borate ester or a boron halide remained the preferred method of synthesis, with the action of the Grignard reagent on boron trifluoride-etherate, as introduced by Krause and Nitsche, being the procedure of choice (*70*).

$$3 \ RMgX + BF_3 \longrightarrow BR_3 + 3 \ MgXF$$

The aliphatic organoboranes are typical non-polar substances, resembling the corresponding hydrocarbons in their physical properties. Thus trimethylborane is a gas, m.p. $-159.8°$, b.p. $-21.8°$, as compared to isobutane, m.p. $-159.6°$, b.p. $-11.7°$. Similarly, triethylborane exhibits the constants, m.p. $-92.5°$, b.p. $95°$, as contrasted with 3-ethylpentane, m.p. $-118.6°$, b.p. $93.5°$. The triarylboranes are generally crystalline solids, e.g., triphenylborane, m.p. $142°$; tri-α-naphthylborane, m.p. $206-207°$.

With the exception of a few organoboranes containing large bulky groups, such as tri-α-naphthylborane and trimesitylborane, the organoboranes are sensitive to oxygen and must be handled in the absence of air. The lower members ignite spontaneously upon exposure to air and burn vigorously, whereas the higher members generally absorb oxygen to form oxidized products without ignition. In contrast to their reactivity toward oxygen, the organoboranes exhibit a remarkable stability toward water, and in many cases may be isolated by washing with water, as well as utilized as a reagent in the presence of water (*56*).

The organoboranes participate in Grignard-like reactions only sluggishly (*50,77*). Since their preparation involved the prior formation of a more reactive organometallic derivative, there was little interest in applying the

150

organoboranes to organic syntheses. Consequently, most of the early investigations involving the organoboranes were stimulated by theoretical considerations.

Thus, the discovery that triarylboranes add sodium and other alkali metals to form addition compounds which are formally analogous to the triarylmethyl free radicals led to the synthesis of many triarylboranes for a study of the influence of structure on the stability of these interesting alkali metal derivatives (*4,42,68*).

$$(C_6H_5)_3B + Na \rightleftharpoons [(C_6H_5)_3B\cdot]^- Na^+$$

Similarly, the ready reaction of organoboranes with amines to form addition compounds has provided a valuable tool for the study of steric effects (*6*).

$$R_3N: + BR_3' \rightleftharpoons R_3N:BR_3'$$

Finally, the similarity in the electronic structures of the trialkylboranes and carbonium ions led Johnson and his co-workers to make the first detailed study of the reactions of organoboranes (*59,60,61,92*).

Recently, it was noted that organoboranes may be readily synthesized from olefins and alkali metal borohydrides or diborane (*24,25*).

$$9\ RCH = CH_2 + 3\ NaBH_4 + AlCl_3 \longrightarrow 3\ (RCH_2CH_2)_3B + AlH_3 + 3\ NaCl$$

$$12\ RCH = CH_2 + 3\ NaBH_4 + 4\ BF_3 \longrightarrow 4\ (RCH_2CH_2)_3B + 3\ NaBF_4$$

$$6\ RCH = CH_2 + B_2H_6 \longrightarrow 2\ (RCH_2CH_2)_3B$$

The reactions are fast and quantitative at room temperature. This new convenient synthesis has led to a renewed interest in the organoboranes as intermediates for organic synthesis.

The chemistry of organoboranes has recently been the subject of detailed reviews (*43,72*). Consequently, this discussion will emphasize the more recent developments, the new synthetic procedures and those reactions of organoboranes which offer promise of utility in organic synthesis. Since the investigations of the author and his students in this area have been directed primarily to the development of new procedures of interest to the research chemist, rather than to the industrial chemist, the discussion will emphasize this viewpoint.

SYNTHESIS OF ORGANOBORANES *VIA* ORGANOMETALLICS

It has already been pointed out that the first synthesis of organoboranes utilized the reaction of dialkylzinc compounds on triethylborate (*48*). With the discovery and wide-spread utilization of the Grignard reagent, it was natural that the latter became the preferred organometallic for this synthetic approach to organoboranes. It was observed that boron trifluoride resulted in better yields than those realized with alkyl borates, so that the dominant synthetic route involved the reaction of the Grignard reagent with boron trifluoride (70).

The greater sluggishness of the reaction of the Grignard reagent with the alkyl borates has been utilized in devising synthetic routes to boronic and borinic esters (and acids). Thus, the aliphatic boronic esters are conveniently synthesized by the addition of the Grignard reagent to methyl borate at low temperatures (75,92), and diarylborinic esters and acids have been obtained by the reaction of the aryl Grignard reagent with tri-isobutyl (78), tri-*n*-butyl borate (73), and trimethoxyboroxine (83).

The recent developments in organoaluminum chemistry by Ziegler and his co-workers (Chapter 5) make these compounds readily available as industrial chemicals. Consequently, there has been renewed interest in the utilization of organoaluminum compounds for the synthesis of the corresponding organoboranes (2,64). It is possible to prepare trialkylboranes from trialkylaluminum in good yield by utilizing either boron trifluoride (99) or borate esters (49). Although the direct reaction of boric oxide with trialkylaluminum has not been successful, it has been possible to utilize the reaction product of trimethylborate and boric oxide, namely, trimethoxyboroxine (2,64).

$$R_3Al + BF_3 \longrightarrow R_3B + AlF_3$$

$$R_3Al + KBF_4 \longrightarrow R_3B + KAlF_4$$

$$R_3Al + B(OCH_3)_3 \longrightarrow R_3B + Al(OCH_3)_3$$

$$3\ R_3Al + (CH_3OBO)_3 \longrightarrow 3\ R_3B + Al(OCH_3)_3 + Al_2O_3$$

Excellent yields have been realized in applying these methods to the synthesis of triethyl-, tri-*n*-propyl-, tri-*n*-butyl- and tri-isobutylborane (2,64). Although these methods should, in principle, be applicable to the synthesis of higher organoboranes, Köster indicates that the experimental difficulties increase with the higher members so that alternate syntheses become preferable (64).

HYDROBORATION

Early Observations

The first description of a reaction between olefins and diborane is that by Hurd in 1948 (58). He reported that he had heated ethylene and diborane in a sealed tube at 100° for four days to obtain a liquid product identified through mass spectrometric analysis as triethylborane. In the case of isobutylene a reaction time of twenty-four hours at 100° sufficed, and it was stated that the addition reaction was even slower at lower temperatures.

In attempting to polymerize acrylonitrile, methyl methacrylate and styrene, Stone and Eméleus reported that only a slow reaction occurs between diborane and these unsaturated molecules at room temperature, yielding complex products (94). More recently, Stone and Graham observed that serious explosions resulted upon heating tetrafluoroethylene with diborane at 80–100° for extended periods of time (95). A simple addition reaction was not observed. Finally, Whatley and Pease utilized temperatures of 130–177° in their study of the kinetics of the reaction of diborane with ethylene and related olefins (98).

In view of these reports of the sluggishness of the reaction of diborane with olefins, this reaction did not appear to offer a promising synthetic route for the synthesis of organoboranes. Fortunately, an unexpected observation in the course of research directed toward other objectives led us to revise our ideas as to the utility of this synthesis.

During the years 1942–1943, in the course of war research at the University of Chicago, Professor H. I. Schlesinger and the present author together with their co-workers had synthesized sodium borohydride for the first time and had developed new practical syntheses for diborane, sodium borohydride and other metal borohydrides (87). In the course of this research it was observed that the alkali metal borohydrides were mild, but useful reducing agents for aldehydes and ketones. Several years later, lithium aluminum hydride was synthesized and observed to be a very powerful reducing agent (47,79).

Unfortunately, the fact that the borohydride investigations had been carried out as war research caused this material to be classified and delayed its publication. Consequently, lithium aluminum hydride was first described in the literature.

It proved to be a very useful reagent and numerous studies were devoted to its application to synthetic organic chemistry (39). However, it was a severe disappointment to the author, as one of the discoverers of sodium borohydride, to note that this promising reagent was being largely ignored in the rush to explore the applicability of its younger brother.

Accordingly, it was decided to institute a research program to explore the effect of solvents (17), substituents (16) and metal ions (23) on the reducing properties of borohydrides. It was observed that the addition of aluminum chloride (or other polyvalent metal halides) to a solution of sodium borohydride in diglyme (dimethylether of diethylene glycol) yielded a solution of greatly enhanced reducing power. At room temperatures esters, such as ethyl stearate and ethyl benzoate, rapidly reacted to form alcohols with the utilization of two "hydrides" per mole of ester. Unexpectedly, ethyl oleate reacted with the disappearance of three "hydrides" per mole of ethyl oleate. Investigation revealed that simple olefins reacted with the reagent with the utilization of one "hydride" per mole of olefin, resulting in the formation of organoboranes, in accordance with the equation (*24*):

$$9 \ RCH = CH_2 + 3 \ NaBH_4 + AlCl_3 \longrightarrow 3 \ (RCH_2CH_2)_3B + AlH_3 + 3 \ NaCl$$

The boron-hydrogen bond of the reagent adds to place the boron atom predominantly at the 1-position of a terminal olefin. These organoboranes are readily oxidized by alkaline hydrogen peroxide to form the corresponding alcohol (*24,60*). Consequently, this reaction offered a new simple procedure for the anti-Markownikoff hydration of double-bonds and a detailed study of the synthesis was undertaken (*27*).

The addition of aluminum chloride to a solution of sodium borohydride in diglyme solution in the stoichiometric quantity ($AlCl_3 + 3 \ NaBH_4$) yields a clear, colorless solution. Addition of an olefin, such as 1-octene, to the solution, results in the precipitation of a white solid as the reaction proceeds. Removal of the clear, supernatant liquid revealed that it contained all of the boron in the form of organically bound boron and only trace amounts of chloride ion and of residual hydride. Analysis of the precipitate indicated the presence of aluminum hydride.

The reaction is relatively fast. Usually the reagent is treated with the olefin for three hours at room temperature and then heated briefly on the steam bath for one-half hour to complete the reaction. In this way ethylene, propylene, 1-pentene, 2-pentene, 1-hexene, 1-octene, cyclopentene, cyclohexene, styrene and α-methylstyrene were converted into the corresponding organoboranes in yields of 80–90% of isolated product.

In converting an olefin directly into the corresponding alcohol, the organoborane need not be isolated. It is possible to oxidize it *in situ* with alkaline hydrogen peroxide. In this way a number of representative olefins were converted into the corresponding alcohols in yields of 60–90 per cent:

> 1-hexene $\longrightarrow$ 1-hexanol, 90 per cent
> 1-decene $\longrightarrow$ 1-decanol, 93 per cent
> styrene $\longrightarrow$ 2-phenylethanol, 81 per cent
> α-methylstyrene $\longrightarrow$ 2-phenyl-1-propanol, 90 per cent
> 1,1-diphenylethylene $\longrightarrow$ 2,2-diphenylethanol, 86 per cent
> *t*-butylethylene $\longrightarrow$ 3,3-dimethyl-1-butanol, 67 per cent
> 2-methyl-2-butene $\longrightarrow$ 3-methyl-2-butanol, 59 per cent
> cyclopentene $\longrightarrow$ cyclopentanol, 80 per cent

The observation that the solution of aluminum chloride and sodium borohydride is clear and does not precipitate sodium chloride (insoluble in diglyme) suggests that the reaction cannot proceed to the formation of aluminum borohydride. However, it is possible that a small equilibrium concentration of aluminum borohydride is formed and that the reaction proceeds through this intermediate. In this connection, it is of interest that aluminum borohydride in ether solution likewise serves to accomplish the hydroboration of olefins.

The use of this reagent for the hydroboration of olefins suffers from the disadvantage that only three of the four "hydrides" in sodium borohydride are utilized for the formation of the organoborane—the fourth is lost in the form of aluminum hydride.

This difficulty is circumvented by the use of either boron trichloride or boron trifluoride in place of the aluminum chloride. With these two Lewis acids of boron, the reaction is amazingly fast—the olefin is converted to organoborane almost instantly at room temperature (*28*).

$$12 \text{ RCH}{=}\text{CH}_2 + 3 \text{ NaBH}_4 + \text{BCl}_3 \longrightarrow 4 \text{ (RCH}_2\text{CH}_2)_3\text{B} + 3 \text{ NaCl}$$

$$12 \text{ RCH}{=}\text{CH}_2 + 3 \text{ NaBH}_4 + 4 \text{ BF}_3 \longrightarrow 4 \text{ (RCH}_2\text{CH}_2)_3\text{B} + 3 \text{ NaBF}_4$$

In the course of these studies it was observed that diborane itself adds quantitatively and with great rapidity at room temperature to a wide variety of olefins. It appears that the reaction is strongly catalyzed by ethers. Thus treatment of carefully purified 1-octene with diborane led to a very slow reaction extending over many hours. Addition of trace amounts of ethers and related weak bases brought about an exceedingly rapid reaction, far too fast to measure (*10*).

Diborane is highly soluble in tetrahydrofuran—a 2 molar solution of diborane may be readily prepared and utilized without significant loss of diborane. Consequently, the direct conversion of olefins to organoboranes is readily carried out in this solvent. Diborane is less soluble in either ether or diglyme, but these solvents may also be utilized for the reaction. Finally, in cases where the presence of sodium borofluoride offers no difficulty, olefins may be conveniently converted into organoboranes by utilizing the action of boron trifluoride etherate on solutions of olefins and sodium borohydride in diglyme or triglyme (dimethylether of triethylene glycol). By careful selection of the solvent (diglyme, b.p. 162°; triglyme, b.p. 216°), one can ensure that it will be readily separable from the product.

The addition of the hydrogen-boron bond to olefins and acetylenes has proven to be a reaction of very wide generality, comparable to the addition of hydrogen or of chlorine to such multiple carbon-carbon linkages. Accordingly, it appears desirable to have a simple means of referring to this reaction and the term hydroboration (HB), has been proposed (*25*).

Experimental Procedures

Sodium borohydride is essentially insoluble in the common ether solvents, but is readily soluble in the new solvents diglyme and triglyme (*17*). Consequently, these solvents were utilized predominantly in our studies of the hydroboration reaction. Their use results in a simple, clean procedure with yields approaching quantitative.

Unfortunately, the unavailability of these solvents abroad has resulted in difficulties in applying the reaction to synthetic problems (*46,103*). Accordingly, a detailed study was made of the possible hydride sources which might be utilized, of acids applicable to these hydride sources, and of solvents which might be applicable to the various systems (*34*). 1-Octene was utilized as the test olefin in this study.

Lithium borohydride is readily soluble in ethyl ether, tetrahydrofuran, as well as other ether solvents. Consequently, it can be utilized in a large variety of solvents with a large variety of acids. For example, in ethyl ether essentially quantitative hydroboration of the 1-octene was achieved with the following acids: boron trifluoride etherate, boron trichloride etherate, aluminum chloride, titanium tetrachloride, hydrogen chloride, and sulfuric acid. Because of their ready availability and ease of handling, it would appear that boron trifluoride etherate, hydrogen chloride and sulfuric acid, all utilized in ethyl ether (EE) solution, offer major advantage. It should be pointed out that lithium borohydride requires only sufficient boron trifluoride to convert the lithium to lithium fluoride, in contrast to sodium borohydride, where sufficient boron trifluoride must be used to form sodium fluoroborate.

$$12 \ RCH{=}CH_2 + 3 \ LiBH_4 + BF_3 \xrightarrow{EE} 4 \ (RCH_2CH_2)_3B + 3 \ LiF$$

$$9 \ RCH{=}CH_2 + 3 \ LiBH_4 + 3 \ HCl \xrightarrow{EE} 3 \ (RCH_2CH_2)_3B + 3 \ LiCl + 3 \ H_2$$

$$9 \ RCH{=}CH_2 + 3 \ LiBH_4 + 1.5 \ H_2SO_4 \xrightarrow{EE}$$
$$3 \ (RCH_2CH_2)_3B + 1.5 \ Li_2SO_4 + 3 \ H_2$$

The sole disadvantage in the use of lithium borohydride is its relatively high cost at the present time.

Sodium borohydride is readily soluble in diglyme (DG) and triglyme, and the hydroboration reactions with boron trifluoride etherate, hydrogen chloride or sulfuric acid proceed rapidly and quantitatively at room temperature. These reactions are the procedures of choice in cases where the solvents are available.

Although the solubility of sodium borohydride in tetrahydrofuran is small, the hydroboration of an olefin is readily achieved by treating a suspension of sodium borohydride in tetrahydrofuran containing the olefin with boron trifluoride etherate. Alternatively a solution of diborane in tetrahydrofuran (THF) can be generated by treating a suspension of sodium borohydride in that solvent at 0° with hydrogen chloride. The hydroboration reaction is then achieved by adding the olefin to this solution.

Finally, it is possible to utilize ethyl ether as the solvent by introducing 10 mole per cent of anhydrous zinc chloride to catalyze the reaction between sodium borohydride and boron trifluoride etherate in ethyl ether.

$$12 \; RCH{=}CH_2 + 3 \; NaBH_4 + 4 \; BF_3 \xrightarrow{DG} 4 \; (RCH_2CH_2)_3B + 3 \; NaBF_4$$

$$12 \; RCH{=}CH_2 + 3 \; NaBH_4 + 4 \; BF_3 \xrightarrow{THF} 4 \; (RCH_2CH_2)_3B + 3 \; NaBF_4$$

$$2 \; NaBH_4 + 2 \; HCl \xrightarrow[0°]{THF} B_2H_6 \; (soln.) + 2 \; NaCl$$

$$6 \; RCH{=}CH_2 + B_2H_6 \xrightarrow{THF} 2 \; (RCH_2CH_2)_3B$$

$$12 \; RCH{=}CH_2 + 3 \; NaBH_4 + 4 \; BF_3 \xrightarrow[10\% \; ZnCl_2]{EE} 4 \; (RCH_2CH_2)_3B + 3 \; NaBF_4$$

Potassium borohydride, although insoluble in triglyme, can be utilized suspended in this solvent with boron trifluoride etherate. Treatment of a mixture of potassium borohydride and lithium chloride with tetrahydrofuran results in the formation of a solution of lithium borohydride in this solvent. The latter solution can be utilized for hydroboration with any of the acids previously established as suitable for lithium borohydride itself.

$$KBH_4 + LiCl \xrightarrow{THF} LiBH_4 + KCl$$

The reaction of lithium aluminum hydride with boron trifluoride etherate in ethyl ether solution appears to be a convenient procedure utilizing a readily available solvent (*103*). In the event boron trifluoride etherate is not available, a mixture of aluminum chloride and methyl borate provides a readily available substitute.

$$12 \; RCH{=}CH_2 + 3 \; LiAlH_4 + 4 \; BF_3 \xrightarrow{EE} 4 \; (RCH_2CH_2)_3B + 3 \; LiAlF_4$$

$$12 \; RCH{=}CH_2 + 3 \; LiAlH_4 + AlCl_3 + 4 \; B(OCH_3)_3 \xrightarrow{EE}$$
$$4 \; (RCH_2CH_2)_3B + 3 \; LiCl + 4 \; Al(OCH_3)_3$$

The simple alkali metal hydrides can also be utilized. Thus, lithium hydride in ethyl ether, tetrahydrofuran or diglyme, or sodium hydride, in tetrahydrofuran or diglyme, react readily with boron trifluoride etherate.

$$6 \; RCH{=}CH_2 + 6 \; LiH + 8 \; BF_3 \xrightarrow{EE} 2 \; (RCH_2CH_2)_3B + 6 \; LiBF_4$$

$$6 \ RCH{=}CH_2 + 6 \ NaH + 8 \ BF_3 \xrightarrow{DG} 2 \ (RCH_2CH_2)_3B + 6 \ NaBF_4$$

The major disadvantage is the relatively large amount of boron tri-fluoride which must be used and the resulting presence of large amounts of lithium or sodium fluoborates in the reaction mixtures.

At elevated temperatures pyridine-borane (*53*) and trimethylamine-borane (*2,63*) can be utilized to achieve the hydroboration of olefins without the use of any solvent or acid.

$$3 \ RCH{=}CH_2 + C_5H_5N : BH_3 \longrightarrow (RCH_2CH_2)_3B : NC_5H_5$$

$$3 \ RCH{=}CH_2 + (CH_3)_3N : BH_3 \longrightarrow (RCH_2CH_2)_3B : N(CH_3)_3$$

In cases where the organoborane may be subjected to the elevated temperatures required (100–200°), this procedure is quite convenient.

Finally, Köster has utilized the displacement reaction of an olefin on tri-isobutylborane, synthesized from tri-isobutylaluminum, as a general synthetic route to the higher trialkylorganoboranes (*64*). Discussion of his results will be deferred to the section dealing with the displacement reactions of organoboranes.

Scope and Stoichiometry

In ether solvents diborane adds with remarkable ease at room temperature to olefins of a wide variety of structural types (*28*). Among the olefins which have been examined for their applicability in this reaction are the following.

> Terminal olefins: 1-hexene, 1-octene, 1-decene, 1-tetradecene, 3-methyl-1-butene, 3,3-dimethyl-1-butene, 4,4-dimethyl-1-pentene, 2-methyl-1-butene, 2-methyl-1-pentene and 2,4,4-trimethyl-1-pentene.
>
> Dialkyl internal olefins: 2-hexene, 3-hexene, 2-octene, 4-methyl-2-pentene, and 4,4-dimethyl-2-pentene.
>
> Cyclic olefins: cyclopentene, cyclohexene, α-pinene and norbornene.
>
> Trialkyl olefins: 2-methyl-2-butene, 2-methyl-2-pentene, 3-ethyl-2-pentene, 1-methylcyclohexene, 2,4,4-trimethyl-2-pentene.
>
> Tetra-alkyl olefins: 2,3-dimethyl-2-butene, 1,2-dimethylcyclopentene and 1,2-dimethylcyclohexene.
>
> Aryl olefins: styrene, α-methylstyrene, 1,1-diphenylethylene, *trans*-stilbene and triphenylethylene.
>
> Substituted olefins: vinyl chloride, allyl chloride, allyl ethyl ether, ethyl oleate and ethyl cinnamate.

In addition, a wide variety of acetylenes and dienes have been demonstrated to undergo hydroboration (see later sections).

In only one case has it been noted that a double bond resists the hydroboration reaction. Wechter has reported that 3,20-bis-cycloethylenedioxy-

5β-pregn-9(11)-ene does not undergo reaction under the usual hydroboration conditions (*97*).

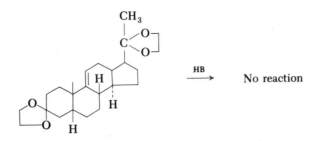

HB
⟶   No reaction

On the other hand, the analogous compound with the A/B-*trans* junction
does undergo hydroboration (*86*).

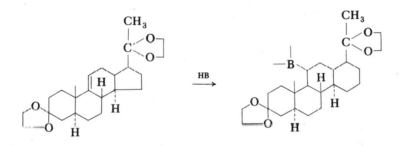

Consequently, it appears that hydroboration is a general reaction of
olefin double bonds with only exceedingly hindered structures exhibiting
any significant resistance toward addition of the reagent. No rearrangement of the carbon skeleton has yet been observed in any hydroboration
reaction.

In the great majority of olefins, reaction appears to proceed to the complete utilization of the active hydrogen of the diborane molecule within a
few minutes at room temperature (*28*).

$$3 \quad \underset{\underset{H}{|}}{\overset{\overset{H_3C}{|}}{C}} = \underset{\underset{H}{|}}{\overset{\overset{CH_3}{|}}{C}} \quad + BH_3 \longrightarrow \left(\underset{\underset{H}{|}}{\overset{\overset{H_3C}{|}}{H-C}} - \underset{\underset{H}{|}}{\overset{\overset{CH_3}{|}}{C}}- \right)_3 B$$

However, trisubstituted olefins, such as 2-methyl-2-butene, react rapidly
at room temperature to utilize only two of the active hydrogens of the
borane group, yielding a dialkylborane (or its dimer) as the reaction
product.

$$2 \quad \underset{\underset{H_3C}{|}\ \underset{H}{|}}{\overset{\overset{H_3C}{|}\ \overset{CH_3}{|}}{C=C}} \quad + \ BH_3 \ \rightarrow \ \left(\underset{\underset{H_3C}{|}\ \underset{H}{|}}{\overset{\overset{H_3C}{|}\ \overset{CH_3}{|}}{H-C-C-}} \right)_2 BH$$

2-Methyl-2-butene will react further with the dialkylborane to form the trialkylborane, but the reaction is very slow, requiring approximately twenty-four hours for completion at room temperature.

In the case of tetrasubstituted olefins, such as tetramethylethylene, the reaction appears to halt at the monoalkylborane stage, RBH_2.

$$\underset{\underset{H_3C}{|}\ \underset{CH_3}{|}}{\overset{\overset{H_3C}{|}\ \overset{CH_3}{|}}{C=C}} \quad + \ BH_3 \ \rightarrow \ \underset{\underset{H_3C}{|}\ \underset{CH_3}{|}}{\overset{\overset{H_3C}{|}\ \overset{CH_3}{|}}{H-C-C-BH_2}}$$

That this phenomenon is largely steric in origin is indicated by the observation that the presence of large bulky groups, such as *t*-butyl, causes the hydroboration to become quite slow at even earlier stages. Thus, *trans-t*-butylmethylethylene undergoes hydroboration rapidly only to the dialkylborane stage (*37*), while *trans*-di-*t*-butylethylene appears to halt at the monoalkylborane stage (*74*). These results are summarized below.

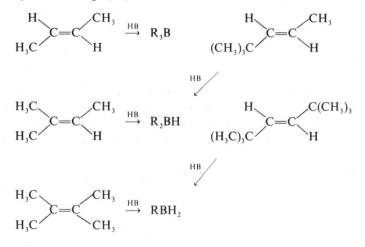

Directive Effects

The original hydroboration experiments had indicated that the hydroboration reaction proceeded to place the boron atom predominately at the least substituted carbon atom of an olefin. However, it appeared desirable to obtain quantitative data on the direction of addition (*37*). Fortunately, the oxidation of organoboranes is a quantitative reaction which serves to place a hydroxyl group in the exact position occupied by the boron atom in the original hydroboration product. Consequently, a careful analysis of the isomeric alcohols obtained in this process provides information as to the influence of the olefin structure on the direction of addition of the boron-hydrogen bond.

Simple straight-chain terminal olefins, such as 1-butene, 1-pentene and 1-hexene, give 93–94 per cent addition of the boron atom to the terminal carbon atom, with only a minor amount of addition, 6–7 per cent, to give the secondary alkyl boron product. Branching of the alkyl group adjacent to the double bond does not influence the direction of addition. Thus, 3-methyl-1-butene, 3,3-dimethyl-1-butene, and 4,4-dimethyl-1-pentene give the same distribution.

Styrene yields 80 per cent addition to the terminal position, 20 per cent to the secondary carbon. The influence of the phenyl group is reduced, but still apparent in allylbenzene, with a 90:10 distribution. It is of special interest that the direction of addition to styrene is strongly influenced by substituents in the *para* position.

In disubstituted terminal olefins, such as 2-methyl-1-butene and 2,4,4-trimethyl-1-pentene, the combined influence of the two alkyl substituents is overwhelming and results in the almost complete addition of the boron atom to the terminal carbon.

These results are summarized in Table 4.1.

TABLE 4.1. DIRECTIVE EFFECTS IN THE HYDROBORATION
OF TERMINAL OLEFINS AT 20°

Olefin	Alcohol Product, %	
	1-ol	2-ol
1-Butene	93	7
1-Pentene	94	6
1-Hexene	94	6
3-Methyl-1-butene	94	6
3,3-Dimethyl-1-butene	94	6
4,4-Dimethyl-1-pentene	93	7
p-Methoxystyrene	91	9
p-Methylstyrene	82	18
Styrene	80	20
p-Chlorostyrene	65	35
Allylbenzene	90	10
2-Methyl-1-butene	99	1
2,4,4-Trimethyl-1-pentene	99	1
α-Methylstyrene	100	trace

In the case of internal olefins, it is possible to examine the competitive effect of two different alkyl groups in directing the addition reaction. However, little difference is observed for different alkyl groups. Thus 2-pentene and 2-hexene undergo addition to place the boron in approximately equal amounts on the 2- and 3-carbon atoms. Branching of one of the two alkyl groups attached to the double bond, as in *trans*-4-methyl-2-pentene and *trans*-4,4-dimethyl-2-pentene, results in a small preference of the boron atom for the carbon atom adjacent to the less branched of the alkyl substituents.

Comparison of the behavior of 1-pentene and styrene (Table 4.1) indicates that the phenyl group is less effective than the alkyl group in directing the boron atom to the terminal carbon. The same relative effect of the phenyl and methyl groups is indicated by the distribution observed for *trans*-1-phenylpropene—85 per cent α- and 15 per cent β.

In the case of trisubstituted olefins, the boron atom goes preferentially to the less substituted of the two carbon atoms.

These results are summarized in Table 4.2.

TABLE 4.2. DIRECTIVE EFFECTS IN THE HYDROBORATION
OF INTERNAL OLEFINS

Olefin	Alcohol Product, %	
	2-ol	3-ol
cis-2-Pentene	55	45
trans-2-Pentene	51	49
cis-2-Hexene	50	50
trans-2-Hexene	46	54
cis-3-Hexene		100
trans-4-Methyl-2-pentene	57	43
trans-4,4-dimethyl-2-pentene[a]	58	42
trans-1-Phenylpropene	85[b]	15[c]
2-Methyl-2-butene[a]	2	98[d]
2,4,4-Trimethyl-2-pentene[a]	2	98[e]

[a]Hydroboration to R_2BH stage.
[b]1-Phenyl-1-propanol.
[c]1-Phenyl-2-propanol.
[d]3-Methyl-2-butanol.
[e]2,4,4-Trimethyl-3-pentanol.

The addition of diborane to olefins must involve at least three distinct stages, in which one, two and three carbon-boron bonds are formed.

$$C{=}C + BH_3 \rightarrow H{-}C{-}C{-}BH_2$$

$$C{=}C + RBH_2 \rightarrow H{-}C{-}C{-}BHR$$

$$C{=}C + R_2BH \rightarrow H{-}C{-}C{-}BR_2$$

Clearly, the final isomer distribution is the result of three successive stages, with the distribution of the boron between the two available carbon atoms of the double bond probably varying with successive substitution of the borane group.

Fortunately, this does not constitute a major problem in considering these data. In the great majority of cases the addition occurs predominantly in one direction. With yields of 94 to 98 per cent of a single isomer realized, it is apparent that the direction of addition cannot vary greatly in the individual stages of these particular reactions. Only in the case of additions to styrene (20 per cent α-) and p-chlorostyrene (35 per cent α-) is there uncertainty as to whether the boron atom prefers the α- or β- carbon atom in the initial stage of the addition reaction.

The failure to observe any significant change in the direction of addition for ethylethylene (93 per cent 1-), isopropylethylene (94 per cent 1-), t-butylethylene (94 per cent 1-), or neopentylethylene (93 per cent 1-) argues against a steric control of the direction of addition. This conclusion is supported by the important influence of substituents in the *para* position of styrene on the direction of addition.

The addition of diborane to cyclic olefins and to acetylenes occurs cleanly *cis*. Consequently, it appears that the addition must involve a four-center transition state.

$$\underset{\substack{| \quad |}}{\underset{\substack{H \quad H}}{R-C=C-H}} + \overset{}{\underset{}{>B-H}} \longrightarrow \underset{\substack{H---B-}}{\underset{\substack{| \quad |}}{\underset{\substack{H \quad H}}{R-C=C}}} \longrightarrow \underset{\substack{B-}}{\underset{\substack{|}}{RCH_2CH_2}}$$

The boron-hydrogen bond is presumably polarized, with the hydrogen having some hydridic character. Consequently, the electronic shifts generally used to account for the normal addition of hydrogen chloride to propylene, can be applied to account for the preferred addition of the boron atom to the terminal position.

In the case of styrene, similar arguments can be used to account for the observed preference of the boron atom for the terminal position.

In order to account for the enhanced substitution which occurs in the *alpha* position, it must be recognized that the phenyl group can also stabilize a negative charge in the *alpha* position, as in the benzyl anion.

This transition state would be stabilized by an electron withdrawing substituent, such as *p*-chloro-, and rendered less stable by an electron supplying substituent, such as *p*-methoxy.

It would be of considerable interest and value to have reliable data on the direction of addition to double bonds containing a variety of substituents. That significant effects may be realized is indicated by the observation of D. Seyferth that trimethylvinylsilane undergoes hydroboration to place 37 per cent of the boron in the secondary position (*85*), as compared to 6 per cent observed for *t*-butylethylene. The problem is currently under investigation (*14*).

Although this discussion has emphasized the importance of electronic effects in directing the addition of the boron-hydrogen bond to olefins, it is possible to bring to bear a measure of steric control by utilizing hydroborating agents of large steric requirements. This question is considered in the following section.

Bis-3-methyl-2-butylborane as a Selective Hydroborating Agent

The reaction of diborane with excess 2-methyl-2-butene at 25° proceeds rapidly to form bis-3-methyl-2-butylborane, but the further reaction of this intermediate with excess olefin is exceedingly slow, requiring approximately twenty-four hours for completion.

$$2 \quad \underset{H_3C}{\overset{H_3C}{>}}C=C\underset{H}{\overset{CH_3}{<}} \; + \; BH_3 \; \xrightarrow{\text{fast}} \; \left(H-\underset{\underset{H_3C}{|}}{\overset{\overset{H_3C}{|}}{C}}-\underset{\underset{H}{|}}{\overset{\overset{CH_3}{|}}{C}}- \right)_2 BH$$

$$\left(H-\underset{\underset{H_3C}{|}}{\overset{\overset{H_3C}{|}}{C}}-\underset{\underset{H}{|}}{\overset{\overset{CH_3}{|}}{C}}- \right)_2 BH \; + \; \underset{H_3C}{\overset{H_3C}{}}C=C\overset{CH_3}{\underset{H}{}} \; \xrightarrow{\text{slow}} \; \left(H-\underset{\underset{H_3C}{|}}{\overset{\overset{H_3C}{|}}{C}}-\underset{\underset{H}{|}}{\overset{\overset{CH_3}{|}}{C}}- \right)_3 B$$

The simplest explanation for the slowness of the last stage is that the large steric requirements of the bis-3-methyl-2-butylborane hinder the formation of the transition state leading to tris-3-methyl-2-butylborane. It appeared that such a reagent might exhibit considerable sensitivity to the steric environments of different double-bonds and thereby make possible a greater degree of selectivity than can be achieved by diborane itself in the direction of hydroboration and in the competitive hydroboration of olefinic structures (*38*).

It was observed that the hydroboration of 1-hexene by bis-3-methyl-2-butylborane results in the formation of 1-hexanol in a purity of at least 99 per cent. Similarly, styrene, which yields 20 per cent of the secondary alcohol with diborane, formed less than 2 per cent of the secondary with the hindered reagent. Finally, the internal olefin, *trans*-isopropylmethylethylene, yields 95 per cent of the less hindered isomer, 4-methyl-2-pentanol.

Representative data are summarized in Table 4.3.

TABLE 4.3. COMPARATIVE RESULTS IN THE HYDROBORATION OF OLEFINS WITH DIBORANE AND WITH BIS-3-METHYL-2-BUTYLBORANE

Olefin	Hydroborating Agent	Alcohol Products, %		
		1-ol	2-ol	3-ol
1-Hexene	B_2H_6	94	6	
	R_2BH^a	99	1	
Styrene	B_2H_6	80	20	
	R_2BH^a	98	2	
p-Methoxystyrene	B_2H_6	91	9	
	R_2BH^a	98	2	
trans-4-methyl-2-pentene	B_2H_6		57	43
	R_2BH^a		95	5

[a]Bis-3-methyl-2-butylborane.

Bis-3-methyl-2-butylborane not only differentiates markedly between the more hindered and less hindered carbon atoms of a double bond, it also differentiates markedly between various olefin types. Thus, the reaction with terminal olefins, such as 1-hexene, 2-methyl-1-butene, and 3,3-dimethyl-1-butene are relatively fast, being complete in a matter of minutes at 0°. Internal olefins are much slower, with cyclopentene reacting faster than *cis*-2-hexene and the latter reacting faster than cyclohexene. *Cis*-2-hexene reacts considerably faster than the *trans* isomer. The presence of bulky groups, such as in *trans-t*-butylmethylethylene, greatly reduces the rate of reaction. Finally, trisubstituted olefins, such as 2-methyl-2-butene, react very slowly.

These relative rates of hydroboration observed with bis-3-methyl-2-

butylborane may be summarized in the following series:

1-hexene ≥ 3-methyl-1-butene > 2-methyl-1-butene > 3,3-dimethyl-1-butene > *cis*-2-hexene ≥ cyclopentene > *trans*-2-hexene > *trans*-4-methyl-2-pentene > cyclohexene ≥ 1-methylcyclopentene > 2-methyl-2-butene ≥ 1-methylcyclohexene ≥ 2,3-dimethyl-2-butene.

The markedly different rates which are observed suggest that the reagent should be quite valuable in achieving the selective hydroboration of one olefin in the presence of another olefin of a different structural type. This possibility was tested by treating a number of representative olefin mixtures with controlled quantities of the reagent and observing the nature of the residual product.

Thus, a mixture of 1-pentene and 2-pentene yielded essentially pure 2-pentene free of the 1-isomer. Similarly, a mixture of 1-hexene and cyclohexene yielded essentially pure cyclohexene. Treatment of a mixture of 1-pentene and 2-methyl-1-pentene resulted in the preferential reaction of the 1-pentene. Treatment of a mixture of 2,4,4-trimethyl-1-pentene and 2,4,4-trimethyl-2-pentene with the reagent resulted in the preferential removal of the terminal olefin to the point where it was not detectable by vapor phase chromatographic analysis of the product.

A mixture of cyclopentene and cyclohexene underwent hydroboration to produce a product containing only minor amounts of the more reactive cyclopentene. Finally, it proved possible to take a commercial sample of *cis*- and *trans*-2-pentene (18 per cent *cis*-, 82 per cent *trans*-) and to remove selectively the *cis* isomer to give a product containing better than 97 per cent of the *trans* isomer.

It should be apparent that this selective hydroborating reagent should be highly useful in the terpene and steroid field for reacting selectively one of several double bonds in the molecule. The utility of the reaction for such selective reactions was demonstrated with 4-vinylcyclohexene and limonene. In each case the exocyclic double bond was selectively hydroborated in excellent yield.

Cyclic Olefins. Stereochemistry of Hydroboration

In applying the hydroboration-oxidation reaction to cyclic olefins it was observed that the reaction proceeds stereospecifically to add the elements of water in a *cis* configuration to the double bond (*32*). Thus, 1-methylcyclopentene is converted into pure *trans*-2-methylcyclopentanol and 1-methylcyclohexene into pure *trans*-2-methylcyclohexanol. The hydrogen peroxide oxidation appears to occur with retention of configuration. Consequently, the hydroboration must involve a *cis*-addition of the hydrogen-boron bond to the double bond of the cyclic olefin.

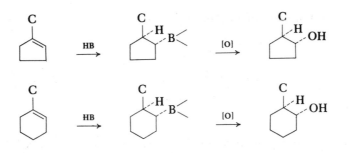

In these cases the *cis* hydration results in the formation of the thermo-dynamically more stable isomer. However, the hydroboration of 1,2-di-methylcyclopentene and 1,2-dimethylcyclohexene yields pure *cis*-1,2-di-methylcyclopentanol and *cis*-1,2-dimethylcyclohexanol. In these cases the elements of water are added *cis* to the double bond even though the products obtained are the thermodynamically less stable isomers.

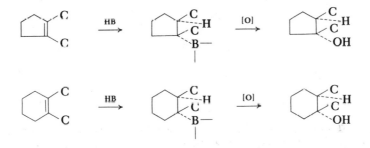

Winstein and his co-workers have utilized this *cis* addition to achieve a convenient synthesis of certain diastereomeric benzyl alcohols (*100*). Thus, *trans*-2-*p*-anisyl-2-butene yielded 72 per cent of almost pure *erythro*-3-*p*-anisyl-2-butanol after a single crystallization. Similarly, *cis*-2-*p*-anisyl-2-butene yielded *threo*-3-*p*-anisyl-2-butanol.

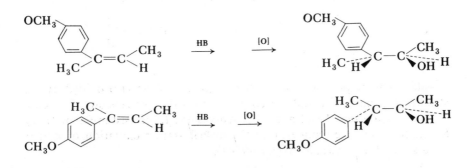

The hydroboration of norbornene takes place to give *exo*-norborneol predominantly.

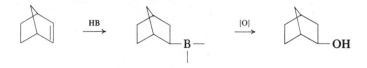

Consequently, the generalization has been proposed that hydroboration proceeds *cis*, preferentially from the less hindered side of a double bond.

In support of this generalization is the observation that α-pinene is readily converted by this procedure into isopinocampheol and β-pinene into *cis*-myrtanol (*8*).

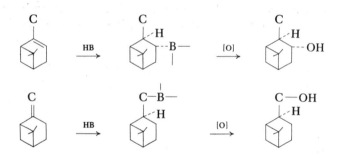

These conclusions are supported by Wechter's observations on the hydroboration of cholesterol (*97*). In this case the predominant reaction product was cholestane-3β, 6α-diol, resulting from a preferential *cis* addition from the less hindered under side of the molecule.

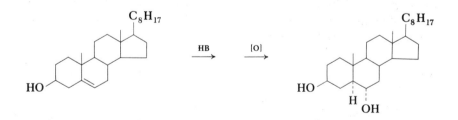

Additional support for the proposed generalization is provided by the studies of Sondheimer and his co-workers on the conversion of Δ^4-cholestene to cholestan-4α-ol and of Δ^5-cholestene to cholestan-6α-ol (*103*). Similarly, it has been shown that the hydroboration-oxidation of isodrin occurs from the less hindered side (*40,44*).

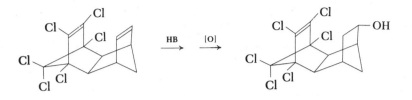

It is evident that the hydroboration reaction should develop into a tool of major importance for the synthesis of stereochemically defined products in the terpene and steroid fields.

Hydroboration of Dienes

The complete hydroboration of dienes, followed by oxidation of the organoboranes initially produced, provides a convenient route to diols (35). Thus, 1,3-butadiene is transformed into 1,4-butanediol, with minor amounts of the 1,3-isomer indicated, and 1,5-hexadiene is converted into 1,6-hexanediol. Consequently, this procedure provides a general route from dienes into the corresponding diols.

Köster has examined the nature of the organoborane formed by butadiene (65). He concludes that it is a cyclic derivative with the structure,

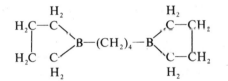

The partial hydroboration of dienes provides a valuable synthetic route to the synthesis of unsaturated alcohols. Thus, 1,5-hexadiene is transformed into 5-hexene-1-ol (35), bicycloheptadiene into exo-dehydronorborneol (35), and cyclopentadiene into Δ³-cyclopentenol (100).

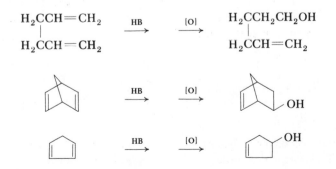

The yields in these reactions are modest, not comparable to the excellent yields realized in the hydroboration of simple olefins. Possibly, the cyclization reaction observed by Köster represents an important side-reaction leading to glycol formation.

The reagent, bis-3-methyl-2-butylborane, has been applied to the selective hydroboration of dienes with excellent results (38). By use of this reagent vinylcyclohexene and limonene have been transformed into the corresponding unsaturated alcohols in yields of 75–80 per cent.

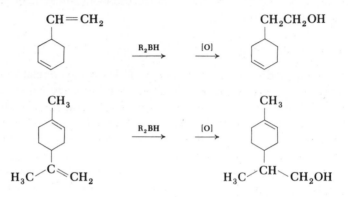

It is evident that this monofunctional reagent, R_2BH, circumvents the tendency toward cyclization inherent in the use of diborane. Consequently, this reagent may well become the reagent of choice for the partial hydroboration of dienes and related polyfunctional molecules.

Hydroboration of Acetylenes

The hydroboration of acetylenes proceeds readily and the reaction can be utilized as a convenient route for the conversion of internal acetylenes into *cis* olefins of high purity and of terminal acetylenes into the corresponding aldehydes (33).

The addition of diborane to internal acetylenes is readily controlled to give predominantly a single addition per acetylene molecule. The resulting products are readily converted to the corresponding *cis* olefins in high purity by treatment with acetic acid at 0°.

$$3 \underset{R}{\overset{R}{\underset{|}{\underset{C}{\overset{C}{\underset{|}{\overset{|||}{C}}}}}} + BH_3 \xrightarrow{0°} (\underset{R-C-}{\overset{R-C-H}{\overset{||}{}}})_3B \xrightarrow[HOAc]{0°} 3 \begin{matrix} R-C-H \\ || \\ R-C-H \end{matrix}$$

Attempts to convert 1-hexyne into a similar organoborane were unsuccessful. Treatment of 3 moles of 1-hexyne with one-half mole of diborane resulted in the complete hydroboration of half of the acetylene with the other half remaining unchanged in the reaction mixture. It is evident that the initial reaction product undergoes further hydroboration more readily than the free acetylene.

Fortunately, the use of the reagent, bis-3-methyl-2-butylborane, circumvented this difficulty, and the monohydroboration product was thereby obtained in high yield. Treatment of the reaction products with acetic acid yields 1-hexene in a yield of 90 per cent, whereas oxidation of the organoborane formed *n*-hexaldehyde in a yield of 88 per cent. The latter result clearly indicates that the boron atom adds to the terminal carbon atom of the triple bond.

$$
\begin{array}{c}
n\text{-}C_4H_9 \\
| \\
C \\
||| \\
C \\
| \\
H
\end{array}
+ R_2BH \rightarrow
\begin{array}{c}
n\text{-}C_4H_9 \quad H \\
\diagdown C \diagup \\
|| \\
\diagup C \diagdown \\
H \qquad BR_2
\end{array}
\begin{array}{l}
\xrightarrow{H+} n\text{-}C_4H_9CH{=}CH_2 \\
\\
\xrightarrow{|O|} n\text{-}C_4H_9CH_2CHO
\end{array}
$$

The dihydroboration of acetylenes proceeds to place two boron atoms on the same carbon atom. Oxidation of the products yields predominantly the ketone from an internal acetylene and the aldehyde from a terminal acetylene. The precise nature of the organoboranes is currently under investigation (*9*).

REACTIONS OF ORGANOBORANES

These studies reveal that through the hydroboration reaction it is possible to convert olefins, dienes and acetylenes under exceedingly mild conditions into organoboranes. This ready availability of organoboranes engenders a new interest in the chemistry of these substances. Although investigations of these compounds were somewhat sparse until recently, the results already available indicate that they have a most interesting chemistry, and they promise to become very important intermediates in organic synthesis.

Thermal Behavior

It was noted by Rosenblum that tri-*n*-butylborane undergoes decomposition slowly at temperatures of 100–130° to form *n*-butyldiboranes and butenes (*84*). Similarly, Köster has reported that in attempting to distill tri-*n*-decylborane he obtained 1-decene and *n*-decyldiboranes (*64*), and Ashby has noted a smooth decomposition of tri-*n*-octylborane, upon attempted distillation at 169° at 0.2 mm., into *trans*-2-octene and tetra-*n*-octyldiborane (*2*).

Although these results are consistent in indicating a decomposition of the organoborane under reduced pressures at temperatures in the neighborhood of 200° into the dialkylborane (or its dimer) and olefin, there is some question as to the structure of the olefin formed in the reaction.

It was observed by Winternitz that tri-*n*-alkylborane behaved differently (*101*). Heated to its boiling point, it evolved hydrogen and *trans*-2-pentene in equimolar amounts, with the formation of a cyclic derivative,

It was also reported that tri-*n*-hexylborane reacts considerably slower, but likewise yields hydrogen, an olefin (*trans*-3-hexene, ?) and the related cyclic compound.

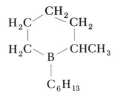

This reaction presumably proceeds through the following mechanism.

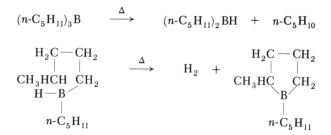

In the hydroboration of *trans*-di-*t*-butyl-ethylene, Logan and Flautt observed that the hydroboration ceases at the monoalkylborane stage. The resulting product could be isolated, but lost hydrogen readily above 100° to form a cyclic organoborane which could be oxidized to a glycol, 2,2,5,5-tetramethyl-1,4-hexanediol (*74*).

Köster has recently reported in a Communication that he has explored

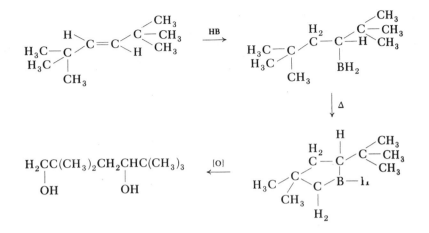

this high temperature route as a general synthesis of glycols from olefins *(67)*. The same reaction has been under exploration in our laboratories *(19)*.

Isomerization

It was observed by G. F. Hennion and his co-workers that secondary organoboranes, synthesized *via* the Grignard reaction, undergo isomerization into the primary derivatives at elevated temperatures *(54)*. Thus they observed the slow isomerization of tri-*sec*-butylborane into tri *n*-butylborane by heating under reflux, 200–215° for 20 to 48 hours.

Under hydroboration conditions the isomerization is far more rapid *(26)*. Thus, tri-*sec*-pentylborane is almost completely isomerized into tri-

TABLE 4.4. ISOMERIZATION OF ORGANOBORANE
FROM 2-HEXENE

Olefin, mmoles	Boro-hydride, mmoles	Boron Trifluoride-Etherate, mmoles	Temp. °C	Time,[a] hr.	Hexanols 1-	2-	3-
50[b]	15[d]	20	150	1	88	7	5
50[c]	15[d]	20	150	1	86	8	6
50[c]	15[d]	20	150	1	85	10	5
50[c]	12.5[e]	16.7	150	1	20	60	20
50[c]	10[f]	13.3	150	1	13	64	23

[a]Heating period to achieve isomerization.
[b]Diborane generated externally and passed into reaction mixture.
[c]Diborane generated internally.
[d]60 mmoles H⁻/50 mmoles olefin = 20% excess.
[e]Stoichiometric equivalent hydride.
[f]Excess olefin.

n-pentylborane in one hour at 160° in diglyme solution. Initially it was thought that the diglyme solvent was mainly responsible for this greatly enhanced rate. However, it has now been established that the small excess of diborane utilized in the hydroboration step to effect complete conversion

TABLE 4.5. ISOMERIZATION OF ORGANOBORANES

Olefin[a]	0 hr.				1 hr.				4 hr.			
C—C—C—C 1 2 3 4	1-	2-	3-	4-	1-	2-	3-	4-	1-	2-	3-	4-
C=C—C(—C)(—C)—C	94	6							99	1		
C=C—⟨phenyl⟩	80	20							80	20		
C=C—C—C—C	94	6			91	7	2		93	5	2	
C—C=C—C—C		52	48		95	4	1		95	4	1	
C=C—C—C—C—C	94	6			93	5	2		94	4	2	
C—C=C—C—C—C		46	54		91	6	3		91	6	3	
C=C(—C)—C—C(—C)(—C)—C	99	1			99	tr.	tr.		99	tr.	tr.	
C—C(—C)=C—C(—C)(—C)—C		1	99		97	1	2		99	tr.	tr.	
C—C=C—C(—C)(—C)—C		57	43		96	2	2		96	2	2	
C=C—C(—C)(—C)—C	94	6			73	1	tr.	26	59	1	tr.	40
C—C=C(—C)—C		98	2		53	1	tr.	47	58	2	tr.	40
C—C—C(—C)=C			1	99	27	1	tr.	72	56	1	tr.	43
C=C—C—⟨phenyl⟩	90	10			85	7	8		86	7	7	
C—C=C—⟨phenyl⟩		15	85		76	10	14		78	9	13	

[a]Hydroboration carried out with 50 mmoles of olefin, 60 mmoles H (from sodium borohydride and boron trifluoride, generated internally), heated under reflux in diglyme solution to achieve isomerization. The zero time values are the distributions observed at 25°. The number applies to the position of the boron from the end of the chain, counting from the left end.

of the olefin plays an important role in the rapid isomerization. Typical results are summarized in Table 4.4.

A detailed study has been made of the isomerization of organoboranes at a temperature of 160° (refluxing diglyme) (*36*). The results are summarized in Table 4.5.

The following conclusions are reached:

1. In the presence of a small quantity of excess "hydride" (boron-hydrogen bonds) the isomerization is essentially complete in one hour.
2. Hydroboration of 1-pentene places the boron on the 1- and 2-carbon atoms in a ratio of 94 to 6. This ratio is not significantly altered during isomerization. However, a small amount of boron appears at the 3-position.
3. The same equilibrium mixtures are obtained from 1- and 2-pentene, from 1- and 2-hexene, and from the three isomeric methylbutenes.
4. The boron atom readily isomerizes past a single carbon branch, as shown by the transformations:

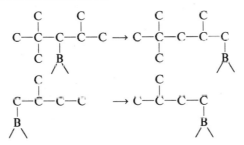

5. The boron atom does not migrate under these conditions past a double branch.*

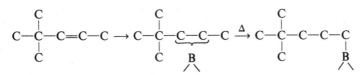

6. In its migration, the boron atom migrates preferentially to the least hindered position in the molecule.

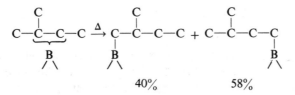

40%   58%

*Note the study of Logan and Flautt (*74*) discussed in the preceding section.

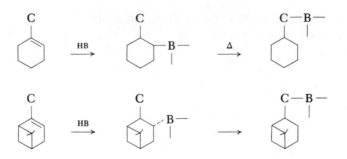

In a number of selected cases, the rates of isomerization were studied. Data for the 2-methylbutene systems are summarized in Table 4.6.

TABLE 4.6. ISOMERIZATION OF ORGANOBORANES FROM THE THREE ISOMERIC 2-METHYLBUTENES

Temp., °C	Time, hr.	C—C—C≡C (C on 3) 1-	2-	3-	4-	C—C=C—C (C on 3) 1-	2-	3-	4-	C=C—C—C (C on 3) 1-	2-	3-	4-
75°	1					9	85	6	tr.				
	2					12	81	6	1				
	4					14	78	6	2				
	8					23	66	5	6				
	24					40	44	4	12				
100°	1	tr.	tr.	tr.	99	38	44	5	13	99	tr.	tr.	1
	2	1	tr.	tr.	99	46	33	3	18	99	tr.	tr.	1
	4	1	tr.	tr.	99	55	17	2	26	99	tr.	tr.	1
	8	1	tr.	tr.	99	63	5	tr.	32	99	tr.	tr.	1
	24	4	tr.	tr.	96	64	2	tr.	34	95	tr.	tr.	5
125°	1	1	1	tr.	98	62	4	tr.	34	95	2	tr.	3
	2	4	1	tr.	95	61	3	tr.	36	95	1	tr.	4
	4	6	tr.	tr.	94	60	2	tr.	38	93	1	tr.	6
	8	12	1	tr.	87	58	2	tr.	40	88	1	tr.	11
	24	34	tr.	tr.	66	58	2	tr.	40	–	–	–	–
150°	1	25	1	tr.	74					81	1	tr.	18
	2	40	1	tr.	59					74	1	tr.	25
	4	46	1	tr.	53					65	1	tr.	34
	8	55	1	tr.	44					61	1	tr.	38
	24	59	1	tr.	40					58	1	tr.	41

The isomerization reaction is inhibited by excess of olefin. This permits the initial isomerization of organoboranes to place the boron atom at a terminal position, followed then by a displacement reaction with another olefin, without interference by a back-isomerization, transferring the boron atom to the new olefin and producing an isomerized olefin (see following section).

The isomerization of the boron atom from an internal position on a carbon chain to the terminal position can be formulated as a succession of eliminations and additions (26).

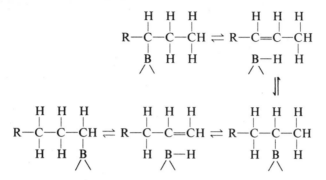

Presumably, the preference of the boron for the terminal position is the result of decreased steric interactions in that location.

All of the available data for the isomerization of organoboranes are consistent with this elimination-addition mechanism.

Displacement Reactions

It is a consequence of the mechanism proposed for the isomerization reaction above that a high concentration of an added olefin should bring about the displacement of that olefin formed in the elimination stage. Ultimately there would result an equilibrium mixture of all of the possible organoboranes and the two olefins (26,64).

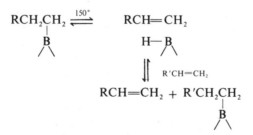

By using a large excess of the displacing olefin, it is possible to shift the equilibrium far toward the formation of the new organoborane. Alternatively, in cases where the displacing olefin is less volatile than the product olefin produced from the organoborane, the reaction is conveniently completed by distilling out the more volatile olefin from the reaction mixture.

$$(RCH_2CH_2)_3B + 3 R'CH{=}CH_2 \xrightarrow{150^\circ} 3 RCH{=}CH_2{\uparrow} + (R'CH_2CH_2)_3B$$

Köster has utilized this reaction extensively as a convenient synthesis of organoboranes (*64*). Thus, tri-isobutylborane, synthesized from tri-iso-butylaluminum, was heated with various olefins to displace isobutylene and to form the corresponding organoborane. In this way he has synthesized tri-*n*-decylborane, tricyclohexylborane and tri-(2-phenylpropyl)-borane.

$$3 \, n\text{-}C_8H_{17}CH{=}CH_2 + [(CH_3)_2CHCH_2]_3B \longrightarrow$$
$$(n\text{-}C_8H_{17}CH_2CH_2)_3B + (CH_3)_2C{=}CH_2$$

$$3 \, C_6H_{10} + [(CH_3)_2CHCH_2]_3B \longrightarrow (C_6H_{11})_3B + 3 \, (CH_3)_2C{=}CH_2$$

$$3 \, C_6H_5C(CH_3){=}CH_2 + [(CH_3)_2CHCH_2]_3B \longrightarrow$$
$$[C_6H_5CH(CH_3)CH_2]_3B + 3 \, (CH_3)_2C{=}CH_2$$

In the investigations of the author and his co-workers, the emphasis has been different (*7,26*). Since hydroboration provides such a convenient route to the organoboranes, the displacement reaction has been explored primarily as a new type of elimination reaction which permits the preparation of olefins under relatively moderate reaction conditions with very mild reagents.

To test the ability of the displacement reaction to produce olefins of various structural types from the corresponding organoboranes, a number of olefins were hydroborated. The reaction products were treated with an excess of 1-decene and the olefin product was distilled out of the reaction mixture at 160°. The yields averaged 80 per cent ± 10 per cent. The reaction products were examined by vapor phase chromatography.

Terminal olefins, such as 1-pentene, 1-hexene, 3-methyl-1-butene and 3-ethyl-1-pentene required approximately 6–8 hours for completion. The products were 90–95 per cent pure 1-olefins, with 5–10 per cent of the 2-olefin. It was noted that the 2-olefin appeared in the initial fraction of the distillate. Apparently it arises from the 6–7 per cent of the 2-alkylboron derivative formed in the hydroboration of a terminal olefin, and this structure must undergo displacement more readily than the 1-alkylborane present.

Terminal olefins, containing two alkyl substituents, such as 2-methyl-1-butene, 2,4,4-trimethyl-1-pentene, methylenecyclohexane, are displaced much more readily under the same conditions, with 2 to 4 hours being adequate for completion. In these cases the olefin products exhibit a purity of 98–99 per cent.

Finally, internal olefins, such as 2-methyl-2-butene, 3-ethyl-2-pentene, 2,4,4-trimethyl-2-pentene, cyclopentene and cyclohexene undergo ready displacement without significant rearrangement.

Under the same conditions it was demonstrated that both α- and β- pinene could be hydroborated and then displaced to yield the original olefin without rearrangement.

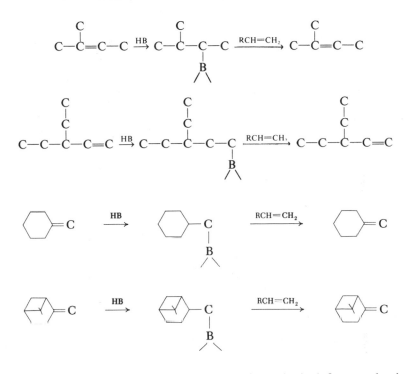

The usual acid catalyzed isomerization of terminal olefins results in a preferential migration of the double bond into the chain or ring, with the final product being predominantly the more thermodynamically stable, most highly substituted olefin.

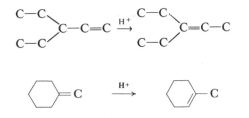

Hydroboration, isomerization of the organoborane, followed by displacement, provides a convenient synthetic route for the reverse transformation.

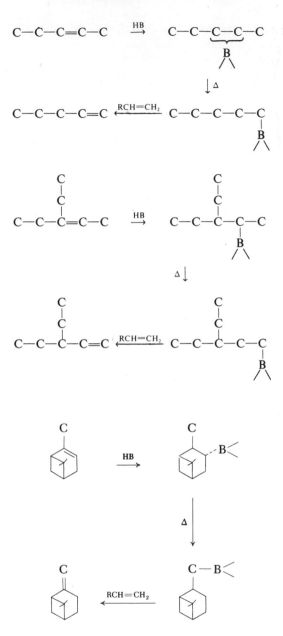

This contra-thermodynamic isomerization of olefins promises to be an exceedingly valuable synthetic procedure.

Redistribution Reactions

It was observed by Schlesinger and his co-workers that diborane reacts readily with trimethyl-, triethyl- and tri-*n*-propylborane to yield a mixture of the corresponding alkyldiboranes (*90,91*).

$$R_3B + B_2H_6 \longrightarrow RBH_2BH_3$$
$$+ R_2BHBH_3$$
$$+ R_2BHBH_2R$$
$$+ R_2BHBHR_2$$

The *sym*-dimethyldiborane, $CH_3BH_2BH_2CH_3$, was later prepared by the reaction of monomethyldiborane with dimethyl ether (*89*), and *sym*-diethyldiborane was recently obtained from the disproportionation of ethyldiborane (*93*).

Consequently, equilibration of trialkylboranes with excess diborane provides a convenient route to the monoalkylboranes (or their dimers). Since these monoalkylboranes are readily alcoholyzed to the corresponding boronic esters, or hydrolyzed to the boronic acids, hydroboration provides a convenient route to these derivatives (*31*).

$$3\ n\text{-}C_3H_7CH{=}CH_2 \xrightarrow[\text{THF}]{\text{HB}} (n\text{-}C_5H_{11})_3B$$

$$\downarrow B_2H_6$$

$$3\ n\text{-}C_5H_{11}B(OCH_3)_2 \xleftarrow{\ 3\ CH_3OH\ } 3\ n\text{-}C_5H_{11}BH_2$$

Treatment of 1-butane- and 1-hexaneboronic acid with ammoniacal silver nitrate converts them into *n*-octane and *n*-dodecane in excellent yield (*92*). Consequently, the conversion of unsaturated compounds into the corresponding boronic acid and then treatment with ammoniacal silver nitrate should provide a useful dimerization procedure for alkenes and certain of their functional derivatives.

$$2\ RCH{=}CH_2 \longrightarrow (RCH_2CH_2)_2$$

By controlling the amount of excess diborane, it is possible to direct the equilibration reaction to the dialkylborane stage. Alternatively, addition of the olefin to excess diborane in tetrahydrofuran solution at 0° results in the formation of the dialkylborane in good yield. By these procedures, hydroboration provides convenient routes to the dialkylborinic acids and esters (*31*).

The reaction of trialkylboranes with boric oxide provides an alternative route to the boronic acids (*52,55*).

$$R_3B + B_2O_3 \longrightarrow (RBO)_3$$

Unfortunately, the reaction requires elevated temperatures and is thereby restricted to organoboranes which do not undergo isomerization. Dr. A. Tsukamoto attempted to react boric oxide with tri-n-pentylborane in refluxing diglyme (162°), but the reaction was only partially complete in 24 hours.

Boron trichloride reacts rapidly with trialkylboranes at temperatures above 100° to give nearly quantitative yields of dialkylchloroboranes (*41, 76*). The reaction has been demonstrated for tri-n-butylborane, tri-iso-butylborane and tri-sec.-butylborane, so that it is relatively insensitive to the structure of the alkyl group.

The dialkylchloroboranes may be distilled without change at temperatures under 100°. At elevated temperatures an equilibrium is set up, $2\,R_2BCl \rightleftharpoons RBCl_2 + R_3B$, from which the more volatile monoalkyldichloroborane may be fractionated. Alternately, the monoalkylchloroborane or the monoalkylfluoroborane may be obtained by heating the trialkylborane and boron halide in an autoclave at 200° (*41*).

It is of considerable interest that triethyl- and tripropylborane fail to undergo exchange below 100° in the absence of a catalyst. In the presences of minor amounts of triethylaluminum, rapid exchange occurs to give the statistically redistributed products, Et_3B, Et_2BPr, $EtBPr_2$, BPr_3 (*66*). Presumably the triethylaluminum, which can form dimers involving alkyl bridges, must form similar bridges with the boron, albeit in low concentrations, and thereby facilitate an exchange of groups.

$$R_3B + R'_3Al \rightleftharpoons R'_2Al\overset{R'}{\underset{R}{\cdots}}BR_2 \rightleftharpoons R'_2AlR + R_2BR'$$

Protonolysis

The trialkylboranes are remarkably stable toward water. Ulmschneider and Goubeau report that the hydrolysis of trimethylborane with an equivalent of water for seven hours at 180° affords a 69 per cent yield of dimethylborinic acid (*96*). After nine hours at 310°, the cleavage of a second methyl group was observed.

Trialkylboranes are more readily hydrolyzed by treating with concentrated mineral acids at reflux temperature. However, under these conditions, only one alkyl group is lost. Thus, Johnson et al., report that in heating tributylborane with 48 per cent hydrobromic acid under reflux a quantitative yield of dibutylborinic acid was obtained in one hour (*59*).

$$(n\text{-}C_4H_9)_3B + HBr \longrightarrow (n\text{-}C_4H_9)_2BBr + n\text{-}C_4H_{10}$$

$$(n\text{-}C_4H_9)_2BBr + H_2O \longrightarrow (n\text{-}C_4H_9)_2BOH + HBr$$

The cessation of reaction at this stage is not due to the rapid hydrolysis of the presumed intermediate dibutylbromoborane, since this compound is readily produced by treatment of tri-n-butylborane with an excess of anhydrous hydrogen bromide at 55–60°, but further dealkylation is not observed unless much more vigorous conditions are employed.

Somewhat unexpectedly, the organoboranes have proven to be more susceptible to attack by carboxylic acids, than to the mineral acids. Thus, it has been observed that under relatively mild conditions triethylborane can be converted into diethylboron acetate and ethane (*51,77*).

$$(C_2H_5)_3B + CH_3CO_2H \xrightarrow{100°} (C_2H_5)_2BOCOCH_3 + C_2H_6$$

A detailed study of the action of carboxylic acids on organoboranes has revealed that two of the three groups can be removed by excess acid at room temperature, and all three groups can generally be removed by refluxing the organoborane in diglyme solution with a slight excess of propionic acid for 2 to 3 hours (*18*).

Consequently, hydroboration of olefins in diglyme, and then refluxing with propionic acid, offers a convenient non-catalytic procedure for the hydrogenation of double-bonds.

$$3\,RCH{=}CH_2 \xrightarrow{HB} (RCH_2CH_2)_3B \xrightarrow{C_2H_5CO_2H} 3\,RCH_2CH_3$$

Use of the solvent triglyme, b.p. 216°, with caprylic acid, permits completion of the protonation stage in 0.5 to 1.0 hour.

Secondary alkyl groups undergo protonolysis less readily than primary. Consequently, in hydrogenating internal olefins, it is preferable that the boron be transferred to the terminal position by heating under reflux prior to addition of the acid.

Since olefins containing active sulfur, chlorine and nitrogen substituents readily undergo hydroboration, this procedure opens up the possibility of hydrogenating olefinic derivatives containing such labile groups. To test this possibility, the conversion of allylmethylsulfide into n-propylmethylsulfide was demonstrated.

Organoboranes of the vinyl type, readily obtained by the hydroboration of acetylenes, undergo protonolysis much more readily. These compounds undergo complete protonolysis with acetic acid at 0°, and the reaction provides a convenient means of converting acetylenes into *cis* olefins of high purity (*33*).

At elevated temperatures, 140–160°, and high pressures of hydrogen, 200–300 atmospheres, organoboranes undergo partial hydrogenation to alkanes and alkylated diboranes. Unfortunately, few details have yet appeared in the scientific literature (*62*), but it appears that the reaction is relatively sluggish (*82*) and not convenient as a means of converting the organoborane into the corresponding alkane.

Mercuration

The ability of triethylborane to function as a Grignard reagent has as yet received little attention. Consequently, considerable interest attaches to the report by Honeycutt and Riddle that they have successfully synthesized diethylmercury by treating mercuric oxide with triethylborane and sodium hydroxide in water at 75° (*56*). The reaction was fast, complete in 10 minutes, with a yield of 95 per cent based on the mercuric oxide.

It is evident that such a transfer of alkyl groups from boron to other elements in aqueous systems should be exceedingly valuable. The phenomenon is currently under study (*56,13*).

Oxidation

The lower alkylboranes are spontaneously inflammable in air, whereas tri-*n*-butylborane and the higher members react with oxygen, but do not inflame (*60*). On oxidation of these higher boranes with moist air, an alkylborinate, R_2BOR, is obtained, whereas under anhydrous conditions, an alkylboronate, $RB(OR)_2$, is formed.

The inhibiting effect of the moisture on the further oxidation of the alkylborinate has been attributed to the formation of a reasonably stable hydrate by the alkylborinate which prevents further coordination by oxygen. Johnson and Van Campen proposed that the oxidation of the organoborane proceeds through an initial addition compound of the trialkylborane and oxygen, $R_2B \cdot O_2$, which they term a "borine peroxide," followed by reaction of this intermediate with a second mole of the trialkylborane.

$$R_3B + O_2 \longrightarrow R_3B \cdot O_2$$

$$R_3B \cdot O_2 + R_3B \longrightarrow 2\,R_2B(OR)$$

The borinate can react further, unless its coördination with oxygen is prevented by water.

Detailed studies of the oxidation have refined this early interpretation. Thus, Petry and Verhoek report that in a flow system (room temperature, 10–15 mm of pressure, contact time of 2–3 minutes) trimethylborane reacts with oxygen quantitatively to form methyldimethylboron peroxide (*81*).

$$(CH_3)_3B + O_2 \longrightarrow (CH_3)_2BOOCH_3$$

Similarly, Abraham and Davies observed that in dilute cyclohexane solution tri-*n*-butylborane absorbed 1.2 moles of oxygen, giving a product that contained 1.06 moles of peroxide (by iodometric titration). Under the same conditions, oxidation of tri-*t*-butylborane (?) (*54*) yielded a peroxide having the formula, *t*-BuB(OO*t*-Bu)$_2$. *t*-Butylhydroperoxide was identified as a product of alkaline hydrolysis (*1*).

Davies and Moodie suggest that the autoöxidation of trialkylboranes proceeds initially by the coördination of the oxygen molecule to the boron atom, followed by a migration of an alkyl group from boron to oxygen (*45*).

$$R_3B + O_2 \longrightarrow R{-}\underset{\underset{R}{|}}{\overset{\overset{R}{|}}{B}}{-}O{-}O^+ \longrightarrow R{-}\underset{\underset{R}{|}}{B}{-}OOR, \text{etc.}$$

It was early demonstrated by Johnson and Van Campen that perbenzoic acid in chloroform solution at 0° reacts quantitatively with tri-*n*-butylborane, and the reaction could be utilized for the quantitative analysis of organoboranes (*60*). A reaction of benzoyl peroxide was also observed, but the results proved to be erratic. In this paper it is stated that aqueous hydrogen peroxide, in the presence of dilute alkalies, effects a complete dealkylation of tri-*n*-butylborane with the formation of boric acid and *n*-butyl alcohol. The reaction was suggested as the basis of a convenient method for the determination of boron in organoboron compounds.

Unfortunately, no experimental details were given. The reaction was developed as an analytical procedure by Belcher, Gibbons and Sykes in 1952 (*3*). However, their conditions were quite vigorous and involved the reaction of the organoborane with excess hydrogen peroxide and concentrated sodium hydroxide under reflux.

Consequently, the early applications of this reaction utilized quite vigorous conditions (*24,25*). However, with continued use of this reaction it was observed that the milder the conditions the better the yield. In view of the growing importance of this reaction in organoboron chemistry, a detailed study of it was finally undertaken (*21*).

It was observed that the treatment of the organoborane from the usual hydroboration of 50 mmoles of 1-hexene in 40 ml of diglyme with 15 mmoles of sodium hydroxide (5 mmoles of a 3 M solution), followed by the slow addition of 60 mmoles of hydrogen peroxide, 20 per cent excess (6.0 ml of 30 per cent hydrogen peroxide) at 25°–30° led to essentially instantaneous oxidation, with yields of 94–97 per cent of alcohol. The reaction proceeded satisfactorily even at 0°, with a yield of 89 per cent indicated.

The oxidation could be achieved with equal ease in tetrahydrofuran. However, the reaction in ether was more sluggish, presumably because of the immiscibility of the solvent with water. However, addition of ethanol as a co-solvent avoided the difficulty and the yield observed was 98 per cent.

Wide variations in the structure of the olefin can be tolerated in this reaction. Numerous substances, such as olefins, acetylenes, dienes, esters, ketones and nitriles, may be present in the reaction mixture without influencing the yield of oxidation product from the organoborane, or exhibiting any attack on themselves.

Although a detailed kinetic study of the reaction has yet to be made, there is available the related study by Kuivila and his co-workers of the reaction of benzeneboronic acid with hydrogen peroxide (71). He proposes the mechanism:

$$H_2O_2 + {}^-OH \rightleftharpoons HO_2{}^- + H_2O$$

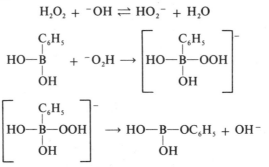

An identical mechanism, in three successive stages, is consistent with all of the available data for the oxidation with alkaline hydrogen peroxide (97). In this mechanism the organic group shifts with its pair of electrons from boron to oxygen. This is consistent with the retention of configuration which is observed in the hydroboration-oxidation of cyclic olefins.

Finally, it should be pointed out that the direct oxidation of organoboranes to ketones with chromic acid has been demonstrated (80). Thus, one can carry out the hydroboration of a cyclic olefin, such as cyclohexene, and oxidize the product in the reaction mixture with aqueous chromic acid directly to cyclohexanone in satisfactory yields (12).

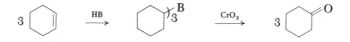

It is hoped that research underway will provide additional synthetic routes from the organoborane to desirable products (12).

ADDITION COMPOUNDS OF ORGANOBORANES

The organoboranes possess a sextet of electrons and exhibit a strong tendency to share an electron-pair with a base, achieving thereby the more stable octet. Indeed, this strong tendency for organoboranes to react with such bases as ammonia and alkali metal hydroxides was recognized as early as 1862 by Frankland (*48*).

$$(CH_3)_3B + NH_3 \longrightarrow (CH_3)_3B:NH_3$$

$$(CH_3)_3B + KOH \longrightarrow [(CH_3)_3B:OH]^- K^+$$

The study of the addition compounds of organoboranes with amines has provided a valuable tool in recent years for the study of steric effects (*6*). Thus, it is observed that trimethylborane forms a more stable addition compound with trimethylamine than with ammonia. This is attributed to the effect of the methyl groups in trimethylamine to increase the electron density on the nitrogen atom and thereby to render it better able to share its electron pair with the boron atom. On the other hand, with tri-iso-propylboron as the reference acid, ammonia forms a more stable addition compound than trimethylamine. This reversal is attributed to the effect of the large steric interactions between the isopropyl groups of the borane and the methyl groups of the amine (*5*).

$$Me_3B:NH_3 + NMe_3 \rightleftharpoons Me_3B:NMe_3 + NH_3$$

$$i\text{-}Pr_3B:NH_3 + NMe_3 \rightleftharpoons i\text{-}Pr_3B:NMe_3 + NH_3$$

These addition compounds dissociate reversibly in the gas phase. An examination of the change with temperature of the equilibrium constant for the dissociation leads to precise values for $\Delta F°$, $\Delta H°$, and $\Delta S°$ of dissociation (*30*).

The heat of dissociation of trimethylamine-trimethylborane is 17.6 kcal/mole, whereas that for triethylamine-trimethylborane is much less, in the neighborhood of 10 kcal/mole. This difference in stability does not appear explicable in terms of the great similarity in the electrical effects of methyl and ethyl groups. It is explicable in terms of the large difference in the steric requirements of the two bases.

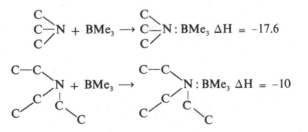

This conclusion is confirmed by an examination of the behavior of quinuclidine, which may be considered to be related to triethylamine

with the three ethyl groups tied back so that they cannot interfere with the trimethylboron molecule. Here we observe an energy of dissociation of 20.0 kcal/mole (29).

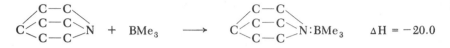

Such studies have contributed greatly to placing the study of steric effects on a quantitative basis (6).

Triarylboranes likewise react readily with amine bases and numerous such compounds have been synthesized (69). Unfortunately, no quantitative data are presently available on the stabilities of these compounds.

It is of interest that tri-α-naphthylborane and trimesitylborane exhibit an unusual stability toward oxygen. Presumably, this is due to the large steric requirements of the three bulky aryl groups. Indeed, trimesitylborane exhibits no tendency to react with any of the usual bases (11).

It was observed in 1940 that lithium ethyl reacts readily to form the quaternary boron derivative, Li B$(C_2H_5)(CH_3)_3$ (92). This was the first quaternary organoborane salt to be synthesized although many other members are now known. This includes lithium tetramethylboron, LiB$(CH_3)_4$ (57), and the very interesting and useful reagent sodium tetraphenylboron, NaB$(C_6H_5)_4$ (102). It is noteworthy that the compound, Li$^+$[B(C_2H_5)-$(CH_3)_3$]$^-$, although formulated as a salt, is easily soluble in the non-polar solvent benzene.

Trimethylborane readily adds in a 1:1 ratio to lithium hydride suspended in ether. The product, lithium trimethylborohydride, is unstable at elevated temperatures and readily dissociates into its components. Consequently, a mixture of ethyl ether and trimethylborane can be considered as a reversible solvent system for lithium hydride (20).

Sodium hydride reacts with triethylborane in the absence of any solvent to form sodium triethylborohydride, stable toward the reverse reaction. The product exhibits the unusual characteristic of being liquid at room temperature, although it must apparently be formulated as an ionic substance (20).

$$LiH + B(CH_3)_3 \longrightarrow Li^+ [HB(CH_3)_3]^-$$

$$NaH + B(C_2H_5)_3 \longrightarrow Na^+ [HB(C_2H_5)_3]^-$$

Similar compounds of alkali metal hydrides and triarylboranes have been synthesized (102).

Finally, it has been observed that in tetrahydrofuran or diglyme solution the alkali metal trimethylborohydrides are capable of adding another molecule of trimethylborane (15).

$$LiH + 2 B(CH_3)_3 \xrightarrow{\text{THF}} Li^+ [(CH_3)_3BHB(CH_3)_3]^-$$

$$NaH + 2 B(CH_3)_3 \xrightarrow{\text{Diglyme}} Na^+ [(CH_3)_3BHB(CH_3)]^-$$

These products presumably involve a single hydrogen bridge related to the double hydrogen bridge in diborane (*22*).

The formation of such quaternary derivatives has received intensive investigation in the related organoaluminum compounds under the impetus of a search for suitable electrolytes to be used in electrochemical syntheses based on these organometallics (Chapter 5).

CONCLUSION

It is evident that the addition of diborane to olefins to form organoboranes is closely related to the reaction of aluminum hydride with olefins discovered by Professor Ziegler and his co-workers (Chapter 5).

$$3 RCH{=}CH_2 + BH_3 \rightarrow (RCH_2CH_2)_3B$$

$$3 RCH{=}CH_2 + AlH_3 \rightarrow (RCH_2CH_2)_3Al$$

In spite of their formal similarity, major differences exist. Thus, the hydroboration reaction is exceedingly fast and takes place with olefins of all types. The corresponding reaction of olefins with aluminum hydride is slow, even at elevated temperatures, and is largely limited to simple terminal olefins. Moreover, the organoaluminum compounds are exceedingly sensitive to both air and moisture, and require highly specialized techniques to handle them satisfactorily. On the other hand, the organoboranes are much less sensitive to these agents and can be handled with the same techniques and precautions normally used for the Grignard reagent.

It therefore appears that in cases where the synthetic route involves a choice between proceeding through the organoaluminum or the organoborane, the latter will prove preferable for laboratory work.

In many instances, the organoaluminum compounds and the organoboranes exhibit individual characteristics not present in the other. Thus chain growth of the alkyl group is an important reaction of the aluminum compounds which has not yet been demonstrated in the boron derivatives. Similarly, the ready isomerization of organoboranes is essentially nonexistent in the organoaluminum derivatives. In such cases the choice will necessarily be dictated by the characteristics of each group of reagents.

Both the organoboranes and the organoaluminum derivatives exhibit many interesting possibilities for industrial processes. In many cases the desired objective can be realized by independent routes based either on organoboron or organoaluminum chemistry. It cannot be definitely stated at this time which will be the more economical route. The situation is rendered even more complex by the interesting processes developed by Professor Ziegler and his co-workers for proceeding from his aluminum chemistry into the borane route.

If the industrial futures of these alternative routes is clouded, there can be little doubt that the organoboranes will prove to be a real boon to the synthetic organic chemist. Intensive work in this field dates only back a few years. Yet the research has already made possible syntheses and transformations which would have been considered impossible earlier. With such accomplishments already realized, the synthetic chemist may look forward with confidence to the continued development of new, powerful tools based on the fascinating chemistry of the organoboranes.

References

(1) Abraham, M. H., and Davies, A. G., *Chemistry and Industry,* 1622 (1957).
(2) Ashby, E. C., *J. Am. Chem. Soc.,* **81,** 4791 (1959).
(3) Belcher, R., Gibbons, D., and Sykes, A., *Microchem. Acta,* **40,** 76 (1952).
(4) Bent, H. E., and Dorfman, M., *J. Am. Chem. Soc.,* **54,** 2132 (1932); *ibid.,* **57,** 1259, 1924 (1935).
(5) Brown, H. C., *J. Am. Chem. Soc.,* **67,** 374 (1945).
(6) Brown, H. C., *J. Chem. Soc.,* 1248 (1956).
(7) Brown, H. C., and Bhatt, M. V., *J. Am. Chem. Soc.,* **82,** 2074 (1960).
(8) Brown, H. C., Bhatt, M. V., and Zweifel, G., *J. Am. Chem. Soc.,* in press.
(9) Brown, H. C., and Bowman, D., research in progress.
(10) Brown, H. C., and Case. I... unpublished observations.
(11) Brown, H. C., and Dodson, V. H., *J. Am. Chem. Soc.,* **79,** 2302 (1957).
(12) Brown, H. C., and Garg, C. P., research in progress.
(13) Brown, H. C., and Hebert, N. C., research in progress.
(14) Brown, H. C., and Keblys, K., research in progress.
(15) Brown, H. C., and Khuri, A., Ph.D. Thesis, Purdue University.
(16) Brown, H. C., Mead, E. J., and Shoaf, C. J., *J. Am. Chem. Soc.,* **78,** 3613 (1956).
(17) Brown, H. C., Mead, E. J., and Subba Rao, B. C., *J. Am. Chem. Soc.,* **77,** 6209 (1955).
(18) Brown, H. C., and Murray, K. J., *J. Am. Chem. Soc.,* **81,** 4108 (1959).
(19) Brown, H. C., Murray, K. J., and Zweifel, G., in press.
(20) Brown, H. C., Schlesinger, H. I., Sheft, I., and Ritter, D. M., *J. Am. Chem. Soc.,* **75,** 192 (1953).
(21) Brown, H. C., Snyder, C., Subba Rao, B. C., and Zweifel, G., manuscript in preparation.
(22) Brown, H. C., Stehle, P., and Tierney, P., *J. Am. Chem. Soc.,* **79,** 2020 (1957).
(23) Brown, H. C., and Subba Rao, B. C., *J. Am. Chem. Soc.,* **78,** 2582 (1956).
(24) Brown, H. C., and Subba Rao, B. C., *J. Am. Chem. Soc.,* **78,** 5694 (1956).
(25) Brown, H. C., and Subba Rao, B. C., *J. Org. Chem.,* **22,** 1136 (1957).

(26) Brown, H. C., and Subba Rao, B. C., *J. Org. Chem.,* **22,** 1136 (1957); *ibid., J. Am. Chem. Soc.,* **81,** 6434 (1959).

(27) Brown, H. C., and Subba Rao, B. C., *J. Am. Chem. Soc.,* **81,** 6423 (1959).

(28) Brown, H. C., and Subba Rao, B. C., *J. Am. Chem. Soc.,* **81,** 6428 (1959).

(29) Brown, H. C., and Sujishi, S., *J. Am. Chem. Soc.,* **70,** 2878 (1948).

(30) Brown, H. C., Taylor, M. D., and Gerstein, M., *J. Am. Chem. Soc.,* **66,** 431 (1944).

(31) Brown, H. C., and Tsukamoto, A., *J. Am. Chem. Soc.,* **82,** 746 (1960). Brown, H. C., Tsukamoto, A., and Bigley, D. B., *J. Am. Chem. Soc.,* in press.

(32) Brown, H. C., and Zweifel, G., *J. Am. Chem. Soc.,* **81,** 247 (1959).

(33) Brown, H. C., and Zweifel, G., *J. Am. Chem. Soc.,* **81,** 1512 (1959).

(34) Brown, H. C., and Zweifel, G., *J. Am. Chem. Soc.,* **81,** 4106 (1959); Brown, H. C., Murray, K. J., Murray, L. J., Snover, J. A., and Zweifel, G., *ibid.,* in press.

(35) Brown, H. C., and Zweifel, G., *J. Am. Chem. Soc.,* **81,** 5832 (1959).

(36) Brown, H. C., and Zweifel, G., *J. Am. Chem. Soc.,* **82,** 1504 (1960); *ibid.,* in press.

(37) Brown, H. C., and Zweifel, G., *J. Am. Chem. Soc.,* in press.

(38) Brown, H. C., and Zweifel, G., *J. Am. Chem. Soc.,* in press.

(39) Brown, W. G., "Reductions by Lithium Aluminum Hydride," in Adams, R., ed., *Organic Reactions*, Vol. VI, Chapt. 10, pp. 469–509, New York, John Wiley and Sons, 1951.

(40) Bruck, P., Thompson, D., and Winstein, S., *Chemistry and Industry*, 405 (1960).

(41) Buls, V. W., Davis, O. L., and Thomas, R. I., *J. Am. Chem. Soc.,* **79,** 337 (1957).

(42) Chu, T. L., *J. Am. Chem. Soc.,* **75,** 1730 (1953).

(43) Coates, G. E., "Organometallic Compounds," Chapt. III, London, Methuen and Co. Ltd., 1956.

(44) Cookson, R. C., and Crundwell, E., *Chemistry and Industry,* 703 (1959).

(45) Davies, A. G., and Moodie, R. B., *Chemistry and Industry,* 1622 (1957).

(46) Dulou, R., and Chrétien-Bessière, Y., *Bull. Soc. Chim. France,* **9,** 1362 (1959).

(47) Finholt, A. E., Bond, A. C. Jr., and Schlesinger, H. I., *J. Am. Chem. Soc.,* **69,** 1199 (1947).

(48) Frankland, E., and Duppa, B. F., *Proc. Roy. Soc. (London),* **10,** 568 (1859); *Ann.,* **115,** 319 (1860). Frankland, E., *J. Chem. Soc.,* **15,** 363 (1862); *Proc. Roy. Soc. (London),* **12,** 123 (1863).

(49) Gilman, H., PB Report 5596, OSRD No. 871 (1942).

(50) Gilman, H., and Marple, K. E., *Rec. trav. chim.,* **55,** 76, 133 (1936).

(51) Goubeau, J., Epple, R., Ulmschneider, D. D., and Lehmann, H., *Angew. Chem.,* **67,** 710 (1955).

(52) Goubeau, J., and Keller, H., *Z. anorg. Chem.,* **267,** 1 (1951).

(53) Hawthorne, M. F., *J. Org. Chem.,* **23,** 1788 (1958).

(54) Hennion, G. F., McCusker, P. A., Ashby, E. C., and Rutkowski, A. J., Abstracts of Papers, 130th Meeting, Amer. Chem. Soc., Sept., 1956, p. 53-0, *ibid., J. Am. Chem. Soc.,* **79,** 5190 (1957).

(55) Hennion, G. F., McCusker, P. A., Ashby, E. C., and Rutkowski, A. J., *J. Am. Chem. Soc.,* **79,** 5194 (1957).
(56) Honeycutt, J. B., Jr., and Riddle, J. M., *J. Am. Chem. Soc.,* **81,** 2593 (1959).
(57) Hurd, D. T., *J. Org. Chem.,* **13,** 711 (1948).
(58) Hurd, D. T., *J. Am. Chem. Soc.,* **70,** 2053 (1948).
(59) Johnson, J. R., Snyder, H. R., and Van Campen, M. G., Jr., *J. Am. Chem. Soc.,* **60,** 115 (1938).
(60) Johnson, J. R., and Van Campen, M. G., Jr., *J. Am. Chem. Soc.,* **60,** 121 (1938).
(61) Johnson, J. R., Van Campen, M. G., Jr., and Grummitt, O., *J. Am. Chem. Soc.,* **60,** 111 (1938).
(62) Köster, R., *Angew. Chem.,* **68,** 383 (1956).
(63) Köster, R., *Angew. Chem.,* **69,** 684 (1957).
(64) Köster, R., *Ann.,* **618,** 31 (1958).
(65) Köster, R., *Angew. Chem.,* **71,** 520 (1959).
(66) Köster, R., and Günter, B., *Ann.,* **629,** 89 (1960).
(67) Köster, R., and Rotermund, G., *Angew. Chem.,* **72,** 138 (1960).
(68) Krause, E., *Ber.,* **57,** 216 (1924). Krause, E., and Polack, H., *Ber.,* **59,** 777 (1926). Krause, E., and Nobbe, P., *Ber.,* **63,** 934 (1930); *ibid.,* **64,** 2112 (1931).
(69) Krause, E., and Grosse, A. von, "Die Chemie der metallorganischen Verbindungen," Berlin, Borntraeger, 1937.
(70) Krause, E., and Nitsche, R., *Ber.,* **54,** 2784 (1921).
(71) Kuivila, H. G., *J. Am. Chem. Soc.,* **76,** 870 (1954); *ibid.,* **77,** 4014 (1955); Kuivila, H. G., and Wiles, R. A., *ibid.,* **77,** 4830 (1955); Kuivila, H. G., and Armour, A. G., *ibid.,* **79,** 5659 (1957).
(72) Lappert, M. F., *Chem. Reviews,* **56,** 959 (1956).
(73) Letsinger, R. L., and Remes, N., *J. Am. Chem. Soc.,* **77,** 2489 (1955).
(74) Logan, T. J., and Flautt, T. J., *J. Am. Chem. Soc.,* in press.
(75) McCusker, P. A., and Glunz, L. J., *J. Am. Chem. Soc.,* **77,** 4253 (1955).
(76) McCusker, P. A., Hennion, G. F., and Ashby, E. C., *J. Am. Chem. Soc.,* **79,** 5192 (1957).
(77) Meerwein, H., Hinz, G., Majert, H., and Sönke, H., *J. prakt. Chem.,* **147,** 226 (1936).
(78) Mel'nikov, N. N., *J. Gen. Chem. (U.S.S.R.),* **6,** 636 (1936); *C.A.,* **30,** 5571 (1936); Mel'nikov, N. N., and Rokitskaya, M. S., *J. Gen. Chem. (U.S.S.R.),* **8,** 1768 (1938); *C.A.,* **33,** 4969 (1939).
(79) Nystrom, R. F., and Brown, W. G., *J. Am. Chem. Soc.,* **69,** 1197 (1947).
(80) Pappo, R., *J. Am. Chem. Soc.,* **81,** 1010 (1959).
(81) Petry, R. C., and Verhoek, F. H., *J. Am. Chem. Soc.,* **78,** 6416 (1956).
(82) Podall, H. E., Petree, H. E., and Zietz, J. R., *J. Org. Chem.,* **24,** 1222 (1959).
(83) Povlock, T. P., and Lippincott, W. T., *J. Am. Chem. Soc.,* **80,** 5409 (1958).
(84) Rosenblum, L., *J. Am. Chem. Soc.,* **77,** 5016 (1955).
(85) Seyferth, D., *J. Inorg. Nucl. Chem.,* **7,** 152 (1958).
(86) Sondheimer, F., and Nussim, M., *Chemistry and Industry,* 400 (1960).
(87) Schlesinger, H. I., and Brown, H. C., in collaboration with Abraham, B., Bond, A. C., Davidson, N., Finholt, A. E., Gilbreath, J. R., Hoekstra, H.,

Horvitz, L., Hyde, E. K., Katz, J. J., Lad, R. A., Mayfield, D. L., Rapp, L., Ritter, D. M., Schwartz, A. M., Sheft, I., Tuck, L. D., and Walker, A. O., *J. Am. Chem. Soc.*, **75**, 186 (1953).
(88) Schlesinger, H. I., and Brown, H. C., *J. Am. Chem. Soc.*, **62**, 3429 (1940).
(89) Schlesinger, H. I., Flodin, N. W., and Burg, A. B., *J. Am. Chem. Soc.*, **61**, 1078 (1939).
(90) Schlesinger, H. I., Horvitz, L., and Burg, A. B., *J. Am. Chem. Soc.*, **58**, 407 (1936).
(91) Schlesinger, H. I., and Walker, A. O., *J. Am. Chem. Soc.*, **57**, 621 (1935).
(92) Snyder, H. R., Kuck, J. A., and Johnson, J. R., *J. Am. Chem. Soc.*, **60**, 105 (1938).
(93) Solomon, I. J., Klein, M. J., and Hattori, K., *J. Am. Chem. Soc.*, **80**, 4520 (1958).
(94) Stone, F. G. A., and Eméleus, H. J., *J. Chem. Soc.*, 2755 (1950).
(95) Stone, F. G. A., and Graham, W. A. G., *Chemistry and Industry*, 1881 (1955).
(96) Ulmschneider, D. D., and Goubeau, J., *Ber.*, **90**, 2733 (1957).
(97) Wechter, W. J., *Chemistry and Industry*, 294 (1959).
(98) Whatley, A. T., and Pease, R. N., *J. Am. Chem. Soc.*, **76**, 835 (1954).
(99) Wiberg, E., and Hertwig, K., cited by J. Goubeau, *FIAT Review*, **23**, 228 (1949).
(100) Winstein, S., Allred, E. L., and Sonnenberg, J., *J. Am. Chem. Soc.*, **81**, 5833 (1959).
(101) Winternitz, P. F., Abstracts of Papers, 135th Meeting, Amer. Chem. Soc., April, 1959, p. 19-M; Winternitz, P. F., and Carotti, A. A., *J. Am. Chem. Soc.*, **82**, 2430 (1960).
(102) Wittig, G., and Rückert, A., *Ann.*, **566**, 101 (1950).
(103) Wolfe, S., Nussim, M., Mazur, Y., and Sondheimer, F., *J. Org. Chem.*, **24**, 1034 (1959); Sondheimer, F., and Wolfe, S., *Can. J. Chem.*, **37**, 1870 (1959).

5. ORGANO-ALUMINUM COMPOUNDS

KARL ZIEGLER

Max-Planck-Institut für Kohlenforschung, Mülheim/Ruhr, Germany

INTRODUCTION

As a consequence of some surprising discoveries made recently, the chemistry of the organo-aluminum compounds has been considerably widened during the past decade. The new findings concern the synthesis and the reactions of aluminum alkyls as well. It has been found that aluminum alkyls have some rather specific properties, distinctly different from those of the magnesium and lithium alkyls. Thus a third important tool for organometallic synthesis has joined the two well-known old ones. It has gained still growing importance also for industrial chemistry and is going to rapidly surpass the two others with regard to large scale technical uses. This chapter reviews the most important facts in the new field, but the limited space does not permit completeness with regard to all details.

Comparatively little progress has been made in the field of aluminum aryls. Therefore no special section will be devoted to these compounds in this chapter. Necessary remarks on aluminum aryls will be made along with the corresponding chemical facts about the aluminum alkyls.

Review articles (*297–308*) on aluminum alkyls have been published during the last 8 years by the author.

SYNTHESIS AND CLASSIFICATION OF ORGANO-ALUMINUM COMPOUNDS

The New "Direct Synthesis" of Aluminum Trialkyls

The principle of the new synthesis is the combination of aluminum hydride with 3 molecules of olefins, according to Eq. (1):

$$AlH_3 + 3 C_nH_{2n} = Al(C_nH_{2n+1})_3. \qquad (1)$$

This simple reaction has been discovered in 1949 by Ziegler and Gellert (*297,298,328,369,373*),* together with the similar addition of olefins to lithium aluminum hydride according to Eq. (2) (which can be combined with (2a) to give also aluminum trialkyls):

*The proposal to execute this reaction under hydrogen pressure at elevated temperatures (*21*) has no practical value.

$$LiAlH_4 + 4 C_nH_{2n} = LiAl(C_nH_{2n+1})_4. \tag{2}$$

$$LiAl(C_nH_{2n+1})_4 + 1/3\ AlCl_3 = 1\ 1/3\ Al(C_nH_{2n+1})_3 + LiCl.* \tag{2a}$$

In 1947 these reactions were new and rather surprising because lithium aluminum hydride had been described to add to $-C{=}O$, $-C{\equiv}N$ and similar groups only but not to $C{=}C$ bonds (*213,252*). The two hydrides normally had been used in ethereal solutions in open vessels. Under such circumstances addition of olefins does not take place, and therefore their reactivity towards olefins had been overlooked. In closed vessels or in the absence of ether it is very easy to accomplish these additions. Some substances (such as $AlCl_3$, $ZnCl_2$, $FeCl_3$, alkali halides, carbonates or phosphates), said to catalyze the reaction (*56,231*), actually have no effect at all.

Olefins suitable for the reaction with aluminum hydride and lithium aluminum hydride are: ethylene, mono- and asymmetrically disubstituted ethylenes, i.e., α-olefins and isobutene-type olefins. 1,2-Disubstituted ethylenes normally do not react; cyclo-olefins with five, seven and eight carbon atoms have been added to $LiAlH_4$ in the limited ratio of 3 to 1 (the same applies to $R_2C:CH_2$). Cyclohexene is practically unreactive (*328*).

This smooth formation of alkyl compounds from the corresponding hydrides by addition of olefins is highly specific for aluminum and boron hydrides only. The first observations have been made by Hurd (*105*) while adding boron hydride to ethylene and isobutylene, and by Brokaw and Pease (*28*) while making a mixture of boron alkyls and an alkylated aluminum hydride by adding ethylene to aluminum boron hydride.

In the course of all these reactions the formation of primary compounds is preferred (*297,298,328,369,373*) (*cf*. p. 217).

The practical value of these additions is limited, because both aluminum hydride and lithium aluminum hydride are rather expensive starting materials; but they are good ways to C_{14}-labelled $AlEt_3$ (*215*). In studying reactions of this type, however, Ziegler and his co-workers (*300,311,332,355, 364,374*) finally discovered a very simple synthesis.† Aluminum hydride cannot be made directly by adding hydrogen to aluminum, but this reaction is possible in the presence of aluminum alkyls. Thus, when an aluminum alkyl is heated with powdered aluminum and hydrogen under pressure, aluminum hydride is formed in a first step and then very quickly stabilized by a reaction with the aluminum trialkyl according to Eq. (3):

$$Al + 1\ 1/2\ H_2 + 2\ Al(C_nH_{2n+1})_3 = 3\ Al(C_nH_{2n+1})_2H \tag{3}$$

---

*This reaction probably is also the essential part of a "thermal splitting of $LiAlR_4$ into $AlR_3 + LiR$" described by P. Smith (I.C.I.) (*245*).

†See also references *42,51,135,141,228–230,232,350,382*.

In this way dialkyl aluminum hydrides* are very easily available from aluminum trialkyls.† They normally are colorless liquids, similar to aluminum trialkyls, and—with lower alkyls—spontaneously flamable. Quite naturally dialkyl aluminum hydrides are able to add one molecule of olefin, e.g.,

$$3 \, Al(C_nH_{2n+1})_2H \, + \, 3 \, C_nH_{2n} \, = \, 3 \, Al(C_nH_{2n+1})_3 \qquad (4)$$

As a result by combination of the two processes, (3) and (4), one more molecule of aluminum trialkyl is synthesized by combining nothing else but aluminum, hydrogen, and olefins. Together with the Schlenk (69,247,249, 250) reaction, i.e., addition of alkali metals to double bonds or radicals, and the splitting of weak C—C bonds by alkali metals (344) (with the exception of the direct substitution of some peculiar hydrocarbons by alkali metals), this is the only synthesis of an organometallic compound in which all valences of the consumed metal are bound to carbon in the reaction product without any loss by formation of metal-halide bonds.

There are two main modifications of the new process: the first, initially realized with aluminum tri-isobutyl, in which all three components are brought into contact in the presence of the aluminum trialkyl as a necessary prerequisite for starting the process; the other, which proceeds in two different steps, is described by Eqs. (3) and (4). With this second modification aluminum triethyl was first synthesized by the new method. In this case certain difficulties are avoided by using the two-step process because, under the conditions of reaction (3), ethylene undergoes additional reactions with aluminum triethyl (see pp. 220–222). Nevertheless, a one-step synthesis of aluminum triethyl is possible also.

It is obvious that the new process allows one to synthesize dialkyl aluminum hydrides as easily as the aluminum trialkyls. Consequently these two main types of organo-aluminum compounds are now quite equally available in large quantities. Modern petrochemistry has opened up ways to many different olefins. Moreover such olefins can be made in a wide variety by certain new processes where aluminum alkyls are used as catalysts (pp. 224–226, 229–241). Therefore, a great number of different organo-aluminum compounds can be obtained from inexpensive materials in a very simple way.

It may be mentioned here that the new synthesis has had a precursor in a

---

*Me$_2$AlH has first been obtained in small quantities and not very pure by Stecher and Wiberg (258; cf. also 54) from Me$_3$Al vapor + H$_2$ in the dark electric discharge. Later Wartik and Schlesinger (269) synthesized it in another way.

†Hydrogen under pressure without any aluminum at 150°–200° causes the smooth reaction R$_3$Al + H$_2$ = R$_2$AlH + RH, a process suitable for the synthesis of the same compounds on a small scale (Lehmkuhl and Köster (157)). Later Podall et al. (226) have studied this hydrogenolysis somewhat more in detail.

reaction discovered by Hall and Nash (*75,76*). These authors synthesized substances like $(C_2H_5)_2AlCl$ and $C_2H_5AlCl_2$ by heating together ethylene, powdered aluminum, and aluminum chloride. Ruthruff (*240*) improved this process by adding hydrogen as one more reaction component. But all these authors obviously believed the aluminum chloride to be necessary for the reaction in stoichiometric quantities.

Other Routes to Organo-Aluminum Compounds

Nearly all former ways to organo-aluminum compounds start from halogenated hydrocarbons as the original reagents. Even the historical synthesis of Buckton and Odling (*29*), by heating together mercury dialkyls* with metallic aluminum (Eq. 5):

$$3\,HgR_2 + 2\,Al = 2\,AlR_3 + 3\,Hg \qquad (5)$$

uses these starting materials, since mercury alkyls are synthesized from alkyl halides. The analogous synthesis of aluminum triaryls is an exception, because mercury triaryls are available *via* the diazo-method (Nesmeyanov *et al.* (*203*)). A synthesis of aluminum alkyls analogous to a synthesis of, e.g., tetraethyllead, by reaction of the halide with a metal-sodium alloy is not possible because aluminum does not give an alloy with sodium. But there exists a similar possibility, that of using magnesium-aluminum alloys (*52,165,368,370*) or even mixtures of ground aluminum and magnesium preferably in anisole as solvent (*60,61*).

Of course aluminum alkyls can be synthesized from Grignard compounds and aluminum chloride (*36,106,114,165,168,236*). This reaction had the widest variability until the new direct synthesis was discovered. (For reactions of $AlCl_3$ with alkyl compounds of metals other than magnesium see p. 202). The disadvantage of the Grignard method lies in the fact that normally only the very stable ether compounds (see pp. 244, 245, 247, 249) of aluminum trialkyls can be obtained and not the aluminum trialkyls themselves. Nevertheless, it is possible to synthesize the ether-free compounds too if the ether is completely removed from the Grignard solutions before their reaction with the aluminum halide (*154*). This can most easily be done by dropping the Grignard solution into well-stirred, boiling toluene and using the suspension of the precipitated Grignard compound in toluene for the reaction (*363*).

The simple addition of the halides to metallic aluminum† (*1,70,73,77,89,*

---

*Renand (*233*) reports to have obtained AlR_3 from MgR_2 with Al under ultrasonic radiation.

†A serious warning is given to all investigators mixing powdered aluminum with organic halides, especially with those of high halogen content (*33*), without appropriate precautions.

168,172), a process which can be compared with a Grignard reaction, is highly limited in its application. It can be realized according to Eq. (6):

$$3 \text{ Rhalogen} + 2 \text{ Al} = \text{RAl(halogen)}_2 + \text{R}_2\text{Alhalogen} \qquad (6)$$

with iodides including C_6H_5I (*1,73,74,266*). The reaction has not yet been realized with aryl chlorides and bromides. With alkyl chlorides and bromides it is possible but only with the methyl and ethyl compounds.* When tried with higher alkyl chlorides or bromides, a very severe and total decomposition is caused by the fact that alkyl halides with more than two carbon atoms in the alkyl group are unstable in contact with alkyl aluminum halides. If, for example, *n*-propyl chloride is mixed with diethylaluminum chloride, a very similar total decomposition can be observed, in the course of which HCl and ethane are evolved and a resinous polymer of propylene is obtained (*272*). Probably the *n*-propyl chloride is first rearranged into isopropyl chloride, and this compound eliminates hydrochloric acid.

Except for this limitation, the formation of the methyl- and ethyl-aluminum so-called "sesquichlorides," i.e., mixtures of $MeAlCl_2 + Me_2AlCl$ and $EtAlCl_2 + Et_2AlCl$, respectively, is a very convenient entrance into the chemistry of the organo-aluminum compounds, and it is the only practicable way to the methyl series.† With aluminum-magnesium alloy (see above), Et_2AlCl and Et_2AlBr also have been prepared without the simultaneous formation of EtAl(halogen)₂ (*73*). CH_3AlCl_2 has been prepared from CH_3OCH_3, $AlCl_3$ and Al (*190*).

Different Types of Organo-Aluminum Compounds with Three Substituents Bound to Aluminum

For better understanding of the following sections the different types of organo-aluminum compounds have first to be described. Three series of such compounds are possible, with 1, 2, and 3 carbon atoms directly bound to aluminum:

$$X_2AlR, \qquad XAlR_2, \qquad AlR_3.$$

The X in $RAlX_2$ may be equal or different; furthermore, X can have quite

---

*The writer has some doubts as to whether the products recently made by Nicolescu and Iovu (*210*) from aluminum and RCl, R = CH_2=CH—CH_2—, —C_4H_9, —CH_2—C_6H_5, —$CHCl_2$, really were the corresponding sesquichlorides as the authors assumed.

†Since the alkyl aluminum mono-, sesqui- and dichlorides having gained considerable importance as components for polyolefin catalysts, a number of proposals have been published to improve their manufacture: (*2,39,45,79,82,108,212, 270*).

different meanings. It is easy to understand that under such circumstances a tremendous variety of organo-aluminum compounds is possible. v.Grosse and Mavity (*73*) have given a formula for the calculation of the number of possibilities for AlXYZ (XYZ being equal or different). For 10 or 20 different substituents 220 or 1540 different compounds respectively are to be expected. For the purposes of this chapter it is sufficient to restrict the meaning of X to H, Halogen, OR, SR, NH_2, NHR, NR_2 and a few others (*1,36, 40,59,73,77,119,145,168,236,328,330,375*). The R also may be an aryl or acyl group. The group, $-NR_2$, also may come from an open or cyclic acid amide (*349*). All these substances are sensitive to air and moisture, some of them are spontaneously flammable. Up to now, products of the type X_2AlR with two different X groups (*5,78,80,95,190,256*) do not play a very important role. Except for substituents with relatively high molecular weights most of these compounds generally are distillable under normal pressure or *in vacuo*. Many of them are liquids, others may be crystallized.

Coördination Complexes of Organo-Aluminum Compounds

Aluminum has 3 valence electrons. Its compounds of type AlX_3 have 6 electrons in the valence sphere. There is an electron deficiency (*179,216, 259*) which is the cause of the tendency of many aluminum compounds, including the organo-aluminum compounds, to add negative ions or neutral molecules with electron-donor properties. This matter shall be discussed later from a more theoretical point of view (see pp. 207 212). It should be mentioned here by way of explanation why, besides the compounds of type AlX_3, many complex compounds do exist in which aluminum has the coördination number four. These compounds can be derived either from lithium aluminum hydride ($LiAlH_4$) or from sodium aluminum tetrachloride ($NaAlCl_4$) by substituting hydrogen atoms or halogen atoms, respectively, by other atoms or groups, and also by substituting Li or Na by other positive ions as well. This relationship is not a purely theoretical one: $LiAlH_4$ can be alkylated to $LiAlEt_4$ either—as already discussed—by ethylene or by diazoethane (*268*).

Such complex compounds usually are obtained by adding certain alkali metal compounds (MX), especially salts, to aluminum compounds of the general formula $AlR_{(3-n)}X_n$ ($n = 2$ to zero). Suitable substances for such additions are: alkali halides (*73,75,310,330,334,375,377*), pseudohalides (*334*), hydrides (*282,346,372,380*), alkyls (*73,83,106,281*) (including rather complicated ones like $-CPh_3$, $-CHPh_2$ (*282*)), aryls (*281–3*) and alkoxyls (*73,352,353*). This does not mean that any possible pair of components is able to give a stable complex compound. There are, on the contrary, certain limits of stability, and there are rules for these stabilities (*307,310,335*). The tendency of the alkali halides to add to organo-aluminum compounds increases with the size of the alkali ions from Li^+ to Cs^+ and decreases with that of the halogen ions from F^- to I^-. If the alkali ion is replaced by a large tetra-alkylammonium ion (84,335,378) the stability of complexes is further increased.

Examples for these rules are: aluminum triethyl adds to all alkali fluorides except LiF and to all alkali chlorides except LiCl and NaCl. Diethyl aluminum chloride adds to KCl but not to NaCl. No alkali iodide adds to $Al(C_2H_5)_3$, but $(C_2H_5)_4NI$ does (152,307,335).

The stability of such complexes is also different for different types of organo-aluminum compounds: mono-ethylaluminum dichloride gives a stable complex compound also with sodium chloride (75). On the other hand, the stability of the complex compounds decreases if the size of the alkyls attached to aluminum increases: all aluminum trialkyls from the methyl up to the butyl derivative add NaF; $Al(C_6H_{13})_3$ does not (307,335). Similarly, the complexes $K[Al(C_nH_{2n+1})_2Br_2]$ are unstable for $n > 4$ (152).

The stability of these complexes has a certain relation to the lattice energy of the added alkali compounds (335). This has been discussed in detail by Lehmkuhl and first reported by Ziegler (307). The lattice energy of the alkali hydrides and alkyls obviously is much lower than that of the alkali halides and therefore $M[AlR_3H]$ and $MAlR_4$ are highly stable. Complex compounds between magnesium and aluminum alkyls also are known. They exist in two different types: $RMg[AlR_4]$ and $Mg[AlR_4]_2$ (310,329). They can be split rather easily by heating in vacuo. MgH_2 does not add to aluminum trialkyls.

Besides the type $MAlR_4$ there exists another, the so-called "1:2" type (307,310,335,346,347,377) in which two molecules of the organo-aluminum compound are added to the alkali compound. Thus in particular $NaF \cdot 2 Al(C_2H_5)_3$, $CsCl \cdot 2 Al(C_2H_5)_3$, $LiH \cdot 2 Al(C_2H_5)_3$, $NaH \cdot 2 Al(C_2H_5)_3$ and $NaCN \cdot 2 AlR_3$ have been found. They are analogs of the purely inorganic complex $KBr \cdot 2 AlBr_3$ (138). Further, more than two AlR_3 can be added to one MX if "AlR_3" is at least partially AlR_2H. In this case, the excess of "AlR_3" is rather weakly fixed (346).

The tendency to give such complex compounds decreases if R is replaced by OR in an aluminum trialkyl. No complex compounds of R_2AlOR and $RAl(OR)_2$ with alkali halides or cyanides are known. Complexes between NaH and R_2AlOR exist but are not very stable (343). The type $[R_3AlOR]$-Na is known and stable (73,352,353); it can likewise be regarded as an addition product of NaOR to AlR_3 or of NaR to AlR_2OR. The most stable addition products are those of the alcoholates, since $Na[R_2Al(OR)_2]$ (343) and $Na[RAl(OR)_3]$ (343) (and even $Na[Al(OR)_4]$ (185)) exist without any limitation.

"Stability" as discussed here has to do with reversible decomposition into the components. In some cases an internal instability has been observed. Alkali carbonates and salts of carboxylic acids or alkali rhodanides easily add to triethyl aluminum, but the complexes soon undergo a rearrangement, the course of which for $CH_3 \cdot CO_2Na + Et_3Al$ is the following (Eq. 7):

$$Na[Et_3AlOCOCH_3] \cdot AlEt_3 \longrightarrow Na]Et_3AlOC(CH_3)(C_2H_5)OAlEt_2] \qquad (335) \qquad (7)$$

Many of the complexes just discussed are rather highly heteropolar, real salts. Nevertheless transition types and even purely homopolar compounds of this kind have been observed. This is elucidated by Table 5.1.

TABLE 5.1. PROPERTIES OF SOME ORGANO-ALUMINUM COMPLEX SALTS

Product	Conductivity κ (of molten product) $\Omega^{-1}cm^{-1}$ 100°	Solubility in saturated hydrocarbons	Remarks
$K[AlEt_4]$ (*343*)	$8.7 \cdot 10^{-2}$	Insoluble	—
$Na[AlEt_4]$ (*343, 83*)	$5.8 \cdot 10^{-2}$ (130°)	Insoluble	Traces distill with the vapors of $AlEt_3$ *in vacuo* (*171*)
$NaF \cdot 2AlEt_3$ (*347, 335*)	$4.2 \cdot 10^{-2}$	Insoluble	—
$CsCl \cdot 2AlEt_3$ (*335*)	$2.3 \cdot 10^{-2}$	Insoluble	—
$CsCl \cdot AlEt_3$ (*335*)	$1.3 \cdot 10^{-2}$	Insoluble	—
$NaF \cdot AlEt_3$ (*347, 335*)	$1.9 \cdot 10^{-4}$	Moderately soluble	Distillable under certain conditions (*335*)
$LiAlEt_4$ (*83*)	$\sim 1 \cdot 10^{-3}$	Moderately soluble	Can be sublimed *in vacuo* (*8, 329*)
$Na[AlEt_3(OC_{10}H_{21})]$ (*343*) (*h*)	$2.1 \cdot 10^{-4}$	Soluble	—
$EtMg[AlEt_4]$ and $Mg[AlEt_4]$	No perceptible conductivity	Highly soluble	$MeMg[AlMe_4]$ is distillable *in vacuo* (*329*)

For $LiAlEt_4$ and the complexes of diethylmagnesium, formulas such as

and

with "electron deficient" or "single electron" bonds have to be discussed also (*318*) (see pp. 207–212).

Aluminum trialkyls and triaryls add electron donors like ethers, thioethers, tertiary amines and tertiary phosphines (*7,36,40,60,88,165,168,236, 273*) to form rather stable and in most cases distillable complex compounds. The formulas are $R_3Al{\leftarrow}OR'_2$, $R_3Al{\leftarrow}SR'_2$, $R_3Al{\leftarrow}NR'_3$ and $R_3Al{\leftarrow}PR'_3$. Formerly proposed compositions such as $Et_3Al \cdot 3/4\ OEt_2$ (*165*) certainly are erroneous (*7,273*). Probably these compounds will dissociate in the vapor phase, at least partially, into their components (experimental proof for $Me_2S{\rightarrow}AlM_3$ (*40*)); nevertheless, a reversible real separation of the two components is not possible by distillation except for some extremely weak anisole compounds (*60*) and for aluminum triaryl etherates (*36,88,168,236*). Bonitz (*22*) has measured heats of formation for some donor complexes of triethylaluminum: aliphatic ethers and dimethyl aniline, 11.0–11.5 kcal; tetrahydrofuran, 14 kcal; tertiary aliphatic amines, 17 kcal; pyridine and benzopyridines, 19–21 kcal; and anisole, 2–3 kcal. The order of complex stability established by these measurements agrees with the order

$$Me_3N > Me_3P > OMe_2 > SMe_2 > SeMe_2 > TeMe_2$$

for the tendency of complex formation mentioned by Coates (*34,36,40*).

Similar to $AlCl_3$ and AlR_3, R_2Al(halogen) and RAl(halogen)$_2$ also add ether and tertiary amines (*3,36,40,70*) but the fluorides, R_2AlF, and alkoxy compounds, R_2AlOR (*330*), do not. The latter fact opens the way for a quantitative determination of true aluminum trialkyls in a mixture with autoöxidation products, (R_2AlOR), by adding ether or trimethyl amine and measuring the increase in weight (*6*).

Stable addition products of NH_3, primary, or secondary amines normally do not exist, due to an internal stabilization by splitting off RH. Exceptions are $(CH_3)_3Al{\leftarrow}NH_3$ (*52*), $(CH_3)_3Al{\leftarrow}NH(CH_3)_2$ (*40*), $(C_6H_5)_3Al{\leftarrow}$ NH_3 (*36,167,168,236*). They lose RH, however, when warmed. A number of well-crystallized and quite different electron-donor complexes of aluminum triaryls have been prepared by Nesmeyanov and Novikova (*201*). $Ph_3P{\rightarrow}AlPh_3$ is also known (*209*).

Interconversion of Organo-Aluminum Compounds

The number of possible interconversions of the different types of organoaluminum compounds is very high. Many of them are routine and therefore, in this chapter, only the most important ones will be mentioned. Very simple replacement reactions are possible in the field of these complex compounds. Tertiary amines replace ethers from the etherates, low-boiling ethers can be replaced by higher boiling ethers; on the other hand, triethylaluminum diethyl etherate splits off diethyl ether when it is heated in a stream of gaseous dimethyl ether (*191*). No replacement occurs if the differences in stability of the complexes involved are too great: anisole does not replace diethyl ether in spite of its high boiling point (*60*).

Mutual transformations of complex salts and electron donor complexes have been described in wide variety. Diethyl ether does not alter $NaF \cdot 2 \, AlMe_3$ or $KF \cdot 2 \, AlEt_3$ but splits $NaF \cdot 2 \, AlEt_3$ into $NaF \cdot AlEt_3 + Et_3Al \leftarrow OEt_2$. $(CH_3)_3N$ (in excess) abstracts one molecule of Et_3Al from $KF \cdot 2 \, AlEt_3$ and two from $NaF \cdot 2 \, AlEt_3$ (*335*).

As a consequence of these observations, triethylaluminum etherate is split by KF into $KF \cdot 2 \, AlEt_3$ and ether. Since $KF \cdot 2 \, AlEt_3$ can be split (by heating *in vacuo*) into $KF \cdot AlEt_3$ and $AlEt_3$, this opens a way for making ether-free aluminum alkyls from the etherates (*335*).

All electron donor complexes can be split by alkali hydrides (*343*), alkali alkyls (*106*) or alkali alcoholates. The same applies to the alkali halide and pseudohalide complexes (*343*). Alkali alcoholates replace alkali hydrides: when the (liquid) salt $Na[AlEt_3H]$ is mixed with a dry sodium alcoholate, the latter dissolves and sodium hydride precipitates (*171*). Similarly, replacement reactions such as (8–10) are possible:

$$K\,[AlEt_2Cl_2] + AlEtCl_2 = AlEt_2Cl + K\,[AlEtCl_3] \quad (354) \quad (8)$$

$$K\,[AlEtCl_3] + AlCl_3 = KAlCl_4 + EtAlCl_2 \quad (354) \quad (9)$$

$$Na[AlEt_3OR] + AlEt_3 = Na[AlEt_4] + AlEt_2OR \quad (352,353) \quad (10)$$

Reaction (10) has some relation to the problem of separating mixtures of $PbEt_4$ and $AlEt_3$ as they are obtained in modern electrolytic processes (see p. 254).

If compounds of the types R_3Al, R_2AlX, $RAlX_2$ and AlX_3 are brought together, very rapid exchanges of substituents are possible. As a rule only two such members of the series which directly follow each other in the order mentioned are stable in mixture with each other, i.e., $R_3Al + AlX_3$ give $R_2AlX + RAlX_2$. $AlR_3 + RAlX_2$ give $2 \, R_2AlX$. $R_2AlX + AlX_3$ give $2 \, RAlX_2$ (*73,74*). The rule also applies for fluorides if AlF_3, used as a component of such mixtures, has been prepared at low temperature (e.g., by the reaction $BF_3 + AlR_3 = BR_3 + AlF_3$) and has not been calcined at high temperature (*116,330*).

In principle the types R_2AlX and $RAlX_2$ may exist in the form of disproportionation equilibria according to Eqs. (11 a and b):

$$2 \, R_2AlX \rightleftarrows R_3Al + RAlX_2 \quad (11a)$$

$$2 \, RAlX_2 \rightleftarrows AlX_3 + R_2AlX, \quad (11b)$$

however, the composition will comply predominantly with the forementioned rule. The disproportionation of R_2AlX, for instance, would give $RAlX_2$ and R_3Al as well. The coëxistence of these two products being extremely unlikely, almost all aluminum is present in the form of the actual molecules R_2AlX.

Nevertheless, disproportionations have been realized in some cases under certain circumstances. Pitzer and Gutowsky (223) have obtained aluminum trimethyl by distillation of methylaluminum sesqui-iodide with an efficient column, the residue being AlI_3. In this case the differences in boiling point between the different possible types in the disproportionation equilibrium are relatively high, and this may be one reason why this·experiment was successful. Besides this singular case disproportionation has been found to be possible only if favored by complex formation: $K[AlR_2Cl_2]$ can be split by distillation according to Eq. 12 (152,307).

$$2 K[AlR_2Cl_2] = KCl + K[AlRCl_3] + AlR_3. \tag{12}$$

If, in this case, the distillate is remixed with the residue, the starting material is regenerated. This possibility has a certain practical value, because the aluminum trialkyl in some cases has a higher reactivity than the diethylaluminum chloride. Thus these two reactions, 1) splitting complex compounds and 2) generating the original product by readdition of the residue to the reaction products, allows the activation and deactivation of the organo-aluminum compound at will (152,339) (see p. 231).

The disproportionation described is not an entirely smooth reaction, since during the distillation only a part of the complex compound disproportionates while another part splits into the original components of the compound, R_2AlCl and KCl. An extremely smooth disproportionation is possible with $Na[AlR_2F_2]$. When heated this complex decomposes smoothly according to Eq. (13) (310,330,375):

$$3 Na[AlR_2F_2] = Na_3AlF_6 + 2 AlR_3. \tag{13}$$

This is a good method for making aluminum trimethyl from the methylaluminum sesquichloride. The monomethylaluminum dichloride in the sesquichloride form can very easily be removed ,by adding sodium chloride to form the nondistillable complex $Na[AlCH_3Cl_3]$.

Another possibility for the removal of the CH_3AlCl_2 from the sesquichloride is the addition of one molecule $Al(CH_3)_3$. The same can be done with the $Na[AlCH_3Cl_3]$ which reacts according to Eq. (14):

$$Na[AlCH_3Cl_3] + Al(CH_3)_3 = NaCl + 2 Al(CH_3)_2Cl. \tag{14}$$

By suitable combination of these reactions with the pyrolysis of $Na[AlR_2F_2]$ the total methyl content of the methylaluminum sesquichloride can be obtained in the form of aluminum trimethyl.

Similar disproportionations are not known at this time for organo-aluminum compounds with alkoxyl groups.

Besides disproportionation the dehalogenation (*2,73,107,140,244,254, 370*) of alkyl aluminum halides has some practical value, e.g.

$$3 Et_2AlCl + 3 Na = 2 Et_3Al + Al + 3 NaCl, \tag{15}$$

and also for conversion of sesquichlorides to dialkyl aluminum mono-chlorides (*139*). The aluminum can again be converted into the sesqui-chloride with methylchloride. Under such circumstances the synthesis of AlEt$_3$ can be realized according to the overall reaction (16) (*244*):

$$3 EtCl + Al + 3 Na = Et_3Al + 3 NaCl \tag{16}$$

Another way to avoid a loss of aluminum is to use sodium for the de-halogenation in the form of sodium hydride (*297,328,380*) (Eq. 17 a and b):

$$(C_2H_5)_2AlCl + NaH = (C_2H_5)_2AlH + NaCl \tag{17a}$$

$$(C_2H_5)_2AlH + C_2H_4 = (C_2H_5)_3Al \tag{17b}$$

Other but similar combinations including the use of sodium hydride have been proposed by Ziegler, Gellert and Martin (*297,372*). Except perhaps for special purposes, the value of such reactions has been decreased by the "Direct Synthesis."

Two similar reactions with and without loss of aluminum, respectively, lead to the alkali-aluminum-tetra-alkyl compounds (*73,308*):

$$4 Al(C_2H_5)_3 + 3 Na = 3 Na[Al(C_2H_5)_4] + Al \text{ and} \tag{18}$$

$$Al(C_2H_5)_3 + NaH = Na[Al(C_2H_5)_3H] \tag{19a}$$

$$Na[Al(C_2H_5)_3H] + C_2H_4 = Na[Al(C_2H_5)_4]. \tag{19b}$$

Processes 19a and b can be expected to gain some importance in the regeneration of electrolytes in the electrolytic synthesis of metal alkyls (see pp. 251–255). The same is true with

$$Al(C_2H_5)_2OR + NaH + C_2H_4 = Na[Al(C_2H_5)_3OR], \tag{20}$$

a reaction which requires the simultaneous addition of NaH and C$_2$H$_4$, because the complex Na[Al(C$_2$H$_5$)$_2$(OR)H] is not very stable (*352,353*).

In the aromatic series the reaction between AlPh$_3$ and sodium (at room temperature) leads to an addition product AlPh$_3$Na analogous to the corresponding boron compound (*166*).

Quite obviously the halogen atoms in the alkyl aluminum halides can be replaced by other groups. Such reactions have been investigated in some detail with the dialkyl aluminum chlorides. In this way reactions with, e.g., LiH, NaH, LiD, NaF, NaCN, NaOR, Na·C≡C·R have led to R$_2$AlX with X = H (*176,297,328,380*), D (*274*), F (*330,375*), CN (*154,169*), OR (*154*), —C≡C—R (*275*). Mixed complexes of the kind, M[R₂AlClX] (M = alkali metal), may be formed, decomposing spontaneously into MCl and R₂AlX. An occasionally favorable modification of such reactions is to work in two steps (*328,380*), e.g., (Eqs. 21 a and b):

$$AlEt_2Cl + 2 LiH = LiCl + Li[AlEt_2H_2] \qquad (21a)$$

$$Li[AlEt_2H_2] + AlEt_2Cl = LiCl + 2 AlEt_2H \qquad (21b)$$

Similarly, a small quantity of AlR₃ (or AlR₂H as well) may be used for dissolving the first part of the added NaH, and then R₂AlCl and NaH may be added continuously in such a way that the reaction always takes place between AlR₂Cl and dissolved NaH (*131*).

Starting from aluminum trialkyls or trialkyl hydrides partial decomposition with compounds having reactive hydrogen atoms (alcohols, phenols, amines, acids, amides, HCN (*52*), thioalcohols, and the like) is a convenient way to products of the types, R₂AlX and RAlX₂ (*36,40,52,66, 200,349,352*). In R₂AlH hydrogen reacts first, and sometimes exclusively, under certain conditions. This has been used for the determination of R₂AlH in mixtures with AlR₃, in the lower members of the series, by adding $CH_3NHC_6H_5$ in a Zerevitinoff apparatus (*206*). In AlR₃ the three R groups are split off with different ease. With water, normal alcohols or acids the decomposition proceeds so rapidly that no differences can be observed. With tertiary alcohols (*103*) or secondary amines (*208*) the differences can be easily demonstrated. Below about 100°C only one Al—R in AlR₃ is alcoholyzed or aminolyzed respectively. This fact can be used for the quantitative determination of the so-called active aluminum (sum of AlR₃ + HAlR₂). AlR₂OR does not react with ammonia or amines at room temperature. AlR₃ and HAlR₂ give H_2NAlR_2, $R'NHAlR_2$, and $R_2'NAlR_2$, respectively. Both fix one molecule of Me₃N. The excess of NH₃ etc. is removed, the residue hydrolyzed, and the volatile N-compound titrated in the usual way (*334*).

Partial (or total) alcoholysis is also possible with NaAlR₄; Na[AlR₃OR'] (*352*) and similar complexes are formed in this simple way.

Compounds like Me₂AlOH, Me₂AlSH, Me₂AlOAlMe₂ and Me₂Al-SAlMe₂are mentioned in the literature (*59*) as products of partial hydrolysis or sulfhydrolysis of Me₃Al. Such products have not as yet been investigated in detail. Me₂AlSH decomposes into MeH and (MeAl=S)ₙ. A complex derivative of (Et₂Al)₂O can easily be obtained from Et₃Al and NaOH (*22*);

$$Et_3Al \xrightarrow{NaOH} Na[AlEt_3OH] \xrightarrow{Et_3Al} Na[AlEt_3OAlEt_2] + C_2H_6 \qquad (\textit{169}) \quad (22)$$

MOLECULAR STRUCTURE AND PROPERTIES OF
ORGANO-ALUMINUM COMPOUNDS

Organo-Aluminum Compounds and Intermolecular Forces

The calculated molecular weights for only a few of the known organo-aluminum compounds have been found in freezing benzene. Aluminum tri-isopropyl (*223*), aluminum tri-isobutyl (*92,336*), aluminum trineopentyl, and quite generally all aluminum trialkyls of the types, $Al(-CH_2-CHRR')_3$ and $Al(-CH_2-CR_3)_3$ (*92*), belong to this group, $AlPh_3$ is partially associated (*167*). All other organo-aluminum compounds known up to now are at least bimolecular (*92,170,223*), trimolecular (*40,92,269*), or in some cases even multimolecular (*330*). The great tendency to associate comes from the electron deficiency of the aluminum atom in its compounds with coördination number 3, leading to the formation of dimers, trimers, polymers with atoms or groups as bridges bound by so-called "electron deficient" (*179,216*) or "half" bonds (*36,238*).

For aluminum trimethyl the symmetrical formula (23a) has been established by X-ray crystal analyses (*36,174*) and other criteria (*224*) (see p. 213). The dimer of aluminum triethyl can be written in a similar manner (23b):

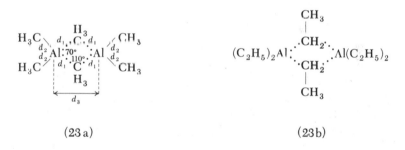

(23a)   (23b)

The distances d_1, d_2, d_3 are 2.24, 1.99, and 2.55Å, respectively, the valence angles at the Al– and bridge C-atoms 110° and 70°, respectively (*36*). The dimers have a distinct tendency to dissociate according to

$$(AlR_3)_2 \rightleftarrows 2\,AlR_3 \qquad (24)$$

This can be clearly demonstrated in the vapor phase at temperatures up to 160°. The heat of dissociation for $(Me_3Al)_2$ is 20.2 kcal (*170*). In solution, especially in freezing benzene, the degree of dissociation is rather low if R is an *n*-alkyl but it is probably higher for the higher alkyl compounds (*35,307,337*). On the other hand, the "monomolecular" aluminum tri-isobutyl and its analogs may—as pure liquids or in highly concentrated solutions—also be associated to some extent (*208,336*) but not enough to increase the normal molecular weight in usual Beckmann measurements. Obviously the tendency to form

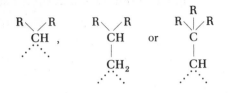

bridges between two aluminum atoms is quite low: the association is sensitive to "steric hindrance" (*92*).

Dialkyl aluminum hydrides are trimolecular in benzene at about $+5°$ (*92,269*); and many of them are similarly trimeric at $100°$ in phenanthrene (*336*). There is no difference between the methyl, ethyl, and isobutyl compounds. The trimers have a ring structure with H-bridges (25). The alkyl groups no longer have any influence.

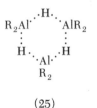

(25)

The tendency to associate has a certain consequence for the stability of aluminum trialkyls in mixture with others. Obviously, while the equilibrium, $2 \text{ AlR}_3 \rightleftarrows (\text{AlR}_3)_2$, exists, the equilibria

$$\text{R}_3\text{Al} + \text{AlR}'_3 \rightleftarrows \text{R}_2\text{Al} \overset{\text{R}}{\underset{\text{R}}{\diagdown\diagup}} \text{AlR}'_2 \rightleftarrows \text{R}_2\text{AlR}' + \text{RAlR}'_2 \qquad (26)$$

are also possible. The rate of such intermolecular reactions is extremely high. Therefore a rapid alkyl interchange is to be expected in the mixture of two different aluminum trialkyls. *Vice versa*, mixed aluminum trialkyls with different alkyls bound to the aluminum should not exist as well defined individual compounds having constant boiling points. This actually has been found (*92,307,336*). Aluminum tri-isobutyl has a melting point very convenient for its use as a solvent for cryoscopic measurements. Immediately after adding other monomolecular aluminum alkyls (aluminum triisoöctyl and others) one third of the calculated molecular weight is found for these products. With an excess of the solvent, the process:

$$2 R_3Al + R'_3Al = 3 R_2R'Al \qquad (27)$$

is the most favored one converting one molecule of R'_3Al into three others. Moreover, Hoffmann (*92*) has found that in benzene solution the number of dissolved particles of aluminum tri-isobutyl is distinctly diminished when $1/4 \ Al_2(CH_3)_6$ is added. It can be clearly demonstrated that (28) occurs first:

$$2 Al(i\text{-}C_4H_9)_3 + 1/2 Al_2(CH_3)_6 = 3 Al(i\text{-}C_4H_9)_2CH_3 \qquad (28)$$

The newly formed molecules of $Al(i\text{-}C_4H_9)_2CH_3$ are able to associate *via* CH_3-bridges; therefore 2 1/2 *N* particles go over into 1 1/2 *N* particles. The reaction is distinctly exothermic (*92,171*). Nevertheless, aluminum trimethyl and tri-isobutyl are recovered if a mixture of these two substances is distilled (Lehmkuhl, reported by Hoffmann, *92*). The mixed aluminum trialkyl is not obtained in this way, but in this special case its dimer is predominantly present in the mixture before distillation, due to the extreme difference in ease of entering the bridges between the two alkyls involved. The alkyl interchange is not surprising in itself since reactions of this type are known by principle (*136*). Nevertheless its rate is astonishing. Model reactions for these interchanges between different aluminum alkyls can be studied with mixtures of aluminum and boron alkyls (*153*) (see p. 243).

Compounds of the type R_2AlX also are associated. The existence of dimers and trimers, (29a–e),

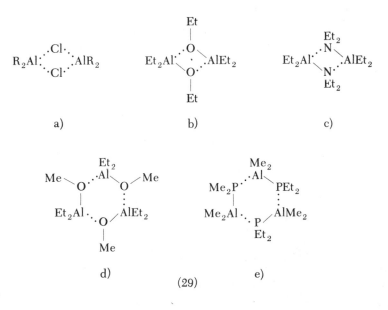

a)   b)   c)

d)   (29)   e)

is well established (*40,92*). Here the oxygen or halogen atoms form the bridges. Nevertheless, an alkyl interchange is possible also between the molecules. It is likely that some alkyl bridging occurs according to:

$$
R_2Al\substack{\cdot\cdot Cl\cdot\cdot\\ \quad\\ \cdot\cdot Cl\cdot}AlR_2 \quad \longleftrightarrow \quad R_2Al\substack{\cdot\cdot Cl\cdot\cdot\\ \quad\\ \cdot R\cdot}Al\substack{Cl\\ \diagup\\ \diagdown R} \tag{30}
$$

and is necessary for the interchange.

$(CH_3)_2AlF$ and $(C_2H_5)_2AlF$ obviously associate to real polymers (*330*). Being distillable at about 200° they are mobile liquids at that temperature but solidify to glass-like products even while still hot. $(C_3H_7)_2AlF$ is a mobile liquid at room temperature and certainly not highly associated.

Finally, the possibility of mixed associations has to be discussed. As a matter of fact dialkyl aluminum hydrides and aluminum trialkyls have a tendency to add, preferably to $R_2Al\substack{\cdot\cdot H\cdot\cdot\\ \quad\\ \cdot\cdot R\cdot}AlR_2$. Di-isobutyl aluminum hydride, trimolecular in benzene at $+5°$, is apparently monomolecular (*92,336*) in (i-$C_4H_9)_3Al$ as solvent at the same temperature. Obviously it is dissociated by adding to the (i-$C_4H_9)_3Al$ molecules.

AlR_3 undergoes an easy alkyl interchange with AlR'_2OR'' or AlR'_2-halogen (*307,336,338*), a fact leading to the conclusion that

$$
R_2Al\substack{\cdot\cdot Cl\cdot\cdot\\ \quad\\ \cdot R\cdot}AlR_2 \quad \text{and} \quad R_2Al\substack{\cdot\cdot O\cdot\cdot\\ \quad\\ \cdot R\cdot}AlR_2 \overset{R'}{}
$$

also exist to a certain extent in equilibrium. On the other hand, and this seems to be surprising, no interchange occurs between aluminum trialkyls and dialkyl aluminum dialkyl amides (*338, cf.* p. 214, 220, 223). Mixed dimers of the types

$$
R_2Al\substack{\cdot\cdot R\cdot\cdot\\ \quad\\ \cdot\cdot N\cdot}AlR_2 \quad \text{or} \quad R_2Al\substack{\cdot\cdot R\cdot\cdot\\ \quad\\ \cdot R\cdot}Al\substack{R\\ \diagup\\ \diagdown NR'_2}
$$

obviously are not possible.

Disaggregation of associated organo-aluminum compounds is further made possible by adding electron donors. The etherates, trialkyl aminates, thio-etherates, and trialkyl phosphine adducts of aluminum trialkyls and dialkyl aluminum halides are monomolecular (40,102). It is not yet known whether dialkyl aluminum fluorides add ether when diluted with this solvent. Stable distillable etherates do not exist (330) as has already been mentioned. Characteristic changes of certain properties occur during the addition of the donors. The addition products have high dipole moments of 4.5–6 Debye units due to a strong polarization (94,95,101,103,262). Neither the associated nor the monomolecular aluminum trialkyls have perceptible dipole moments. This difference can be used for a dielectric titration of aluminum trialkyls (103).

The formation of electron donor complexes is also accompanied by characteristic changes in the electrolytic conductivity. Pure aluminum trialkyls and dialkyl aluminum hydrides have, as concentrated liquids, electrical conductivities as low as 10^{-10} (and even these values probably are too high, see below). For etherates, trialkyl aminates and the like, values of $\kappa = 1 - 20 \cdot 10^{-7} \Omega^{-1} cm^{-1}$ have been measured (22,207). This considerable increase can be used for conductivity titrations of aluminum trialkyls (Bonitz (22), later repeated by Grayevsky et al. (68)). (Potentiometric measurements are also possible (22).) Obviously the electron donor complexes are crypto-ionic substances. The nature of the ions formed has been discussed by Bonitz (22) and more in detail by Neumann (207).*

Changes in the crypto-ionic character also occur if aluminum trialkyls and dialkyl aluminum hydrides are mixed. Neumann has found a sharp maximum ($1.8 \cdot 10^{-8} \Omega^{-1} cm^{-1}$) for the conductivity in 1 : 1 molar mixtures of $AlEt_3$ and $AlEt_2H$ without solvent. Probably even the lowest value $1 \cdot 10^{-10}$ found for aluminum triethyl is due to a trace of $AlEt_2H$ present, and the pure $AlEt_3$ will have a much lower value. The maximum in the conductivity observed by Neumann once more demonstrates the existence of a special relation between $AlEt_3$ and $AlEt_2H$ in the mole ratio 1 : 1.

Dialkyl aluminum hydrides add ethers reversibly as can be recognized by changes in the infrared spectrum (95,256). The addition products of tertiary amines, e.g., $(C_2H_5)_2\overset{H}{\underset{|}{Al}} \leftarrow N(C_2H_5)_3$, are more stable. (See also Wiberg, (54).) The Al—H bond, not occupied by forming bridges, is characterized by a rather sharp infrared band at 1753 cm^{-1} suitable for spectroscopic >AlH determinations, whereas the absorption of the AlH in bridges is very broad and not suitable for quantitative measurements (256).

$(R_2AlOR)_n$, $n = 2$ or 3, is not disaggregated by ethers or tertiary amines although the complex, $Me_2AlSMe \cdot N(CH_3)_3$, does exist (40). Also, dialkyl

---

*Conductivity measurements of CH_3AlBr_2 and its dimethyl etherate in CH_3Br have been made by Jacober and Kraus (109).

aluminum dialkyl amides have a tendency to add tertiary amines (*207*). A special type of these molecular compounds is formed by addition of two molecules of azomethines to R_2AlH, e.g.,

$$Ph \cdot CH : N \cdot Ph \xrightarrow{R_2AlH} Ph \cdot CH_2 \cdot \overset{\cdot}{N} \cdot Ph \longrightarrow Ph \cdot CH_2 \cdot \overset{\cdot}{N} \cdot Ph \qquad (31)$$
$$R_2Al \qquad\qquad R_2Al \leftarrow N : CH \cdot Ph$$
$$Ph$$

Instead of benzalaniline, pyridine, quinoline or isoquinoline can be used. Such 1 : 2 adducts all are deeply colored (Bonitz (*22*), Neuman (*206*)) and can be used for a spectrophotometrical determination of the > AlH bond or as indicators for a titration of aluminum trialkyls with isoquinoline. The color is caused by a charge-transfer band (*207*). The fixation of electron donors by the aluminum atom is also possible within the same molecule. Bähr and Müller (*6*) synthesized the compound (32a) and similar ones with NEt_2 and SEt groups (and 5-membered chelate rings). Zakharkin and Savina (*292*) added di-isobutyl aluminum hydride to allyl ethers, thioethers, and allyl diethylamine to molecules such as (32b):

$$Et_2Al \overset{\displaystyle CH_2 - CH_2}{\underset{\displaystyle \overset{\cdot}{O} \longrightarrow CH_2}{\diagup}} CH_2 \qquad (iso\text{-}Bu)_2Al \overset{\displaystyle CH_2 - CH_2}{\underset{\displaystyle X \longrightarrow CH_2}{\diagup}} \Big|$$
$$Et$$
$$X = EtO,\ EtS,\ C_3H_7O,\ Et_2N$$

a)   b)

(32)

In these compounds the mixed type of an aluminum trialkyl obviously is stabilized by the chelate rings.

Spectroscopic and Miscellaneous Physical Properties of Organo-Aluminum Compounds

Organo-aluminum compounds normally do not absorb visible or ultraviolet light. Of course absorptions can be caused by certain substituents such as aryls. Electron donor-acceptor complexes with open-chain or cyclic aldimines (e.g., benzalaniline, pyridine, and benzopyridines) are slightly or strongly colored as has already been mentioned. The colors can be utilized for different quantitative measurements.

Investigations on infrared and Raman spectra have been carried out by Hoffmann and Schomburg (*95–101*) and by others (*50,71,223,224*). One result of this research is the demonstration of "negative hydrogen bridges" in the associated dialkyl aluminum hydrides and the splitting of the bridges by electron-donor molecules (*95,96,101*) as has already been discussed.

Quite generally, the following can be said. Most of the infrared absorptions caused by bonds to aluminum itself or in its close vicinity are extraordinarily intense or at least considerably stronger in intensity, than the corresponding absorptions in hydrocarbons. This arises from the increased polarity of such bonds. (The C—H stretching frequencies on the α-C atoms are normal in position and intensity, whereas some deformation vibration types have changed considerably in both frequency and intensity.) The frequencies of these absorptions are highly sensitive to substitution on, or addition of electron-donor molecules to, the aluminum atom (*95,96,101*). This applies also to the addition complexes, which means association of the organo-aluminum compounds themselves. Besides this, of course, the bridge bonds cause a set of new frequencies, some of which are highly Raman active. The entirely symmetrical bridge structure of $[(CH_3)_3Al]_2$ has first been proposed by Kohlrausch and Wagner (*163*) on account of Raman spectra and some additional calculation. This was later confirmed by Pitzer and Sheline (*224*) by infrared measurements and by Lewis and Rundle (*174*) by X-ray analysis. The recent infrared and Raman investigations have established the same type of bridge structure for the dimers of the higher aluminum alkyls (*98,100*). Similar investigations with corresponding results have been made for some alkyl aluminum chlorides (*71,98,99,100*). Also the infrared spectrum of AlPh₃ has been described (*38*).

The few monomolecular nonassociated organo-aluminum compounds known differ distinctly from the associated types in the low frequency range (Al—C bonds, 400–700 cm⁻¹) of the molecular spectra. Clearly, the frequencies characteristic for the bridge bonds have disappeared (*98–100*). Naturally these frequencies also disappear after the addition of electron-donor molecules. It has not been possible to identify with certainty a special infrared or Raman frequency of the new dipolar bond between the aluminum and the electron donor atom. The special polarization leading to the highly intense absorption of the Al—C bonds can be clearly recognized in the chemical shifts of proton magnetic resonance spectra (*93,100*). The signals of the CH₂-protons in aluminum ethyl compounds and in diethyl ether appear on different sides (*9,93,100*) of the nearly fixed signal of the CH₃-protons according to the inverse polarization of the $-\overset{\delta-}{O}-\overset{\delta+}{C}H$ and the $\overset{\delta+}{Al}-\overset{\delta-}{C}H$ groups. The nuclear resonance spectra show with particular distinctness the changes in electronegativity of the aluminum atom caused by substitution and formation of complexes (*100*). Besides this, these spectra confirm the existence of the very rapid alkyl interchange between different aluminum trialkyl molecules (*97*); e.g., $[Al(CH_3)_3]_2$ shows one single signal for the protons of all methyl groups!

Measurements of several physical properties have been published by different authors but no really systematic investigation exists up to now on this problem. It would exceed the scope of this chapter to collect all these data. Some references may be sufficient: 1) simple constants like densities, boiling points, refractive indices (*145,168,223,236*); 2) solubility (of Ph_3Al) (*261*); 3) viscosity (*145*); 4) vapor pressures, heats of evaporation, Trouton constants, Antoine equations (*10,36,40,145,164,170,223,236*); 5) heats of combustion (*47,178,211*); 6) magnetic susceptibility (*223*); 7) electron diffraction (*27,41*); and 8) dielectric values (in addition to those cited above) (*86,262,280*).

REACTIONS OF ORGANO-ALUMINUM COMPOUNDS

Introduction

The reactivity of the organo-aluminum compounds can quite generally be described by the following statements.

1) The highest reactivity is observed if all three valences are bound to C or C and H only. The reactivity decreases considerably if one or even two valences of the aluminum are attached to other atoms than C or H. According to this rule there exists a certain group of reactions which are (under moderate conditions) possible only with aluminum alkyls and not with the types AlR_2X and $AlRX_2$ (*300–302*). In such reactions, so far as the total number of Al—C + Al—H bonds is not altered, they can be realized also with AlR_2X (exception X = $-NR_2$) if some aluminum trialkyl is present as a catalyst (*307,338,351*). This catalysis is caused by the alkyl interchange discussed above. The reactions take place with the aluminum trialkyls only, but the changes are transferred to the AlR_2X compounds *via* alkyl interchange (see pp. 208–210). Similar catalysis is not possible for the type $RAlX_2$ because small amounts of added R_3Al immediately go over into R_2AlX and large amounts of AlR_3 convert all $RAlX_2$ present into R_2AlX, and then we have a catalytical transformation not of $RAlX_2$ but of R_2AlX. The sharp difference in reactivity between R_3Al and R_2AlX again demonstrates that under normal circumstances no appreciable amount of R_2AlX can be disproportionated. Otherwise R_2AlX should react slowly in a similar manner. On the other hand, it has been observed that some reactions highly specific for aluminum trialkyls at moderate temperatures become possible with R_2AlX at very inconvenient temperatures of 100–200° higher (*76*). Under these conditions some disproportionation quite obviously occurs.

2) Many reactions are related to the electron deficiency of aluminum in

its compounds of the type $AlR_{3-n}X_n$ (n = 2 to zero). The saturation of the electron deficiency considerably diminishes the reactivity. Thus, the etherates, trialkyl aminates etc. of the aluminum trialkyls are much less reactive than the donor-free parent compounds (*302,318,342*). The same applies to the complex compounds of type, $MAlR_4$ or $MAlR_3X$ (*302,318*). This leads to the conclusion that reactions start predominantly with the parent monomolecular aluminum compounds; and indeed this has been well proved as far as suitable decisive experiments were possible (*302,318,348*). Probably this electron deficiency normally causes the start of many reactions (*235*).

3) Certain reversible relations exist between the Al—C and the Al—H bond (*301,302,336*). In connection with the "Direct Synthesis" the addition of olefins to dialkyl aluminum hydrides has been mentioned;

$$(C_nH_{2n+1})_2AlH + C_nH_{2n} \rightleftarrows Al(C_nH_{2n+1})_3.$$

We must now add that the reverse ← reaction is also possible; that is, the equation has to be written as an equilibrium. The consequences of this fact shall be discussed below.

4) Not only the aluminum-hydrogen bond but also the aluminum-carbon bond can be added to C=C double bonds (*297,298,300,337,369,373*) (and to C≡C bonds as well (*275,302*)). This makes a rather valuable expansion of organometallic synthesis possible. By combining this reaction with that numbered under 3) a new type of purely catalytic, organometallic synthesis has been developed. To a certain extent also the addition of "Al—C" to C=C is reversible (*219,302,340*).

5) Organo-aluminum compounds undergo a series of reactions more or less characteristic for many metal alkyls in which the aluminum is removed from carbon (*300,303,305,306,308*). Although some reactions of this type may be rather important for practical reasons, they are not entirely new and mostly not very surprising. Moreover the limitations discussed under 1) often play a role.

6) An interesting new field has been opened up by using complex compounds like $NaF \cdot 2\ AlR_3$ or $NaAlR_4$ as means for making highly reactive alkyl radicals, especially ethyls, by electrolysis, suitable for dissolving metals to metal alkyls. Therefore, a special section has been devoted to electrolytic processes later in the chapter (see pp. 251–255).

Reactions in which the Sum of Al—C + Al—H Bonds (+ Free Al) Remains Constant

Relationships between Al—C and Al—H Bonds. All aluminum alkyls with alkyls higher than methyl have a certain tendency to split off one molecule of olefin. If the alkyls are branched in the α position actual equilibria like

$$Al(CH_2-CH(CH_3)_2)_3 \rightleftharpoons HAl(CH_2-CH(CH_3)_2)_2 + CH_2=C(CH_3)_2 \quad (33)$$

can be observed and have been measured (336). As a consequence it is very easy to convert aluminum tri-isobutyl into di-isobutylaluminum hydride by heating it to temperatures between 120 and 150° (145,300,313,336,357). Isobutylene is split off, and the residue after distillation *in vacuo* is pure isobutylaluminum hydride. *Vice versa*, when this hydride is heated with an excess of isobutylene to about 60–70°, aluminum tri-isobutyl having very little hydride content is recovered. The excess of olefin must be removed at a temperature as low as possible. Aluminum tri-isobutyl, being solid below +5° C (145,181,328,355) is very easy to obtain in a high degree of purity.

Similar reversible transformations can be realized with other aluminum alkyls, including those with normal alkyls. The ease with which the olefins can be split off is different. It depends somewhat on the boiling point, for the products have to be heated in a vacuum; and if the boiling point is low, so is the decomposition rate. Aluminum tri-*n*-hexyl, for example, has been completely converted into the corresponding hydride by prolonged heating *in vacuo* to *ca.* 150°, whereas aluminum triethyl has to be refluxed for a long time under a pressure somewhat lower than 1 atmosphere at 160–180° to be partially converted into the hydride (23,357). It is interesting that the olefin split off is mainly butene-(1) and not ethylene (213,297,357). The explanation for this observation is that aluminum triethyl first adds the ethylene set free to form diethyl aluminum butyl, and the aluminum butyl group is decomposed more easily than the aluminum ethyl group.

Obviously, the aluminum trialkyl—dialkyl aluminum hydride—olefin equilibrium is also possible as a mechanism for an alkyl interchange between different aluminum trialkyls. If two different aluminum alkyls dissociate reversibly, the olefins can be mutually interchanged, and the result is the same as if alkyl groups had been directly interchanged. The direct alkyl interchange discussed on pp. 208–210 proceeds by many orders of magnitude faster than this interchange *via* the hydrides and olefins. The decomposition of aluminum trialkyls to the hydrides + olefins is very slow below 100°. But the alkyl interchange takes place rapidly at temperatures of 0° and below. This has been confirmed in a rather nice experiment by Pino, Lardicci and Lorenzi (222). They demonstrated that at low temperatures interchange of optically active primary alkyls with the asymmetrical carbon atom in position 2 is possible without loss of optical activity, whereas the activity disappears rapidly at higher temperatures.

Another problem to be discussed in connection with the dissociation equilibria is the question as to whether secondary and tertiary aluminum alkyls can be obtained. Quite naturally secondary aluminum alkyls can be derived from cyclic olefins because there is no other possibility. The tendency to add aluminum hydride groups is different for different cycloölefins. Cyclobutyl, cyclopentyl, and cyclooctyl aluminum compounds can be obtained much more easily than the cyclohexyl and cycloheptyl derivatives (328).

The real problem is what happens in the competitive formation of primary and secondary aluminum compounds during the addition of the Al—H group. In this case the Markownikoff rule applies. The aluminum hydride bond is polarized according to $\overset{\delta+}{Al}$—$\overset{\delta-}{H}$ and can be compared with $\overset{\delta+}{H}$—$\overset{\delta-}{Br}$ (297,298). This means that the formation of primary aluminum compounds is favored. As a matter of fact all reactions related to this problem have been formulated according to this rule in the preceding part of this chapter. The difference in the ease with which secondary and primary aluminum alkyls are formed when Al—H is added to double bonds has been compared by reaction rate measurements (328). 1,2-Disubstituted ethylenes add the Al—H bond about 100 times slower than α-olefins do. Therefore one should expect that about 1 per cent of secondary aluminum alkyls would be formed along with 99 per cent of primary ones if Al—H is added to an α-olefin. Probably this estimate from the measured reaction rates of different olefins is not very accurate. The real proportion seems to lie more in the region $1:20$–$1:30$ (337). The exact value is not yet known. Styrene is an exception. Natta et al. (198) have found here a proportion of secondary : primary alkyl $= 1:\sim 3$.

It is easy to understand that no pure aliphatic secondary aluminum compounds can be obtained from aluminum hydrides and olefins if the formation is in competition with that of primary compounds. The only practicable way in such a case seems to be the reaction of, e.g., mercury diisopropyl with metallic aluminum. The aluminum tri-isopropyl (223), a well-defined, crystallizable substance, recently has been demonstrated to rearrange to aluminum tri-n-propyl (296) by being heated to 110–$130°$C, an observation which after all is not very surprising. Dialkyl aluminum hydrides can be added to olefins with internal double bonds (328). The fragments arising from the olefins probably are primarily bound to aluminum as secondary groups. They may be rearranged subsequently.

Obviously there is very little change to synthesize tertiary aluminum trialkyls. This has been established in the following way. Aluminum alkyls are catalysts for the shifting of double bonds of olefins in the chain. Of course this catalysis is due to reversible addition and splitting-off of "Al—H" at the double bond. Olefins with the group $H_2C{=}C{\Big\langle}{\begin{array}{l} CH_2{-}CH_2 \ldots . \\ CH_2{-}CH_2 \ldots . \end{array}}$ are extremely easily and to a high degree rearranged to other ones with the group H$_3$C—C$\begin{smallmatrix}\diagup CH_2-CH_2\ldots\\ \diagdown CH-CH_2\ldots\end{smallmatrix}$ by acid catalysts. Nevertheless, if they are heated for a rather long time with aluminum alkyls or dialkyl aluminum hydrides, only traces are rearranged (*337*). This demonstrates that the addition of "Al—H" to form a tertiary group is nearly impossible.

The stability of the different types of primary aluminum trialkyls has been compared by measurements of decomposition rates (*336*). This can be realized by heating aluminum trialkyls with suitable olefins. Thus, when aluminum tripropyl is boiled with 2-ethyl-hexene-(1) (120°) propylene is evolved exactly following a first-order rate law. The rate remains unchanged if the reaction mixture is diluted with octane (having the same boiling point) or if the excess of the olefin is altered, or the 2-ethyl-hexene-(1) is replaced by 2-methylstyrene. In this latter case, of course, the original boiling point (120°) has to be carefully adjusted by using the olefin in a mixture with octane and heptane.

The olefins in these experiments are added for the removal of the dipropyl aluminum hydride set free by decomposition. The boiling action of the reaction mixture removes the propylene very quickly.

Under such circumstances the readdition of propylene to the hydride is made impossible, and therefore the true rate of the original decomposition can be studied. At 120° aluminum tripropyl has a half-life period of *ca.* 6 hours (*336*), at 160°, 20 minutes (*260*). The decomposition rates of other aluminum tri-*n*-alkyls are practically the same. Similar experiments with aluminum triethyl have shown that ethylene is split off at about 1/40 of the rate of propylene from aluminum tripropyl (*336*).

The decomposition rate of aluminum tri-isobutyl certainly is much higher than that of the normal aluminum alkyls (*333*), but it has not yet been measured exactly.

During these experiments the reaction rate is a function of the monomolecular decomposition of the aluminum trialkyls only. Nevertheless the overall reaction to be observed is a replacement of one olefin by another one from its compound with aluminum hydride, which can be described by Eq. (34):

$$Al(C_3H_7)_3 + 3\ C_8H_{16} = Al(C_8H_{17})_3 + 3\ C_3H_6 \qquad (34)$$

Obviously if the equilibrium

$$\text{Aluminum-alkyl}^I \rightleftarrows \text{Aluminum-H} + \text{Olefin}^I \qquad (35)$$

exists, wherein the "Aluminum-H" shall mean the Al—H bond in dialkyl aluminum hydrides, the following double equilibrium must also be possible:

Aluminum-alkyl^I + Olefin^{II} $\rightleftarrows$ Aluminum-H + Olefin^I + Olefin^{II} $\rightleftarrows$

Aluminum-alkyl^{II} + Olefin^I.

Normally the concentration of the hydride in equilibria such as these is very low, and therefore we can write the equilibrium of replacement in this way:

Aluminum-alkyl^I + Olefin^{II} $\rightleftarrows$ Aluminum-alkyl^{II} + Olefin^I.

The concentration of the different components in equilibria like these depends on the structure of the olefins and aluminum alkyls involved. The equilibrium constant is 1 or close to 1 if the two competing olefins are similar in structure (*336*), e.g., if both are normal α-olefins or isobutene type olefins; but the constants are highly different from 1 if the two olefins belong to different types (*336*). The three "types" investigated in detail up to now are

$$C_2H_4 \qquad\qquad R{-}CH{=}CH_2 \qquad\qquad R_2C{=}CH_2 \qquad (36)$$

Type 1 $\qquad\qquad$ Type 2 $\qquad\qquad$ Type 3

The equilibrium constant is about 40 for equilibria in which either types 2 and 3 or types 1 and 2 are involved (*336*). Obviously the equilibrium constant for ethylene competing with type 3 must have an order of magnitude of 1600. These values are measured or calculated for simplified equilibria written as

$$alR^I + Olefin^{II} \rightleftarrows alR^{II} + Olefin^I \quad al = \tfrac{1}{3} Al \qquad (37)$$

This involves the assumption that the individual aluminum-carbon bonds in aluminum trialkyls are not influenced if different alkyl radicals are bound to the other two valences (*336*). We must recall in this connection that, due to the alkyl interchange and the differences in the tendencies to associate, we have a rather complicated composition in such equilibrium mixtures. Nevertheless the equilibria measurements can be described correctly by the formula:

$$\frac{[alR^{II}][Olefin^I]}{[alR^I][Olefin^{II}]} = K \qquad (38)$$

if all measurements are made under similar conditions of concentration.

We can describe the results just discussed in a somewhat different way by saying that the affinity of olefins to "Al—H" decreases considerably from type 1 to type 3. Nothing definite can be said about the 1,2-disubstituted ethylenes, but certainly their affinity to "Al—H" is lower than that of type 2.

The practical value of the replacement equilibria lies in the fact that they allow one to interconvert aluminum alkyls at will. The extreme ease with which aluminum tri-isobutyl loses isobutylene makes this readily available aluminum trialkyl a very convenient starting material for the synthesis of any other desired aluminum trialkyl (267,333,374), (also with C_{14}-labeled Et (215)). Nothing else is necessary but to boil this aluminum trialkyl (or the corresponding di-isobutyl aluminum hydride) with other olefins or to heat the isobutyl compounds with lower olefins in excess under pressure. This allows one to limit the large-scale synthesis of aluminum alkyls to that of the aluminum isobutyl compounds only, as well as to make the other products on a small scale by convenient laboratory methods.

Regardless of the ease with which such replacements are possible with the isobutyl compounds, the replacement can also be used for the interconversion of other aluminum alkyls. For example, aluminum tripropyl can be used instead of aluminum tri-isobutyl if we increase the temperature of the replacement or if we use the trick of adding a trace of colloidal nickel (299,309,317,336,337,339,371) a catalyst in the replacement at low temperatures. When aluminum trihexyl is heated to 150–160° and a stream of gaseous propylene is passed through, α-hexene distills off and aluminum tripropyl is obtained (336). Vice versa, if we start with aluminum tripropyl and pass the vapor of α-hexene through it at 150°, propylene is evolved and all is converted into aluminum trihexyl (336). Such replacements are important in connection with the synthesis of straight-chained α-olefins from ethylene (see pp. 229–231).

The replacement reaction belongs to that group of reactions which are possible only with true aluminum trialkyls. It can be used in a simple experiment to demonstrate the catalytic activity of some aluminum trialkyls added to reagents of the type R_2AlX (X = Halogen, OR, or SR). Methoxyaluminum di-isobutyl has been refluxed with 2-ethyl-hexene-(1) for many hours without any trace of isobutene being evolved. After a few per cent of aluminum tri-isoöctyl (or any other aluminum trialkyl) has been added, the isobutene escapes from the mixture and the displacement soon reaches completion (338). The addition of nickel without aluminum trialkyl has no effect. An analogous experiment with di-isobutyl aluminum diethylamide fails (338), thus demonstrating that no alkyl interchange occurs between the aluminum trialkyls and dialkyl aluminum dialkylamides.

Addition of Al—C Groups to the C=C Bond. *Addition to Ethylene, the "Stepwise Organometallic Synthesis."* The addition of organometallic compounds to C=C double bonds and the principle of the so-called "stepwise organometallic synthesis" were discovered more than 30 years ago for alkali alkyls and butadiene or styrene and other phenylated ethylenes, respectively (319–326,345). Gilman and Kirby (63) demonstrated that aluminum triphenyl also adds to olefins activated by phenyl groups. Later Ziegler and Gellert (*327*) found the similar but also simpler (with regard to the structure of the products) addition of lithium alkyls to ethylene according to Eq. (39):

$$LiC_2H_5 \xrightarrow{C_2H_4} Li-CH_2-CH_2-C_2H_5 \xrightarrow{C_2H_4} Li[CH_2-CH_2]_n-C_2H_5 \qquad (39)$$

It was indeed a surprise when the same authors discovered an analogous reaction for ethylene and (normal) aluminum trialkyls (Eq. 40) (*297,298, 337,369,373*):

$$Al\begin{cases} C_2H_5 \\ C_2H_5 \\ C_2H_5 \end{cases} + 3\,m\,C_2H_4 = Al\begin{cases} (C_2H_4)_nC_2H_5 \\ (C_2H_4)_pC_2H_5 \\ (C_2H_4)_qC_2H_5 \end{cases} \left(\frac{n+p+q}{3} = m\right) \qquad (40)$$

or more simply,

$$R-al + n\,C_2H_4 = R[C_2H_4]_n al.$$

In combination with the "direct synthesis" of $Al(C_2H_5)_3$ the same process can be written

$$al + \tfrac{1}{2}H_2 + n\,C_2H_4 = al(C_2H_4)_n H \qquad (41)$$

This so-called "growth reaction" requires a pressure of *ca.* 100 atmospheres and temperatures between 90 and 120°. At lower pressures the addition proceeds too slowly, and then appreciable amounts of olefins are formed as by-products. These originate by the spontaneous decomposition of the aluminum trialkyls into olefins and dialkyl aluminum hydrides, the latter being scavenged immediately by the ethylene present to give aluminum triethyl. The rate of this "replacement" is independent of the ethylene pressure. At 1 atmosphere the ratio "growth" to "replacement" is about 1:1, at 10 atmospheres 10:1, at 100 atmospheres 100:1, i.e., the rate of replacement is not altered but that of the "growth" (bimolecular for the single step) is increased proportionally to the pressure (*332*). At 110° and with 100 atmospheres of C_2H_4 about one molecule of ethylene is added per mole of aluminum trialkyl in one hour. This means that 3 hours are necessary for converting aluminum triethyl to a product with the average composition of aluminum tributyl. Higher temperatures may be used and higher reaction rates may be realized (*381*), but it is somewhat difficult to have a smooth reaction under such circumstances. With aluminum tri-isobutyl, the growth products of aluminum triethyl are obtained predominantly due to the extreme ease with which isobutene is split off from tri-isobutyl aluminum (*297*).

It is important to avoid all traces of catalysts for the replacement during the growth reaction. The picture just discussed for aluminum triethyl is correct for an absolutely uncatalyzed system only. In the presence of even extremely small quantities of colloidal nickel (or other substances with a similar activity) rather confused results can be obtained (299,309,317,332). In such cases complicated mixtures of normal and branched olefins with aluminum alkyls can be obtained, or even exclusively butene-(1), together with aluminum triethyl (and the olefin corresponding to the aluminum tri-alkyl used, if this has not been $Al(C_2H_5)_3$). Steel, copper, or glass are materials suitable for the reaction vessels.

If the experiment is properly made the reaction product contains only a few per cent of free olefins. Its average composition corresponds to the amount of ethylene added per mole of aluminum trialkyl. The distribution of the different chains grown on the aluminum comes very near to that calculated under the assumption that all Al—C bonds present in the reaction mixture have the same probability of adding to ethylene during the entire period of the experiment. This distribution follows the so-called Poisson law (Eq. 42) (271,337):

$$X_{(p)} = \frac{n^p \cdot e^{-n}}{p!} \tag{42}$$

wherein n is given by the equation

$$Ral + n\,C_2H_4 = R(C_2H_4)_n al.$$

$X_{(p)}$ represents the proportion of chains with $(C_2H_4)_p$ to the total number of chains formed.

The good agreement between calculation and experiment is illustrated by Fig. 5.1 (337). Ziegler has recently discussed reasons why the formation of longer chains may perhaps be somewhat favored (307,337).

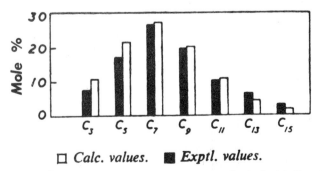

□ Calc. values.   ■ Exptl. values.

Figure 5.1. Distribution of hydrocarbons yielded by hydrolysis of products from $C_3H_7Al_{1/3} + 2 \cdot 2\,C_2H_4$

The rate of ethylene absorption* per aluminum atom present increases considerably when the aluminum trialkyls are diluted with inert (hydrocarbon) solvents (*301,302,318,337*). Suitable experiments have been made by measuring the initial absorption rate for 1 atmosphere of ethylene by dissolved $Al(C_2H_5)_3$. Under these conditions the only reaction taking place is

$$Al(C_2H_5)_3 + C_2H_4 = Al(C_4H_9)(C_2H_5)_2, \qquad (43)$$

and the possible subsequent evolution of butene-(1) can be neglected. The ratio of the absorption rates (per Al present) for a 1 M and a 0.01 M solution comes very near to 10 (*348*), thus demonstrating that this absorption rate per mole AlR_3 follows the square root of the dilution. The same has been found very exactly for the absorption of acetylene, the measurement of which is somewhat simpler than that of the ethylene absorption. On the other hand, monomolecular tri-isobutyl aluminum has always the same absorption rate for acetylene (per Al atom) quite independently of the dilution. (The rate for ethylene cannot be measured due to rapid replacement.) These observations are rather impressive proofs for the assumption that monomolecular aluminum trialkyls are the active principle of the growth reaction, that they are quite generally the active forms, and that the dimers are unreactive. Not only does this self-complexity hinder the "growth"; heterocomplexity does so too. Thus, $Na[Al(C_2H_5)_3F]$ and $Na[Al(C_2H_5)_4]$ add ethylene but only with great sluggishness (*318*)

The addition of ethylene cannot be continued without limits. Even at relatively low temperatures the ratio of the number of addition steps to the number of replacement steps does not exceed about 100 (for 100 atmospheres of ethylene), i.e., for 100 molecules of added ethylene, about 1 molecule of an aluminum-free olefin is to be expected. It is easy to understand that in the case of an expected synthesis of a molecule, $R(C_2H_4)_{100}al$, about equal amounts of long-chain aluminum alkyls and olefins will be formed (*317*). The consequence of this complication is that the growth reaction may be predominantly used for the synthesis of straight-chain aliphatic compounds between C_4 and about C_{30}.

Again the growth reaction can also be realized with substances of the type R_2AlX (except for $X = -NR_2$) in the presence of small amounts of aluminum trialkyls as catalysts (*307,338,351,354*). This fact is utilized in a certain modification of the α-olefin synthesis from ethylene (see pp. 230–231).

Special conditions are required in synthesizing odd-numbered aluminum alkyls by the growth reaction. Using aluminum tripropyl as starting material, the reaction proceeds quite normally if catalysts for the replacement

*Absorption rate measurements have also been made by Natta et al. (*199*).

are carefully avoided. The only rather unimportant difference between the synthesis of even-numbered and odd-numbered products is that in the course of the side reaction, i.e., the replacement, some aluminum triethyl is formed, and this leads to the formation of a small quantity of even-numbered by-products (*337*).

More interesting is the fact that the growth reaction is really impossible with aluminum trimethyl. This lowest member of the series has a very low reactivity toward ethylene (*301,302,337*); and if under rather strong conditions, a reaction finally does take place, the first traces of the aluminum propyl formed react much faster with the ethylene than the aluminum trimethyl does. Under such circumstances no smooth growth reaction can be realized. No relation exists between the molar ratio of aluminum trimethyl and the ethylene used, and most of the aluminum trimethyl remains unchanged. It is interesting that aluminum trimethyl is able to transfer its unreactivity (*302,337*) to other aluminum trialkyls, e.g., aluminum triethyl. Mixtures of aluminum trimethyl and triethyl add ethylene much slower than would be calculated if nothing else had happened but the dilution. A possible explanation can be found in the assumption that by alkyl interchange mixed aluminum methyl-ethyls are formed having a much more significant tendency to associate than has the pure aluminum triethyl. Of course the low reaction rate of aluminum trimethyl can be explained in a similar way also. It is self-evident that the reactive component in mixtures of the two mentioned aluminum alkyls is the aluminum ethyl only. It undergoes a normal growth reaction to give even-numbered growth products; and, on decomposition of the reaction product with water, methane is obtained together with the even-numbered paraffins (*337*).

It would be helpful for its utilization if the growth reaction could be accelerated by catalysts. Catalysts for the original form of this reaction are not known. But a new modification of the growth reaction has been found in the Goodrich-Gulf Company by Roha and Beears (*237*) which perhaps includes such a catalysis. Dialkyl aluminum chlorides add ethylene in the presence of $TiCl_3$ especially in aromatic hydrocarbons as solvents. The mechanism of this reaction is not yet entirely known. The reaction products obviously have the formula $ClAl[(C_2H_4)_n-R]_2$. Hydrolysis leads to paraffins; oxidation to primary alcohols (see pp. 238–239). The reaction probably is the connecting link between the growth of pure organoaluminum compounds and the true low-pressure polymerizations by complex catalysts (*307*) and therefore does not properly belong to the subject matter of this chapter.

Aluminum Alkyls and Higher Olefins. In the course of the growth reaction the type of the aluminum alkyls involved remains unchanged. This does not apply when an aluminum alkyl is added to a monosubstituted ethylene, e.g., propylene. The aluminum atom, preferring the primary carbon atom, adds predominately according to Eq. (44) (*297,298,337,373*):

$$C_3H_7al + CH_3\text{—}CH\text{=}CH_2 = CH_3\text{—}\underset{\underset{C_3H_7}{|}}{CH}\text{—}CH_2al \qquad (44)$$

The addition product has a structure similar to that of aluminum isobutyl. Therefore the first addition is immediately followed by a replacement (Eq. 45):

$$CH_3\text{—}\underset{\underset{C_3H_7}{|}}{CH}\text{—}CH_2al + C_3H_6 = CH_3\text{—}\underset{\underset{C_3H_7}{|}}{C}\text{=}CH_2 + C_3H_7al \qquad (45)$$

Even if equimolecular amounts of aluminum propyl and propylene are used we do not obtain smoothly an addition product but predominantly 2-methyl-pentene-(1), a dimer of propylene; and aluminum tripropyl remains unchanged (*337*).

Nevertheless, the addition product can be obtained if the reaction mixture is heated for a comparatively long time. After the main part of propylene has been consumed, the reaction mixture contains 2-methyl-pentene-(1) in high concentration. It gives, with aluminum tripropyl, the equilibrium

$$C_3H_7al + C_6H_{12} \rightleftarrows C_3H_6 + C_6H_{13}al \qquad (46)$$

Regardless of an equilibrium constant of about 40, unfavorable for the formation of free propylene, small amounts of propylene are formed because the concentration of isohexene is high. The propylene reacts further according to equation (44), and so, after a long reaction time, we obtain $C_6H_{13}Al$ in high concentration (*337*).

This method of making isohexylaluminum is not the recommended one. It is preferable first to realize the rather rapid overall reaction, (44) + (45). In this case propylene is employed in excess. What happens then is nothing other than the catalytic dimerization (*297,298,337,356,369*) of propylene to 2-methyl-pentene-(1), which, if desired, can be converted into the corresponding isohexylaluminum by the "Direct Synthesis."

The dimerization of propylene to 2-methyl-pentene-(1) by heating with small amounts of aluminum tripropyl to temperatures of 140 to 200° is one of the smoothest, homogeneous, catalytic processes whose mechanism is known in complete details. A few per cent of aluminum tripropyl is sufficient, and, if the propylene is pure, this can be recovered again and again by distilling off the methylpentene. Instead of aluminum tripropyl, any other aluminum trialkyl can be used as a catalyst, e.g., aluminum triethyl. It is very soon converted into aluminum tripropyl in the reaction mixture, and a small amount of 2-methyl-butene-(1) can be distilled off in the forerun of 2-methyl-pentene.

Analogous catalytic dimerizations can be realized with butene-(1) and all α-olefins, the general formula of the dimers being

$$R-C=CH_2$$
$$\overset{|}{R-CH_2-CH_2}$$

(297,298,337,369,373). It is remarkable that during these dimerizations only very little trimer is obtained. The trimer of, e.g., propylene could originate by an addition of aluminum isohexyl to propylene, but this reaction obviously proceeds very slowly.

Detailed study of the dimerization has led to a rather good estimation of the ratio between the Markownikoff and the "anti-Markownikoff" addition of the aluminum alkyls to α-olefins *(337)*. The result of an "anti-Markownikoff" addition is a secondary aluminum alkyl with a normal chain (Eq. 47):

$$R-CH_2-CH_2al + CH_2=CH-R = R-CH_2=CH_2-CH_2-\overset{|}{\underset{al}{CH}}-R \quad (47)$$

If R is a relatively large normal aliphatic radical and if the olefins formed in the dimerization are hydrogenated, a mixture of a monomethyl paraffin and a straight-chain paraffin is obtained. The two products can be very easily separated by crystallization and in this way about 5 per cent of the "anti-Markownikoff" products have been found for dimerizations made at 180–200° *(234)*. Probably the ratio depends on the temperature of the dimerization. At lower temperature the Markownikoff process is even more highly favored *(337)*.

If the alkyl group in the aluminum alkyl and in the α-olefin have different numbers of carbon atoms, the fastest process, when they are heated together in equimolar amounts, is the mutual replacement of olefins. That is, the mixture of the two compounds first is converted into the equilibrium mixture

$$\underset{A}{R-CH_2-CH_2-\ al\ +\ R'-CH=CH_2} \rightleftarrows$$

$$\underset{B}{R-CH=CH_2\ +\ R'-CH_2-CH_2-\ al} \quad (48)$$

and then addition processes occur between all four components of the equilibrium *(303,337)*. Therefore, normally four different dimers will be obtained: A_2, AB, BA, B_2. A smooth codimerization to a single product is not possible in this way. An exception to this rule is found in reactions of aluminum triethyl, because this aluminum alkyl is highly favored in the replacement equilibrium. Therefore an α-ethylation of α-olefins by means of aluminum triethyl is relatively smooth, especially if the aluminum triethyl is used in excess (*337*). This problem has a certain relation to the co-dimerization of ethylene and propylene to 2-methyl-butene, a fore-product of isoprene (*302,337*).

Cycloölefins also have been dimerized, e.g., cyclopentene (*302,337*) to:

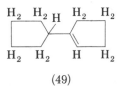

(49)

For open-chain olefins with a double bond in the chain, dimerization has not yet been realized. If such olefins are heated together with aluminum alkyls, the shift of the double bond, catalyzed by the aluminum alkyl, is the fastest process. If the double bond has reached the end of the molecule, dimerization occurs. Therefore, at least the lower β-, γ-, *etc.* olefins can be converted into the dimers of the α-olefins (*297,298,337*).

All of the reactions discussed in detail above were catalytic variants of an original organometallic synthesis, rather specific for aluminum alkyls. The decisive step in making this catalysis possible is the instability of aluminum alkyls having a tertiary hydrogen atom at a branched carbon atom-2. Therefore a smooth formation of an aluminum alkyl might be expected from reaction between an aluminum alkyl and, e.g., isobutylene. It has been found that isobutylene-type hydrocarbons have no great tendency to add aluminum alkyls. If such olefins are heated together with aluminum alkyls, a replacement equilibrium leading to other olefins more reactive than isobutylene and its analogs occurs. Therefore the total course of the reaction is a highly complicated one. Only one smooth addition of this type has been realized up to now, namely that of aluminum trimethyl to isobutylene at about 200°. In this way aluminum trineopentyl is formed (*219,290,302*). It is most interesting that this addition is reversible. The aluminum trineopentyl can be distilled in a high vacuum at 50° without decomposition; but when distilled at 210°, aluminum trimethyl and isobutylene are recovered. Therefore we have to write the following equilibrium:

$$(CH_3)_2C{=}CH_2 + CH_3al \rightleftarrows (CH_3)_3C{-}CH_2al \qquad (50)$$

These observations are a very clear proof of the reversibility of the organometallic synthesis at high temperatures.

Pyrolysis of Aluminum Trialkyls (Reversibility of the Organometallic Synthesis). It seems useful at this point to say something more about the thermal instability of aluminum trialkyls, in addition to the decomposition of aluminum trineopentyl just mentioned.

The formation of dialkyl aluminum hydrides by moderately heating aluminum trialkyls already has been discussed. These hydrides can be entirely decomposed at still higher temperatures (*313,340*), e.g., di-isobutyl aluminum hydride decomposes rather smoothly at 250° according to (Eq. 51):

$$(i\text{-}C_4H_9)_2AlH = Al + 1\tfrac{1}{2}H_2 + 2\,i\text{-}C_4H_8 \tag{51}$$

This, together with the formation of the di-isobutyl hydride (Eq. 33), is nothing other than a complete reversal of the "Direct Synthesis." The reaction has been proposed for the refining of aluminum by a reversible dissolution of aluminum with isobutylene and hydrogen and decomposition of the aluminum tri-isobutyl thus obtained (*313,376*). But this process is somewhat complicated by the fact that normally a little bit of aluminum carbide is obtained as a by-product, originating by another type of decomposition. First, consider the pyrolysis of aluminum trimethyl (*340*). At 200–250° reactions such as (52 a-c) occur:

a) $Al(CH_3)_3 = 1/n\,[CH_2\!=\!Al\!-\!CH_2]_n + CH_4$

b) $1/n\,[CH_2\!=\!Al\!-\!CH_2]_n + CH_4 = 1/n\,[Al\!\equiv\!CH]_n + 2\,CH_4$ $\qquad(52)$

c) $4\,Al(CH_3)_3 = Al_4C_3 + 9\,CH_4$

This overall reaction is comparable to the dehydration of metal hydroxides which, *via* several intermediates, finally leads to the metal oxides. In limited reaction periods, products are formed which can be regarded as complicated cross-linked compounds of $CH_2\!=$, $CH\!\equiv$, $C\!\equiv$ groups on the one side and a corresponding amount of aluminum atoms on the other, which of course still can contain unchanged methyl groups. These products are yellowish-white and insoluble. The end product after long heating is the amorphous modification of aluminum carbide (*340*), a product which had already been obtained in 1946 from heated $Al(CH_3)_3$ vapor by Yeddanapalli and Schubert (*286*).

The decomposition of aluminum tri-isobutyl into aluminum, hydrogen and isobutene takes place eventually if the heating is done in an open vessel or in a vacuum. If the same aluminum compound is heated in a closed vessel, so that the isobutene cannot escape, quite another decomposition is observed. Methane is evolved, and yellowish-white insoluble products are formed similar to those obtained from aluminum trimethyl (*340*). The explanation is simple: aluminum isobutyl can be regarded as an addition product of aluminum methyl to propylene. Above 200° the addition is reversible; the aluminum isobutyl splits into aluminum methyl and propylene. The aluminum methyl undergoes its normal decomposition, and the propylene is converted into its dimer and other products.

This course of the pyrolysis of an aluminum alkyl is again an example of the reversibility of the organometallic synthesis. The same reversibility has been demonstrated for aluminum[2-ethyl-hexyl]. In this case the decomposition can follow two different paths, (53a) and 53b) (besides the simple formation of R_2AlH + olefin):

$$C_4H_9 \cdot \underset{\overset{|}{C_2H_5}}{CH} \cdot CH_2 \cdot al \underset{b}{\overset{a}{<}} \begin{array}{l} C_4H_9al + C_2H_5 \cdot CH:CH_2 \\ \\ C_2H_5al + C_4H_9 \cdot CH:CH_2 \end{array} \qquad (53)$$

Products corresponding to both possibilities have been found (*340*).

Synthesis of Straight-Chain α-Olefins From Ethylene. Aluminum trialkyls were efficient catalysts for the synthesis of branched olefins having the general formula $RR'C{=}CH_2$. When heated with ethylene under suitable conditions, no catalysis was observed, and the so-called growth products were obtained smoothly (*297,298,337,373*). Now we shall discuss the possibility of making straight-chain α-olefins, using ethylene and aluminum alkyls as starting materials, without any appreciable loss of the aluminum alkyl. The most simple way to realize this is to perform the growth reaction in the presence of a trace of colloidal nickel. Under such circumstances the first addition step, forming aluminum butyl groups, is immediately followed by an extremely rapid replacement catalyzed by the nickel, and butene-(I) is obtained in high yield as sole reaction product (*299,309,311,339,371*).* The whole process is improved when a trace of acetylene or an acetylene derivative is added, stabilizing the nickel cocatalyst (*339,371*). In the course of this reaction the rate of the replacement is many times faster than that of the growth, and this is the only condition for a good yield of butene-(1). It does not make any difference whether the ratio between the two rates is 100, 1000, or 10^6. The changes for such differences would lie within the limit of the last per cent of the yield. But if this ratio was lowered to 10 or below, the yield of butene-(1) would decrease markedly (*299,339*). It has been proposed that one can arrive at any desired average molecular weight of olefins by regulating this ratio to still lower but absolutely constant values. This idea is not practicable because the co-catalyst too quickly changes its activity during the reaction (*339*). A better possibility is to omit any co-catalyst but to choose a reaction temperature much higher than the temperatures of the

---

*A similar dimerization of ethylene can be realized with the combination, $Ti(OR)_4$ + AlR_3. The process is rather fast under conditions of temperature and pressure at which the normal "growth reaction" does not occur. The mechanism of this process is not yet elucidated (*182,358*).

normal growth (*339*). For a certain ethylene pressure, given ratios of the rates of the growth and replacement reactions belong to a prescribed temperature, and the higher the temperature, the more is the replacement favored. In addition, the ratio can be influenced by changing the pressure. In the region of 200° and above, it is actually possible to realize a full cycle of the following reactions:

a) $alH + C_2H_4 = alC_2H_5$

b) $alC_2H_5 + (n\text{-}1)C_2H_4 = al(C_2H_4)_{n\text{-}1}(C_2H_5)$ (54)

c) $al(C_2H_4)_{n\text{-}1}C_2H_5 = alH + CH_2{=}CH(C_2H_4)_{n\text{-}2}C_2H_5,$

---

d) $nC_2H_4 = (C_2H_4)_n$

The organometallic synthesis of higher α-olefins from ethylene thus is realized in the form of a complete catalysis. The catalyst is the "alH" of course, present in the reaction mixture as dialkyl aluminum hydride (*297, 298,339*).

The disadvantage of this purely catalytic polymerization of ethylene is the very broad distribution of the olefins formed. The mentioned cycle of reactions leads to the following formula (55) for the distribution (*271*):

$$X_{(p)} = \frac{\beta}{(1 + \beta)^p}, \text{ where}$$ (55)

$\beta = \dfrac{K \text{ (replacement)}}{K \text{ (growth)}}$; $X_{(p)}$ represents the proportion of olefins $(C_2H_4)_p$ to the total number of olefin molecules formed.

This distribution is much broader than that of the Poisson formula (Eq. 42). This unfavorable fact is one reason why the aluminum-organic synthesis of α-olefins preferably has been practised in a two-step process. This process is characterized by first synthesizing normal growth products with the relatively sharp Poisson distribution and then splitting off the olefins by replacement reaction in an extra step (*299,339,371*). Of course in this way the olefin mixtures still must have the original Poisson distribution. One way for carrying out the replacement is to add nickel to the growth product and to replace the long-chained olefins by ethylene. The reaction product then is a mixture (aluminum triethyl, olefins, and nickel) which has to be separated. Nickel has to be removed since it interferes with the reuse of the aluminum trialkyl. The problems involved in this task are somewhat complicated, and so several modifications have been proposed (*339*). The difficulty lies in the fact that during the separation of the aluminum triethyl and the olefins the nickel is still present. This can lead to a redisplacement of ethylene by higher olefins during operations. One rather satisfactory solution of the problem is the following modification (*307,339*) in which a cycle of reactions is started from the complex compound, $K[AlEt_2Cl_2]$. This first is decomposed according to Eq. (56a and b) (see also p. 204):

$$
\begin{array}{lll}
a) & KCl + K[EtCl_3] + AlEt_3 & \\
& \nearrow & \\
2\, K[AlEt_2Cl_2] & & (56) \\
& \searrow & \\
b) & 2\, KCl + 2\, EtAlCl &
\end{array}
$$

The distillate is a mixture of about 50 per cent $AlEt_3$ (a) + 50 per cent $AlEt_2Cl$ (b). The residue is a mixture of $KCl + K[AlEtCl_3]$. Distillate and residue are strictly equivalent. If they were recombined the original two molecules of $K[AlEt_2Cl_2]$ would be recovered. The distillate is used for the growth reaction, during which the aluminum trialkyl catalyzes the growth also for diethylaluminum chloride. To the growth product nickel is added, and the mixture is treated with ethylene. A mixture of olefins, aluminum triethyl, diethyl aluminum chloride, and nickel is obtained. This is mixed with the residue of the first decomposition whereupon the free aluminum triethyl entirely disappears. Therefore, no further changes in the reaction mixture are possible, since further reactions are possible only in the presence of free aluminum trialkyl. Moreover, the complex compound $K[Al(C_2H_5)_2Cl_2]$ is insoluble in the olefins and separates spontaneously. The complex compound goes back to the first step of the cycle.

Evidently this rather efficient process is a combination of some reactions specific for organo-aluminum compounds, described in the preceding sections and discovered in the course of the development during the last decade. It may be mentioned here that quite recently further progress has been made in simplifying the α-olefin synthesis from ethylene (*381*).

Of course the olefin synthesis can be started from any aluminum trialkyl. For realizing a complete cycle it is necessary to use in the replacement step the olefin corresponding to the alkyl of the original aluminum compound. Thus, by starting from aluminum tripropyl and using propylene for the replacement the odd-numbered series of α-olefins can easily be obtained. Additional possibilities have been discussed for narrowing the Poisson distribution curve by separating the primary olefin mixture using the lower single olefins for the replacement and adding more ethylene to the lower aluminum alkyls obtained in this way (*299,339*). It is impossible to discuss this in detail in this limited space, but the techniques of all these reactions have now been sufficiently developed to realize such experiments in a rather simple way.

Aluminum Alkyls and Acetylenic Hydrocarbons. Reactions between aluminum alkyls and acetylenic hydrocarbons have been first attempted by Ziegler and Nagel (*191*) and later studied in detail by Wilke and H. Müller (*275,301,302*). As a rule, the active hydrogen atoms of acetylene itself and of monosubstituted acetylenes do not react (as they do in contact with magnesium or alkali alkyls).* The Al—H (*274,276,278*) and the Al—C bonds (*275*) add smoothly to the C≡C bond. In this way aluminum trialkyls can be obtained having vinyl-type substituents (57 and 58):

a $(C_2H_5)_2AlH$ $\xrightarrow{\quad CH\equiv C-C_2H_5 \quad}$

b $(C_2H_5)_3Al$ $\xrightarrow{\quad CH\equiv CH \quad}$ $(C_2H_5)_2Al-CH=CH-C_2H_5$ $\qquad$ (57)

a $(iso-C_4H_9)_3Al$ $\xrightarrow{\quad CH\equiv CH \quad}$ $(iso-C_4H_9)_2Al-CH=CH-CH_2-CH(CH_3)_2$

b $(iso-C_4H_9)_3Al$ $\xrightarrow{\quad C_6H_5C\equiv CH \quad}$ $(iso-C_4H_9)_2Al-CH=C\diagup^{\displaystyle CH_2-C(CH_3)_2}_{\diagdown\displaystyle C_6H_5}$ $\qquad$ (58)

Reaction 58a (with a monomolecular aluminum trialkyl) proceeds at room temperature (*275,302*); (57b) (with an associated one) requires about 40–60°. (For reaction rate measurements, see p. 223.) Consequently, the aluminum trialkyl etherates (trialkyl aminates etc.) do not react with acetylene up to about 100° (*200,275*). No "displacement" is observed as a side reaction of the additions, (57) and (58). The dialkyl aluminum alkenyls obviously are not capable of an interchange as in Eq. (59):

$$2\,(C_2H_5)_2Al-CH=CH-C_2H_5 \rightleftarrows (C_2H_5)_3Al + C_2H_5Al(CH=CHC_6H_5)_2 \quad (59)$$

since only one Al—C_2H_5 group reacts with the alkyne. In an equilibrium like (59) the aluminum triethyl on the right side should add more acetylene. Obviously such mixed aluminum trialkyls are stable. Probably the interchange is impossible only for the unsaturated substituents. This would mean that these substituents do not enter the "bridges." (The dialkyl aluminum alkenyls are associated, with factors amounting to 2.0–2.5 (*275*).) The dialkyl aluminum alkenyls undergo intramolecular condensations when heated to 100° and above (*275,279*).

A dialkyl aluminum alkynyl has been synthesized according to:

$$(C_2H_5)_2AlCl + NaC\equiv C-C_2H_5 = NaCl + (C_2H_5)_2Al-C\equiv C-C_2H_5 \quad (60)$$

It is a liquid, distillable in a high vacuum (*275*).

*Consequently, metallation of aromatic compounds by means of AlEt$_3$ seems to be impossible also (*64,81*).

The addition of the "Al—H" group to acetylenic bonds can be continued. In this way products with more than one Al—C bond in the molecule are formed (*275,302*). There is experimental proof that the different Al atoms are bound to the same carbon atom (61 and 62):

$$2\,(\text{iso-}C_4H_9)_2AlH + HC{\equiv}C{-}C_4H_9 \longrightarrow$$

$$\begin{array}{l} (\text{iso-}C_4H_9)_2Al \\ \qquad\qquad\quad{\searrow} \\ (\text{iso-}C_4H_9)_2Al \end{array}CH{-}CH_2{-}C_4H_9 \quad (61)$$

$$2\,(C_2H_5)_2AlH + (C_2H_5)_2Al{-}C{\equiv}C{-}C_2H_5 \longrightarrow$$

$$[(C_2H_5)_2Al{-}]_3C{-}CH_2{-}C_2H_5 \quad (62)$$

Disubstituted acetylenes normally (exception: tolane (*275*)) do not add aluminum trialkyls smoothly, but they still add one "AlH" group. The addition products are able to add (at about 90°) to another such acetylene (*202,275,301,302*), the reactive group being $Al{-}\overset{|}{C}{=}\overset{|}{C}{-}$ and not $Al{-}\overset{|}{\underset{|}{C}}{-}\overset{|}{\underset{|}{C}}{-}$ Hydrolysis then leads to 1,2,3,4-tetra-alkylbutadienes (also, tetraphenylbutadiene can be made from tolane in this way):

$$R{-}C{\equiv}C{-}R \xrightarrow{\ \text{alH}\ } R{-}CH{=}\underset{\underset{\text{al}}{|}}{C}{-}R \longrightarrow R{-}CH{=}\overset{\overset{R}{|}}{C}{-}\overset{\overset{R}{|}}{\underset{\underset{\text{al (H)}}{|}}{C}}{=}C{-}R \quad (63)$$

At a still higher temperature (140°) and with more alkyne, hexasubstituted benzenes (hexaëthyl, hexaphenyl) are formed in a Diels-Alder reaction from the tetra-alkyl- (-aryl) butadienyl aluminum, followed by a loss of "alH." (For more details about all these reactions see Wilke et al. (*275, 302*).)

Although the reactions between alkynes and organo-aluminum compounds have opened up some rather interesting new aspects, their practical value cannot be compared with that of the different olefin reactions. The main reason is the decrease in reactivity of the aluminum-carbon bond 2 and 3 after the first one has been transformed into $-\overset{|}{C}{=}\overset{|}{C}{-}$al. The addition of an aluminum trialkyl to acetylene includes a method for a systematic "homologization" (*302*) of α-olefins:

$$R{-}CH{=}CH_2 \longrightarrow R{\cdot}CH_2{-}CH_2{-}al \longrightarrow R{-}CH_2{-}CH_2{-}CH{=}CH{-}al \longrightarrow$$

$$R{-}CH_2{-}CH_2{-}CH{=}CH_2 \quad (64)$$

but two-thirds of the olefins are lost by hydrolysis of the two unreactive $R{-}CH_2{-}CH_2{\cdot}al$ equivalents present. Therefore this reaction cannot compete with the α-olefin synthesis with ethylene *via* the "growth reaction," except for $R_2C=CH_2 \rightarrow R_2CH-CH_2-CH=CH_2$, because this latter reaction is highly complicated by the "displacement" in the case of the ethylene method.

Bi- and Polyfunctional Organo-Aluminum Compounds. Pyrolysis of aluminum methyl compounds and addition of aluminum hydride groups to alkynes or alkynyl aluminum compounds obviously lead to bi- and trifunctional organo-aluminum compounds as has been discussed in the preceding pages. All the products described were di- or trifunctional with regard to the same carbon atom. Special synthetic uses for these compounds have not yet been found.

Bifunctional aluminum compounds with the aluminum atom attached to two different C-atoms, especially compounds of the type $al(CH_2)_nal$, would be rather interesting with a view to a possible synthesis of long-chain bifunctional compounds by adding ethylene and then converting the aluminum compounds into other products. The realization of this idea is hindered by a strong barrier which has not yet been surmounted. This is the fact that ring-closure reactions occur when two aluminum atoms are fixed in a certain distance in a carbon chain. Thus, diallyl- and aluminum tri-isobutyl or di-isobutyl hydride do not give 1,6-dialumino-hexane derivatives like (65) or (66):

$$(i\text{-}C_4H_9)_2AlCH_2-CH_2-CH_2-CH_2-CH_2-CH_2Al(i\text{-}C_4H_9)_2 \qquad (65)$$

$$Al[(CH_2)_6]_3Al \qquad (66)$$

—the latter would of course be a cross-linked three-dimensional, high molecular weight compound. Only methylene-cyclopentene and cyclopentyl-methyl aluminum compounds are obtained (*301,302*). The ring closure (*67*) is an intramolecular analog of the olefin dimerization (Eqs. 44 and 45)

$$(67)$$

occurring much more easily (below 100°) than the dimerization of propylene (150°). Quite extraordinary reactions have been realized due to this increased tendency for ring closures. 2,5-Dimethyl-hexadiene-(1,5) quantitatively undergoes reaction (68) when slightly heated with aluminum isobutyl compounds:

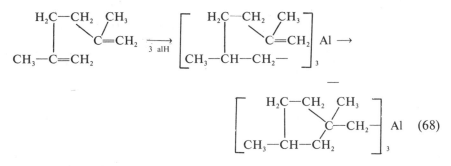

$$\tag{68}$$

This is a smooth synthesis (155) of an aluminum trialkyl closely related to aluminum trineopentyl under extremely mild conditions ($\sim 100°$), whereas isobutylene adds aluminum trialkyls only with extreme difficulty.

Bivalent boron compounds can be made easily from B_2H_6 or certain BH_3 complexes like $H_3B \cdot NR_3$ and butadiene (the reactions of suitable aluminum alkyls with butadiene have not yet been studied in detail). The main product of such a reaction is

$$\tag{69}$$

Köster (119) has converted this compound into the bivalent aluminum compound, $Et_2Al(CH_2)_4AlEt_2$ (see p. 243), the reactions of which have not yet been studied in detail. On the other hand, Köster and Larbig (155) have already investigated whether the 3 four-carbon-chains in (69) can be converted into $-(CH_2)_4-[CH_2-CH_2]_n-$ chains by a growth reaction with ethylene, catalyzed by added aluminum trialkyls (see p. 223, 231 and pp. 243–244). Again, methylene-cyclopentene and cyclopentyl-methyl boron (and aluminum) compounds were obtained. The six-carbon atom chain formed in the first addition step undergoes ring closure also in this case.

Gellert and Kempkes (137) tried to proceed from allene to aluminum triallyl or bifunctional 1,3-dialuminopropanes. Both products would be suitable for the synthesis of bifunctional compounds by adding ethylene. No smooth reaction was obtained in the desired sense. Complicated ring closures including 3 molecules of allene were observed. (The synthesis of allyl aluminum halides has been reported by Prevost and Gaudemar (57. 227).) Perhaps addition products of aluminum hydride or alkylated aluminum hydrides to certain allyl derivates (ethers (292)) or alcoholates of allyl alcohol) will be more suitable starting materials for such experiments. Early experiments of Gellert (*62*) in this direction have not yet been successful. A somewhat obscure report (*48*), mentioning the reactions (70a–c)

$$Li[AlH_4] \xrightarrow[a)]{3\ C_2H_2} LiAl[(CH{=}CH_2)_3H] \xrightarrow[b)]{3n\ C_2H_4}$$

(70)

$$Li[(Al(CH_2{-}CH_2)_n{-}CH{=}CH_2)_3H] \xrightarrow{c)}$$
$$3\ CH_2{=}CH{-}(CH_2{-}CH_2)_{n-1}{-}CH{=}CH_2 + Li[AlH_4]$$

and crediting them to the author of this chapter, is a conception of the fancy of the anonymous reporter.

Experiments such as those discussed here probably will have better chances of success if they can be started from products having already a certain minimum chain length. At least 7 or 8 carbon atoms would be probably all right. Suitable starting materials are not easily available at the moment. Some of these have been quite recently synthesized by Marvel and Garrison (*183*) and used for polymerization experiments with so-called Ziegler catalysts (*308,316*) (not to be treated in this chapter; see p. 250). Undecylene-(10)-ol-(1) seems to be promising for such investigations.

Finally some former attempts to make bivalent organo-aluminum halides from $(CH_2)(halogen)_2$ and $(C_2H_4)(halogen)_2$ may be cited (*49, 55,264*).

Reactions of Organo-Aluminum Compounds with Cleavage of Al—C and Al—H Bonds

Aluminum Trialkyls and Dialkyl Hydrides as Reducing Agents. The olefin interchange between an easily available aluminum trialkyl, e.g., aluminum tri-isobutyl, or the addition of a dialkyl aluminum hydride to an olefin (eventually followed by an additional olefin interchange) opens ways for reducing olefins to paraffins by hydrolyzing the aluminum alkyls formed. Such a possibility occassionally may be of interest, especially for partial reductions by utilizing the difference in the reaction rates of the olefins with internal and external double bonds (*328,331*). Combination of the "growth reaction" with hydrolysis is a means for a "hydropolymerization" or "hydro-copolymerization" of ethylene or propylene + ethylene respectively to the straight-chain paraffins. This is probably the best way now known, at least for the odd-numbered series, to synthesize such paraffins in a high degree of purity.

The addition of dialkyl aluminum hydrides to alkynes, followed by the hydrolysis, is a possibility for a partial or complete reduction of acetylene and its homologs. The reaction allows a smooth synthesis of many pure *cis*-1,2-disubstituted ethylenes (*276*). Furthermore it has been used for making unsaturated and saturated deuterium-substituted hydrocarbons having the deuterium atoms in well-defined positions (*274*).

The Al—H group adds also to other multiple bonds. Therefore dialkyl aluminum hydrides are convenient reducing agents for the groups $-\overset{\overset{\displaystyle H}{|}}{C}=O$,

$>\!C\!=\!O$, $-C\overset{\displaystyle \nearrow O}{\underset{\displaystyle \searrow OR}{}}$, $-C\!=\!N\!-$, $C\!\equiv\!N$, and others (*188,220,221,288,300,*

315,331,359). After hydrolysis alcohols are obtained from the first three

carbonyl compounds$\left(2 >\!AlH \text{ required for } -C\overset{\displaystyle \nearrow C}{\underset{\displaystyle \searrow OR}{}}\right)$, amines from the

azomethines, and either aldimines and aldehydes or amines from the nitriles (with 1 or 2 moles of AlH respectively). These reactions are similar to those of $LiAlH_4$. Toward many aldehydes, di-isobutyl aluminum hydride and aluminum tri-isobutyl behave like mixtures of aluminum hydride and 2 or 3 molecules of isobutene, respectively. That is to say 2 or 3 moles of isobutene are split off, respectively, and 3 moles of the aldehyde are reduced (in a kind of "displacement" reaction) by 1 mole of the aluminum compound (*300,315,331*):*

$$
\begin{array}{l}
Al(i\text{-}C_4H_9)_2H \\
\qquad\qquad\qquad + 3\ R\!-\!CHO = Al(OCH_2\cdot R)_3 + \begin{smallmatrix}2\\ \\3\end{smallmatrix}\ i\text{-}C_4H_8 \qquad (72) \\
Al(i\text{-}C_4H_9)_3
\end{array}
$$

All ketones, esters, nitriles, and open-chain azomethines react (also with $Al(i\text{-}C_4H_9)_3$) in the ratio of $1:1$ only† (red complexes in the molar ratio $2 > C\!=\!N\!-: 1\ R_2AlH$, see p. 212, Eq. 31). Cyclic azomethines (pyridine,

---

*A precursor of this reaction has been found by Meerwein et al. (*186*) in 1936: the highly specific trichloroacetaldehyde reacts similarly with aluminum triethyl in the ratio 1 : 3,

$$3\ Cl_3CCHO + Al(C_2H_5)_3 = 3\ C_2H_4 + Al(OCH_2\cdot CCl_3)_3 \qquad (71)$$

†In these cases two equivalents of "AlR" are lost for each $>C\!=\!O$ and four equivalents for each $>COOR$ group. It is possible (Köster, *158,159*) to concentrate the reductive capacity of R_2AlH by the reaction

$$3\ R_2AlH + AlCl_3 = AlH_3 + 3\ R_2AlCl$$

and to synthesize a solid product with about 50 per cent $(AlH_3)_x$ together with the recovery of nearly all the organometallic equivalents such as R_2AlCl.

238 *ORGANOMETALLIC COMPOUNDS*

quinoline, isoquinoline) react similarly in the first step at room temperature (*22,204,205*). At elevated temperatures the heterocycles are split (*205*), e.g., (73) and (74):

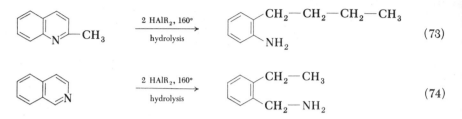

Alkyl Halides and Aluminum Halides from Organo-Aluminum Compounds. Aluminum trialkyls should react with halogens according to the following Eq. (75):

$$AlR_3 + 3 \, hal_2 = 3 \, Rhal + Al(hal)_3 \qquad (75)$$

Such reactions can be realized with iodine (*11,52,272,328*), but it is not easy to split off the third R. It is difficult to make alkyl chlorides or bromides in this way since the synthesis is complicated by the second reaction product, the highly active aluminum halide. With the lowest alkyl aluminum compounds reactions like

$$Et_2AlCl + Cl_2 = EtCl + EtAlCl_2 \qquad (75a)$$

have been employed in making mono-ethylaluminum dichloride from the sesquichloride (*37*). (The reaction $R_2AlCl + 2 \, HCl = AlCl_3 + 2 \, RH$ has been proposed for making finely divided $AlCl_3$ in a solvent for catalytic processes (*184*).) In the presence of substances adding aluminum halides to form complex compounds, rather smooth reactions are possible (also with higher aluminum alkyls (*272,290,296*)). One of the best additives for this purpose is pyridine. The reaction leads *via* the aluminum alkyls from olefins to primary alkyl halides and is a valuable supplement to the addition of HBr to vinyl groups in the presence of peroxides.

Oxidation of Aluminum Trialkyls (and Reaction with Sulfur and Selenium). Gilman and Marple (*67*) obtained poor yields of cresol by oxidation of aluminum tritolyl.

Aluminum trialkyls react with oxygen rather smoothly to form aluminum alcoholates (Ziegler *et al.*, *300,302,303,314,341,379*; see also *46,143*). The overall reaction is

$$AlR_3 \xrightarrow{1 \; 1/2 \; O} Al(OR)_3 \qquad (76)$$

The first two $O_2/2$ are absorbed rapidly, the third one rather slowly. Peroxides are the initial reaction products (*90,91,243,341*). They disappear quickly by reacting with still unchanged organo-aluminum compounds:

$$\text{al—R} \xrightarrow[O_2]{} \text{al—O—O—R} \xrightarrow{\text{AIR}} 2 \text{ alOR.} \qquad (77)$$

This autoöxidation combined with the "Direct Synthesis" of the aluminum alkyls and with hydrolysis of the alcoholates is a convenient method for synthesizing primary alcohols from olefins having the group $=CH_2$. The yields in laboratory experiments are 70–90 per cent. The alcohols obtained can be regarded as "anti-Markownikoff" addition products of water to the olefins. (But notice the somewhat abnormal reaction of styrene (*198*).) In addition the method is a practicable way for making long-chain fatty alcohols from ethylene or from propylene + ethylene *via* the "growth products" of aluminum triethyl and tripropyl. Also the olefins from wax-cracking are a good source for similar fatty alcohols (*300*). Here the process can be realized with broad fractions because the accompanying paraffins can easily be separated from the alcoholates by distillation. The technically competing oxo-process requires rather narrow cuts of hydrocarbons, otherwise no pure alcohols can be obtained. Besides the fatty alcohols already discussed, the following alcohols, e.g., have been synthesized (for the first two see (*243*); all others (*300,314,341*)).

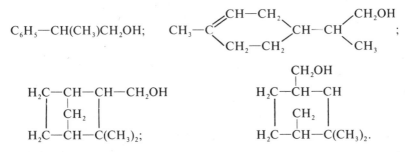

A similar alcohol synthesis described in a patent of the Goodrich-Gulf Company (*237*) arises from the oxidation of the $TiCl_3$-catalyzed growth products of $(C_2H_5)_2AlCl$, mentioned on p. 224. A technical disadvantage of this process lies in the fact that pure alumina cannot be obtained directly by hydrolysis of the oxidation products. The distribution of the different molecular sizes in these alcohols is no narrower than that in the original process.

A reaction with sulfur, selenium and (perhaps) tellurium, analogous to the autoöxidation of aluminum trialkyls, has been described by Jenkner (*119*). Normally the reaction seems not to come to completion. Triethylaluminum has been converted into Et_2AlSEt. Et_2S_2 and a polymer of SAlEt have been formed as by-products. With selenium, a mixture of $Et_2AlSeEt$ and $EtAl(SeEt)_2$ is obtained. By hydrolysis of the main products thio- and seleno-alcohols are available in moderate yields.

Reactions with Carbonyl Compounds. The possibility of using aluminum alkyls for making alcohols by reactions with carbonyl compounds is highly limited. There is no proper analogy to the Grignard reactions in this field. Normally only one aluminum-carbon bond is able to add to carbonyl compounds. A second one seems to react slowly at elevated temperature in the case of aluminum triaryls (*67*). Moreover, in some cases a simple reduction of the carbonyl compounds is favored (*186,331*), as has been described on pp. 236–237. Examples of smooth additions are:

$$Cl_3C-CHO + AlMe_3 = Cl_3C-CH(Me)OAlMe_2 \qquad (255) \qquad (78)$$

$$Ph \cdot CH{=}CH \cdot CHO + AlEt_3 = Ph \cdot CH{=}CH(Et)OAlEt_2 \qquad (186) \qquad (79)$$

$$Ph_2CO + AlPh_3 = Ph_3COAlPh_2 + \text{some } Ph_3COAl(Ph)OCPh_3 \qquad (67) \qquad (80)$$

$$Ph-CH{=}CH-COPh + AlPh_3 = (Ph)_2CH-C(Ph)OAlPh_2 \, (63,142,282) \qquad (81)$$

In spite of the maximum yields being no higher than $33\frac{1}{3}$ per cent with regard to the organometallic component, such reactions may be useful since the aluminum alkyls can be made so easily from olefins. It is easy to understand that the dialkyl aluminum compounds R_2AlX do not add to carbonyl compounds (*72*). Nevertheless reaction with the enol forms of the carbonyl compounds may occur (*331*). In some cases only self-condensations have been observed (*31,70,173*), or secondary condensations of primarily formed normal reaction products (*282*) (of AlR_3). The complex compounds, $Na[AlPh_4]$ and $Na[AlPh_3(CPh_3)]$, behave more like the corresponding alkali alkyls with lowered reactivity (*282*).

Tertiary alcohols can be made from aluminum alkyls and carbon dioxide. When this gas is slowly led into aluminum triethyl, one molecule of triethylcarbinol can be obtained from 3 molecules of the aluminum compound (*302,303,342*):

$$3 AlEt_3 + CO_2 = Et_2Al-O-AlEt_2 + Et_3C-O-AlEt_2 \qquad (82)$$

Synthesis of Carboxylic Acids. The first step in the overall reaction (82) is the formation of the diethyl aluminum propionate:

$$AlEt_3 + CO_2 = Et-\underset{\underset{O}{\|}}{C}-O-AlEt_2 \qquad (83)$$

This salt is able to undergo reaction with two Al—C bonds of two more molecules of $AlEt_3$. In this way we arrive at equation (82). The complex $LiAlEt_4$ is converted by CO_2 into $Et \cdot COOH + Et_2CO$ (*268*).

The complicating additional reaction steps can be avoided if aluminum trialkyls are slowly added to an excess of carbon dioxide dissolved in a hydrocarbon. Thus, high yields (with regard to 1 aluminum-carbon bond) of carboxylic acids are obtained if a rapid stream of carbon dioxide is passed through a well-stirred hydrocarbon, and an aluminum trialkyl is slowly added to this mixture (*342*). The use of solid carbon dioxide cannot be recommended, since under such circumstances the temperature is too low (*67,342*). Another way of suppressing additional reactions is through the use of aluminum trialkyl etherates (*289;342*). These react at about 100° (no reaction at room temperature (*8*)), forming one molecule of carboxylic acid. A second aluminum-carbon bond can be utilized if either the etherates or the dialkyl aluminum salts of the acids made in the way described above are heated with carbon dioxide under pressure to 200–220° (*289,342*). The third aluminum-carbon bond does not react at all with carbon dioxide.

It is easy to see that under normal circumstances, compounds of the type R_2AlX do not react with carbon dioxide (*70*). Therefore, this gas can be used instead of nitrogen or argon for handling aluminum compounds such as Et_2AlCl and $EtAlCl_2$.

The aluminum-carbon bonds remaining unchanged in the reaction products with carbon dioxide still can be oxidized; and in this way a combination of an acid and an alcohol synthesis is possible. High yields of acids and alcohols can thus be obtained by utilization of all three aluminum-carbon bonds (*189,342*).

The formation of carboxylic acids from aluminum triaryls and carbon dioxide has been known for nearly 25 years (*67*). In the presence of ether only one Al—C bond reacts. Without ether and after a very long treatment with carbon dioxide in boiling xylene, the second Al—C bond is partially attacked.

Synthesis of Ketones. Adkins and Scanley (*1*) have found that acid chlorides react with alkyl aluminum chlorides to give ketones. Aluminum trialkyls cannot be used for a smooth ketone synthesis because the first aluminum-carbon bond is too reactive. The whole process is thus complicated by an additional reaction between the ketone and the aluminum trialkyl. In the reaction of Adkins and Scanley only one alkyl group of the dialkyl aluminum chloride is utilized:

$$R_2AlCl + ClCOR' = RAlCl_2 + RCOR' \qquad (84)$$

The mono-alkyl aluminum dichlorides also can be smoothly converted into ketones with acid chlorides:

$$RAlCl_2 + ClCOR' = AlCl_3 + RCOR' \qquad (85)$$

The reason why the reaction (84) does not proceed with a second molecule of acid chloride to (85) lies in the fact that the reaction products on the right side of Eq. (84) combine to a very stable complex compound which is unreactive toward the acid chloride. In Eq. (85) $AlCl_3$ gives the most stable complex compound with RCOR' and therefore $RAlCl_2$ is able to react completely, since it cannot combine with the ketone formed (272).

A consequence of these statements is that for ketone synthesis, the aluminum trialkyl first must be converted into 3 $RAlCl_2$ with 2 $AlCl_3$.

A normal Grignard-like ketone synthesis from a nitrile has been described by Gilman and Marple (67). Furthermore Ph · COMe and PhCOPh were obtained from [Ph_4Al] Li and MeCOCl and PhCOCl, respectively (282).

Reactions with Sulfur Dioxide. All three aluminum-carbon bonds are reactive towards sulfur dioxide (303,342,365). It is easy to convert all aluminum tri-n-alkyls into aluminum salts of sulfinic acids:

$$AlR_3 + 3 SO_2 = Al[O-\underset{\underset{O}{\|}}{S}-R]_3 \qquad (86)$$

by introducing them slowly into an excess of liquid or dissolved sulfur dioxide. Aluminum trialkyls, branched at carbon atom 2, give very poor yields because complicating reduction processes occur (342).

The normal procedure for such a reaction, i.e. passing gaseous sulfur dioxide through the aluminum trialkyls, also leads to a decrease in yield due to similar complications discussed in the case of the CO_2 reaction. The complication can be avoided either by using the aluminum trialkyl etherates (8) or by converting the aluminum trialkyls, prior to the SO_2 reaction, into diethyl aluminum chlorides with $AlCl_3$ (246).

N_2O_4 and NO add to aluminum triethyl etherate to give products which yield upon hydrolysis, Et_2NOH and (probably!) $EtN(NO)OH$ respectively (8).

Reactions in which Al—C Bonds Are Broken but Total Number of Metal-Carbon Bonds Remains Constant (Synthesis of Other Metal Alkyls)

Organo-aluminum compounds are suitable reagents for introducing alkyls to other metals or elements. The synthesis of sulfinic acids was the first example of such a possibility. It is self-evident that organo-aluminum compounds are able to react with metal halides and other metal compounds, and in this way a wide variety of different products can be obtained. If the "other metal compound" also is a metal alkyl, or an "element alkyl," the only possible reactions are alkyl interchanges. Such reactions have been described by Calingaert et al (*30*), e.g., (Eq. 87):

$$HgMe_2 + PbEt_4 \rightleftarrows HgMeEt + PbEt_3Me \rightleftarrows HgMe_2 + PbEt_2Me_2, \text{ etc.} \quad (87)$$

In these cases catalysts, especially small amounts of $AlCl_3$, are necessary, and the reaction mixtures must be heated for some hours. Very rapid alkyl interchanges without catalyst occur between aluminum and boron trialkyls as has been found by Köster and Bruno (*153,307*).* Alkyls of a similar constitution, e.g., ethyl and *n*-butyl, distribute equally between the aluminum and boron atoms. In the case of less closely related substituents, aluminum prefers those alkyls leading to the highest degree of association of the aluminum trialkyl (88–90), al $= \frac{1}{3}$ Al, b $= \frac{1}{3}$ B:

$$al(nC_4H_9) + b \cdot Et \rightleftarrows alEt + b(n\text{-}C_4H_9) \quad (88)$$

has an equilibrium constant of 1,

$$al(isoC_4H_9) + b \cdot Et \rightleftarrows alEt + b(i\text{-}C_4H_9) \quad (89)$$

and

$$al(nC_4H_9) + bCH_3 \rightleftarrows alCH_3 + b(n\text{-}C_4H_9) \quad (90)$$

have 3,5 and $\sim$12, respectively.

Obviously aluminum trialkyls and boron trialkyls have a certain tendency to give a "mixed association," making an interchange possible (*161, 307,336*), whereas boron trialkyls do not associate at all (and do not interchange alkyls under moderate conditions) (*307,336*).

This interchange has practical value in the synthesis of some otherwise difficultly available organo-aluminum compounds, e.g., aluminum tribenzyl, tricyclohexyl, and especially triaryls (*161,336*). In these cases it is easier to synthesize the corresponding boron compounds first (*via* the Grignard method or by direct boration of aromatic hydrocarbon, especially benzene (*150*)), then add aluminum triethyl and distill:

$$B(CH_2 \cdot Ph)_3 + AlEt_3 \longrightarrow BEt_3 + Al(CH_2 \cdot Ph)_3 \quad (91)$$

(BEt_3 has a boiling point about $100°$ lower than $AlEt_3$).

The easily available bifunctional, bicyclic boron compound (69) has been converted, with 2 $AlEt_3$, into the distillable $(CH_2)_4BEt$ and the bifunctional aluminum compound, $Et_2Al(CH_2)_4AlEt_2$ (*149*).

Moreover, the alkyl interchange allows one to transmit the "growth reaction" to the boron alkyls by adding some aluminum alkyls as catalysts,

*Zakharin and Ochlobystin (*291*) also observed this interchange but did not recognize its extreme ease.

similar to what has been possible with the unreactive aluminum compounds of type R_2AlX (see p. 223, 231) (*366*).

If the "other metal compound" added to the aluminum alkyl is not a metal alkyl, a great many different possibilities exist for using organo-aluminum compounds in the alkylation of other elements. The general equation for such alkylations is (92), i.e., an equilibrium:

$$alR + elX \rightleftarrows alX + elR, \qquad (92)$$

wherein al means $\frac{1}{3}$ Al, el means an equivalent of other suitable elements, and X means any other atom, group, or equivalent of negative character. We have to distinguish among the following three cases: 1) reactions involving the transformation of alR, i.e., the right side of the equilibrium (92) is highly favored; 2) the equilibria containing both alR and elR; and 3) the left side of the equation (92) is the most stable system, in which case of course an alkylation by means of organo-aluminum compounds is impossible. On the contrary, in the latter case an aluminum halide would be alkylated by the "element alkyl" added.

The equation (92) is an oversimplification since these reactions occur, not with the equivalents, but with the compounds of multivalent elements. Under these circumstances we have to distinguish valence 1, 2, 3, ... n of the element and valence 1, 2, 3 of the aluminum. The activities of the compounds involved in the reactions depend upon their whole structures. That means, reactions possible for the first AlR in AlR_3 do not necessarily occur with an AlR in AlR_2X, and similar differences may exist in the reactivities of ElX_n, $ElRX_n$, ElR_2X_{n-2}, etc. The three different possibilities for the course of the alkylation, explained above with the example of equation (92), can all be realized between an organo-aluminum compound and a compound of the same second element, depending upon the valences of aluminum and of that second element involved.

With regard to these possible complications the alkylation of boron and silicon with organo-aluminum compounds is very simple. In contact with suitable boron and silicon compounds, any aluminum-carbon bond reacts, and if sufficient boron or silicon valences are available no alkyl remains on the aluminum.

Boron and silicon compounds suitable for the alkylation are the fluorides, complex fluorides, especially KBF_4 and Na_2SiF_6 (*53,112,118, 120,122,123,125,146,239,287*), esters of boric (*113,147,151,156*) or silicic (*121,124*) acid, and compounds with SiO- and BO-groups, except for the highly unsoluble and unreactive types.* Such compounds can be obtained by dissolving B_2O_3 in a boric acid ester or in a boron trialkyl; the reaction

---

*B_2O_3 gives poor yields of BR_3 with AlR_3 (*218*).

products have mainly cyclic structures:

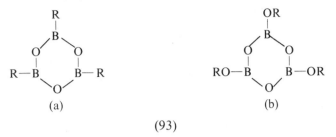

(a)   (b)

(93)

These can be regarded as solutions of B_2O_3 in a boric acid ester or a boron trialkyl; and the overall reaction, especially in the case of using a boron alkyl as solvent, can be formulated as (94) (*4,134,147,148,160,217, 294*):

$$B_2O_3 + 2\,AlR_3 = Al_2O_3 + 2\,BR_3 \qquad (94)$$

For silicon a similar, simple possibility for transforming SiO_2 into SiR_4 is not known; however Si—O—Si groups can be split by aluminum alkyls (*110,117*).

Of course it is also possible to alkylate boron and silicon compounds partially by using, e.g., BF_3 or SiF_4 in excess. In this way the compounds, $EtSiF_3$, Et_2SiF_2, and Et_3SiF, have been obtained, the separation of which by distillation is a most simple problem compared with the rather difficult separation of the corresponding methylsilicon chlorides (*115*).

The reaction between $SiCl_4$ and aluminum trialkyls (*257*) does not go to completion under all circumstances. Equilibria such as

$$RSiCl_3 + AlCl_3 \rightleftarrows SiCl_4 + RAlCl_2 \qquad (95)$$

have been observed (*284,285*) which obviously also occur during the disproportionation of $SiCl_4 + SiR_4$ to alkyl silicon chlorides with $AlCl_3$ as catalyst. The reversibility can be suppressed by adding alkali chlorides to the mixtures of 3 $SiCl_4 + 4\,AlR_3$, and capturing the highly reactive $AlCl_3$ to form the much less reactive $NaAlCl_4$ (*127*).

Reactions between BCl_3 and AlR_3 have not come to the attention of the author. Schlesinger et al. (*253*) reported that B_4Cl_4 and $AlMe_3$ react to form liquid and solid substances, whereas higher aluminum alkyls do not give any well characterized products.

If dialkyl aluminum hydrides are brought together with suitable silicon compounds, the hydrogen migrates to the silicon prior to the alkyls. The introduction of, e.g., SiF_4, $SiCl_4$, or $Si(OR)_4$ into an excess of dialkyl aluminum hydrides leads to SiH_4, and in a similar way $RSiH_3$, R_2SiH_2, R_3SiH can be obtained (*111,126,154*). Instead of R_2AlH the alkylated complex hydrides, $Na[AlR_3H]$ and $Na[AlR_2H_2]$ (*132*), can be used or the reductions can be achieved with NaH, activated by some AlR_3 (*130*). Of course such hydrogenations are also possible with aluminum hydride or lithium aluminum hydride, and so the alkylated aluminum hydrides are not required. Since aluminum alkyls have a certain tendency to split into olefins and dialkyl aluminum hydrides, partially alkylated silanes have been observed as by-products from such alkylations (*110,117*).

In mixtures of boric acid esters with dialkyl aluminum hydrides only the alkyl groups migrate to the boron (*154*):

$$2\ B(OR)_3 + 3\ AlR_2H = 2\ BR_3 + 3\ Al(OR)_2H \qquad (96)$$

The trialkyl boroxols (93a) behave towards R_2AlH like the boron halides and not like esters. Also the hydrogen migrates to boron, and alkylated diboranes are obtained (*162*). Similarly, boron alkyls can be made from diborane and aluminum alkyls:

$$B_2H_6 + 6\ AlR_3 = 6\ AlR_2H + 2\ BR_3 \qquad (97)$$

With more B_2H_6, $B(AlH_4)_3$ is eventually formed (*251*).*

The alkylation of germanium by means of organo-aluminum compounds has not yet been described. But something is known about the alkylation of tin. If $SnCl_4$ is mixed with an aluminum alkyl, a rather complicated equilibrium mixture is obtained, containing all various individual compounds possible. Here the case no. 2) explained for equation (92) is realized rather clearly. Many different reactions between $SnCl_4$ and organo-aluminum compounds can be formulated, e.g. (98–101):

$$SnCl_4 + AlR_3 = RSnCl_3 + AlR_2Cl \qquad (98)$$

$$SnCl_4 + 2\ AlR_3 = Sn_2Cl_2R_2 + 2\ AlR_2Cl \qquad (99)$$

$$SnCl_4 + 3\ AlR_3 = SnR_3Cl + 3\ AlR_2Cl \qquad (100)$$

$$SnCl_4 + 4\ AlR_3 = SnR_4 + 4\ AlR_2Cl. \qquad (101)$$

Two similar additional series can be written for 1–4 molecules of R_2AlCl and $RAlCl_2$. In addition, it is possible to combine the resulting reactions into many others, e.g.,

$$SnCl_4 + AlR_3 = R_3SnCl + AlCl_3, \text{ etc. etc.} \qquad (102)$$

It is obvious that if at least some of these different possibilities correspond to equilibria, and in some of them the reverse process is preferred,

---

*Wartik and Schlesinger (*269*) observed an inverse migration of hydrogen in the reaction

$$LiAlH_4 + BR_3 = LiBH_3R.$$

complicated mixtures of different reaction products will be obtained. The composition of these mixtures will depend upon the ratio and the nature of the components used. Moreover Köster (*154*) has found that between aluminum chloride and alkyl tin chlorides relatively stable crystallizable complex compounds (e.g., $Et_2SnCl_2 \cdot AlCl_3$ and $Et_3SnCl \cdot AlCl_3$) are formed, complicating the course of the reaction.

Again the whole picture can be greatly simplified if an alkali halide such as sodium chloride is added to the reaction mixture. It gives the most stable complex compound, $NaAlCl_4$, with the aluminum chloride and leads in this way to the smooth formation of tin tetra-alkyls with complete consumption of the stoichiometric amount of aluminum alkyls (Jenkner (*128*)):

$$3\,SnCl_4 + 4\,AlR_3 + 4\,NaCl = 3\,SnR_4 + 4\,NaAlCl_4 \qquad (103)$$

W. P. Neumann (*208*) has found that the same objective can be reached by using the etherates or tertiary aminates of aluminum trialkyls, or quite generally by working in the presence of ethers or tertiary amines. In this case $Cl_3Al \cdot OR_2$ and $Cl_3Al \cdot NR_3$, respectively, are the most stable complex compounds possible.

Starting from halides of bivalent tin similar reactions are possible. In this case—as is known from other similar reactions—half of the tin is recovered as tin metal. The reaction has been mentioned for tin difluoride (*112*).

The alkylation of lead compounds by means of aluminum alkyls has been widely studied in connection with the synthesis of tetraethyllead. The classical method for making tetraethyllead from ethyl chloride and sodium-lead alloy has some disadvantages which have not yet been overcome; and therefore all new possibilities for making this important metal alkyl have been thoroughly investigated.

It is easy to make tetraethyllead by reaction between $PbCl_2$ and $AlEt_3$. But it is impossible in this way to utilize all the valuable aluminum ethyl groups. Thus, the following two reactions (*65,272*):

$$PbEt_4 + EtAlCl_2 = PbEt_3Cl + AlEt_2Cl \qquad (104)$$

and

$$PbEt_3Cl + AlEt_3 = PbEt_4 + AlEt_2Cl \qquad (105)$$

are known. This means that the complete ethylation of lead is only possible with the first AlEt group of $AlEt_3$, and this fact would complicate the process. Of course another difficulty would arise from the use of $PbCl_2$ as starting material because this again leads to a formation of lead metal in the first reaction step.

It has been found by Blitzer and Pearson of the Ethyl Corporation (*16,20*) that complete utilization of the aluminum ethyl groups is possible by using lead compounds like PbO, PbS or salts of lead with carboxylic acids, e.g., 106:*

$$6 \, PbS + 4 \, AlEt_3 = 3 \, Pb + 2 \, Al_2S_3 + 3 \, PbEt_4 \qquad (106)$$

Of course the recovery of half the lead as lead metal cannot be avoided in this way.

This difficulty may be overcome by a multi-step cyclic method proposed by Sims (*242*). This author additionally introduces into the process organocadmium compounds and ethyl iodide as reacting components. The overall reaction is:

$$6 \, PbAc_2 + 6 \, AlEt_3 + 6 \, EtI = 6 \, PbEt_4 + 4 \, AlAc_3 + 2 \, AlI_3, \qquad (107)$$

the two AlI_3 of course being used for the resynthesis of EtI.

Two essential steps in this process are

$$6 \, PbAc_2 + 4 \, AlEt_3 = 3 \, Pb + 3 \, PbEt_4 + 4 \, AlAc_3 \qquad (108)$$

and

$$3 \, Pb + 6 \, EtI + 3 \, CdEt_2 = 3 \, PbEt_4 + 3 \, CdI_2 \qquad (109)$$

The CdI_2 is converted to $CdEt_2$ with $AlEt_3$. Thus the cadmium compounds are continuously recycled and do not appear in the overall reaction (107).

An essential intermediate step in this process probably may be a reaction between the precipitated lead and the cadmium dialkyl:

$$Pb + 2 \, CdEt_2 = PbEt_4 + 2 \, Cd, \qquad (110)$$

cadmium then being able to add EtI to 2 EtCdI (and reacting further with $AlEt_3$ to $CdEt_2$), whereas lead is not able to add EtI.

In the fifth group of the Periodic Table alkylations by means of aluminum alkyls have been reported for all four members of the group. The reaction between PCl_3 and organo-aluminum compounds has been investigated by Weyer (*272*) at the Max-Planck-Institut für Kohlenforschung and by Ochlobystin and Zakharkin (*214*). Depending upon the ratio of the aluminum alkyl and the PCl_3 used, it is equally possible to obtain either alkyl dichloro-phosphines or trialkyl phosphines. Weyer obtained yields of trialkyl phosphines up to 50–60 per cent; the yields of the Russian authors were somewhat lower. Both authors made alkyl dichloro-phosphines rather smoothly. Weyer has found that dialkyl monochloro-phosphines can be rather easily obtained by the reaction of $EtAlCl_2$ and PCl_3. Weyer has also studied the reaction between $POCl_3$ and aluminum trialkyls and finds that this is not a good method for the synthesis of trialkyl phosphine

*Other proposals from inventors of Ethyl Corporation: (*17–19,263*).

oxides. A better way to these compounds is by the oxidation of trialkyl phosphines made from PCl_3.

Smooth alkylations have been reported to occur in the reactions between AsF_3, SbF_3, and BiF_3 with aluminum alkyls (*123*). Zakharkin and Ochlobystin made trialkyl stibines and alkyl chloroarsines from $SbCl_3$ and $AsCl_3$ (*287*). In these cases (including $BiCl_3$) it is again recommended to add sodium chloride in order to secure complete reaction (*133*). The inverse splitting of $SbPh_3$ and $BiPh_3$ by $AlCl_3$ has been described by Manulkin and Tatarenko (*180*).

In the second group of the Periodic Table the synthesis of zinc, cadmium, and mercury alkyls using aluminum alkyls has been reported. Diethylcadmium has just been mentioned as intermediate in a new tetraethyllead synthesis. The reaction between organo-aluminum compounds and $HgCl_2$ is characterized by the fact that if all alkyls on the aluminum are utilized only one alkyl can be brought to mercury. This means that the following three types of reactions are possible (*144,175*):

a) $\quad 3\,HgCl_2 + R_3Al = 3\,RHgCl + AlCl_3$

b) $\quad HgCl_2 + R_2AlCl = 2\,RHgCl + AlCl_3 \qquad\qquad (111)$

c) $\quad HgCl_2 + RAlCl_2 = RHgCl + AlCl_3.$

Mercury dialkyls are formed in moderate yields with AlR_3 in excess ("equimolar to $HgCl_2$ (*287*)" = 50 per cent excess) and in high yields in the presence of sodium chloride (*129*).

Mixtures of aluminum trialkyls with $ZnCl_2$ behave quite differently from those with $HgCl_2$. It is easy to make directly, and without any additional help, zinc dialkyls, but only one alkyl group on the aluminum trialkyl can be utilized (*303,305,367*):

$$ZnCl_2 + 2\,AlR_3 = ZnR_2 + 2\,AlR_2Cl \qquad\qquad (112)$$

Normally, the two reaction products have differences in their boiling points sufficient for their separation. However, the R_2AlCl may be transformed into the nonvolatile complex compound, $K[AlR_2Cl_2]$, by adding potassium chloride. Consequently, $ZnCl_2$ and AlR_2Cl do not react with each other and $EtZnCl$ can be used to alkylate $AlCl_3$ to Et_2AlCl (*24*).

The combination of Eq. (112) with the disproportionations expressed by Eqs. (12) and (13) (*190a*) opens possibilities for utilizing the second and even the second and the third AlR in AlR_3.

In the third group of the Periodic Table the synthesis of boron trialkyls from aluminum trialkyls has already been mentioned. Eisch and Wilke (*44*) have studied reactions between aluminum trialkyls and the chlorides of gallium and indium. $GaCl_3$ adds 3 molecules of $ClAlEt_2$ to give a complex $Ga[AlEt_2Cl_2]_3$. Therefore $GaEt_3$ is obtained in 50 per cent yield only when triethyl aluminum and $GaCl_3$ are mixed:

$$2 \, GaCl_3 + 3 \, AlEt_3 = Ga[AlEt_2Cl_2]_3 + GaEt_3 \qquad (113)$$

With 6 moles of $AlEt_3$ a mixture of $GaEt_3$ and $AlEt_3$ is obtained, the separation of which is difficult. Potassium chloride splits the complex and the yield is considerably increased:

$$GaCl_3 + 3 \, AlEt_3 + 3 \, KCl = 3 \, K[AlEt_2Cl_2] + GaEt_3 \qquad (114)$$

The reaction

$$GaBr_3 + 3 \, AlEt_3 = GaEt_3 + 3 \, AlEt_2Br \qquad (115)$$

can be realized with more than 80 per cent yield.

Similar reactions have led to indium triethyl.

The alkylation of thallium compounds with AlR_3 has not yet been described.

This chapter demonstrates that organo-aluminum compounds are suitable reagents for making other element alkyls by alkylation processes. All types of element alkyls made were already known. Only one entirely new compound (or group of compounds) has been found using aluminum alkyls as reagents. This is monomethyl titanium trichloride (and its very unstable homologs) from the reaction discovered by Beermann and Bestian in the Farbwerke Hoechst A.G. (12,14):

$$TiCl_4 + (CH_3)_2AlCl + NaCl = Na[AlCH_3Cl_3] + CH_3TiCl_3 \qquad (116)$$

This compound is related (13,15) to the so-called organometallic complex catalysts discovered by Ziegler, Holzkamp, Breil and Martin (304–308, 317), which are highly active catalytic systems for quite a variety of different polymerizations (low-pressure linear polyethylene, isotactic polypropylene and poly-α-olefins, different types of polybutadiene, synthetic "natural rubber," cyclododecatriene from butadiene). These catalysts can be obtained quite generally by mixing compounds of group IV B–VII B (and also VIII B) metals with different metal alkyls, especially those of aluminum. Reduction processes normally occur in such mixtures. Since their discovery, many publications have been dedicated to these new catalysts by numerous authors, and interesting new complex compounds between organo-aluminum compounds and compounds of such other elements (especially Ti) have been discovered (25,32,177,194–97). Reviewing this new and rather wide field of modern catalysis would exceed the planned size of this chapter. Some investigations of general interest derived from the basic work of Ziegler et al. may be cited: (26,43,58,104,192,193,216, 265).

The mentioned compounds, $RTiCl_3$, are not very stable. They decompose mainly to $TiCl_3$. Therefore the reactions between compounds of "group B" metals and aluminum trialkyls may be quite generally explained by the assumption that highly unstable metal alkyls are the primary products which decompose very rapidly. The compounds of the different "group B" metals differ in the degree to which they are reduced in this way. In many cases the reduction proceeds to the metals themselves (a reaction discovered nearly 40 years ago with Grignard compounds by Schlenk and Weichselfelder (248)). The metals—e.g., Ni, Fe, Pt, Cn, Ag—can be obtained readily in a high degree of dispersion or even in colloidal form, suitable for uses as catalysts (299) (a good Ni-hydrogenation catalyst has been prepared in this way by Wilke (277)) or for making them more reactive. Podall (225) used nickel made in such a way for the preparation of $Ni(CO)_4$. Zakharkin et al. (295) obtained in similar fashion the hexacarbonyls of Cr, Mo and W. Sarton and Costa (241) studied the reaction between cobalt acetylacetonate and $AlEt_3$ and $AlPh_3$.

Electrolysis of Organo-Aluminum Compounds

In 1922-1926 Hein et al. (83-85,87) described the electrolysis of "ethylsodium dissolved in diethylzinc and triethylaluminum." They found that ethyl radicals were evolved at the anode, stabilizing to ethane + ethylene if the anode was an indifferent metal, and forming the corresponding metal ethyl with anodes of, e.g., lead or bismuth. The process on the cathode was not very thoroughly investigated. In the case of the system, sodium ethyl + diethyl zinc, a deposit of zinc was obtained.

The so-called solutions of ethylsodium in other metal ethyls really were complex compounds like sodium zinc ethyl and sodium aluminum tetraethyl.

About 30 years later, Ziegler and Lehmkuhl (347,360,378) started new research on the electrolysis of complex organo-aluminum compounds. Meanwhile, progress in the synthesis of the aluminum alkyls had made such complexes readily available.

The aim of the first experiments made with the compound $NaF \cdot 2\ AlEt_3$ was to investigate whether electrolytes of this type could be used for electrolytic refining of aluminum or for electroplating other metals with a very pure aluminum. The results were quite promising. The authors elucidated the conditions necessary for a deposit of aluminum on the cathode. They found that complexes like $Na[AlEt_3F]$ or $Na[AlEt_4]$ do not give a pure aluminum on the cathode but predominantly sodium. For the deposition of aluminum it is necessary that, besides the complex compound, an additional noncomplex organo-aluminum compound should be present in the electrolyte. The 1:2 complex, $NaF \cdot 2\ AlEt_3$, can be written as $Na[AlEt_3F] \cdot AlEt_3$. The second $AlEt_3$ is not very strongly fixed and can be regarded, for the purpose of this consideration, as free $AlEt_3$. (Some years earlier

Menzel (*187*) had proposed another bath for electroplating aluminum. It is questionable whether this bath contained an aluminum-organic compound at all.)

Later Ziegler, Lehmkuhl, and Lindner (*346,361*) published a modification of this electrolytic process in which electrolytes having high contents of hydride were decomposed by the electric current with anodes of special metals such as copper or silver. On these metals hydrogen is evolved predominantly. The overall reaction during the electrolysis is a decomposition of AlH_3. As a by-product pure $AlEt_3$ separates from the electrolyte during the electrolysis. This can be used together with the hydrogen evolved on the anode for dissolving fresh raw aluminum and recovering the electrolyte by adding the $AlEt_2H$ thus obtained.

Another promising use for such electrolytic processes is the synthesis of metal alkyls, especially metal ethyls. These experiments correspond to those already started by Hein et al. In principle all metals able to combine with alkyls can be transformed into their ethyl compounds if they are used as anodes in $NaF \cdot 2 AlEt_3$ as electrolyte. Aluminum is deposited on the cathode; and since this metal can be converted into aluminum triethyl with hydrogen and ethylene, the electrolysis opens a way for a general synthesis of metal alkyls through the overall reaction

$$M + 1/2 \ H_2 + C_2H_4 = M(C_2H_5) \quad (300,306,312) \tag{117}$$

The author has used the expression "in principle," because it is not simple to realize the idea for any desired metal alkyl. However, in a very simple apparatus consisting of an anode, a cathode and the electrolyte it is possible to make $SbEt_3$, $SbPr_3$, and $SnEt_4$ in good yields and with no difficulty. On the cathode an equivalent amount of aluminum is obtained (*343*).

In the case of some other metals, especially lead and mercury, the metal alkyl dissolving in the electrolyte is partially decomposed by the aluminum precipitated on the cathode. In these cases the yields of alkyl compounds are lowered, and the precipitated aluminum has a rather high content of the other corresponding metal (*343*).

In other cases, practically no metal alkyls can be obtained because the decomposition of the alkyl compounds by aluminum on the cathode is complete (Zn, Cd, Bi, Tl, Te). In this event only a transport of the metal from the anode to the cathode occurs (*343*).

The difficulties have been overcome by different methods, e.g., by electrolysis in a high vacuum. Under such circumstances the sensitive metal alkyls distill from the electrolyte before they can be decomposed on the cathode, and good yields of the ethyl compounds of Zn, Hg, Cd, Pb, Bi, etc. can be obtained (*343*).

Another way to overcome the difficulties is by the use of electrolytic cells having diaphragms separating the space around the anode from that around the cathode. Suitable equipments have been described especially in connection with the electrolytic synthesis of tetraethyllead (*362*).

Another problem in utilizing the electrolysis just discussed arises from the fact that a solid metal is precipitated on the cathode. This makes it difficult to develop a continuous electrolytic process. Even if the aluminum precipitates on the cathode in the form of a fine powder, as can be effected by using high current densities on the cathode, it is not easy to remove this deposit continuously and quantitatively; short circuits then may occur in the cell. Therefore, considerable progress was made when a modification of the electrolysis was developed which deposited liquid sodium on the cathode instead of metallic aluminum (*308*).

Liquid sodium separates if the electrolyte contains no free $AlEt_3$. The simplest way to realize this is to use molten $NaAlEt_4$ as electrolyte; i.e., the original electrolyte of Hein. The separation of liquid sodium can very easily be demonstrated if molten $NaAlEt_4$ is electrolyzed between a cathode of any metal and an anode of liquid sodium. In such an experiment all the sodium finally is transported from the anode to the cathode. With anodes of indifferent metals, e.g., copper or iron, pure sodium separates only at the very beginning. The electrolytic process is the following:

$$Na[AlEt_4] + \text{electrical energy} = Na + AlEt_3 + Et \qquad (118)$$

Certainly the first product formed at the anode is the neutral radical, $AlEt_4$, which immediately decomposes into $Et + AlEt_3$. The Et disproportionates in the well-known manner to ethane + ethylene. Very shortly after current flow begins, the electrolyte contains free $AlEt_3$; and then solid aluminum precipitates together with sodium at the cathode. Under such circumstances the metal deposit is a very disagreeable sponge. However, a very smooth electrolysis can be realized if the experiment is made in a vacuum. $AlEt_3$ distills off and nothing but liquid sodium separates on the cathode.

If this experiment is made with an aluminum anode the overall reaction of the electrolysis is:

$$3\,[NaAlEt_4] + Al + \text{electrical energy} = 3\,Na + 4\,AlEt_3 \qquad (119)$$

After electrolysis the sodium obtained can be converted into sodium aluminum tetraethyl by hydrogenation to 3 NaH and addition of 3 $AlEt_3$ and 3 C_2H_4. It is evident that in this way an electrolytic synthesis of aluminum triethyl is possible, in which three-fourths of the batch is recycled to recover the electrolyte, and one-fourth is removed as final product. The total course of the process resembles the two-step direct synthesis of aluminum triethyl described by equations (3, 4) in which two-thirds of the batch is recycled and one-third is removed. The electrolytic synthesis is possible with compact aluminum anodes; atomizing of aluminum is not necessary. The pressures required for the hydrogenation of sodium and the addition of ethylene in the recovery of the electrolyte are about 10 atmospheres. These two reactions have a very high rate. Therefore, the somewhat more complicated electrolytic synthesis of aluminum triethyl perhaps can compete with its direct synthesis from aluminum, hydrogen, and ethylene (*343*).

Besides the electrolysis in an evacuated system there of course exist other ways of avoiding the presence of free aluminum triethyl around the cathode, hindering reaction between the sodium and the aluminum triethyl formed. One possibility is again the use of a disphragm, but there are others also.

The principle just described can be successfully used in the synthesis of tetraethyllead and other metal alkyls. With a lead anode the vacuum electrolysis of $Na[AlEt_4]$ gives the mixture of 4 $AlEt_3$ + 1 $PbEt_4$ in practically quantitative yield. There exist several possibilities for the separation of the two components of this mixture, e.g., that of converting $AlEt_3$ into a suitable complex compound, distilling off the TEL, and recovering the $AlEt_3$ from the complex.

Direct separation of the two components by distillation is very difficult due to a very small difference in boiling points.

Another possibility for this separation is to add 4 molecules of a complex compound $Na[AlEt_3OR]$. This compound immediately converts the $AlEt_3$ into $Na[AlEt_4]$, insoluble in the other components of the mixture. In this way a liquid layer consisting of 4 $AlEt_2OR$ + $PbEt_4$ is obtained, whose difference in the boiling points can be adjusted at will by suitable choice of the OR. Now the separation by distillation is possible. The diethylaluminum alkoxyl is treated with sodium hydride (the sodium coming from the electrolysis) and ethylene to give again $Na[AlEt_3OR]$ (*343,353*).

In another modification of the electrolytic synthesis of tetraethyllead, $Na[AlEt_3OR]$ is used as a part of the electrolyte together with sodium or potassium aluminum tetraethyl. The complexes containing OR have too low an electrolytic conductivity to be used without other such complexes of higher conductivities. Of course in these cases a mixture of 4 $AlEt_2OR$ + $PbEt_4$ is obtained directly during the electrolysis, and the compound $Na[AlEt_3OR]$ has to be continuously added throughout the course of the process (*352*).

Again, vacuum electrolysis is not the only existing way for by-passing reactions of liquid sodium with the metal alkyls formed. In these cases not only $AlEt_3$ but also the desired alkyl compounds of other metals can be decomposed by the sodium. The description of technical details for these electrolytic processes would exceed the planned size of this chapter. It may be mentioned, however, that very promising results have been obtained also in the electrolytic synthesis of magnesium diethyl which probably will become readily available by this process.

References

(1) Adkins, H., and Scanley, C., *J. Am. Chem. Soc.*, **73**, 2854 (1951).

(2) Ambros, O., Keller, G., Rindtorff, E., and Schmitt, K. (to Bergwerksgesellschaft Hibernia A.-G.), German Patent (DAS) 1,018,061 (Oct. 24, 1957).

(3) Apperson, L. D., *C.A.*, **36**, 4476 (1942).

(4) Ashby, E. C., *J. Am. Chem. Soc.*, **81**, 4791 (1959).

(5) Badische Anilin und Soda Fabric A.-G., British Patent 804,059 (Nov. 5, 1958); *C.A.*, **53**, 7990*b* (1959).

(6) Bähr, H., and Müller, H. E., *Chem. Ber.*, **88**, 251, 1765 (1955).

(7) Baker, E. B., and Sisler, H. H., *J. Am. Chem. Soc.*, **75**, 4828 (1953).

(8) Baker, E. B., and Sisler, H. H., *J. Am. Chem. Soc.*, **75**, 5193 (1953).

(9) Baker, E. B., *J. Chem. Phys.*, **26**, 960 (1957).

(10) Bamford, C. H., Levi, D. L., and Newitt, D. M., *J. Chem. Soc.*, 468, (1946).

(11) Bartkiewicz, S. A., and Robinson, J. W., *Anal. Chim. Acta*, **20**, 326 (1959); *C.A.*, **53**, 21434*g* (1959).

(12) Beermann, C., *Angew. Chem.*, **71**, 195 (1959).

(13) Beermann, C., and Bestian, H., *Angew. Chem.*, **71**, 618 (1959).

(14) Beermann, C., Bestian, H., and Graf, R. (to Farbwerke Hoechst A.-G.), German Patent 1,023,766 (Feb. 6, 1958); Belgian Patent 553,477 (Dec. 17, 1956).

(15) Beermann, C., and Bestian, H. (to Farbwerke Hoechst A.-G.), German Patent (DAS) 1,026,964 (March 27, 1958); Belgian Patent 553,478 (Dec. 17, 1956).

(16) Blitzer, S. M., and Pearson, T. H. (to Ethyl Corporation), U. S. Patent 2,859,225 (March 25, 1955).

(17) Blitzer, S. M., and Pearson, T. H. (to Ethyl Corporation), U. S. Patent 2,859,227 (March 28, 1955).

(18) Blitzer, S. M., and Pearson, T. H. (to Ethyl Corporation), U. S. Patent 2,859,228 (March 28, 1955); Belgian Patent 553,228 (Dec. 7, 1956).

(19) Blitzer, S. M., Milde, R. L., Pearson, T. H., and Redmann, H. E. (to Ethyl Corporation), Belgian Patent 548,439 (June 7, 1956).

(20) Blitzer, S. M., and Pearson, T. H. (to Ethyl Corporation), Austrian Patent Application 5 A 7343/56 (Oct. 15, 1959); Belgian Patent 553,653 (Dec. 22, 1956).

(21) Blitzer, S. M., and Pearson, T. H. (to Ethyl Corporation), German Patent Application Blitzer, S. M., and Pearson, T. H. (to Ethyl Corporation), German Patent Application E 10 906 IVb/12o (Aug. 30, 1956).

(22) Bonitz, E., *Chem. Ber.*, **88**, 742 (1955).

(23) Bonitz, E., Max-Planck-Institut fuer Kohlenforschung, Muelheim-Ruhr, private communication to the author.

(24) Bos, H. (to Stamicarbon N. V.), German Patent (DAS) 1,018,865 (Nov. 7, 1957); *C.A.*, **53**, 16963*g* (1959).

(25) Breslow, D. S., and Newburg, N. R., *J. Am. Chem. Soc.*, **79**, 5072 (1957); **81**, 81 (1959).
(26) Breslow, D. S., Long, W. P., and Newburg, N. R., *Rubber & Plastics Age*, **41**, 155 (1960).
(27) Brockway, L. O., and Davidson, N. R., *J. Am. Chem. Soc.*, **63**, 3287 (1941).
(28) Brokaw, R. S., and Pease, R. N., *J. Am. Chem. Soc.*, **72**, 3237 (1950).
(29) Buckton, G. B., and Odling, W., *Ann. Supplementum*, **4**, 109 (1865).
(30) Calingaert, G., Soroos, W., and Shapiro, H., *J. Am. Chem. Soc.*, **63**, 947 (1941).
(31) Calloway, N. O., and Green, L. D., *J. Am. Chem. Soc.*, **59**, 809 (1937).
(32) Chien, J. C. W., *J. Am. Chem. Soc.*, **81**, 86 (1959).
(33) Clogston, C. C., *Underwriters' Lab. Bull. Research*, No. **34**, 5 (1945).
(34) Coates, G. E., *J. Chem. Soc.*, 2003 (1951).
(35) Coates, G. E., and Glockling, F., *J. Chem. Soc.*, 22 (1954).
(36) Coates, G. E., "Organo-Metallic Compounds," New York, John Wiley & Sons, 1956.
(37) Coates, G. E., Hunter, W. H., and Topley, B. (to the Minister of Supply, in Her Majesty's Government of the United Kingdom of Great Britain and Northern Ireland), U. S. Patent 2,712,546 (July 5, 1955).
(38) Costa, G., and Calcinari, R., *Univ. studi. Trieste, Fac. sci. Ist. chim.*, No. **20**, 15 (1957); *C.A.*, **53**, 19569*g* (1959).
(39) Cottle, D. L. (to Esso Research and Engineering Company), U. S. Patent 2,848,472 (Aug. 12, 1955); *C.A.*, **53**, 1148*d* (1959); British Patent 790,822 (Aug. 19, 1958); *C.A.*, **52**, 16202*d* (1958).
(40) Davidson, N., and Brown, H. C., *J. Am. Chem. Soc.*, **64**, 316 (1942).
(41) Davidson, N., Hugill, S. A. C., Skinner, H. A., and Sutton, L. E., *Trans. Faraday Soc.*, **36**, 1212 (1940).
(42) Dobratz, E. H. (to Koppers Company, Inc.) German Patent (DAS) 1,071,705 (Dec. 24, 1959); Belgian Patent 549,410–413.
(43) Eirich, F., and Mark, H., *J. Colloid Sci.*, **11**, 748 (1956).
(44) Eisch, J., Preprinted Abstract of ACS Cincinnati Section, "Symposium on Organometallic Compounds" (Oct. 1958).
(45) Esso Research and Engineering Company, British Patent 790,822 (Feb. 19, 1956); *C.A.*, **52**, 16202*c* (1958).
(46) Esso Research and Engineering Company, British Patent 808,055 (Jan. 28, 1956); *C.A.*, **53**, 12174*f* (1959).
(47) Ethyl Corporation, *Techn. Bull.*
(48) *European Scientific Notes*, Vol. **6**, No. 13, p. 178, London, Office of Naval Research, July 1, 1952.
(49) Faillebin, *Compt. rend.*, **174**, 112 (1922).
(50) Fehér, F., and Kolb, W., *Naturwissenschaften*, **27**, 615 (1939).
(51) Fernald, H. B. (to Goodrich-Gulf Chemicals Inc.), Belgian Patent 559,404 (July 22, 1957).
(52) FIAT review of German Science, 1939–1946, Wiesbaden, Dieterich'sche Verlagsbuchhandlung, (edited by Klemm, W.); Bähr, G., "Metallorganische Verbindungen," 1948, tome **24**, p. 157–163.
(53) FIAT Review of German Science, 1939–1946, Wiesbaden, Dieterich'sche Ver-

lagsbuchhandlung, (edited by Klemm, W.); Goubeau, J., "Boron Compounds," 1948, tome **23**, p. 215–238.

(54) FIAT Review of German Science, 1939–1946, Wiesbaden, Dieterich'sche Verlagsbuchhandlung, (edited by Klemm, W.); Wiberg, E., "Hydrogen Compounds," 1948, tome **23**, p. 126–166.

(55) Fürstenhoff, J. A., *Chem. Zentr.*, **75-I**, 785 (1904).

(56) Fulton, G. R. (to Imperial Chemical Industries, Ltd.), British Patent 757,524 (Sept. 19, 1956); *Chem. Zentr.*, 8069 (1957); French Patent 1,113,546 (Dec. 5, 1955).

(57) Gaudemar, M., *Compt. rend.*, **239**, 1303 (1954).

(58) Gaylord, N. G., and Mark, H. F., "Linear and Stereoregular Addition Polymers," Polymer Reviews Vol. **2**, New York, Interscience Publishers, 1959.

(59) Geiersberger, K., and Galster, H., *Z. anorg. Chem.*, **274**, 289 (1953).

(60) Geiseler, G., and Knothe, W., *Chem. Ber.*, **91**, 2446 (1958); *C.A.*, **53**, 6065g (1959).

(61) Geiseler, G., and Knothe, W. (to VEB Leuna-Werke). Austrian Patent Application 4804/57-3 (Aug. 15, 1958); German Patent (DAS) 1,041,959 (Oct. 30, 1958).

(62) Gellert, H. G., Max-Planck-Institut fuer Kohlenforschung, Muelheim-Ruhr, private communication to the author.

(63) Gilman, H., and Kirby, R. H., *J. Am. Chem. Soc.*, **63**, 2046 (1941).

(64) Gilman, H., Haubein, A. H., O'Donnell, G., and Woods, L. A., *J. Am. Chem. Soc.*, **67**, 922 (1945).

(65) Gilman, H., and Apperson, L. D., *J. Org. Chem.*, **4**, 162 (1939).

(66) Gilman, H., and Mayhue, M. L., *Rec. trav. chim.*, **51**, 47–50 (1932).

(67) Gilman, H., and Marple, K. E., *Rec. trav. chim.*, **55**, 133 (1936).

(68) Grayevsky, A. I., Shchegol, S. S., and Smolyan, Z. S., *Doklady Akad. Nauk S.S.S.R.*, **119**, 101 (1958); *C.A.*, **53**, 205d (1959).

(69) Greenberg, H. (to National Distillers and Chemical Corporation) U. S. Patent 2,749,364 (June 5, 1956).

(70) Grignard, V., and Jenkins, R., *Compt. rend.*, **179**, 89 (1924).

(71) Groenewege, M. P., *Z. physik. Chem.*, (N.E.), **18**, 147 (1958).

(72) Groizeleau, L., *Compt. rend.*, **242**, 1491–92 (1956); *Chem. Zentr.*, 10444 (1957).

(73) von Grosse, A., and Mavity, J. M., *J. Org. Chem.*, **5**, 106 (1940).

(74) von Grosse, A., (to Universal Oil Products Company), U. S. Patent 2,270,292 (Jan. 20, 1942).

(75) Hall, F. C., and Nash, A. W., *J. Inst. Petrol. Technologists*, **23**, 679 (1937).

(76) Hall, F. C., and Nash, A. W., *J. Inst. Petrol. Technologists*, **24**, 471 (1938).

(77) Hallwachs, W., and Schafarik, A., *Ann.*, **109**, 206 (1859).

(78) Hamprecht, G., and Mühlbauer, H. (to Badische Anilin-und Soda Fabrik A.-G.), British Patent 804,059 (Nov. 5, 1958); *C.A.*, **53**, 7990b (1959); U. S. Patent 2,867,643 (Jan. 1, 1959); *C.A.*, **53**, 14938a (1959).

(79) Hamprecht, G., and Mühlbauer, H. (to Badische Anilin-und Soda Fabrik A.-G.), German Patent (DAS) 1,006,856 (Apr. 25, 1957).

(80) Hamprecht, G., Oertel, H., and Schwarzmann, M. (to Badische Anilin-und Soda Fabrik A.-G.), German Patent (DAS) 1,070,179 (Dec. 3, 1959).

(81) Haubein, A. H., *Iowa State Coll. J. Sci.*, **18**, 48 (1943).

(82) Hawkins, E. G. E., and Watt, I. M. (to National Distillers and Chemical Corporation), British Patent 800,615 (Aug. 25, 1958).

(83) Hein, F., Petzchner, E., Segitz, F. A., and Wagler, K., Z. anorg. Chem., 141, 161 (1924).

(84) Hein, F., and Segitz, F. A., Z. anorg. Chem., 158, 153 (1926).

(85) Hein, F., Z. Elektrochem., 28, 469 (1922).

(86) Hein, F., and Schramm, H., Z. physik. Chem., 149 A, 408 (1930).

(87) Hein, F., and Pauling, H., Z. physik. Chem., 165 A, 338 (1933).

(88) Hilpert, S., and Gruettner, G., Ber., 45, 2828 (1912).

(89) Huizda, V. F., and Kraus, C. A., J. Am. Chem. Soc., 60, 2276 (1938).

(90) Hock, H., Ernst, F., and Kropf, H., Angew. Chem., 71, 541 (1959).

(91) Hock, H., and Ernst, F., Chem. Ber., 92, 2716, 2723, 2732 (1959).

(92) Hoffmann, E. G., Ann., 629, 104 (1960).

(93) Hoffmann, E. G., Z. anal. Chem., 170, 177 (1959).

(94) Hoffmann, E. G., Z. Elektrochem., 61, 1014 (1957).

(95) Hoffmann, E. G., and Schomburg, G., Z. Elektrochem., 61, 1101 (1957).

(96) Hoffmann, E. G., and Schomburg, G., Z. Elektrochem., 61, 1110 (1957).

(97) Hoffmann, E. G., Z. Elektrochem., 64, in press (1960).

(99) Hoffmann, E. G., and Schomburg, G., communicated at the III. European Meeting on Molecular Spectroscopy, Freiburg (Brsg.) 1957.

(100) Hoffmann, E. G., and Schomburg, G., Proceedings of the IV. European Meeting on Molecular Spectroscopy at Bologna 1951, in press, London, Pergamon Press, 1960.

(101) Hoffmann, E. G., and Schomburg, G., IUPAC Symposium on Hydrogen Bonding, p. 509, London, Pergamon Press, 1959.

(102) Hoffmann, E. G., Max-Planck-Institut fuer Kohlenforschung, Muelheim-Ruhr, private communication to the author.

(103) Hoffmann, E. G., and Tornau, W., Muelheim-Ruhr, unpublished results.

(104) Horne, S. E., Folt, V. L., Gibbs, C. F., Kiehl, J. P., and Shipmann, J. I., et al., Ind. Eng. Chem., 48, 784 (1956). (B. F. Goodrich Research Center, Breckville, Ohio).

(104a) Hüther, E., cf. (367).

(105) Hurd, D. T., J. Am. Chem. Soc., 70, 2053 (1948).

(106) Hurd, D. T., J. Org. Chem., 13, 711 (1948).

(107) Imperial Chemical Industries, Ltd., Belgian Patent 568,231 (Dec. 1, 1958).

(108) Iyoda, J., and Shiihara, I., J. Chem. Soc. Japan, (Ind. Chem. Sect.), 62, 1106 (1959).

(109) Jacober, J., and Kraus, C. A., J. Am. Chem. Soc., 71, 2405, 2409 (1949).

(110) Jenkner, H., Z. Naturforsch., 146b, 133 (1959).

(111) Jenkner, H., and Schmidt, H. W. (to Kali-Chemie A. G.), U. S. Patent 2,857,414 (Oct. 21, 1958); British Patent 781,533 (Aug. 21, 1957); C.A., 52, 2049g (1958); German Patent (DAS) 1,038,553 (Sept. 11, 1958).

(112) Jenkner, H. (to Kali-Chemie A.G.), British Patent 768,765 (Apr. 12, 1955).

(113) Jenkner, H. (to Kali-Chemie A.G.), British Patent 812,787 (Apr. 29, 1959).

(114) Jenkner, H. (to Kali-Chemie A.G.), German Patent 944,249 (June 14, 1956); *Chem. Zentr.*, 1798 (1957).

(115) Jenkner, H. (to Kali-Chemie A.G.), German Patent 948,975 (March 15, 1956); *Chem. Zentr.*, 5113 (1957); British Patent 756,612; *Chem. Zentr.*, 5704 (1957).

(116) Jenkner, H. (to Kali-Chemie A.G.), German Patent 1,009,630 (June 6, 1957); *C.A.*, **53**, 21667*b* (1959).

(117) Jenkner, H. (to Kali-Chemie A.G.), German Patent (DAS) 1,009,631 (June 6, 1957); *Chem. Zentr.*, 14135 (1957).

(118) Jenkner, H., and Schmidt, H. W. (to Kali-Chemie A.G.), German Patent 1,014,541 (Aug. 29, 1957); *C.A.*, **53**, 19881*h* (1959).

(119) Jenkner, H. (to Kali-Chemie A.G.), German Patent (DAS) 1,031,306 (June 4, 1958).

(120) Jenkner, H. (to Kali-Chemie A.G.), German Patent Application K 18391 IVb/12o (Feb. 2, 1956).

(121) Jenkner, H., and Schmidt, H. W. (to Kali-Chemie A.G.), German Patent Application K 18392 IVb/12o (Apr. 19, 1956).

(122) Jenkner, H. (to Kali-Chemie A.G.), German Patent Application K 20032 IVb/12o (March 15, 1956).

(123) Jenkner, H. (to Kali-Chemie A.G.), German Patent Application K 20071 IVb/21o (Apr. 5, 1956); German Patent Application K 22285 IVb/12o.

(124) Jenkner, H. (to Kali-Chemie A.G.), German Patent Application K 22141 IVb/12o (Dec. 20, 1956).

(125) Jenkner, H., and Schmidt, H. W. (to Kali-Chemie A.G.), German Patent Application K 26023 IVb/12o (Sept. 27, 1956).

(126) Jenkner, H. (to Kali-Chemie A.G.), German Patent (DAS) 1,033,660 (July 10, 1958).

(127) Jenkner, H. (to Kali-Chemie A.G.), German Patent (DAS) 1,034,174 (July 17, 1958).

(128) Jenkner, H., and Schmidt, H. W. (to Kali-Chemie A.G.), German Patent (DAS) 1,048,275 (Jan. 8, 1959).

(129) Jenkner, H. (to Kali-Chemie A.G.), German Patent (DAS) 1,048,581 (Jan. 15, 1959).

(130) Jenkner, H. (to Kali-Chemie A.G.), German Patent (DAS) 1,055,511 (Apr. 23, 1959).

(131) Jenkner, H. (to Kali-Chemie A.G.), German Patent (DAS) 1,058,478 (June 4, 1959).

(132) Jenkner, H. (to Kali-Chemie A.G.), German Patent (DAS) 1,061,302 (July 16, 1959).

(133) Jenkner, H. (to Kali-Chemie A.G.), German Patent (DAS) 1,064,513 (Sept. 3, 1959).

(134) Jenkner, H. (to Kali-Chemie A.G.), German Patent (DAS) 1,067,814 (Oct. 29, 1959).

(135) Johnson, W. K. (to Monsanto Chemical Company), U. S. Patent 2,900,402 (Aug. 18, 1959).

(136) Jones, R. G., and Gilman, H., *Chem. Reviews*, **54**, 835 (1954).

(137) Kempkes, A., Doctoral Thesis, T.-H. Aachen (1958).

(138) Kendall, J., Crittenden, E. D., and Miller, K. H., *J. Am. Chem. Soc.*, **45**, 963 (1923).

(139) King, R. W., and Movsovic, D. J. (to Petrochemicals Ltd.), British Patent 798,599 (July 23, 1958).

(140) King, R. W., and Movsovic, D. J. (to Petrochemicals Ltd.), British Patent 811,076 (Apr. 2, 1955); *C.A.*, **53**, 15980*d* (1959); German Patent (DAS) 1,044,081 (Nov. 20, 1958).

(141) Kinter, R., and Pfeifer, C. R. (to Dow Chemical Company), British Patent 801,674 (Sept. 15, 1958); *C.A.*, **53**, 4135*g* (1959); Belgian Patent 548,652 (June 14, 1956).

(142) Kirby, R. H., *Iowa State Coll. J. Sci.*, **12**, 137 (1937).

(143) Kirshenbaum, I., and Stanley, B. M. (to Esso Research and Engineering Company) U. S. Patent 2,863,895 (Dec. 9, 1958); British Patent 811,976 (Apr. 15, 1959).

(144) Kluge, F., and Schaeffer, G. (to Farbwerke Hoechst A.-G.), German Patent Application F 17 351 IVb/12 0.

(145) Knap, J. E., Leech, R. E., Reid, A. J., and Tamplin, W. S., *Ind. Eng. Chem.*, **49**, 874 (1957).

(146) Köster, R., *Angew. Chem.*, **68**, 383 (1956).

(147) Köster, R., and Ziegler, K., *Angew. Chem.*, **69**, 94 (1957).

(148) Köster, R., *Angew. Chem.*, **70**, 371 (1958).

(149) Köster, R., *Angew. Chem.*, **71**, 520 (1959).

(150) Köster, R., Reinert, K., and Müller, K. H., *Angew. Chem.*, **72**, 78 (1960).

(151) Köster, R., *Ann.*, **618**, 31 (1958).

(152) Köster, R., and Kroll, W. R., *Ann.*, **629**, 50 (1960).

(153) Köster, R., and Bruno, G., *Ann.*, **629**, 89 (1960).

(154) Köster, R., Max-Planck-Institut fuer Kohlenforschung, Muelheim-Ruhr, private communication to the author.

(155) Köster, R., and Larbig, W., Max-Planck-Institut fuer Kohlenforschung, Muelheim-Ruhr, private communication to the author.

(156) Köster, R., (to Studiengesellschaft Kohle m.b.H.), Canadian Patent 580,529 (July 28, 1959).

(157) Köster, R., Bruno, G., and Lehmkuhl, H. (to Studiengesellschaft Kohle m.b.H.), Austrian Patent 202,566 (Jan. 25, 1957), German Patent (DDR) 16,560 (Febr. 5, 1957).

(158) Köster, R. (to Studiengesellschaft Kohle m.b.H.), German Patent 1,024,062 (May 28, 1958).

(159) Köster, R. (to Studiengesellschaft Kohle m.b.H.), German Patent 1,039,041 (Jan. 9, 1959), Patent of Addition to 1,024,062 (158).

(160) Köster, R. (to Studiengesellschaft Kohle m.b.H.), German Patent 1,056,127 (Aug. 11, 1959).

(161) Köster, R. (to Studiengesellschaft Kohle m.b.H.), German Patent 1,057,600 (Sept. 2, 1959).

(162) Köster, R. (to Studiengesellschaft Kohle m.b.H.), German Patent 1,060,400 (Oct. 15, 1959).

(163) Kohlrausch, K. W. F., and Wagner, J., Z. physik. Chem., B 52, 185 (1942).

(164) Koppers Technical Bulletin, C-B-253.

(165) Krause, E., and Wendt, B., Ber., 56, 466 (1923).

(166) Krause, E., and Polack, H., Ber., 59, 777, 1428 (1926).

(167) Krause, E., and Dittmar, P., Ber., 63, 2401 (1930).

(168) Krause, E., and von Grosse, A., "Die Chemie der metallorganischen Verbindungen," Berlin, Gebr. Bornträger, 1937.

(169) Kroll, W. R., Max-Planck-Institut fuer Kohlenforschung, Muelheim-Ruhr, private communication to the author.

(170) Laubengayer, A. W., and Gilliam, W. F., J. Am. Chem. Soc., 63, 477 (1941).

(171) Lehmkuhl, H., Max-Planck-Institut fuer Kohlenforschung, Muelheim-Ruhr, private communication to the author.

(172) Leone, P., Gazz. chim. ital., 55, 294 (1925).

(173) Leone, P., and Braicovic, A., Gazz. chim. ital., 55, 301 (1925).

(174) Lewis, P. H., and Rundle, R. E., J. Chem. Phys., 21, 986 (1953).

(175) Lindsey, R. V., Jr. (to E. I. du Pont de Nemours & Co.), U. S. Patent 2,473,434 (June 14, 1949).

(176) Lindsey, R. V., Jr. (to E. I. du Pont de Nemours & Co.), U. S. Patent 2,765,329 (Oct. 2, 1956).

(177) Long, W. P., J. Am. Chem. Soc., 81, 5312 (1959).

(178) Long, L. H., and Norrish, R. G. W., Trans. Roy. Soc. London, A 241, 587 (1949).

(179) Longuet-Higgins, H. C., Quart. Reviews, 11, 121 (1957).

(180) Manulkin, Z. M., and Tatarenko, A. N., Zhur. Obshchei Khim., 21, 93 (1951).

(181) Martin, H., Doctoral Thesis, T.-H. Aachen (1952).

(182) Martin, H., Angew. Chem., 68, 306 (1956).

(183) Marvel, C. S., and Garrison, W. E., Jr., J. Am. Chem. Soc., 81, 4737 (1959).

(184) Mavity, J. M. (to Universal Oil Products Company), U. S. Patent 2,388,428 (Nov. 6, 1945).

(185) Meerwein, H., and Bersin, T., Ann., 476, 113 (1929).

(186) Meerwein, H., Hinz, G., Majert, H., and Sönke, H., J. prakt. Chem., (2), 147, 226 (1937).

(187) Menzel, W., Z. anorg. Chem., 269, 52 (1952).

(188) Miller, A. E. G., Biss, I. W., and Schwarzmann, M., J. Org. Chem., 24, 627 (1959).

(189) Mirviss, St. B., and Inchalik, E. J. (to Esso Research and Engineering Company), U. S. Patent 2,827,458 (March 18, 1958); C.A., 52, 13778h (1958).

(190) Mühlbauer, H., and Hamprecht, G. (to Badische Anilin und Soda Fabrik A.-G.), German Patent (DAS) 1,004,179 (March 14, 1957).

(190a) Müller, H. (to Badische Anilin und Soda Fabrik A.-G.), German Patent (DAS) 1,054,454 (Apr. 9, 1959).

(191) Nagel, K., Max-Planck-Institut fuer Kohlenforschung, Muelheim-Ruhr, private communication to the author.

(192) Natta, G., Angew. Chem., 68, 393 (1956).

(193) Natta, G., Pasquon, I., and Giachetti, E., Angew. Chem., 69, 213 (1957).

(194) Natta, G., and Corradini, P., Angew. Chem., 72, 39 (1960).

(195) Natta, G., Mazzanti, G., Giannini, U., and Cesca, S., *Angew. Chem.*, **72,** 39 (1960).

(196) Natta, G., Mazzanti, G., Corradini, P., Giannini, U., and Cesca, S., *Atti acad. naz. Lincei*, **26,** No. 2, 150 (1959).

(197) Natta, G., Pino, P., Mazzanti, G., and Giannini, U., *J. Am. Chem. Soc.*, **79,** 2975 (1957).

(198) Natta, G., Pino, P., Mazzanti, G., Longi, P., and Bernardini, F., *J. Am. Chem. Soc.*, **81,** 2561 (1959).

(199) Natta, G., Farina, M., and Pino, P., *Ricerca sci. Suppl.*, **A 25,** 120–133 (1955); *Chem. Zentr.*, 12182 (1957).

(200) Nelson, J. F., *Iowa State Coll. J. Sci.*, **12,** 145 (1937); *C.A.*, **32,** 3756g (1938).

(201) Nesmeyanov, A. N., and Novikova, N. N., *Bull. acad. sci. U.R.S.S.*, 372 (1942); *C.A.*, **39,** 1637⁶ (1945).

(202) Nesmeyanov, A. N., Borisov, A. E., and Savel'eva, J. S., *Izvest. Akad. Nauk S.S.S.R.*, 1034 (1959).

(203) Nesmeyanov, A. N., and Kahn, E. I., *Ber.*, **62,** 1018 (1929); "Organic Synthesis," Vol. **12,** pp. 46, 54, New York, John Wiley & Sons, Inc., 1932.

(204) Neumann, W. P., *Angew. Chem.*, **69,** 730 (1957).

(205) Neumann, W. P., *Ann.*, **618,** 90 (1958).

(206) Neumann, W. P., *Ann.*, **629,** 23 (1960).

(207) Neumann, W. P., Thesis for Habilitation, University of Giessen, Germany (1959).

(208) Neumann, W. P., Max-Planck-Institut fuer Kohlenforschung, Muelheim-Ruhr, private communication to the author.

(209) Neunhoeffer, O., and Weigel, W., *J. prakt. Chem.*, **4,** 201 (1957).

(210) Nicolescu, V., and Iovu, M., *Analele univ.*, "C. J. Parhon," *Bucuresti, Ser. Stiint, nat.*, **15,** 97 (1957); *C.A.*, **53,** 1181f (1959).

(211) Nobis, J. F., *Ind. Eng. Chem.*, **49,** 44 A (1957).

(212) Nowlin, G., and Lyons, H. D. (to Phillips Petroleum Company), U. S. Patent 2,852,544 (Sept. 16, 1958).

(213) Nystrom, R. F., and Brown, W. G., *J. Am. Chem. Soc.*, **69,** 1197 (1947).

(214) Ochlobystin, O. J., and Zakharkin, L. I., *Izvest. Akad. Nauk S.S.S.R.*, 1006 (1958); *C.A.*, **53,** 1122g (1959).

(215) Pajaro, G., *Ann. chim. Rome*, **48,** 193 (1958); *C.A.*, **52,** 18194g (1958).

(216) Patat, F., and Sinn, H., *Angew. Chem.*, **70,** 496 (1958).

(217) Perrine, J. C., Jr. (to Olin Mathieson Corporation), U. S. Patent 2,853,526 (Sept. 23, 1958); *C.A.*, **53,** 4133 (1959).

(218) Perrine, J. C., Jr. (to Olin Mathieson Corporation), U. S. Patent 2,853,527 (Sept. 23, 1958); *C.A.*, **53,** 4133 (1959).

(219) Pfohl, W., *Ann.*, **629,** 207 (1960).

(220) Philips Gloeilampen Fabrieken, Belgian Patent 550,991.

(221) Philips Gloeilampen Fabrieken, Belgian Patent 556,450.

(222) Pino, P., Landicci, L., and Lorenzi, G. P., "XVII. IUPAC-Congress," Abstracts Vol. 1, p. 9, Muenchen, 1959; *C.A.*, **53,** 19851e (1959).

(223) Pitzer, K. S., and Gutowsky, H. S., *J. Am. Chem. Soc.*, **68,** 2204 (1946).

(224) Pitzer, K. S., and Sheline, R. K., *J. Chem. Phys.*, **16,** 552 (1948).

(225) Podall, H. E., *J. Am. Chem. Soc.*, **80**, 5573 (1958).
(226) Podall, H. E., Petree, H. E., and Zietz, J. R., *J. Org. Chem.*, **24**, 1222 (1959).
(227) Prevost, C., and Gaudemar, M., *Compt. rend.*, **239**, 282 (1954).
(228) Redman, H. E. (to Ethyl Corporation), U. S. Patent 2,787,626 (July 8, 1955); *C.A.*, **52**, 1202h (1958).
(229) Redman, H. E. (to Ethyl Corporation), U. S. Patent 2,885,314 (March 28, 1957); *C.A.*, **53**, 16967e (1959).
(230) Redman, H. E. (to Ethyl Corporation), U. S. Patent 2,886,581 (March 28, 1957); *C.A.*, **53**, 18865f (1959).
(231) Reed, H. W. B., and Smith, W. R. (to Imperial Chemical Industries, Ltd.), U. S. Patent 2,872,470 (May 28, 1956); British Patent 789,236 (March 2, 1959); Belgian Patent 548,959 (June 5, 1955); German Patent (DAS) 1,040,028 (June 5, 1956).
(232) Reed, H. W. B. (to Imperial Chemical Industries, Ltd.); British Patent Application 788,671 (Jan. 8, 1958).
(233) Renand, P., *Bull. soc. chim. France*, 1044 (1950).
(234) Rienäcker, R., Doctoral Thesis, University of Bern (1958).
(235) Robinson, R., *Chem. Age*, **74**, 997 (1956).
(236) Rochow, E. G., Hurd, D. T., and Lewis, R. N., "The Chemistry of Organometallic Compounds," New York, John Wiley and Sons, Inc., 1957.
(237) Roha, M. E., and Beears, W. L. (to Goodrich-Gulf Chemicals, Inc.), Belgian Patent 553,721.
(238) Rundle, R. E., *J. Am. Chem. Soc.*, **69**, 1327 (1947).
(239) Ruthruff, R. F. (to Chempats, Inc.), U. S. Patent 2,247,821 (July 1, 1941).
(240) Ruthruff, R. F. (to Chempats, Inc.), U. S. Patent 2,271,956 (Feb. 3, 1942); *C.A.*, **36**, 3513 (1942).
(241) Sarton, G., and Costa, G., *Z. Elektrochem.*, **63**, 105 (1959).
(242) Sims, L. L., Ethyl Corporation, *Chem. Eng. News*, Apr., 1958, 66.
(243) Sladkov, A. M., Avich, I. A., Chernov, V. N., Luneva, L. K., and Markevich, V. A., *Proc. Acad. Sci. U.S.S.R.*, **119**, 307 (1958).
(244) Smith, P. (to Imperial Chemical Industries, Ltd.); U. S. Patent 2,863,894 (Dec. 9, 1958); *C.A.* **53**, 3061g (1959); French Patent 1,120,572 (Apr. 23, 1956); German Patent (DAS) 1,032,741 (June 26, 1958).
(245) Smith, P. (to Imperial Chemical Industries, Ltd.), British Patent 757,525 (Sept. 19, 1956); French Patent 1,113,547 (Dec. 5, 1955); *Chem. Zentr.*, 8069 (1959).
(246) Scherer, O., and Osswald, P., Frankfurt/M.-Hoechst, FIAT FINAL Report. No. 1313, p. 357 (1948).
(247) Schlenk, W., Appenrodt, J., Michael, H., and Thal, A., *Ber.*, **47**, 473 (1914).
(248) Schlenk, W., and Weichselfelder, Th., *Ber.*, **56**, 2230 (1923).
(249) Schlenk, W., and Marcus, E., *Ber.*, **47**, 1665 (1914).
(250) Schlenk, W., and Bergmann, E., *Ann.*, **463**, 1 (1928).
(251) Schlesinger, H. I., Sanderson, R. T., and Burg, A. B., *J. Am. Chem. Soc.*, **62**, 3421 (1940).
(252) Schlesinger, H. I., Finholt, A. E., and Bond, A. C., Jr., *J. Am. Chem. Soc.*, **69**, 1199 (1947).

(253) Schlesinger, H. I., Wartik, T., and Grant, N., *J. Am. Chem. Soc.*, **74**, 5809 (1950).

(254) Schmitt, K., Rindtorff, E., and Schaeler, B. (to Bergwerksgesellschaft Hibernia A.-G.), German Patent (DAS) 1,030,343 (May 22, 1958).

(255) Schneider, K., Max-Planck-Institut fuer Kohlenforschung, Muelheim-Ruhr, private communication to the author.

(256) Schomburg, G., and Hoffmann, E. G., *Z. Elektrochem.*, **61**, 1110 (1957).

(257) Stamicarbon, N. V., Belgian Patent 554,994 (Feb. 14, 1957).

(258) Stecher, O., and Wiberg, E., *Ber.*, **75 B**, 2003 (1942).

(259) Stone, F. G. A., *Quart. Reviews*, **9**, 174 (1955).

(260) Storto, M., Doctoral Thesis, T.-H. Aachen (1960).

(261) Strohmeier, W., and Hümpfner, K., *Chem. Ber.*, **90**, 2339 (1957).

(262) Strohmeier, W., and Hümpfner, K., *Z. Elektrochem.*, **61**, 1010 (1957).

(263) Tanner, H. M., and Giraitis, A. P., Belgian Patent 548,440 (Sept. 9, 1956).

(264) Thomas, V., *Compt. rend.*, **174**, 464 (1922).

(265) Uelzmann, H., *J. Polymer Sci.*, **32**, 457 (1958).

(266) Vdovtsova, E. A., and Tsukervanik, I. P., *Zhur. Obshchei Khim.*, **24**, 558 (1954).

(267) Walsh, W. L. (to Goodrich-Gulf Chemicals, Inc.), Belgian Patent 571,731 (Oct. 3, 1959).

(268) Walter, H. A. (to Monsanto Chemical Company), U. S. Patent 2,864,842 (Dec. 16, 1958).

(269) Wartik, T., and Schlesinger, H. I., *J. Am. Chem. Soc.*, **75**, 835 (1953).

(270) Weber, H., and Strache, H. (to Chemische Werke Hüls A.-G.) German Patent (DAS) 1,054,455 (Apr. 9, 1959).

(271) Wesslau, H., *Ann.*, **629**, 198 (1960).

(272) Weyer, K., Doctoral Thesis, T.-H., Aachen (1956).

(273) Wiberg, E., and Stecher, O., *Angew. Chem.*, **52**, 372–73 (1939).

(274) Wilke, G., and Müller, H., *Ann.*, **618**, 267 (1958); *C.A.*, **53**, 13040*h* (1959).

(275) Wilke, G., and Müller, H., *Ann.*, **629**, 222 (1960).

(276) Wilke, G., and Müller, H., *Chem. Ber.*, **89**, 444 (1956).

(277) Wilke, G., Max-Planck-Institut fuer Kohlenforschung, Muelheim-Ruhr, private communication to the author.

(278) Wilke, G. (to Ziegler, K.), German Patent 1,044,082 (March 3, 1959); Canadian Patent 581,625 (Aug. 18, 1959); French Patent 1,152,113 (Sept. 2, 1957).

(279) Wilke, G. (to Ziegler, K.), German Patent 1,052,987 (July 1, 1959).

(280) Wiswall, R. H., Jr., and Smyth, C. P., *J. Chem. Phys.*, **9**, 352 (1941).

(281) Wittig, G., *Angew. Chem.*, **62**, 231 (1950).

(282) Wittig, G., and Bub, O., *Ann.*, **566**, 113 (1950).

(283) Wittig, G., and Keicher, G., *Naturwissenschaften*, **34**, 216 (1947).

(284) Yakubovich, A. Y., and Motsarev, G. V., *Doklady Akad. Nauk S.S.S.R.*, **88**, 87 (1953).

(285) Yakubovich, A. Y., and Motsarev, G. V., *Zhur. Obshchei Khim.*, **23**, 771 (1953).

(286) Yeddanapalli, L. M., and Schubert, C. C., *J. Chem. Phys.*, **14**, 1 (1946).

(287) Zakharkin, L. I., and Ochlobystin, O. J., *Doklady Akad. Nauk S.S.S.R.*, **116**, 236 (1957); *C.A.*, **52**, 6167*c* (1958).

(288) Zakharkin, L. I., and Chorlina, I. M., *Doklady Akad. Nauk S.S.S.R.*, **116**, 422 (1957).
(289) Zakharkin, L. I., and Gavrilenko, V. V., *Doklady Akad. Nauk S.S.S.R.*, **118**, 713 (1958); *C.A.*, **52**, 11738e (1958).
(290) Zakharkin, L. I., and Gavrilenko, V. V., *Izvest. Akad. Nauk S.S.S.R.*, 166 (1959).
(291) Zakharkin, L. I., and Ochlobystin, O. J., *Izvest. Akad. Nauk S.S.S.R., Otdel. Khim. Nauk*, 181 (1959).
(292) Zakharkin, L. I., and Savina, L. A., *Izvest. Akad. Nauk S.S.S.R., Otdel. Khim. Nauk*, 444 (1959); *C.A.*, **53**, 21626d (1959).
(293) Zakharkin, L. I., and Chorlina, I. M., *Doklady Akad. Nauk S.S.S.R.*, 550 (1959).
(294) Zakharkin, L. I., and Ochlobystin, O. J., *Doklady Akad. Nauk S.S.S.R.*, 1135 (1959).
(295) Zakharkin, L. I., Gavrilenko, V. V., and Ochlobystin, O. J., *Izvest. Akad. Nauk S.S.S.R., Otdel. Khim. Nauk*, 100 (1958).
(296) Zakharkin, L. I., and Ochlobystin, O. J., *Izvest. Akad. Nauk S.S.S.R., Otdel. Khim. Nauk*, 1278 (1958); *C.A.*, **53**, 4115c (1959).
(297) Ziegler, K., *Angew. Chem.*, **64**, 323 (1952).
(298) Ziegler, K., *Brennstoff-Chem.*, **33**, 193 (1952); *Chem. Zentr.*, 1745 (1953).
(299) Ziegler, K., *Brennstoff-Chem.*, **35**, 321 (1954); *Chem. Zentr.*, 11196 (1955).
(300) Ziegler, K., *Experientia Suppl. II*, 274 (1955).
(301) Ziegler, K., "Perspectives in Organic Chemistry," p. 185, New York, Interscience Publishers, Inc., 1956.
(302) Ziegler, K., *Angew. Chem.*, **68**, 721 (1956).
(303) Ziegler, K., *Suomen Kemistilehti A*, **30**, 109 (1957); *Chem. Zentr.*, 1733 (1959).
(304) Ziegler, K., *Collection Czechoslov. Chem. Commun.*, **22**, 295 (1957).
(305) Ziegler, K., *Compte-rendu du XXXIe Congrès International de Chimie Industrielle*, Liège (1958).
(306) Ziegler, K., *Erdöl u. Kohle*, **11**, 766 (1958)..
(307) Ziegler, K., Special Publ. No. 13, London, The Chemical Society, 1959 (Int. Conf. Coörd Chem.).
(308) Ziegler, K., *Brennstoff-Chem.*, **40**, 209 (1959).
(309) Ziegler, K., *Angew. Chem.*, **67**, 33 (1955).
(310) Ziegler, K., Holzkamp, E., Köster, R., and Lehmkuhl, H., *Angew. Chem.*, **67**, 213 (1955).
(311) Ziegler, K., Gellert, H.-G., Zosel, K., Lehmkuhl, H., and Pfohl, W., *Angew. Chem.*, **67**, 424 (1955).
(312) Ziegler, K., and Lehmkuhl, H., *Angew. Chem.*, **67**, 424 (1955).
(313) Ziegler, K., and Gellert, H.-G., *Angew. Chem.*, **67**, 424 (1955).
(314) Ziegler, K., Krupp, F., and Zosel, K., *Angew. Chem.*, **67**, 425 (1955).
(315) Ziegler, K., Schneider, K., and Schneider, J., *Angew. Chem.*, **67**, 425 (1955).
(316) Ziegler, K., Holzkamp, E., Breil, H., and Martin, H., *Angew. Chem.*, **67**, 426 (1955).
(317) Ziegler, K., Holzkamp, E., Breil, H., and Martin, H., *Angew. Chem.*, **67**, 541 (1955).
(318) Ziegler, K., *Angew. Chem.*, **71**, 623 (1959).

(319) Ziegler, K., Grössmann, H., Kleiner, H., and Schaefer, O., *Ann.*, **473**, 1 (1929).
(320) Ziegler, K., and Kleiner, H., *Ann.*, **473**, 54 (1929).
(321) Ziegler, K., Dersch, F., and Wollthan, H., *Ann.*, **511**, 13 (1934).
(322) Ziegler, K., and Jakob, L., *Ann.*, **511**, 45 (1934).
(323) Ziegler, K., Jakob, L., Wollthan, H., and Wenz, A., *Ann.*, **511**, 64 (1934).
(324) Ziegler, K., and Schaefer, W., *Ann.*, **511**, 101 (1934).
(325) Ziegler, K., Grimm, A., and Willer, R., *Ann.*, **542**, 90 (1939).
(326) Ziegler, K., Eimers, E., Hechelhammer, W., and Wilms, A., *Ann.*, **567**, 43 (1950).
(327) Ziegler, K., and Gellert, H.-G., *Ann.*, **567**, 195 (1950).
(328) Ziegler, K., Gellert, H.-G., Martin, H., Nagel, K., and Schneider, J., *Ann.*, **589**, 91 (1954).
(329) Ziegler, K., and Holzkamp, E., *Ann.*, **605**, 93 (1957).
(330) Ziegler, K., and Köster, R., *Ann.*, **608**, 1 (1957).
(331) Ziegler, K., Schneider, K., and Schneider, J., *Ann.*, **623**, 9 (1959).
(332) Ziegler, K., Gellert, H.-G., Lehmkuhl, H., Pfohl, W., and Zosel, K., *Ann.*, **629**, 1 (1960).
(333) Ziegler, K., Martin, H., and Krupp, F., *Ann.*, **629**, 14 (1960).
(334) Ziegler, K., and Gellert, H.-G., *Ann.*, **629**, 20 (1960).
(335) Ziegler, K., Köster, R., Lehmkuhl, H., and Reinert, K., *Ann.*, **629**, 33 (1960).
(336) Ziegler, K., Kroll, W. R., Larbig, W., and Steudel, O. W., *Ann.*, **629**, 53 (1960).
(337) Ziegler, K., Gellert, H.-G., Zosel, K., Holzkamp, E., Schneider, J., Söll, M., and Kroll, W. R., *Ann.*, **629**, 121 (1960).
(338) Ziegler, K., and Kroll, W. R., *Ann.*, **629**, 167 (1960).
(339) Ziegler, K., Gellert, H.-G., Holzkamp, E., Wilke, G., Duck, E., and Kroll, W. R., *Ann.*, **629**, 172 (1960).
(340) Ziegler, K., Nagel, K., and Pfohl, W., *Ann.*, **629**, 210 (1960).
(341) Ziegler, K., Krupp, F., and Zosel, K., *Ann.*, **629**, 241 (1960).
(342) Ziegler, K., Krupp, F., Weyer, K., and Larbig, W., *Ann.*, **629**, 251 (1960).
(343) Ziegler, K., Dislich, H., Hüther, E., and Lehmkuhl, H., Muelheim-Ruhr, unpublished results.
(344) Ziegler, K., and Thielmann, F., *Ber.*, **56**, 1740, 2453 (1923).
(345) Ziegler, K., and Bähr, K., *Ber.*, **61**, 253 (1928).
(346) Ziegler, K., Lehmkuhl, H., and Lindner, E., *Chem. Ber.*, **92**, 2320 (1959).
(347) Ziegler, K., and Lehmkuhl, H., *Z. anorg. Chem.*, **283**, 414 (1956).
(348) Ziegler, K., Hoberg, H., and Ruppenthal, F., Muelheim-Ruhr, unpublished results.
(349) Ziegler, K., Köster, R., Breil, H., Martin, H., and Holzkamp, E. (to Ziegler, K.), Austrian Patent 199,368 (June 27, 1958); *Chem. Zentr.*, 1345 (1960); German Patent (DAS) 1,016,023 (Sept. 19, 1957); *C.A.*, **53**, 20912c (1959).
(350) Ziegler, K., Lehmkuhl, H., Pfohl, W., and Zosel, K., (to Ziegler, K.), Austrian Patent 201,610 (Nov. 22, 1958); German Patent (DDR) 14,808 (March 9, 1956).
(351) Ziegler, K., Köster, R., and Kroll, W. R. (to Ziegler, K.), Belgian Patent 575,319 (Aug. 3, 1959).

(352) Ziegler, K., and Lehmkuhl, H. (to Ziegler, K.), Belgian Patent 575,595 (Aug. 11, 1959).

(353) Ziegler, K., and Lehmkuhl, H. (to Ziegler, K.), Belgian Patent 575,641 (Aug. 12, 1959).

(354) Ziegler, K., Köster, R., and Kroll, W. R. (to Ziegler, K.), Belgian Patent 575,992 (Aug. 21, 1959).

(355) Ziegler, K., and Gellert, H.-G. (to Ziegler, K.), British Patent 770,707 (July 10, 1957); *C.A.*, **52**, 1202*c* (1958); German Patent 961,537 (Jan. 30, 1957); *C.A.*, **53**, 11226*c* (1959); German Patent 1,000,818 (Apr. 29, 1957); *C.A.*, **54**, 1299*d* (1960); German Patent 1,008,733 (Dec. 12, 1957); *C.A.*, **53**, 21666*h* (1959); German Patent 1,031,792 (Oct. 2, 1958).

(356) Ziegler, K., and Zosel, K. (to Ziegler, K.), British Patent 775,384 (March 3, 1957); *C.A.*, **52**, 12893*d* (1958); German Patent 925,291 (Jan. 10, 1955); *C.A.*, **52**, 1197*b* (1958).

(357) Ziegler, K., Gellert, H.-G., and Bonitz, E. (to Ziegler, K.), British Patent 778,098 (July 3, 1957); *C.A.*, **51**, 15081*i* (1957); French Patent 1,132,972 (Nov. 12, 1956); *Chem. Zentr.*, 14529 (1958); German Patent 942,026 (Feb. 14, 1956); *C.A.*, **53**, 7014*f* (1959).

(358) Ziegler, K., and Martin, H. (to Ziegler, K.), British Patent 787,438 (Apr. 18, 1958); *C.A.*, **52**, 19107*h* (1958); French Patent 1,128,369 (Aug. 20, 1956); *Chem. Zentr.*, 1268 (1959); German Patent 1,018,857 (Feb. 21, 1958); Italian Patent 538,581 (Jan. 26, 1956); Japanese Patent 236,128 (Oct. 23, 1957).

(359) Ziegler, K., Schneider, K., and Schneider, J., (to Ziegler, K.), British Patent 803,178 (Feb. 11, 1959); *C.A.*, **53**, 6985*c* (1959).

(360) Ziegler, K., and Ruthardt, K. (to Ziegler, K., and Ruthardt, K.), British Patent 816,574 (July 15, 1959); Canadian Patent 564,493 (Oct. 14, 1958); French Patent 1,130,678 (Oct. 1, 1956); *Chem. Zentr.*, 2580 (1959).

(361) Ziegler, K., and Lehmkuhl, H. (to Ziegler, K.), French Patent 1,174,100 (Nov. 3, 1958).

(362) Ziegler, K., and Lehmkuhl, H. (to Ziegler, K.), Canadian Patent 582,016 (Aug. 25, 1959); French Patent 1,139,719 (Feb. 18, 1957); *Chem. Zentr.*, 3300 (1959); French Patent 1,208,430 (Sept. 14, 1959).

(363) Ziegler, K., Breil, H., Martin, H., and Holzkamp, E., (to Ziegler, K.), German Patent (DAS) 1,016,022 (Sept. 9, 1957); *C.A.*, **53**, 20912*c* (1959).

(364) Ziegler, K., and Zosel, K. (to Ziegler, K.), German Patent 1,048,276 (Apr. 30, 1959).

(365) Ziegler, K. (to Ziegler, K.), German Patent 1,050,762 (May 29, 1959).

(366) Ziegler, K., Köster, R., and Kroll, W. R. (to Ziegler, K.), German Patent 1,055,534 (Aug. 5, 1959); *Chem. Zentr.*, 650 (1960).

(367) Ziegler, K. (from Hüther, E.), Italian Patent 567,577 (Oct. 14, 1957).

(368) Ziegler, K., and Zosel, K. (to Ziegler, K.), U. S. Patent 2,691,668 (Oct. 12, 1954); *C.A.*, **49**, 11685*b* (1955); British Patent 772,174 (Apr. 10, 1957); *C.A.*, **51**, 14786*d* (1957); German Patent 916,167 (May 14, 1954); *Chem. Zentr.*, 4933 (1955).

(369) Ziegler, K., and Gellert, H.-G., (to Ziegler, K.), U. S. Patent 2,695,327 (Nov. 23, 1954); *C.A.*, **50**, 1073*g* (1956); U. S. Patent 2,699,457 (Jan. 11, 1955); *C.A.*, **49**, 6651*e* (1955); British Patent 713,081 (June 12, 1956); *C.A.*, **49**, 3576*d*

(1955); British Patent 742,642 (Apr. 18, 1956); *C.A.,* **51,** 2846*g* (1957); German Patent 878,560 (Feb. 17, 1953); *C.A.,* **51,** 9670*i* (1957).

(370) Ziegler, K., and Nagel, K. (to Ziegler, K.), U. S. Patent 2,744,127 (May 1, 1956); *C.A.,* **51,** 459*c* (1957); British Patent 767,400 (Nov. 23, 1956); *C.A.,* **51,** 9673*e* (1957); German Patent 911,731 (Feb. 19, 1954); *Chem. Zentr.,* 7745 (1954).

(371) Ziegler, K., Holzkamp, E., and Wilke, G. (to Ziegler, K.), U. S. Patent 2,781,410 (Feb. 12, 1957); *C.A.,* **51,** 9211*e* (1957); British Patent 773,536 (Aug. 14, 1957); British Patent 777,152 (Oct. 9, 1957); *C.A.,* **51,** 12543*g* (1957); French Patent 68,554 (Dec. 30, 1957); *Chem. Zentr.,* 16161 (1959); French Patent 964,642 (March 26, 1957); German Patent 1,001,981 (May 20, 1957); *C.A.,* **53,** 20912*a* (1959); German Patent 1,034,169 (Oct. 28, 1958).

(372) Ziegler, K., Gellert, H.-G., and Martin, H. (to Ziegler, K.), U. S. Patent 2,786,860 (March 26, 1957); *C.A.,* **51,** 12130*a* (1957); British Patent 777,701 (Oct. 16, 1957); *C.A.,* **51,** 15569*h* (1957); German Patent 920,071 (Aug. 23, 1954); *Chem. Zentr.,* 7553 (1955).

(373) Ziegler, K., and Gellert, H.-G. (to Ziegler, K.), U. S. Patent 2,826,598 (March 11, 1958); *C.A.,* **52,** 7352*i* (1958); British Patent 763,824 (Apr. 9, 1957); *C.A.,* **52,** 1203 (1958); German Patent 917,006 (June 4, 1954); *Chem. Zentr.,* 5179 (1955).

(374) Ziegler, K., and Gellert, H.-G. (to Ziegler, K.), U. S. Patent 2,835,689 (May 20, 1958); *C.A.,* **53,** 1148*h* (1959); British Patent 794,359 (Aug. 20, 1958); *C.A.,* **53,** 13056*h* (1959); German Patent 1,038,043 (Dec. 17, 1958).

(375) Ziegler, K., and Köster, R. (to Ziegler, K.), U. S. Patent 2,839,556 (June 17, 1958); *C.A.,* **52,** 13777*b* (1958); U. S. Patent 2,909,547 (Oct. 20, 1959); British Patent 779,873 (July 24, 1957); *C.A.,* **51,** 17981*a* (1957); German Patent 921,450 (Sept. 30, 1954); *C.A.,* **52,** 13791*b* (1958); German Patent 934,649 (Aug. 20, 1955); *C.A.,* **52,** 18216*i* (1958); German Patent 936,630 (Oct. 3, 1955); *C.A.,* **53,** 2093*b* (1959).

(376) Ziegler, K., and Gellert, H.-G. (to Ziegler, K.), U. S. Patent 2,843,474 (July 15, 1958); *C.A.,* **52,** 15405*g* (1958); British Patent 788,619 (Apr. 23, 1958); *C.A.,* **52,** 8920*a* (1958).

(377) Ziegler, K., Köster, R., and Lehmkuhl, H. (to Ziegler, K.), U. S. Patent 2,844,615 (July 22, 1958); *C.A.,* **52,** 16202*c* (1958); British Patent 779,874 (July 24, 1957); *C.A.,* **52,** 2050*d* (1958); German Patent 925,348 (Jan. 16, 1955); *C.A.,* **52,** 14654*c* (1958); German Patent 931,107 (May 16, 1955); *C.A.,* **52,** 16201*i* (1958).

(378) Ziegler, K., and Lehmkuhl, H. (to Ziegler, K.), U. S. Patent 2,849,349 (Aug. 26, 1958); *C.A.,* **52,** 19619*d* (1958); British Patent 813,446 (Sept. 2, 1959); *C.A.,* **53,** 13845*e* (1959); German Patent (DAS) 1,047,450 (Dec. 24, 1958); German Patent (DAS) 1,056,377 (Apr. 30, 1959).

(379) Ziegler, K. (to Ziegler, K.), U. S. Patent 2,892,858 (June 30, 1959); British Patent 804,335 (March 4, 1959); *C.A.,* **53,** 12173*e* (1959); French Patent 1,134,907 (Dec. 10, 1956); German Patent 1,014,088 (Nov. 20, 1959); *C.A.,* **53,** 17975*i* (1959).

(380) Ziegler, K., Gellert, H.-G., and Nagel, K. (to Ziegler, K.), U. S. Patent

2,915,541 (Dec. 1, 1959); British Patent 774,516 (May 8, 1957); *C.A.*, **52,** 2050*b* (1958); German Patent 918,928 (July 21, 1954); *Chem. Zentr.*, 7312 (1955).

(381) Zosel, K., and Holzkamp, E., Max-Planck-Institut fuer Kohlenforschung, Muelheim-Ruhr, private communication to the author.

(382) Zosel, K. (to Ziegler, K.), British Patent 809,310 (June 10, 1959); German Patent 1,028,096 (July 30, 1958); *Chem. Zentr.*, 13326 (1958).

6. ORGANOSILYLMETALLIC CHEMISTRY

HENRY GILMAN and HANS J. S. WINKLER

Iowa State University, Ames, Iowa

HISTORICAL REVIEW

It had long been thought that organosilylmetallic compounds were formed as intermediates in the preparation of disilanes from chlorosilanes and alkali metals (*111,144,152,155*), but no attempts were made to use the intermediate silylmetallic substances as such on a preparative scale during these early investigations. In the nineteen twenties and early nineteen thirties a series of publications appeared which described the preparation and reactions of transient alkali metal derivatives of organosilanes (*117–124*). These early attempts to prepare stable silylmetallic compounds failed, partly because of the inherent difficulty in preparing alkylsubstituted silylmetallic compounds, and partly because of the high reactivity of the silylmetallic compounds towards the solvents used, liquid ammonia and ethylamine. However, Kraus and co-workers were successful in preparing alkali metal derivatives of the other Group IV-B elements and later similar routes to silylmetallic compounds were followed although different substituents, solvents, and reaction conditions were used. Attempts to duplicate the early experiments by Kraus on the preparation of organosilylmetallic compounds were unsuccessful (*9,179*).

In the following decades a new approach to silylmetallic compounds was made through reaction of iodosilane with magnesium (*33*), mercury (*32*), and zinc (*160*). However, these reactions did not clearly show the existence of silylmetallic compounds.

The preparation of tris-(triphenylgermyl)-silyllithium marks the first successful synthesis of a stable organosilylmetallic compound (*133*). This preparation and the early work by Benkeser showed without doubt that silylmetallic compounds could be prepared. Triphenylsilylpotassium was formed together with α,α-dimethylbenzylpotassium by cleaving α,α-dimethylbenzyltriphenylsilane with sodium-potassium alloy in ether (*10*):

$$(C_6H_5)_3SiC(CH_3)_2(C_6H_5) + 2 K \longrightarrow (C_6H_5)_3SiK + C_6H_5(CH_3)_2CK$$

However, the preparation was not a very useful route to the silylmetallic reagent since a reactive organometallic compound was also present in the reaction mixture.

In the same year appeared the first of an extensive series of papers by others describing the formation and reactions of silylmetallic compounds (*86*).

Several procedures for the preparation of R_3SiM compounds were described (*170*). One of broad applicability is concerned with the cleavage of disilanes (*70,71,86*), and in this regard, two general factors should be considered.

$$R_3SiSiR_3 + 2\ Li \longrightarrow 2\ R_3SiLi$$

One of these is the nature of the R group, and the other is the solvent or medium in which the cleavage is carried out. R_3SiM compounds are readily prepared when one, two, or three groups are aryl (*71*). When the three groups are alkyl, it is possible to prepare such compounds, but the reaction is not so effective from a preparative viewpoint as when one or more of the R groups are aryl.

Several solvents have been examined for the formation of R_3SiM types, one of the earliest being diethyl ether (*86*). For example, the cleavage of a compound like hexaphenyldisilane by sodium-potassium alloy proceeds satisfactorily in this medium. However, this mode of preparation has two drawbacks. First, there is an excess of sodium-potassium alloy; and second, the triphenylsilylpotassium is insoluble in ether. The excess of sodium-potassium alloy was readily removed by the use of mercury to form an amalgam. A subsequent development came in the replacement of diethyl ether by ethylene glycol dimethyl ether, a medium in which the triphenyl-silylpotassium was soluble (*14*). However, the R_3SiM compounds are unstable in this solvent, which is cleaved appreciably over a period of time and particularly on heating. For example, when a solution of triphenylsilyl-potassium in ethylene glycol dimethyl ether is refluxed for one hour all the triphenylsilylpotassium is used up, as evidenced by a negative Color Test I (*82,153*). In a corresponding reaction of triphenylsilyllithium, the chief product formed by the cleavage is methyltriphenylsilane (*164*). Triphenyl-silylpotassium was also prepared from triphenylsilane (*7*), chlorotriphenyl-silane (*7,92*), and alkoxytriphenylsilane (*7,92*) with sodium-potassium alloy.

Later came the procedure for the preparation of triphenylsilyllithium by cleavage of hexaphenyldisilane in tetrahydrofuran (*71*). The yields by this synthesis are excellent; the R_3SiLi compound is soluble; and the solutions are satisfactorily stable. On protracted refluxing, or on heating at a more elevated temperature, the tetrahydrofuran is cleaved to give (subsequent to hydrolysis) 4-triphenylsilylbutanol-1 (*168*).

$$(C_6H_5)_3SiLi + \underline{CH_2CH_2CH_2CH_2O} \xrightarrow{\text{(H}_2\text{O)}} (C_6H_5)_3SiCH_2CH_2CH_2CH_2OH$$

For most purposes, reactions with triphenylsilyllithium in tetrahydrofuran proceed sufficiently satisfactorily so that there is no problem of contamination by any appreciable quantity of the 4-triphenylsilylbutanol-1.

The triphenylsilyllithium can also be prepared by cleavage in tetrahydropyran. The rate of formation of triphenylsilyllithium in this solvent is slower than in tetrahydrofuran, but the resulting R_3SiLi compound is more stable.

A more recent development in the preparation of R_3SiM compounds is that involving the direct reaction of R_3SiX with lithium in tetrahydrofuran (*40b,80*). In short, these compounds can now be prepared by the simple convenient procedure used for the preparation of Grignard reagents and for the preparation of organolithium compounds. This so-called direct preparation appears to involve the intermediate formation of a disilane, which is then cleaved by the metal present. The disilane can be isolated when the preparation is halted at an appropriate stage. This production of the disilane may be preceded by the direct formation of the R_3SiLi compound which is known to react very promptly with an R_3SiX compound to give a disilane. The synthesis may involve the following transformations:

$$R_3SiX + 2\ M \longrightarrow R_3SiM + MX$$

$$R_3SiM + R_3SiX \longrightarrow R_3SiSiR_3$$

$$R_3SiSiR_3 + 2\ M \longrightarrow 2\ R_3SiM$$

Cleavage is generally not accomplished by metals such as magnesium or sodium even though the initial condensation of chlorosilanes to the corresponding disilanes does proceed with these metals (*40b,80*).

The condensation of chlorotriphenylsilane with magnesium is noteworthy since it appears that the reaction proceeds through a silyl-Grignard reagent. Similar procedures have recently been published which may involve the transient silyl-Grignard reagent. One of these is the reaction of chlorotriphenylsilane with cyclohexylmagnesium bromide (*148*); the other is the coupling of diphenylchlorosilane with magnesium to give *sym*-tetraphenyldisilane (*84*).

PREPARATION OF ORGANOSILYLMETALLIC COMPOUNDS

This presentation is arranged systematically in order of the bond being cleaved. Thus, the first section, "Preparation of Organosilylmetallic Compounds," covers the reactions of metals with compounds containing silicon-hydrogen bonds, silicon-silicon bonds, and other silicon-nonmetal bonds. These reactions lead mainly to the formation of silylmetallic compounds either as intermediates or as end products. The individual elements are arranged within a section according to columns in the periodic chart and subordinated according to increasing atomic number.

Metal Cleavage of Bond between Silicon and Hydrogen

Preparations of trialkylsilylmetallic reagents from the cleavage of hexa-alkylated-disilanes have so far failed. Similarly when triethylsilane was treated with sodium-potassium alloy in ether and derivatized with chloro-triethylsilane, only starting material could be recovered (7,67). During the early work of Kraus (122) the reaction of triethylsilane with lithium in ethylamine was studied. It was shown that N-ethyltriethylsilazane was formed, and it was postulated that the lithium acted as a catalyst only (122):

$$(C_2H_5)_3SiH + Li + C_2H_5NH_2 \longrightarrow (C_2H_5)_3SiNHC_2H_5 + H_2 + Li$$

The following reactions may be involved:

$$(C_2H_5)_3SiH + LiHNC_2H_5 \longrightarrow LiH + (C_2H_5)_3SiNHC_2H_5$$

$$LiH + NH_2C_2H_5 \longrightarrow H_2 + LiNHC_2H_5$$

Triphenylsilane was shown to react slowly with lithium in ether to give triphenylsilanol and hexaphenyldisilane on hydrolysis (51). The reaction is more rapid in tetrahydrofuran. On derivatization with chlorotrimethyl-silane, there was obtained tetraphenylsilane and 1,1,1-trimethyl 2,2,2-tri-phenyldisilane (98). The following reaction scheme may be proposed:

$$(C_6H_5)_3SiH + 2\ Li \longrightarrow (C_6H_5)_3SiLi + LiH$$

$$(C_6H_5)_3SiLi + (CH_3)_3SiCl \longrightarrow (C_6H_5)_3SiSi(CH_3)_3 + LiCl$$

$$(C_6H_5)_3SiLi + (C_6H_5)_3SiH \longrightarrow (C_6H_5)_4Si + other\ products$$

In addition to the tetraphenylsilane there were isolated various other phenylsilanes (4,5,7).

Similar disproportionation products have been found in the reaction of phenylsilane, diphenylsilane, and triphenylsilane with sodium-potassium alloy in ether (4,5,7). Tribenzylsilane reacts with sodium-potassium alloy in decalin to give tetrabenzylsilane. This interfering disproportionation makes the preparation of silylmetallic compounds from silanes impractical in contrast to a carbon analog such as triphenylmethane (121,123). It was observed that benzyltriphenylsilane was formed from triphenylsilane and sodium-potassium alloy in hot toluene (7). It is conceivable that the inter-mediate triphenylsilylpotassium metalated toluene and that benzylpotas-sium reacted rapidly with unreacted triphenylsilane. The postulated metala-tion of toluene by an intermediate phenylsodium could likewise account for the product. For further details of these disproportionation reactions see the section on metal cleavage of silicon-carbon bonds.

Triphenylsilane reacts with sodium in liquid ammonia to give bis-(triphenylsilyl)-amine, a product which may have been formed from the interfering side reaction of the silylmetallic compound with the solvent (140). Another possible route of reaction is:

$$(C_6H_5)_3SiH + NaNH_2 \longrightarrow (C_6H_5)_3SiNH_2 + NaH \xrightarrow{Na} (C_6H_5)_3SiNHNa$$

$$\downarrow {\scriptstyle (C_6H_5)_3SiH}$$

$$[(C_6H_5)_3Si]_2NH$$

Silylmetallic compounds can, however, be prepared from silanes and alkali metals in selected cases. Thus, tri-*p*-xenylsilane reacts with sodium-potassium alloy in ether to give the silylpotassium reagent which couples readily with *p*-bromobiphenyl to give a tetra-*p*-xenylsilane in good yield (7). Tris-(triphenylgermyl)-silane reacts similarly with lithium in ethylamine to give the intermediate silyllithium compound which on standing reacts with the solvent (133), or on derivatization with ethyl bromide gives tris-(triphenylgermyl)-ethylsilane (133), or with triphenyltin chloride gives tris-(triphenylgermyl)-triphenylstannylsilane(97).

$$[(C_6H_5)_3Ge]_3SiH + 2 Li \longrightarrow [(C_6H_5)_3Ge]_3SiLi + LiH$$

$$[(C_6H_5)_3Ge]_3SiLi + C_2H_5Br \longrightarrow [(C_6H_5)_3Ge]_3SiC_2H_5 + LiBr$$

$$[(C_6H_5)_3Ge]_3SiLi + (C_6H_5)_3SnCl \longrightarrow [(C_6H_5)_3Ge]_3SiSn(C_6H_5)_3 + LiCl$$

The reaction of methyldiphenylsilane and dimethylphenylsilane with sodium-potassium alloy in decalin indicated that the phenyl group rather than the alkyl group is displaced from the silicon; thus from the former only methyltriphenylsilane was isolated, and from the latter only dimethyldiphenylsilane (5).

Metal Cleavage of Bond between Silicon and Silicon

Many unsuccessful attempts have been made to prepare trialkylsilylmetallic reagents by cleavage of hexa-alkyldisilanes. The procedures which had been shown to cleave hexa-aryldisilanes caused no significant cleavage. Thus hexamethyldisilane (23,67) and hexaethyldisilane (179) were not cleaved in ethers by sodium-potassium alloy. Similarly, hexaethyldisilane did not undergo cleavage by lithium in tetrahydrofuran (103,125); by sodium-potassium alloy at elevated temperatures without solvents (67,149), or in solvents such as tetrahydrofuran (67,103) and ethylene glycol dimethyl ether (67); by lithium in ethylene glycol dimethyl ether or triethylamine (*125*); or by sodium in liquid ammonia (*67,149*). The alkali metals rubidium (*67,149*) and cesium (*67*) were also unreactive towards hexa-ethyldisilane.

Hexa-aryldisilanes, such as hexaphenyldisilane have been cleaved under a wide variety of conditions. Various solvents have been used for the cleavage of hexaphenyldisilane with lithium, and the stabilities of the solutions of triphenylsilyllithium examined. Tetrahydrofuran is superior to other solvents (*125*) used since it is cleaved only slowly, on prolonged heating, to the corresponding 4-triphenylsilylbutanol-1 (*168*).

$$(C_6H_5)_3SiSi(C_6H_5)_3 + 2\ Li \longrightarrow 2\ (C_6H_5)_3SiLi$$

$$(C_6H_5)_3SiLi + \underline{CH_2CH_2CH_2CH_2O} \xrightarrow{(H_2O)} (C_6H_5)_3SiCH_2CH_2CH_2CH_2OH$$

Solutions of triphenylsilyllithium in ethylene glycol dimethyl ether are stable for only about one hour (*14*). The cleavage of hexaphenyldisilane in tetrahydropyran or dioxane is slower than in tetrahydrofuran (*39,164*). For this reason these solvents are considered less advantageous than tetra-hydrofuran even though they are more stable toward cleavage by the silylmetallic compound. The attempted use of pyridine as a solvent for the cleavage of hexaphenyldisilane gave a quantitative yield of triphenylsilyl-lithium. However, the triphenylsilyllithium reacted promptly with the solvent to give 4-triphenylsilyl-1,4-dihydropyridine (*167*). Lithium in quinoline is ineffective in causing the cleavage of hexaphenyldisilane even after prolonged heating (*127*).

$$(C_6H_5)_3SiLi + C_5H_5N \longrightarrow$$

Ether was used in the first cleavage of hexaphenyldisilane by sodium-potassium alloy (*92,93*), resulting in a suspension of triphenylsilylpotas-sium. This led to the use of ethylene glycol dimethyl ether as solvent which was found to dissolve the R_3SiM compound (*14*). It was further found that the excess alloy could readily be removed by amalgamation (*92*). The cleavage of hexaphenyldisilane by sodium-potassium alloy has been accomplished with marginal success in such solvents as petroleum ether and benzene (*92*).

Potassium metal in di-*n*-butyl ether causes cleavage of hexaphenyldi-silane (*86*), but this procedure has no advantage over the one described above. Sodium in liquid ammonia likewise cleaves hexaphenyldisilane but the silylmetallic compound reacts readily with the solvent to form silazanes

(*93,180*) in addition to tetraphenylsilane. Sodium dispersion in ether, tetralin (*179*), xylene, or dioxane (*86*) did not effect cleavage of hexaphenyldisilane. When ethylene glycol dimethyl ether was used as a solvent (*14*) the cleavage by sodium went smoothly. However, the reagent has not been used so extensively as the corresponding triphenylsilyllithium or -potassium.

Cesium and rubidium were found to cleave hexaphenyldisilane in ether and di-*n*-butyl ether, respectively (*92*), but the cost of the metals coupled with the danger of handling them makes these silylmetallic compounds less attractive. Calcium (*125*) and magnesium (*14,92*) were found not to react with hexaphenyldisilane under corresponding conditions.

From the above it may be concluded that triphenylsilyllithium in tetrahydrofuran is currently the most accessible silylmetallic compound. It should be mentioned that some samples of lithium have been shown to be inactive in cleaving disilanes (*46,129,163*). A correlation seems to exist between the purity of the metal and its activity toward cleavage of disilanes. Traces of sodium present in the lithium seem to enhance the cleavage while the absence of sodium or a larger percentage of sodium seems to slow down the cleavage if not to prevent it entirely (*46*). Prior studies on this phenomenon were observed in the preparation of some RLi compounds (*46*).

Substituted aromatic disilanes such as hexa-*p*-tolyldisilane (*179*) and 1,2-di-*p*-tolyl-1,1,2,2-tetraphenyldisilane (*90*) have been cleaved to the corresponding silylmetallic compounds by sodium-potassium alloy in ether. Octaphenyltrisilane and decaphenyltetrasilane (*165*) have been shown to undergo cleavage by lithium in tetrahydrofuran. The cleavage of these polysilanes may be complicated by subsequent reaction of the remaining silicon-silicon bonds with the resulting silylmetallic compounds (see p. 291).

$$(C_6H_5)_3Si(C_6H_5)_2SiSi(C_6H_5)_3 + 2\,Li \longrightarrow (C_6H_5)_3Si(C_6H_5)_2SiLi + (C_6H_5)_3SiLi$$

An interesting cleavage of *sym*-tetraphenyldisilane has recently been reported (*84*).

$$(C_6H_5)_2SiHSiH(C_6H_5)_2 + 2\,Li \longrightarrow 2\,(C_6H_5)_2SiHLi$$

The subsequent reaction of diphenylsilyllithium with unreacted starting material or the competitive reaction of the silicon-hydrogen bond with the metal may explain the low yields of products obtained (see pp. 295, 273).

In contrast to the failure of cleaving hexa-alkyldisilanes, *sym*-dimethyltetraphenyldisilane and *sym*-tetramethyldiphenyldisilane can be cleaved in tetrahydrofuran by lithium (*71*) to the corresponding methyldiphenyl- and dimethylphenylsilyllithium reagents. These R_3SiLi types are comparable chemically in many respects, to triphenylsilyllithium. It has been found that bis-5,5'-dimethyldibenzosilole cleaved readily with lithium in tetrahydrofuran (*62*).

The comparable reactions of *sym*-dimethyltetraphenyldisilane (*67,149*) and *sym*-tetramethyldiphenyldisilane with sodium-potassium alloy in ether did not proceed satisfactorily (*149*). In the hope of obtaining evidence for the intermediate formation of trialkylsilylmetallic compounds by indirect methods, 1,1,1-trialkyl-2,2,2-triaryldisilanes were cleaved by metals. Thus 1,1,1-trimethyl-2,2,2-triphenyldisilane was treated with lithium in tetrahydrofuran and subsequently with chlorotriethylsilane, but only starting material was recovered (*125*). However, when 1,1,1-triethyl-2,2,2-triphenyldisilane was cleaved by lithium in tetrahydrofuran at low temperatures and rapidly hydrolyzed, triethylsilane, hexaethyldisilane, and triphenylsilane were obtained in yields of 11, 14, and 92 per cent, respectively (*125*).

$$(C_2H_5)_3SiSi(C_6H_5)_3 + Li \xrightarrow{(H_2O)} (C_2H_5)_3SiH + (C_2H_5)_3SiSi(C_2H_5)_3 + (C_6H_5)_3SiH$$

When sodium-potassium alloy was used in these cleavage reactions further evidence was obtained for the formation of trialkylsilylmetallic compounds. Thus, 1,1,1-trimethyl-2,2,2-triphenyldisilane was cleaved in ether and the silylmetallic compound derivatized with bromobenzene (*67,92*) to yield tetraphenylsilane, hexaphenylsilane, and some phenyltrimethylsilane (*67,149,179*). (The formation of hexaphenyldisilane is explained later by a halogen-metal interconversion reaction between triphenylsilylpotassium and bromobenzene.) Similar cleavages of 1,1,1-triethyl-2,2,2-triphenyldisilane followed by subsequent derivatization with bromobenzene yielded tetraphenylsilane and traces of triethylphenylsilane (*149*).

Metal Cleavage of Bond between Silicon and Group IV Elements other than Silicon

An early attempt to prepare trialkylsilylmetallic compounds involved the cleavage of triethylsilyltriphenylgermane by lithium in ethylamine (*122*). Triethylsilane and triphenylgermane were isolated from the reaction after hydrolysis. If the cleavage products were treated with ethyl bromide, tetraethylsilane and ethyltriphenylgermane were isolated. Both of these reactions indicate the transient existence of triethylsilyllithium. This shows that trialkylsilylmetallic compounds may exist, although their stability is limited due to rapid reaction with the solvent.

$$(C_2H_5)_3SiGe(C_6H_5)_3 + 2\,Li \longrightarrow (C_2H_5)_3SiLi + (C_6H_5)_3GeLi$$

$$(C_2H_5)_3SiLi + (C_6H_5)_3GeLi + 2\,C_2H_5Br \longrightarrow (C_2H_5)_4Si + (C_6H_5)_3GeC_2H_5$$

A similar reaction of triphenylsilyltrimethyltin with sodium in liquid ammonia yielded triphenylsilylsodium in addition to trimethyltinsodium (*117*). The triphenylsilylsodium thus formed reacted with the solvent to form triphenylsilazane. Addition of methyl iodide to the same reaction mixture resulted in the formation of tetramethyltin and methyltriphenylsilane (*117*).

Similarly, triphenylsilyltriphenylgermane was cleaved by sodium-potassium alloy in ether. On carbonation there was obtained a mixture of triphenylsilanol and triphenylgermanecarboxylic acid (*58*).

Many attempts to cleave silicon-carbon bonds for the specific preparation of trialkylsilylmetallic compounds have been carried out. The following compounds were not cleaved under the conditions indicated: trimethylphenylsilane (*67*), triethylphenylsilane (*67,103*), trimethyl-*o*-biphenylsilane (*103*), and trimethyl-*o*-tolylsilane (*103*) by sodium-potassium alloy in ether; phenyltriethylsilane by sodium in liquid ammonia or lithium in ethylamine (*122*); allyltrimethylsilane by lithium in ether (*103*); trimethyl-*o*-tolylsilane, trimethylphenylsilane, triethylphenylsilane by lithium in ether or tetrahydrofuran (*103*); and trimethyl-*o*-xenylsilane by lithium in ethylene glycol dimethyl ether (*103*). The series 9-fluorenyltrimethylsilane, 9-methyl-9-fluorenyltrimethylsilane, and 9,9-bis-(trimethylsilyl) fluorene were likewise unaffected by lithium in ether or tetrahydrofuran (*103*). Dimethyldibenzosilole was stable towards lithium in tetrahydrofuran (*62*). It was also shown that the compounds methyltriphenyl-, dimethyldiphenyl-, and trimethylphenylsilane were unaffected by sodium-potassium alloy in decalin (*5*).

Mention was made earlier that benzyltriethylsilane (*67,122*) and benzyltriphenylsilane (*179*) were not cleaved by lithium in liquid ammonia, by sodium-potassium alloy in ether, or by sodium dispersion in ether. However, benzyltrimethylsilane, diphenylmethyltrimethylsilane, and triphenylmethyltrimethylsilane were cleaved by potassium in liquid ammonia (*101*). The cleavage of benzyltrimethylsilane was established by isolation of toluene, bis-(trimethylsilyl)amine, and hexamethyldisiloxane (*101*). Benzyltriphenylsilane was later cleaved similarly by lithium in tetrahydrofuran (*75*).

The cleavage of a carbon to silicon bond marked the first successful identification of an organosilylmetallic compound as mentioned in the introduction (*10*). It should be noted that the above-mentioned work by Hauser (*101*) appeared at about the same time as that of Benkeser (*10*), as did the work on the cleavage of silicon-silicon bonds for the formation of silylmetallic compounds (*93*).

Benkeser successfully cleaved silicon-carbon bonds with sodium-potassium alloy in ether in selected systems. He found that a *tert*-butyl group attached to silicon was not cleaved whereas an α,α-dimethylbenzyl group was cleaved readily (*10*). The formation of the silylmetallic compound was proven by subsequent derivatization with bromobenzene, water, and chlorotrimethylsilane. The yields were low, possibly because of interfering side-reactions between the simultaneously formed organometallic compound and the derivatizing agents. When triphenylmethyltriphenylsilane was cleaved by sodium-potassium alloy and carbonated, a mixture of triphenylacetic acid and triphenylsilanol was isolated (*17*). The triphenylsilanol was formed from the triphenylsilanecarboxylic acid by decarbonylation during the isolation procedure.

$$(C_6H_5)_3SiC(C_6H_5)_3 + 2K \longrightarrow (C_6H_5)_3SiK + (C_6H_5)_3CK$$
$$ \text{I} \qquad\qquad \text{II}$$

$$CO_2 + I + II \xrightarrow{(H_2O)} (C_6H_5)_3SiCOOH + (C_6H_5)_3CCOOH$$
$$\phantom{CO_2 + I + II \xrightarrow{(H_2O)} (C_6H_5)_3}\downarrow$$
$$\phantom{CO_2 + I + II \xrightarrow{(H_2O)}} (C_6H_5)_3SiOH + CO$$

From the above it may be concluded that at least one phenyl group attached to the carbon linked to the silicon is necessary if silicon-carbon cleavage is to occur with sodium-potassium alloy. The resonance stabilizations of the silylmetallic compound and the organometallic compound may account for this enhanced cleavage. The favored cleavage of a tri-aryl-silyl group, as compared to a tri-alkyl-silyl group, from a silicon atom or from a carbon atom by a metal in organic solvents is consistent with this stability. Cleavages by potassium in liquid ammonia appear to be anomalous in this respect (*101*).

Tetraphenylsilane has been cleaved by sodium-potassium alloy (*92*) in ether and by lithium in tetrahydrofuran (*98*).

$$(C_6H_5)_4Si + 2Li \longrightarrow (C_6H_5)_3SiLi + C_6H_5Li$$
$$\downarrow 2(CH_3)_3SiCl$$
$$C_6H_5Si(CH_3)_3 + (C_6H_5)_3SiSi(CH_3)_3 + 2LiCl$$

Several strained systems have been found to promote carbon to silicon cleavage by metals. Thus tris-(*o*-biphenyl)silane cleaves readily in the presence of lithium to give biphenyl (*98*).

A large amount of work has been published on the reactions of triphenylsilylcarbinols. These substances were shown to rearrange readily in the presence of traces of metals (*13,22*).

$$(C_6H_5)_3Si(C_6H_5)_2COH + Na \xrightarrow{(H_2O)} (C_6H_5)_2CHOSi(C_6H_5)_3$$

Traces of metals catalyzed the rearrangement of trimethylsilyldiphenylcarbinol to benzhydryloxytrimethylsilane, suggesting that a concerted molecular rearrangement is involved rather than the formation of a silyl-metallic species (*22*).

$$(CH_3)_3Si(C_6H_5)_2COH + Na \xrightarrow{(H_2O)} (CH_3)_2SiOCH(C_6H_5)_2$$

The disproportionation reaction of silanes in the presence of metals has already been mentioned. This type of reaction has only been observed in the cases where at least one hydrogen atom is present on the silicon atom (see p. 273). A thorough investigation showed that aryl groups and not alkyl groups are cleaved from the silicon atom (*5*). The time of reaction and the metal used have been shown to have a pronounced effect on the composition of the products. When diphenylsilane was treated with lithium in tetrahydrofuran for 84 hours a 77 per cent yield of triphenylsilane was obtained (*98*). Treating diphenylsilane with sodium-potassium alloy in ether for eight hours yielded 80 per cent of tetraphenylsilane and 8 per cent of triphenylsilane (*4*). Triphenylsilane when treated with lithium in tetrahydrofuran for 4 and 7.5 hours, respectively, and then derivatized with chlorotrimethylsilane, gives 58 and 0 per cent of 1,1,1-trimethyl-2,2,2-triphenyldisilane, respectively. It was observed that diphenylsilane gave tetraphenylsilane on treatment with sodium-potassium alloy. Triphenylsilane was reacted with the sodium-potassium alloy to give triphenylsilylpotassium which was derivatized by chlorotrimethylsilane to yield 1,1,1-trimethyl-2,2,2-triphenyldisilane. Triphenylsilylpotassium on the other hand showed no tendency to cleave a silicon-carbon bond. The following reactions were postulated (*4*):

$$(C_6H_5)_2SiH_2 + 2 K \longrightarrow C_6H_5K + C_6H_5SiH_2K$$

$$(C_6H_5)_2SiH_2 + C_6H_5K \longrightarrow (C_6H_5)_3SiH + KH$$

$$(C_6H_5)_3SiH + K \longrightarrow (C_6H_5)_3SiK \xrightarrow{(H_2O)} (C_6H_5)_3SiOH$$

$$(C_6H_5)_3SiH + C_6H_5K \longrightarrow (C_6H_5)_4Si + KH$$

It was shown that diphenylsilane reacted with lithium in tetrahydrofuran to give triphenylsilane (77 per cent). Methyltriphenylsilane was the only product isolated from the reaction of triphenylsilane with lithium in tetrahydrofuran, followed by addition of dimethyl sulfate (*98*). Triphenylsilane reacted with lithium metal to give tetraphenylsilane and 1,1,1-trimethyl-2,2,2-triphenyldisilane after treatment with chlorotrimethylsilane (*98*).

Metal Cleavage of Bond between Silicon and Group VI Elements

It has recently been found that certain siloxanes cleave readily with lithium, cesium, and rubidium metal in tetrahydrofuran (*37*). Lithium silanolates and silyllithium compounds are formed from the cleavage with lithium. It was observed that hexamethyldisiloxane was not cleaved by sodium-potassium alloy in ether, or by lithium and cesium in tetrahydrofuran. Hexaphenyldisiloxane cleaved readily with lithium in tetrahydrofuran, methyltetrahydrofuran or tetrahydropyran to give, subsequent to hydrolysis, triphenylsilane and triphenylsilanol in good yields (*37*):

$$(C_6H_5)_3SiOSi(C_6H_5)_3 + 2 Li \longrightarrow (C_6H_5)_3SiOLi + (C_6H_5)_3SiLi$$

The symmetrical 1,1,3,3 - tetramethyl - 1,3 - diphenyldisiloxane likewise cleaved normally. Hexaphenyldisiloxane also undergoes cleavage by cesium or rubidium (*37*). Unsymmetrical siloxanes, such as 1,1,1-trimethyl-3,3,3-triphenyldisiloxane, cleave in agreement with previous results to yield triphenylsilylmetallic compounds.

$$(C_6H_5)_3SiOSi(CH_3)_3 + 2 Li \longrightarrow (C_6H_5)_3SiLi + LiOSi(CH_3)_3$$

$$(C_6H_5)_3SiLi + LiOSi(CH_3)_3 + 2(C_6H_5)_3SiCl \longrightarrow$$

$$(C_6H_5)_6Si_2 + (C_6H_5)_3SiOSi(CH_3)_3$$

It appears that the silyllithium compound does not react with the starting material to form the corresponding disilane, since 1,1,1-trimethyl-3,3,3-tri-*p*-tolyldisiloxane, when cleaved by lithium and derivatized by chlorotriphenylsilane, yields only 1,1,1-tri-*p*-tolyl-2,2,2-triphenyldisilane and no hexa-*p*-tolyldisilane.

$$(p\text{-}CH_3C_6H_4)_3SiOSi(CH_3)_3 + 2 Li \longrightarrow (p\text{-}CH_3C_6H_4)_3SiLi + LiOSi(CH_3)_3$$

$$(p\text{-}CH_3C_6H_4)_3SiLi + (C_6H_5)_3SiCl \longrightarrow (p\text{-}CH_3C_6H_4)_3SiSi(C_6H_5)_3 + LiCl$$

Alkoxytriarylsilanes have been cleaved with sodium-potassium alloy in ether (*7,92*) but no appreciable reaction takes place with sodium in xylene (*149*).

No cleavage of ethoxytrimethylsilane by lithium was observed in ether or tetrahydrofuran (*103*); by sodium-potassium alloy in ether or tetrahydrofuran (*103,179*); or by cesium in ether (*149*). During the early work by Kipping, it was observed that diphenylphenoxychlorosilane reacted with sodium in toluene to give a silicohydrocarbon, the identity of which has not been fully established (*110*).

$$(C_6H_5)_2Si(OC_6H_5)Cl \xrightarrow{Na} [(C_6H_5)_2Si]_4$$

Metal Cleavage of Bond between Silicon and Group VII Elements

The first attempts to prepare silylmetallic compounds were made by reaction of halosilanes with various metals. This reaction was known to give disilanes in most cases. Since it was reasoned that an intermediate silylmetallic reagent may have been formed in this Wurtz type reaction, it was thought possible to arrest the reaction at the intermediate silylmetallic compound under the proper conditions.

Early attempts to form silylmetallic compounds included the reaction of bromotriethylsilane with lithium in ethylamine (*122*), but there was isolated only N-ethyltriethylsilazane, the condensation product with the solvent.

Due to the apparent high reactivity of the alkylsilylmetallic compounds, attention was turned towards arylsilylmetallic compounds. This approach was further encouraged by the finding that triphenylmethyl chloride reacted readily with sodium in liquid ammonia (*121*). At that time it was thought that a solvated organosilicon free radical was formed from the reaction between bromotriphenylsilane and lithium in ethylamine (*121*). Repetition of this work indicated that no solvated free radical could be isolated (*9*). However, from the reaction of bromotriphenylsilane with lithium in ethylamine there was isolated N-ethyltriphenylsilazane in good yields (*9*). It was found that aromatic substances such as benzene and phenyl substituted silanes when dissolved in ethylamine take up lithium metal to form polylithium addition compounds (*9*). It may have been this absorption in part which led Kraus to believe that a solvated free radical had been formed and reacted with lithium to yield triphenylsilyllithium (*117*). It was later shown that apparently neither the silylmetallic compound nor the solvated free radical was formed under these conditions since no tetraphenylsilane could be isolated after addition of bromobenzene (*179*). This reaction had been reported to proceed during the earlier work (*117*). The reaction of chlorotriphenylsilane with sodium in liquid ammonia gave triphenylsilazane only (*123*).

It was only after the use of sodium-potassium alloy in ether or of lithium in tetrahydrofuran that silylmetallic reagents were prepared on a useful scale from halosilanes. It has been shown, however, that the silylmetallic compound is formed by metal cleavage of the disilane obtained from a primary condensation of the halosilane, (p. 272). Thus hexaphenyldisilane could be isolated in a 64 per cent yield if the reaction was interrupted at an early state (*40b,80*). On longer reaction times, chlorotriphenylsilane reacted with excess lithium in tetrahydrofuran to give triphenylsilyllithium which on condensation with chlorotrimethylsilane gave 82–83 per cent of 1,1,1-trimethyl-2,2,2-triphenyldisilane (*40b,80*).

$$2\,(C_6H_5)_3SiCl + 2\,Li \longrightarrow (C_6H_5)_3SiSi(C_6H_5)_3 + 2\,LiCl$$

$$(C_6H_5)_3SiSi(C_6H_5)_3 + 2\,Li \longrightarrow 2\,(C_6H_5)_3SiLi$$

$$(C_6H_5)_3SiLi + (CH_3)_3SiCl \longrightarrow (C_6H_5)_3SiSi(CH_3)_3 + LiCl$$

Partly alkylated silylmetallic compounds, methyldiphenylsilyllithium, dimethylphenylsilyllithium, and 1-phenyl-1-silacyclohexyllithium have been prepared similarly (40b,80,136).

The first step in this sequence may in reality be a two-step process. That is, chlorotriphenylsilane may react with lithium directly to give triphenylsilyllithium which then couples with unreacted chlorotriphenylsilane to give hexaphenyldisilane. In special cases it has been possible to find evidence for the formation of an organosilylmetallic compound directly from a chlorosilane. Highly hindered chlorosilanes such as chlorotri-o-xenylsilane have been found to give silanes on reaction with sodium in xylene followed by hydrolysis (135). In this case the reaction does not proceed beyond the formation of the silylmetallic intermediate because the sterically hindered silylmetallic compound fails to couple with unreacted chlorosilane (135). Chlorotri-o-tolylsilane (15) reacts similarly with lithium in tetrahydrofuran (40b).

$$(o\text{-}CH_3C_6H_4)_3SiCl + 2\,Li \longrightarrow (o\text{-}CH_3C_6H_4)_3SiLi + LiCl$$

This is in agreement with the unsuccessful attempts to introduce more than four o-tolyl groups in a disilane. Thus, hexachlorodisilane reacts with o-tolyllithium to produce sym-dichlorotetra-o-tolyldisilane while phenyllithium under the same conditions reacts to form hexaphenyldisilane (83).

$$Cl_3SiSiCl_3 + 4\,o\text{-}CH_3C_6H_4Li \longrightarrow (o\text{-}CH_3C_6H_4)_2SiClSiCl(o\text{-}CH_3C_6H_4)_2 + 4\,LiCl$$

$$Cl_3SiSiCl_3 + 6\,C_6H_5Li \longrightarrow (C_6H_5)_3SiSi(C_6H_5)_3 + 6\,LiCl$$

Tri-p-tolylsilanecarboxylic acid was prepared in a 69 per cent yield by the reaction of chlorotri-p-tolylsilane with sodium-potassium alloy in ether and subsequent carbonation (18). Rubidium and cesium were found to be satisfactory for the preparation of silylmetallic compounds directly from chlorosilanes (40b,80).

Diphenylchlorosilane was found to react with lithium in tetrahydrofuran to give diphenylsilyllithium, a silylmetallic compound containing hydrogen and an alkali metal on the same silicon atom (84).

$$(C_6H_5)_2SiHCl + 2\,Li \longrightarrow (C_6H_5)_2SiHLi$$

The use of other less active metals was indicated early. It was thought possible in this way to reduce the extent of condensation of a silylmetallic compound with the unreacted halosilane. Alkali metal derivatives normally react smoothly with excess halide, to form disilanes which, in specific solvents, readily undergo cleavage by excess metal.

Zinc reacts with iodosilane to produce silane and hydrogen (33). It was postulated that an intermediate silylzinc iodide was formed here but this was later disputed (2,126). Mercury apparently reacts with iodosilane to produce disilane (*33*). Magnesium reacts very slowly with bromosilane in di-*n*-butyl ether or iodosilane in di-isoamyl ether, but there is no evidence for the formation of intermediate silylmetallic compounds (*33,160*) Iodotriethylsilane gave no apparent reaction with magnesium (*32*). An intermediate silyl-Grignard reagent has, however, been postulated in reactions of certain arylated silanes with magnesium in tetrahydrofuran (*84*) and more recently in the very interesting study (*148*) of the reactions of cyclohexylmagnesium bromide with chlorosilanes (*99,148*).

$$(C_6H_5)_3SiCl + 2 C_6H_{11}MgBr \longrightarrow (C_6H_5)_3SiMgBr + C_6H_{12} + C_6H_{10} + MgClBr$$

$$(C_6H_5)_3SiMgBr + (C_6H_5)_3SiCl \longrightarrow (C_6H_5)_6Si_2 + MgClBr$$

Disilanes are formed when halosilanes are treated with sodium in hydrocarbon solvents. This method of preparation of disilanes has long been known, and has been used extensively. Some of the first cases of the preparation of tetrasubstituted organosilanes involved Wurtz type condensations of aryl and alkyl halides with chlorosilanes such as trichlorosilane and silicon tetrachloride (*138,155*).

$$4 RX + SiX_4 + 8 Na \longrightarrow R_4Si + 8 NaX$$

It has not been established whether these reactions proceed through silylmetallic compounds.

Iodosilane (*33*), chlorotriethylsilane (*67*), and bromotriethylsilane (*122*) on heating with sodium without a solvent give the corresponding disilanes. Sealed tube techniques have also been used (*144*). Normally, however, high boiling solvents such as toluene and xylene are used for the condensation of halosilanes to the corresponding symmetrical disilanes (*5,18,51,67,71,90, 107*). The success of this condensation is explained by the observation that sodium does not cleave hexasubstituted disilanes in these solvents. The following interesting condensations proceed quite satisfactorily (*62*):

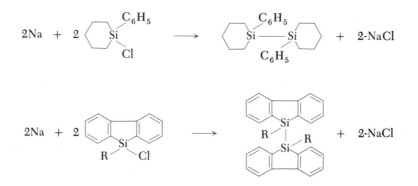

Potassium or sodium-potassium alloy has been found to effect the condensation satisfactorily (23). Thus chlorotrimethylsilane reacts with potassium in the absence of any solvent to give hexamethyldisilane in 92 per cent yield (23). It is especially significant that solvents such as ethylene glycol dimethyl ether (23) or tetrahydrofuran (23) have been used for the condensation of chlorotrimethylsilane with excess potassium or lithium (35, 171). This again indicates the difficulty of cleaving hexa-alkyldisilanes. The mixed condensation has only been used in a few cases because of interfering reactions. Thus chlorotriphenylsilane and benzyl chloride gave benzyltriphenylsilane in addition to a large amount of hexaphenyldisilane (179).

$$2 M + C_6H_5CH_2Cl + (C_6H_5)_3SiCl \longrightarrow C_6H_5CH_2Si(C_6H_5)_3 + 2 MCl$$

Silanes containing two or more halogens have been condensed to give high molecular weight silicohydrocarbons (5,108-114,157), some of which have been identified. Thus, lithium or sodium-potassium alloy reacts with dichlorodiphenylsilane to give silicohydrocarbons which are difficult to separate (136,163,179).

Chlorotrimethylsilane does not undergo coupling with sodium, either in the absence of solvent or in solvents such as xylene, tetrahydrofuran, or di-n-butyl ether (23). It has been shown that chlorotriphenylsilane does not react with magnesium in ether (92). However, chlorotriphenylsilane does react with magnesium in tetrahydrofuran to give 60 per cent of hexaphenyldisilane when the reaction is initiated with ethyl iodide (40b,80). Chlorophenylmethylsilane, chlorophenylethylsilane, chlorodiphenylsilane, and bromodiphenylsilane likewise condense with magnesium in tetrahydrofuran to give the symmetrical disilanes (84,151):

$$2 (C_6H_5)_2SiHCl + Mg \longrightarrow (C_6H_5)_2SiHSiH(C_6H_5)_2 + MgCl_2$$

The condensation of dimethylfluorosilylmethyl-dimethylchloromethylsilane with magnesium presumably is a condensation of a Grignard reagent with a fluorosilane (115):

$$(CH_3)_2SiFCH_2Si(CH_3)_2CH_2Cl + Mg \longrightarrow \underline{(CH_3)_2SiCH_2Si(CH_3)_2CH_2}$$

An interesting case of the formation of a silylmetallic compound from a chlorosilane has recently been reported (137).

$$\pi\text{-}C_5H_5Fe(CO)_4\pi\text{-}C_5H_5 + Na(Hg) \longrightarrow \pi\text{-}C_5H_5Fe(CO)_2Na$$

$$\pi\text{-}C_5H_5Fe(CO)_2Na + (CH_3)_3SiCl \longrightarrow \pi\text{-}C_5H_5Fe(CO)_2Si(CH_3)_3 + NaCl$$

Recently a study has been made of silicon-aluminum types (144a).

Analytical Chemistry of Organosilylmetallic Compounds

Qualitatively, organosilylmetallic compounds can be detected by various color tests. Moderately reactive and highly reactive organometallic compounds react with Michler's ketone to produce strongly colored dyes on oxidation with iodine in acetic acid (Color Test I) (*82*). All organosilylmetallic compounds give a positive Color Test I.

During the early studies of the preparation of triphenylsilylpotassium in ether it was found that a negative Color Test I was obtained from the supernatant ether, if the silylmetallic compound was allowed to settle; whereas the ether insoluble silylmetallic compound gave a strong positive Color Test I. This observation indicates clearly that the silylpotassium compound is insoluble in ether.

By the use of Color Test IIA, it is possible to distinguish between highly reactive organometallic compounds (such as alkyllithium compounds) which give a positive test, and less reactive organometallic reagents (such as aryllithium compounds) since the latter give a negative test. Color Test IIA (*85a*), involves the reaction of the organometallic compound with *p*-bromodimethylaniline followed by treatment with benzophenone and concentrated hydrochloric acid. In a positive test, the first step involves a halogen-metal interconversion to produce the *p*-dimethylaminophenyl-metallic reagent which reacts with benzophenone and concentrated hydrochloric acid to give a red, triarylmethyl type dye. If the color test is negative, no halogen-metal interconversion has occurred and the organometallic compound may or may not react with benzophenone. The triarylcarbinol thus formed does not give a colored ion with hydrochloric acid because of the absence of the dimethylamino group. Organosilyllithium compounds give a negative Color Test IIA (*163*), unless the benzophenone is added immediately (*171*). An interfering reaction may be a rapid coupling of the bromosilane and the *p*-dimethylaminophenyllithium (both formed by the halogen-metal interconversion) to give the corresponding *p*-dimethylaminophenylsilicon derivative. Organosilylmetallic compounds give green-blue colors when added to benzophenone (*125*). This color may in part be due to ketyl formation.

Quantitatively, organosilylmetallic reagents can be determined by titration with acid (*71,80*). This method gives high results if the silylmetallic compound reacts with the solvent to form alkali metal alkoxides. The estimation would thus exceed the true value. For this reason the so-called double titration (*64,100*) has been used with advantage with silylmetallic compounds (*14*). The total amount of alkali is determined first from one aliquot; then a second aliquot is treated with benzyl chloride, which reacts with the silylmetallic compound only, and the unreacted alkoxides are determined as above. The difference between the two determinations represents the total content of silylmetallic compound.

REACTIONS OF ORGANOSILYLMETALLIC COMPOUNDS

This section is arranged according to the bond with which the silylmetallic reagent reacts. Silylmetallic compounds reacting with elements or inorganic compounds precedes the major section which includes the reactions of silylmetallic compounds with organic compounds. This last section is divided according to the columns of the periodic chart.

With Elements

Reactions of triphenylsilyllithium with oxygen have recently been studied (39). It was found that triphenylsilanol, triphenylsilane, and hexaphenyldisilane were produced in tetrahydropyran or tetrahydrofuran at low temperatures (60, 13, 0.6 per cent at −25°). A larger amount of hexaphenyldisilane and a smaller amount of triphenylsilanol were formed at elevated temperatures (33, 29, 19 per cent at +25°). A free-radical mechanism was proposed for this reaction.

$$(C_6H_5)_3SiLi + O_2 \longrightarrow (C_6H_5)_3SiOOLi$$

$$(C_6H_5)_3SiOOLi + (C_6H_5)_3SiLi \longrightarrow 2\,(C_6H_5)_3SiOLi$$

$$(C_6H_5)_3SiOOLi \longrightarrow (C_6H_5)_3SiO\cdot + \cdot OLi$$

$$(C_6H_5)_3SiO\cdot + (C_6H_5)_3SiLi \longrightarrow (C_6H_5)_3SiOLi + (C_6H_5)_3Si\cdot$$

$$(C_6H_5)_3Si\cdot + solvent \longrightarrow (C_6H_5)_3SiH$$

$$2\,(C_6H_5)_3Si\cdot \longrightarrow (C_6H_5)_3SiSi(C_6H_5)_3$$

The first step in this mechanism is similar to the one postulated earlier by Walling and Buckler (162), who considered the oxidation of the Grignard reagent by molecular oxygen to be a two-step process involving bimolecular association followed by rearrangement of an R group through migration. The hydroperoxide salt thus formed could then react either with triphenylsilyllithium by an ionic mechanism or decompose by a homolytic cleavage. The formation of the triphenylsilyl free radical could explain the isolation of triphenylsilane and hexaphenyldisilane. Thus, the formation of a triphenylsilyl free radical by the fourth step could be rationalized. The presence of triphenylsilyl free radicals in the reaction of triphenylsilane with di-tert-butyl peroxide in chlorobenzene was indicated by the isolation of chlorotriphenylsilane (28). The variation of the yield of triphenylsilanol with temperature is in agreement with the variation of phenolic products isolated at various temperatures from the oxidation of aromatic Grignard reagents (105).

The reaction of triphenylsilyllithium with sulfur was found to proceed smoothly to the lithium salt of triphenylsilanethiol which coupled with various halides to yield such compounds as methylthio-, benzylthio-, and benzoylthiotriphenylsilane in good yields (125):

$$(C_6H_5)_3SiLi + S_x \longrightarrow (C_6H_5)_3SiSLi$$

$$(C_6H_5)_3SiSLi + CH_3I \longrightarrow (C_6H_5)_3SiSCH_3 + LiI$$

With Inorganic Compounds

Triphenylmethylsodium reacts with water to give triphenylmethane (121). Triphenylsilylpotassium reacts with water to give triphenylsilanol (92), but under acid conditions triphenylsilane is produced (10). This difference is due to the instability of the silicon-hydrogen bond towards the base liberated on hydrolysis:

$$(C_6H_5)_3SiK + H_2O \longrightarrow (C_6H_5)_3SiH + KOH$$

$$(C_6H_5)_3SiH + H_2O \xrightarrow{KOH} H_2 + (C_6H_5)_3SiOH$$

For reactions of silylmetallic compounds with ammonia and carbon dioxide see pp. 270, 325.

The reactions of triphenylsilyllithium with a variety of metal halides have been studied and the pertinent experimental conditions are presented in Table 6.1.

TABLE 6.1. REACTIONS OF TRIPHENYLSILYLLITHIUM WITH
METALLIC HALIDES AND ORGANOMERCURY COMPOUNDS[a]

Number	Metal halide	R_3SiM/MX_n ratio	Temperature	% Ph_6Si_2	Other products (%)
1	Mercury(II) chloride	1 : 1	Room temp.	18.1	Chlorotriphenylsilane[b] 45
2	Mercury(II) bromide	2 : 1	Room temp.	63.3	Triphenylsilanol 18.1
3	Mercury(II) bromide	2 : 1	$-70°$	50.3	Triphenylsilanol 33.3 Hexaphenyldisiloxane 11.2
4	Lead(II) chloride	1 : 1	Room temp.	17	Chlorotriphenylsilane[b] 17
5	Tin(IV) chloride	1 : 1	Room temp.	30	Chlorotriphenylsilane[b] 25
6	Mercury(I) chloride	1 : 1	Room temp.	33	Chlorotriphenylsilane[b] 18

TABLE 6.1. (*continued*)

Number	Metal halide	R_3SiM/MX_n ratio	Temperature	% Ph_6Si_2	Other products (%)
7	Silver chloride	1:1	Room temp.	41	Triphenylsilane[b] 3
8	Copper(II) chloride	1:1	Room temp.	26	Triphenylsilane[b] 29
9	Iron(III) chloride	1:1	Room temp.	20	Triphenylsilane[b] 30
10	Tin(II) chloride	1:1	Room temp.	16	Trace of triphenylsilane[b]
11	Aluminum chloride	1:1	Room temp.	0	No products identified
12	Zinc chloride	1:1	Room temp.	0	No products identified
13	Cadmium chloride	1:1	$-60°$	0	Cd metal. No other products identified
14	Phenylmercuric bromide	1:1	Room temp.	5.8	Tetraphenylsilane 73.3. Triphenylsilanol 2.2. Mercury 78.8
15	Phenylmercuric bromide	2:1	$-70°$	2.4	Tetraphenylsilane 15.6. Triphenylsilanol 55.2. Mercury 50
16	Diphenylmercury	1:1	Room temp.	0	Benzoic acid[c] 74. Tetraphenylsilane 69.4. Recovered diphenylmercury 11.9
17	Di-*p*-tolylmercury	1:1	Room temp.	0	*p*-Toluic acid[c] 71.3. Triphenyl-*p*-tolylsilane 88. Triphenylsilanol 6.5
18	Di-*p*-tolylmercury	2:1	$0°$	0	*p*-Toluic acid[c] 51. Triphenyl-*p*-tolylsilane 45.7. Triphenylsilanol 45.9. Hexaphenyldisiloxane 4

[a] All reactions listed in this Table are described in reference *40a*. The reactions were carried out in tetrahydrofuran, and the triphenylsilyllithium was added to the inorganic halide.
[b] The reaction was worked up anhydrously.
[c] The reaction mixture was carbonated.

It was hoped that organosilylmetallic compounds containing different metals would result. It was rationalized that the products obtained from reaction 1 were formed by the following steps:

$$HgCl_2 + (C_6H_5)_3SiLi \longrightarrow [(C_6H_5)_3SiHgCl]$$

$$[(C_6H_5)_3SiHgCl] \longrightarrow (C_6H_5)_3SiCl + Hg$$

$$(C_6H_5)_3SiCl + (C_6H_5)_3SiLi \longrightarrow (C_6H_5)_3SiSi(C_6H_5)_3 + LiCl$$

This route may have been followed in reactions Nos. 4, 5, and 6. The formation of triphenylsilane and the absence of triphenylsilanol in reactions 7, 8, 9, and 10 are less readily understood.

The formation of tetraphenylsilane from phenylmercuric bromide or diphenylmercury points to a possible unstable silylmercury intermediate, (Nos. 14 and 15):

$$C_6H_5HgBr + (C_6H_5)_3SiLi \longrightarrow C_6H_5HgSi(C_6H_5)_3 + LiBr$$

$$C_6H_5HgSi(C_6H_5)_3 \longrightarrow (C_6H_5)_4Si + Hg$$

Diphenylmercury and di-*p*-tolylmercury reacted similarly to produce benzoic acid and *p*-toluic acid on carbonation (Nos. 16, 17, and 18), in addition to tetraphenylsilane and triphenyl-*p*-tolylsilane, as shown in the following sequence of equations:

$$(C_6H_5)_2Hg + (C_6H_5)_3SiLi \longrightarrow [C_6H_5HgSi(C_6H_5)_3] + C_6H_5Li$$

$$C_6H_5Li + CO_2 \longrightarrow C_6H_5COOLi$$

$$[C_6H_5HgSi(C_6H_5)_3] \longrightarrow (C_6H_5)_4Si + Hg$$

Reactions between triphenylsilyllithium and halides of Group V elements have been presented in Table 6.2. It was the object of these experiments to prepare compounds containing silicon linked to Group V elements.
A route similar to the one discussed above for phenylmercuric bromide may explain the formation of the products isolated in reaction 7.

$$(C_6H_5)_3SiLi + BiCl_3 \longrightarrow (C_6H_5)_3SiBiCl_2 + LiCl$$

$$(C_6H_5)_3SiBiCl_2 \longrightarrow (C_6H_5)_3SiCl + BiCl$$

$$(C_6H_5)_3SiCl + (C_6H_5)_3SiLi \longrightarrow (C_6H_5)_3SiSi(C_6H_5)_3 + LiCl$$

$$3\ BiCl \longrightarrow BiCl_3 + 2\ Bi$$

The products of reactions 1, 2, 3, 5, and 6, may be explained similarly by the transient formation of complexes containing silicon-phosphorus, silicon-arsenic, or silicon-antimony bonds. Reaction 4 is of interest because of the large percentage of hexaphenyldisilane obtained. In this case one of the chlorine atoms may have reacted rapidly with triphenylsilyllithium to

TABLE 6.2. REACTIONS OF TRIPHENYLSILYLLITHIUM WITH
HALIDES OF GROUP V ELEMENTS[a]

Number	Group V halide[b]	Temperature[c]	% Ph_6Si_2	Other products (%)
1	Phosphorus trichloride[d]	−70°	68.1	Triphenylsilanol 9.1
2	Phosphorus tribromide	−50°	80.5	Triphenylsilanol 9.7
3	Phosphorus tribromide	−50°	81.5	Triphenylsilanol 6
4	Phosphorus oxychloride	Room temp.	90	Triphenylsilanol 2
5	Arsenic trichloride	Room temp.	44	Triphenylsilane 13.2 Triphenylsilanol 13.3 Hexaphenyldisiloxane 5.1
6	Antimony trichloride	Room temp.	50.1	Triphenylsilane 5.1 Triphenylsilanol 21.1 Hexaphenyldisiloxane 6.2 Antimony 90.5
7	Bismuth trichloride	Room temp.	78.8	Triphenylsilane 3.4 Triphenylsilanol 7.6 Hexaphenyldisiloxane 2.1 Bismuth 81.3

[a]All reactions listed in this Table are described in reference *39*.
[b]A molar ratio of triphenylsilyllithium to halide of 3 : 1 was used throughout.
[c]All reactions were carried out in tetrahydrofuran by adding triphenylsilyllithium to the halide except in reaction 2 where reverse addition was used.
[d]A mixture of tetrahydrofuran and ether was used in this reaction.

form chlorotriphenylsilane which is known to couple readily with excess triphenylsilyllithium to give hexaphenyldisilane.

With Organic Compounds

Bonds Between Two Like Atoms. From the few examples of reactions of silylmetallic compounds with compounds containing one or more silicon-silicon bonds it may be concluded that this bond is susceptible to cleavage by silylmetallic and organometallic compounds. The reactions of triphenylsilyllithium with either chloropentaphenyldisilane or pentaphenyldisilane yield hexaphenyldisilane (42.3 and 78 per cent, respectively) while the trisilane was formed from the chloropentaphenyldisilane only (25.7 per cent) (*165*).

$(C_6H_5)_3SiLi + (C_6H_5)_3Si(C_6H_5)_2SiCl \longrightarrow$

$(C_6H_5)_3SiSi(C_6H_5)_3 + (C_6H_5)_3Si(C_6H_5)_2SiSi(C_6H_5)_3$

The higher yield of coupling product in the reaction of the chlorosilane with the silyllithium reagent may be due to the very rapid consumption of the silylmetallic compound in preference to a slower attack of the silylmetallic reagent on the silicon-silicon bond in pentaphenyldisilane, resulting in the formation of hexaphenyldisilane.

A series of reactions was carried out to determine the relative reactivities of methyldiphenylsilyllithium and dimethylphenylsilyllithium (73c). The addition of dimethylphenylsilyllithium to an equimolar suspension of hexaphenyldisilane in tetrahydrofuran gave 1,1,2,2-tetramethyl-1,2-diphenyldisilane (56 per cent), triphenylsilanol (21 per cent), and hexaphenyldisilane (65 per cent). The following reactions may account for these products:

$$(CH_3)_2(C_6H_5)SiLi + (C_6H_5)_3SiSi(C_6H_5)_3 \longrightarrow$$
$$(CH_3)_2(C_6H_5)SiSi(C_6H_5)_3 + (C_6H_5)_3SiLi$$
$$(CH_3)_2(C_6H_5)SiLi + (CH_3)_2(C_6H_5)SiSi(C_6H_5)_3 \longrightarrow$$
$$(CH_3)_2(C_6H_5)SiSi(C_6H_5)(CH_3)_2 + (C_6H_5)_3SiLi$$

Evidence for the existence of a transient trialkylsilylmetallic compound is afforded by lithium cleavage of 1,1,1-triethyl-2,2,2-triphenyldisilane in tetrahydrofuran (73c). The products isolated from this reaction were, after acid hydrolysis, hexaethyldisilane, triethylsilane and triphenylsilane. Isolation of the first compound indicates the formation of triethylsilyllithium which by cleavage of 1,1,1-triethyl-2,2,2-triphenyldisilane gives hexaethyldisilane.

$$(C_6H_5)_3SiSi(C_2H_5)_3 \xrightarrow{2\ Li} (C_6H_5)_3SiLi + (C_2H_5)_3SiLi$$
$$(C_6H_5)_3SiSi(C_2H_5)_3 + (C_2H_5)_3SiLi \longrightarrow (C_2H_5)_3SiSi(C_2H_5)_3 + (C_6H_5)_3SiLi$$

If it is assumed that the silicon-silicon bond strength remains about the same with varying numbers of alkyl and aryl substituents on the silicon atoms, then on the basis of such cleavage reactions silyllithium compounds may be arranged in the following reactivity series (73c):

$$(C_2H_5)_3SiLi > (CH_3)_2(C_6H_5)SiLi > (CH_3)(C_6H_5)_2SiLi > (C_6H_5)_3SiLi$$

This reactivity scale refers to the cleavage of silicon-silicon bonds by silylmetallic compounds. Hexaphenyldigermane is cleaved by excess triphenylsilyllithium to give triphenylgermyllithium and hexaphenyldigermane (125).

It has been seen that silicon-silicon bonds are cleaved readily by silylmetallic compounds. This cleavage has also been observed with organometallic compounds. Thus in the preparation of hexasubstituted disilanes by the reaction of a Grignard reagent with hexachlorodisilane, varying quantities of tetrasubstituted silanes account for the low yields of disilanes often obtained (24,25,146). The cleavage was found to be more extensive in the case of hexabromodisilane than in the case of hexachlorodisilane on treatment with phenylmagnesium bromide (*73a,146*). Hexaphenyldisilane does not cleave in the presence of phenylmagnesium bromide (*35*). Hexabenzyldisilane has been prepared from hexachlorodisilane and benzylmagnesium chloride (*147*).

In some early investigations of the possible use of a mixed Wurtz type reaction for the preparation of substituted disilanes it was found that extensive cleavage occurred (*145*).

$$14 \text{ Na} + Cl_3SiSiCl_3 + 8 \text{ RX} \xrightarrow{\text{Ether}} 2 \text{ R}_4Si + 8 \text{ NaX} + 6 \text{ NaCl}$$

R = ethyl, *n*-amyl, phenyl, *p*-biphenyl; X = chlorine or bromine.

Similar cleavages were encountered in reactions between *p*-biphenyllithium (*51,179*), *p*-tolyllithium, and phenylsodium (*147*) with hexachlorodisilane. It was found, however, that less cleavage occurred when the organometallic compounds were prepared separately and then added to hexachlorodisilane (*147*). The preparation of 5,5'-spirobi-(dibenzosilole) from *o,o'*-dilithiobiphenyl and hexachlorodisilane (*62*) indicates that extensive cleavage of the silicon-silicon bond had occurred.

In general it may be stated that chlorinated polysilanes (and alkoxysilanes) react with phenyllithium to give the desired coupling product if normal addition of the organometallic reagent to the chlorinated polysilane is used. In this way the organometallic reagent is at no time in great excess. Thus, chloropentaphenyldisilane (*164*), formed coupling products with methyllithium (*71*), ethyllithium (*164*), and *p*-tolyllithium (*179*) in good yields. Ethoxypentaphenyldisilane and pentaphenyldisilane likewise reacted with phenyllithium to give hexaphenyldisilane (*61*). Neither was any extensive cleavage observed when disilanes with adjacent hydrogen or chlorine atoms on silicon were treated with *p*-tolyllithium (*151,163*).

$$(C_6H_5)_2SiHSiH(C_6H_5)_2 + p\text{-}CH_3C_6H_4Li \longrightarrow$$
$$(C_6H_5)_2(p\text{-}CH_3C_6H_4)SiSi(C_6H_5)_2(p\text{-}CH_3C_6H_4)$$

If, however, a *gem*-dichlorodisilane is allowed to react with *p*-tolyllithium, a low yield of the desired coupling product is formed (*179*).

Earlier work had shown that hexaethyldisilane (*149*) or hexaphenyldisilane (*125,179*) did not react with aryllithium compounds. Reinvestigation of this work (35) revealed that hexaphenyldisilane did indeed undergo cleavage by phenyllithium or tolyllithium if there were prolonged heating and if a solvent like tetrahydrofuran were used. Thus, when *p*-tolyllithium and hexaphenyldisilane were heated 48 hours in tetrahydrofuran and then carbonated, there was isolated triphenylsilane, triphenyl-(*p*-tolyl)-silane, triphenylsilanol, and 4-triphenylsilylbutanol-1. When a similar reaction mixture of phenyllithium and hexaphenyldisilane was heated 48 hours and then treated with chlorotrimethylsilane the following compounds could be isolated: hexaphenyldisilane, tetraphenylsilane, 1,1,1-trimethyl-2,2,2-tri-phenyldisilane, and 4-triphenylsilylbutanol-1.

$$C_6H_5Li + (C_6H_5)_3SiSi(C_6H_5)_3 \longrightarrow (C_6H_5)_4Si + (C_6H_5)_3SiLi$$

$$(C_6H_5)_3SiLi + (CH_3)_3SiCl \longrightarrow (C_6H_5)_3SiSi(CH_3)_3 + LiCl$$

$$(C_6H_5)_3SiLi + \underline{CH_2CH_2CH_2CH_2O} \xrightarrow{(H_2O)} (C_6H_5)_3SiCH_2CH_2CH_2CH_2OH$$

Bond between Hydrogen and Group IV, V, and VI Elements. The reaction of an organometallic compound with hydrogen bonded to carbon in an organic molecule to form a new organometallic compound is defined as a metalation reaction. Various compounds have been metalated by triphenylsilyllithium. In general it may be concluded that triphenylsilyllithium is a poorer metalating agent than alkyllithium compounds since only substances with quite acidic hydrogens are known to undergo metalation. Triphenylsilylpotassium, -sodium, and -lithium have been reported to metalate triarylmethanes to produce the corresponding organometallic compounds (49). Thus, triphenylsilylpotassium reacts with triphenylmethane to give a 95 per cent yield of triphenylacetic acid on carbonation (49). This is to be contrasted with the low yield of 2,2'-dicarboxydiphenyl ether obtained by metalation and carbonation of diphenyl ether (164), and the failure of dibenzofuran and naphthalene to form organometallic compounds by treatment with triphenylsilyllithium (127,158).

Recently a number of heterocyclic compounds was metalated by triphenylsilyllithium (31). Thiaxanthene and 10-ethylphenothiazine yielded the following acids on carbonation: 10-thiaxanthenecarboxylic acid, 10-ethylphenothiazene-4-carboxylic acid. No acids were obtained by the analogous treatment of 10-ethylphenothiazene-5-oxide (31), and dibenzo-thiophene-5,5-dioxide (173). Fluorene (127), phenylacetylene (88), diphenylmethane (127), and xanthene (158) have all been metalated successfully by triphenylsilyllithium in tetrahydrofuran.

It is of particular interest that silanes such as tri-*p*-tolylsilane do not couple with triphenylsilylpotassium (15) in a manner similar to organolithium compounds (74,94,130,131). Instead silicon-carbon cleavage occurs under forced conditions (p. 295).

The reaction of silylmetallic compounds with amines often leads to the formation of silazanes. Thus, triphenylsilyllithium reacts with *n*-butylamine and di-*n*-butylamine to produce triphenylsilyl-*n*-butylamine and triphenyl-silyldi-*n*-butylamine (*125*). The corresponding reactions of methyldiphenyl-silyllithium and dimethylphenylsilyllithium with di-*n*-butylamine gave good yields of the trisubstituted amines (*125*). Excellent yields of triphenylsilyl-substituted amines were obtained by the reaction of triphenylsilyllithium with piperidine, morpholine, and piperazine (*125*), but dicyclohexylamine (*31*) and diphenylamine (*125*) failed to couple with triphenylsilyllithium. This indicates that the formation of silylamines from silylmetallic compounds and amines is a two-step process:

$$(C_6H_5)_3SiLi + R_2NH \longrightarrow (C_6H_5)_3SiH + R_2NLi$$

$$(C_6H_5)_3SiH + R_2NLi \longrightarrow (C_6H_5)_3SiNR_2 + LiH$$

The second step of this process has been used for the preparation of silylamines (*66,102*). The failure of an intermediate lithium diphenylamide to displace the hydride ion from the silicon may be due to the negative inductive effect of the phenyl groups compared to alkyl groups.

So far only a very limited study has been made on the reaction of silyl-metallic compounds with alcohols. From preliminary studies it was found that triphenylcarbinol, tri-*p*-tolylcarbinol, benzyl alcohol, and benzhydrol reacted with triphenylsilylpotassium to yield tetraphenylsilane (*88,179*). These reactions may proceed stepwise as shown, although lower yields of tetraphenylsilane were obtained from reactions of silylmetallic compounds with triphenylsilane (*15*).

$$(C_6H_5)_3SiK + (C_6H_5)_3COH \longrightarrow (C_6H_5)_3SiH + (C_6H_5)_3SiOK$$

$$(C_6H_5)_3SiK + (C_6H_5)_3SiH \longrightarrow (C_6H_5)_4Si + KH + \text{other products}$$

Bond between Carbon and Group IV Elements other than Carbon. Cleavage of the carbon-silicon bond by silylmetallic compounds usually does not occur if silicon is bonded to four carbon atoms. Thus tetraphenyl-silane is not cleaved by triphenylsilyllithium (*173*), methyldiphenylsilyl-lithium, or dimethylphenylsilyllithium (*125*). Similarly no cleavage of tri-phenylmethyltriphenylsilane by triphenylsilyllithium has been observed (*73c*).

A reaction does occur, however, if silicon is bonded to at least one atom different from carbon. Triphenylsilane is cleaved by triphenylsilyl-lithium to yield tetraphenylsilane (*98*).

$$(C_6H_5)_3SiLi + (C_6H_5)_3SiH \longrightarrow (C_6H_5)_4Si + LiH + \text{other products}$$

A more complete study of the reaction between triphenylsilane and tri-phenylsilylmetallic compounds showed that the sodium and potassium compounds reacted differently (15). No clear-cut mechanism can be postulated on the basis of these data.

The reaction of triphenylsilylmetallic compounds with substances containing weakly acidic hydrogen atoms leads to tetraphenylsilane. Triphenylsilanol, benzyl alcohol, triphenylcarbinol, and phenylacetylene react with triphenylsilylpotassium to give tetraphenylsilane, probably by way of triphenylsilane as an intermediate (88,179).

$$(C_6H_5)_3SiK + C_6H_5C\equiv CH \longrightarrow C_6H_5C\equiv CK + (C_6H_5)_3SiH$$

$$(C_6H_5)_3SiH + (C_6H_5)_3SiK \longrightarrow (C_6H_5)_4Si + KH + \text{other products}$$

Phenylpropiolic acid has been isolated on carbonation of a reaction mixture, in accordance with the above reaction path. See p. 298 for another type of silicon-carbon cleavage in a nitrogen-containing molecule.

Two cases of germanium-carbon cleavage are known. When methyl triphenylgermanecarboxylate is treated with triphenylsilyllithium there is obtained triphenylgermyltriphenylsilane (54).

$$(C_6H_5)_3SiLi + (C_6H_5)_3GeCOOCH_3 \longrightarrow (C_6H_5)_3SiGe(C_6H_5)_3 + CH_3OLi + CO$$

Triphenylsilyltriphenylgermane underwent similar cleavage by triphenylsilyllithium to give triphenylgermyllithium and hexaphenyldisilane (125).

Cleavage of the carbon-silicon bond by organometallic compounds has been observed in a number of different cases. However, no carbon-silicon bond cleavage by n-butyllithium was observed with some simple tetrasubstituted alkyl- or aryl-silanes (48) or with the more strained 5,5-diphenyldibenzosilole (62). It was however observed that 1,4-dilithiobutane reacted with chlorotriphenylsilane to give 1,1-diphenyl-1-silacyclopentane in addition to tetraphenylsilane, n-butyltriphenylsilane, and 1,4-bis-(triphenylsilyl)-butane (168). By the independent synthesis of 1,1-diphenyl-1-silacyclopentane from 4-bromobutyltriphenylsilane (168), it was established that the reaction of chlorotriphenylsilane with 1,4-dilithiobutane involved first a coupling and then a cleavage of the silicon-phenyl bond.

$$Li(CH_2)_4Li + (C_6H_5)_3SiCl \longrightarrow (C_6H_5)_3Si(CH_2)_4Li$$

$$(C_6H_5)_3Si(CH_2)_4Li \longrightarrow (C_6H_5)_2Si(CH_2)_4 + C_6H_5Li$$

By varying the temperature of the reaction and carbonating the reaction mixture it was possible to isolate benzoic acid and δ-triphenylsilylpentanoic acid from the intermediate organolithium compounds in agreement with this reaction path.

Groups such as trichloromethyl (19), β-styryl (171), and phenylethynyl (63) have been cleaved from triphenylsilyl moieties by n-butyl- or phenyllithium. Although 5,5-diphenyldibenzosilole was not cleaved by n-butyllithium, 5,5'-spiro-bi-(dibenzosilole) was cleaved by phenyllithium to yield

5-*o*-biphenyl-5-phenyldibenzosilole (*62*):

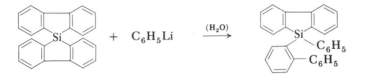

Benzyltriphenylsilane (*63*) and 9-fluorenyltrimethylsilane (*48*) underwent metalation to yield on carbonation 9-fluorenylcarboxylic acid and phenyl-acetic acid, since α-silylcarboxylic acids decomposed readily.

$$(C_6H_5)_3SiCH_2C_6H_5 \xrightarrow[\text{H}_2\text{O}]{n\text{-C}_4\text{H}_9\text{Li}} (C_6H_5)_3SiCHLiC_6H_5 \xrightarrow{\text{CO}_2}$$

$$(C_6H_5)_3SiCHC_6H_5 \xrightarrow{(\text{H}_2\text{O})} (C_6H_5)_3SiOH + C_6H_5CH_2COOH$$
$$\underset{\text{COOH}}{|}$$

Silanes containing bonds to atoms other than carbon have been cleaved by organometallic compounds in selected cases. The reaction of trisub-stituted silanes with organometallic compounds usually leads to coupling reactions (*74,76,94,130*), but cleavage has been observed to occur in a few special cases. Thus, from *n*-butyllithium and triphenylsilane was obtained tetraphenylsilane in addition to *n*-butyltriphenylsilane (*76*).

$$n\text{-C}_4H_9Li + (C_6H_5)_3SiH \longrightarrow n\text{-C}_4H_9Si(C_6H_5)_3 + (C_6H_5)_4Si$$

Reaction of triphenylsilanol with *n*-butyllithium followed by carbonation yielded *n*-butyldiphenylsilanol, in addition to benzoic acid (*48*).

$$(C_6H_5)_3SiOH + n\text{-C}_4H_9Li \longrightarrow n\text{-C}_4H_9Si(OLi)(C_6H_5)_2 + C_6H_5Li$$

$$C_6H_5Li + CO_2 \longrightarrow C_6H_5COOLi$$

Tri-*p*-xenylsilanol similarly gave *p*-phenylbenzoic acid on reaction with phenyllithium and subsequent carbonation (*51*). Chlorosilanes usually couple very readily with silylmetallic compounds but the following special case of silicon-carbon cleavage is known (*62*):

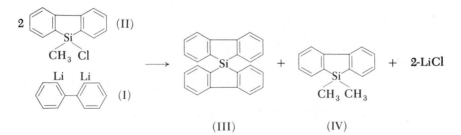

It appears that I first participated in a coupling reaction with II; then the methyl group is cleaved off as methyllithium, which couples with unreacted II to give IV; and a new carbon-silicon bond is formed simultaneously to produce the spiro compound III.

Two unrelated cases of carbon-silicon cleavage by phenyllithium involve triphenylsilyldiphenylcarbinol (*13*) and benzoyltriphenylsilane (*12*). Tetraphenylsilane was formed in both of these reactions.

$$(C_6H_5)_3SiCOH(C_6H_5)_2 \xrightarrow{C_6H_5Li} (C_6H_5)_3SiOCLi(C_6H_5)_2$$

$$(C_6H_5)_3SiOCLi(C_6H_5)_2 + C_6H_5Li \xrightarrow{(H_2O)} (C_6H_5)_4Si + (C_6H_5)_2CHOH$$

$$(C_6H_5)_3SiCOC_6H_5 + C_6H_5Li \longrightarrow (C_6H_5)_4Si + \text{fragments}$$

Cleavage of carbon-silicon bonds by allylmagnesium chloride has recently been demonstrated (*85b*). It was found that allylmagnesium chloride reacted with tribenzylsilane in tetrahydrofuran to give allyldibenzylsilane. The reaction apparently involved the displacement of a benzyl group by an allyl group. The formation of benzylmagnesium chloride was substantiated in a separate experiment from which phenylacetic acid was isolated, subsequent to carbonation, according to the following reaction scheme (*85b*):

$$CH_2{=}CHCH_2MgCl + (C_6H_5CH_2)_3SiH \longrightarrow$$
$$(CH_2{=}CHCH_2)(C_6H_5CH_2)_2SiH + C_6H_5CH_2MgCl$$

$$C_6H_5CH_2MgCl + CO_2 \xrightarrow{(H_2O)} C_6H_5CH_2COOH$$

Bond between Carbon and Group V Elements. The reactions of triphenylsilyllithium with carbon-nitrogen bonds are discussed in this section. Only one reaction of triphenylsilyllithium with a tertiary amine has been reported (*35*). No carbon-nitrogen bond cleavage was detected and only a secondary reaction leading to hexaphenyldisilane was observed:

$$(C_6H_5)_3SiLi + (CH_3)_2NCHC_6H_5Si(C_6H_5)_3 \xrightarrow{(H_2O)} (C_6H_5)_6Si_2 + (CH_3)_2NCH_2C_6H_5$$

A series of reactions of amides and imides with triphenylsilyllithium has been carried out (*35*). It had earlier been found that N,N-dimethylformamide did not react (*125*) with organosilylmetallic compounds to give any identifiable compounds, but it was later observed that N,N-diphenylacetamide reacted to yield diphenylamine and various silicon-containing substances. In contrast, N,N-dimethylacetamide yielded N,N-dimethyl-α-(triphenylsilyl)ethylamine and, similarly, N,N-diphenylbenzamide and N,N-dimethylbenzamide yielded N,N-diphenyl-α-(triphenylsilyl)benzylamine and N,N-dimethyl-α-(triphenylsilyl)benzylamine, respectively. It was found that if, before hydrolysis, methyl iodide were added to the reaction mixture from which the last mentioned amine had been isolated, there was obtained N,N-dimethyl-α-(triphenylsilyl)-α-methyl-benzylamine. The following reaction path is consistent with the products obtained from these reactions:

$$C_6H_5CON(C_6H_5)_2 + (C_6H_5)_3SiLi \longrightarrow C_6H_5\underset{\substack{| \\ O \\ | \\ Si(C_6H_5)_3}}{C}LiN(C_6H_5)_2 \quad I$$

$$I + (C_6H_5)_3SiLi \longrightarrow C_6H_5\underset{\substack{Si(C_6H_5)_3 \\ |}}{\overset{}{C}}LiN(C_6H_5)_2 + (C_6H_5)_3SiOLi \quad II$$

$$II + CH_3I \longrightarrow C_6H_5\underset{\substack{| \\ CH_3}}{\overset{\substack{Si(C_6H_5)_3 \\ |}}{C}}-N(C_6H_5)_2 + LiI$$

$$II + H_2O \longrightarrow C_6H_5-\underset{\substack{| \\ H}}{\overset{\substack{Si(C_6H_5)_3 \\ |}}{C}}-N(C_6H_5)_2$$

Phthalimides reacted with triphenylsilyllithium to form cleavage products and large amounts of hexaphenyldisilane (35). Thus, when N-methylphthalimide was allowed to react with triphenylsilyllithium, hexaphenyldisilane and o-formyl-N-methylbenzamide were formed.

Triphenylsilyllithium has been found to react with various phenylated Group V-B compounds (35). No compounds were, however, isolated which contained silicon linked to the Group V-B element. Thus triphenylsilyllithium reacted with triphenylarsine, triphenylstibine, and triphenylbismuthine to produce tetraphenylsilane, in addition to hexaphenyldisilane, and various other products dependent on the mode of isolation. If the reaction mixtures were carbonated, varying quantities of benzoic acid were isolated, indicating that an organometallic compound is formed as an intermediate.

The following reaction path is in agreement with the products isolated in the reaction of triphenylsilyllithium with triphenylstibine:

$$(C_6H_5)_3SiLi + (C_6H_5)_3Bi \longrightarrow (C_6H_5)_3SiBi(C_6H_5)_2 + C_6H_5Li$$
$$I$$

$$2(C_6H_5)_3SiLi + (C_6H_5)_3Bi \longrightarrow [(C_6H_5)_3Si]_2BiC_6H_5 + 2C_6H_5Li$$
$$II$$

$$I + C_6H_5Li \longrightarrow (C_6H_5)_4Si + (C_6H_5)_2BiLi$$
$$III$$

$$I + (C_6H_5)_3SiLi \longrightarrow (C_6H_5)_6Si_2 + (C_6H_5)_2BiLi$$
$$III$$

$$II + C_6H_5Li \longrightarrow (C_6H_5)_4Si + (C_6H_5)_3SiBiLiC_6H_5$$
$$IV$$

$$II + (C_6H_5)_3SiLi \longrightarrow (C_6H_5)_6Si_2 + (C_6H_5)_3SiBiLiC_6H_5$$
$$IV$$

$$3(C_6H_5)_2BiLi \longrightarrow (C_6H_5)_3Bi + 3 C_6H_5Li + 2 Bi$$

Triphenylstibine and triphenylarsine may react by a similar path.

Bond between Carbon and Group VI Elements. Cleavage of ethers by silylmetallic compounds was first observed when ethylene glycol di-methyl ether was used as a solvent. The absence of cleavage products from diethyl ether and triphenylsilylpotassium may be due mainly to the insolubility of the silylmetallic compound in this solvent. When triphenyl-silyllithium was heated for one hour in ethylene glycol dimethyl ether a large yield of methyltriphenylsilane resulted (*164*).

Cyclic ethers of the general formula $(CH_2)_nO$ were found to cleave in the presence of triphenylsilyllithium. The ease of cleavage apparently decreases with increasing size of the ring. Epoxides ($n = 2$) and trimethylene oxide ($n = 3$) react very readily with triphenylsilyllithium and much faster than the next larger member of the series, tetrahydrofuran ($n = 4$). The reactions of these cyclic ethers with triphenylsilyllithium were carried out in tetrahydrofuran as a solvent, and good yields of 2-(triphenylsilyl)-ethanol and 3-(triphenylsilyl)-propanol, respectively, were isolated (*45, 168*).

$$\underset{\diagdown O \diagup}{CH_2CH_2} + (C_6H_5)_3SiLi \xrightarrow{(H_2O)} (C_6H_5)_3SiCH_2CH_2OH$$

$$\underset{\underset{CH_2-O}{|}{\diagdown}}{CH_2CH_2} + (C_6H_5)_3SiLi \xrightarrow{(H_2O)} (C_6H_5)_3SiCH_2CH_2CH_2OH$$

Several epoxides were found to react with triphenylsilyllithium to give the corresponding alcohols with the triphenylsilyl group in the *beta*-position. In these reactions triphenylsilyllithium resembles organolithium compounds which react selectively (*27*), in contrast to the Grignard reagent which often gives a mixture of two or more isomers (*36*).

Triphenylsilyllithium reacted with ethylene oxide or symmetrically substituted epoxides to give alcohols. Unsymmetrically substituted epoxides such as propylene oxide and styrene oxide reacted at the least sterically hindered carbon atom of the oxirane ring. Thus, 1-(triphenylsilyl)-propanol-2 and 1-phenyl-2-(triphenylsilyl)-ethanol resulted from the above reactions.

$$RCHCH_2 + (C_6H_5)_3SiLi \xrightarrow{(H_2O)} RCH(OH)CH_2Si(C_6H_5)_3$$

The reactions of epichlorohydrin and epibromohydrin with triphenylsilyl-lithium will be discussed later (p. 307).

Tetrahydrofuran ($n = 4$) was cleaved very slowly at room temperature but somewhat more rapidly at elevated temperatures. After three hours of heating at 125° in a sealed tube there was obtained a 71 per cent yield of 4-(triphenylsilyl)-butanol-1 (*168*). The largest member of the series which was investigated was tetrahydropyran ($n = 5$). This cyclic ether underwent cleavage slowly at elevated temperatures but no well defined products were isolated (*164*).

It may be seen that tetrahydrofuran is an advantageous solvent for the preparation and reactions of organosilylmetallic compounds since it is cleaved only slowly at room temperature. In addition, tetrahydrofuran is a preferred solvent inasmuch as such solutions react very promptly with many reactants.

Cyclic ethers containing more than one oxygen have also been found to react with organosilylmetallic compounds. Dioxane reacted slowly with tri-phenylsilyllithium at elevated temperatures to give ethylene-*bis*-(triphenyl-silane) (*168*).

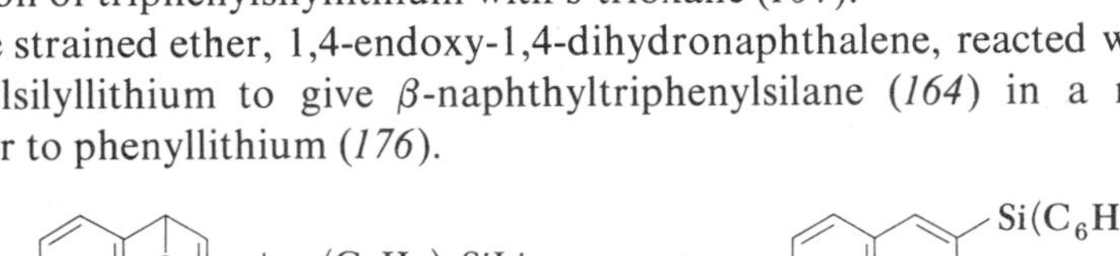

$$2(C_6H_5)_3SiLi + O\overset{CH_2CH_2}{\underset{CH_2CH_2}{\diagup\diagdown}}O \longrightarrow (C_6H_5)_3SiCH_2CH_2Si(C_6H_5)_3$$

However, no definite compound could be obtained from the attempted reaction of triphenylsilyllithium with s-trioxane (*164*).

The strained ether, 1,4-endoxy-1,4-dihydronaphthalene, reacted with tri-phenylsilyllithium to give β-naphthyltriphenylsilane (*164*) in a manner similar to phenyllithium (*176*).

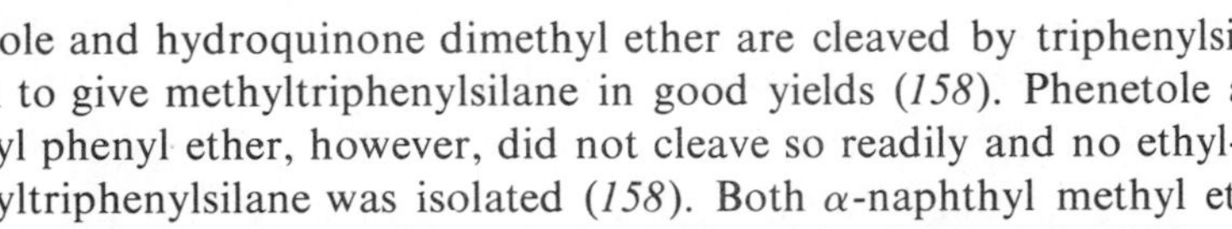

+ $(C_6H_5)_3SiLi$ $\longrightarrow$ $-Si(C_6H_5)_3$

Anisole and hydroquinone dimethyl ether are cleaved by triphenylsilyl-lithium to give methyltriphenylsilane in good yields (*158*). Phenetole and *n*-propyl phenyl ether, however, did not cleave so readily and no ethyl- or *n*-propyltriphenylsilane was isolated (*158*). Both α-naphthyl methyl ether and β-naphthyl methyl ether reacted readily with triphenylsilyllithium to yield methyltriphenylsilane and the corresponding naphthols (*158*).

When benzyl methyl ether was allowed to react with triphenylsilyllithium there was formed an 8 per cent yield of 1-phenylethanol (*164*). This compound could have been formed by a rearrangement similar to that observed by Wittig and coworkers on treatment of benzyl methyl ether with phenyllithium (*175,177*).

$$(C_6H_5)_3SiLi + C_6H_5CH_2OCH_3 \longrightarrow (C_6H_5)_3SiH + C_6H_5CHLiOCH_3$$

$$C_6H_5CHLiOCH_3 \longrightarrow C_6H_5CHCH_3$$
$$| $$
$$OLi$$

$$(C_6H_5)_3SiH + (C_6H_5)_3SiLi \longrightarrow (C_6H_5)_4Si + \text{other products}$$

The reaction of triphenylsilane with triphenylsilyllithium as discussed earlier (p. 295), produced mainly tetraphenylsilane.

Triphenylsilyllithium reacted with 1-(*n*-butoxymethyl)-piperidine to give 1-triphenylsilylmethylpiperidine (*164*), but apparently no *n*-butyltriphenylsilane. Diphenyl ether is not cleaved but is metalated by triphenylsilyllithium (see p. 294).

$$\text{(piperidine ring)} + (C_6H_5)_3SiLi \longrightarrow \text{(piperidine ring)} + n\text{-}C_4H_9OLi$$

Reactions of alkylated phosphates and sulfates with silylmetallic compounds involve cleavage of the alkyl group attached to oxygen (*35,62*). From triphenylsilyllithium and trimethyl-, tri-isobutyl-, and tri-*n*-butylphosphate in molar ratios of 1:1 high yields of the corresponding alkyltriphenylsilanes were obtained in addition to minor amounts of hexaphenyldisilane, triphenylsilanol, and hexaphenyldisiloxane (*35*). Triaryl phosphates reacted differently. None of the aryltriphenylsilanes was obtained, but varying amounts of hexaphenyldisilane, triphenylsilanol, and triphenylsilane were isolated (*35*).

Various sulfur containing aromatic compounds react with silylmetallic compounds. Diphenyl sulfide reacted with triphenylsilyllithium, followed by carbonation, to produce hexaphenyldisilane and benzoic acid; whereas from the reaction with triphenylsilylpotassium only triphenylsilanol and tetraphenylsilane were isolated (*173*). It appears that an intermediate thiosilyl ether was formed in the first case and that this reacted with excess triphenylsilyllithium to produce hexaphenyldisilane.

$$(C_6H_5)_2S + (C_6H_5)_3SiLi \longrightarrow C_6H_5Li + (C_6H_5)_3SiSC_6H_5$$

$$(C_6H_5)_3SiSC_6H_5 + (C_6H_5)_3SiLi \longrightarrow (C_6H_5)_6Si_2 + C_6H_5SLi$$

Under suitable conditions it should be possible to isolate triphenyl-

(phenylthio)-silane. In agreement with the above reaction path, triphenyl-(p-tolylthio)-silane was found to react readily with triphenylsilyllithium to give hexaphenyldisilane (167,172). This reaction is analogous to that of triphenyl-(methylthio)-silane with phenyllithium which yielded tetraphenyl-silane (125).

$$(C_6H_5)_3SiSR + (C_6H_5)_3SiLi \longrightarrow (C_6H_5)_6Si_2 + RSLi$$

$$(C_6H_5)_3SiSR + C_6H_5Li \longrightarrow (C_6H_5)_3SiC_6H_5 + RSLi$$

Diphenyl sulfoxide reacted with triphenylsilylpotassium to produce tetraphenylsilane, hexaphenyldisiloxane, and hexaphenyldisilane (173). The reaction between triphenylsilyllithium and diphenyl sulfone gave higher yields of tetraphenylsilane in addition to m-bis-(triphenylsilyl)-benzene (173). When the reaction was carried out at very low temperatures and the reaction mixture carbonated, it was possible to isolate benzoic acid. Similarly p-toluic acid was obtained from di-p-tolyl sulfone. It is evident from these reactions that one phenyl group is cleaved from the sulfur atom to give tetraphenylsilane, whereas the triphenylsilyl group attached to sulfur reacts with excess triphenylsilyllithium to form hexaphenyldisilane. The reaction may partly be depicted as follows:

$$C_6H_5SO_2C_6H_5 + (C_6H_5)_3SiLi \longrightarrow$$

$$C_6H_5Li \quad (C_6H_5)_3SiSO_2C_6H_5 \xrightarrow{(CO_2,H_2O)}$$

$$(C_6H_5)_3SiOH + C_6H_5COOH + C_6H_5SO_2H$$

Bond between Carbon and Group VII Elements. Extensive studies have been carried out on the reactions of silylmetallic compounds with aryl and alkyl halides. The reactions are divided according to four main sections: one halogen bonded to aliphatic carbon; two or more halogens bonded to aliphatic carbon; one halogen bonded directly to an aromatic nucleus; and two or more halogens bonded directly to an aromatic nucleus.

The reactions lead to the formation of two main types of products formed by the following routes:

Coupling: $R_3SiLi + R'X \longrightarrow R_3SiR' + LiX$

Halogen-metal interconversion:

$$R_3SiLi + R'X \longrightarrow R_3SiX + R'Li$$

$$R_3SiX + R_3SiLi \longrightarrow R_3SiSiR_3 + LiX$$

Alkyl Halides (mono). Alkyl halides like methyl iodide have frequently been used to prepare derivatives of silylmetallic compounds. The mode of addition and other experimental conditions influence the yield of tetrasub-stituted silane formed. The halogen and the alkyl group to which the halogen is attached likewise affect the yield considerably. Table 6.3 summarizes

TABLE 6.3. REACTIONS OF TRIPHENYLSILYLMETALLIC
COMPOUNDS WITH ALKYL HALIDES (MONO)

Number	Metal in R_3SiM	Alkyl halide[a]	Ph_6Si_2 (%)	Other products (%)	Ref.
1	Li	Methyl iodide[b,c]	29.3	Methyltriphenylsilane, 44	159
2	Li	Methyl iodide[d]	22.7	Methyltriphenylsilane, 42.2	159
3	Na	Methyl iodide		Methyltriphenylsilane	117
4	K	Methyl iodide[d,c]	52	Methyltriphenylsilane, 33	7
5	Li	Ethyl chloride	0	Ethyltriphenylsilane, 80	159
6	Li	Ethyl chloride[d]	0	Ethyltriphenylsilane, 75.5	159
7	Li	Ethyl bromide	29.3	Ethyltriphenylsilane, 45.5	159
8	Li	Ethyl bromide[d]	25.3	Ethyltriphenylsilane, 54.5	159
9	Li	Ethyl iodide	40	Ethyltriphenylsilane, 28.2	159
10	Li	Ethyl iodide[d]	36.7	Ethyltriphenylsilane, 30.0	159
11	Li	1-Chloropropene-1[c]	13	1,2-Bis-(triphenylsilyl)-propane, 26.8	1
12	Li	1-Chloropropene-1[e]	13.5	1,2-Bis-(triphenylsilyl)-propane, 45.5	1
13	Li	1-Chloropropene-1[d,c,e]	14	1,2-Bis-(triphenylsilyl)-propane, 36.4	1
14	Li	Allyl chloride	0	Allyltriphenylsilane, 56	45
15	Li	Epichlorohydrin	0	Allyltriphenylsilane, 8	45
16	Li	Epichlorohydrin[c,e]	0	1,3-Bis-(triphenylsilyl)-propanol-2, 43.3	1
17	Li	Epichlorohydrin[e]	0	1-Triphenylsilyl-3-chloropropanol-2, 60.5	1
18	Li	Epichlorohydrin	0	1,3-Bis-(triphenylsilyl)-propanol-2, 22	1
19	Li	Epibromohydrin	68.6		45
20	Li	Epibromohydrin[d]	72.6	Allyltriphenylsilane, 1	45
21	Li	Epibromohydrin[c,e]	79		1
22	Li	Isopropyl chloride	6.7	Isopropyltriphenylsilane, 71.2	30
23	Li	Isopropyl bromide	73.5	Isopropyltriphenylsilane, 5.8	30
24	Li	1-Bromobutene-1	63.5		1
25	Li	n-Butyl chloride	0	n-Butyltriphenylsilane, 75	44

TABLE 6.3. (*continued*)

Number	Metal in R_3SiM	Alkyl halide[a]	Ph_6Si_2 (%)	Other products (%)	Ref.
26	Li	*n*-Butyl bromide	60	*n*-Butyltriphenylsilane, 10	*44*
27	Li	Isobutyl chloride[d]	3.25	Isobutyltriphenylsilane, 62	*30*
28	Li	*sec*-Butyl chloride[d]	13.25	*sec*-Butyltriphenylsilane, 24.8	*30*
29	Li	*tert*-Butyl chloride[d]	3.5	Triphenylsilane, 56.7	*30*
30	Cs	*tert*-Butyl chloride	0	Triphenylsilanol, 20	*30*
31	Rb	*tert*-Butyl chloride[d]	0	*tert*-Butyltriphenylsilane, 9.5 Triphenylsilanol, 25.4	*30*
32	Li	*tert*-Butyl bromide[d]	52	*tert*-Butyltriphenylsilane, 1.82	*30*
33	Li	Cyclopentyl chloride	9.3	Cyclopentyltriphenylsilane, 40	*44*
34	K	Cyclohexyl bromide[f]	56	Hexaphenyldisiloxane, 24 Bicyclohexyl, 2	*11*
35	K	Cyclohexyl bromide[d,g]	80	Triphenylsilane, 6 Bicyclohexyl, 37	*11*
36	Li	Benzyl chloride	7	Benzyltriphenylsilane, 50	*30*
37	K	Benzyl chloride	5	Benzyltriphenylsilane, 22	*92*
38	K	Benzyl chloride[d]	26	Benzyltriphenylsilane, 60 Bibenzyl, 25	*11*
39	K	Benzyl chloride	7	Benzyltriphenylsilane, 40 Hexaphenyldisiloxane, 21 Bibenzyl, 15	*11*
40	Li	β-Phenethyl chloride		β-Phenethyltriphenylsilane, 53	*30*
41	Li	β-Phenethyl bromide	50.8	β-Phenethyltriphenylsilane, 9.3 Triphenylsilanol, 3	*30*
42	K	1,1-Diphenyl-2-chloroethane		2,2-Diphenyl-1-triphenylsilylethane, 47	*183*
43	K	Triphenylchloromethane		Hexaphenyldisiloxane, 50 Hexaphenylethane, 88[h]	*17*
44	K	Triphenylchloromethane	16	Hexaphenyldisiloxane, 53 Hexaphenylethane, 62[h]	*17*

TABLE 6.3. (continued)

Number	Metal in R_3SiM	Alkyl halide[a]	Ph_6Si_2 (%)	Other products (%)	Ref.
45	K	Triphenylchloromethane[e]	45	Hexaphenyldisiloxane, 14 Hexaphenylethane, 63[h] Triphenylacetic acid, 14[i]	17
46	Li	n-Octyl fluoride[d]	0	n-Octyltriphenylsilane, 86.6	30
47	Li	n-Octyl bromide[d]	44.4	n-Octyltriphenylsilane, 26.4	30
48	K	n-Decyl bromide[d]	62	n-Decyltriphenylsilane, 6.32	78
49	Li	n-Dodecyl chloride	0	n-Dodecyltriphenylsilane, 28.7	45
50	K	n-Dodecyl chloride[d]	9	n-Dodecyltriphenylsilane, 33	78
51	Li	10-(2-Chloroethyl)-phenothiazine	58.6	10-(2-Triphenylsilylethyl)-phenothiazine, 32.9	31
52	K	n-Octadecyl bromide[d]	59	n-Octadecyltriphenylsilane, 6 n-Hexatriacontane, 35	78
53	Li	Chloromethyltrimethylsilane	0	Trimethylsilyl-triphenyl phenylsilylmethane, 55	1
54	Li	Chloromethyldimethylvinylsilane[d]	0	Triphenylsilylmethyl-dimethylvinylsilane, 54.5	1
55	Li	β-Chloroethyltriphenylsilane[d]	74	1,2-Bis-(triphenylsilyl)-ethane, 29.5	185
56	Li	β-Bromoethyltriphenylsilane[d]	47.4	1,2-Bis-(triphenylsilyl)-ethane, 2.4	185

[a] All reactions were performed at room temperature unless otherwise noted. Tetrahydrofuran was used as solvent in all cases involving silyllithium compounds and ether was used in all cases involving silylpotassium compounds, with the exception of No. 51 in which a 2:1 mixture of tetrahydrofuran to ether was used.

[b] Normal addition of the silylmetallic reagent was used in all cases but those marked otherwise.

[c] A ratio of 1:1 between the silylmetallic compound and the halide was used in all cases but Nos. 4 and 16, where it was 2:1 and in Nos. 11 and 13 where excess silylmetallic compound was used.

[d] Reverse addition of the alkyl halide to the silylmetallic compound was used.

[e] In these reactions the addition was carried out at $-60°$ except No. 13 at $0°$; and No. 18 at reflux temperature, and No. 45 at $-30°$.

[f] In addition there was isolated cyclohexyl bromide, 31%, and triphenylsilanol, 2% (11).

[g] In addition there was isolated cyclohexyl bromide, 5%, hexaphenyldisiloxane, 10%, cyclohexene, 9%, cyclohexane, 14% (11).

[h] Isolated as peroxide.

[i] The reaction mixture was carbonated before isolation of the products.

the reactions of silylmetallic compounds with alkyl halides containing one halogen.

It is evident that no halogen-metal interconversion occurs in the reaction of *tert*-butyl chloride with triphenylsilylrubidium or -cesium (Nos. 30, and 31).

From the reactions of a particular halide under various conditions, a number of conclusions may be drawn. It may be observed that in some cases more halogen-metal interconversion occurs by reverse addition than by normal addition (35 *vs.* 34); that is, if an excess of silylmetallic compound is present a larger yield of hexaphenyldisilane is obtained. However, this is not a general phenomenon since the reverse is true in a number of reactions, even with different halogens (1 *vs.* 2, 7 *vs.* 8, 9 *vs.* 10). The halogen has a pronounced effect on the yield of coupling product as well as on the extent of halogen-metal interconversion, (5–10). Thus there seems to be increased halogen-metal interconversion with the series Cl, Br, I as illustrated by the increased yield of hexaphenyldisilane in the series ethyl chloride, ethyl bromide, and ethyl iodide. The yield of coupling product decreases with the increase in extent of halogen-metal interconversion (Nos. 5–10). It is interesting to note that the choice of methyl iodide for derivatizing the silylmetallic compounds was among the poorest possible selections even though the aforementioned effect is less pronounced with methyl halides than with ethyl halides. The increased extent of halogen-metal interconversion of bromides over chlorides can be extremely pronounced when one compares epichlorohydrin with epibromohydrin (15 and 18 *vs.* 19 and 21), and isopropyl chloride with isopropyl bromide (22 *vs.* 26, 46 *vs.* 47, 50 *vs.* 52). It is thus evident that halogen-metal interconversion is negligible in the case of alkyl fluorides and chlorides, but very pronounced in the case of bromides and iodides.

The alkyl substituent to which the halogen is attached further influences the reaction as already mentioned. Thus the following series seems to hold for increasing extent of halogen-metal interconversion and decreasing amounts of coupling for a given halogen such as chlorine:

CH_3—; C_2H_5—; n-C_4H_9—; n-$C_{12}H_{25}$—; $C_6H_5CH_2CH_2$—;

i-C_4H_9—; s-C_4H_9—; $C_6H_5CH_2$—; $(C_6H_5)_3C$—

It should be noted that the abnormal yields of hexaphenyldisilane obtained in specific cases such as triphenylmethyl chloride may be due to the secondary carbon-silicon bond cleavage discussed earlier, p. 295. Both *tert*-butyl chloride and *tert*-butyl bromide behave quite differently from secondary and primary halides. From the reaction of *tert*-butyl chloride with triphenylsilyllithium there were isolated triphenylsilane and only a trace of hexaphenyldisilane. The process is currently considered to involve dehydrohalogenation.

$(C_6H_5)_3SiLi + (CH_3)_3CCl \longrightarrow (C_6H_5)_3SiH + (CH_3)_2C{=}CH_2 + LiCl$

The reaction between epichlorohydrin and triphenylsilyllithium, in a molar ratio of 1:1, is in reality a competitive reaction. The reaction products show that the opening of an epoxy-ring is favored over the coupling with an alkyl halide. Various aryllithium compounds react analogously with epichlorohydrin to form compounds of the 3-aryl-1-chloropropanol-2 type (65). A dioxane derivative was obtained in one case from a bimolecular coupling of an intermediate (No. 15). From the reaction of two moles of triphenylsilyllithium with one mole of epichlorohydrin there was isolated 1,3-bis-(triphenylsilyl)-propanol-3 (No. 16). The various reaction products discussed may have been formed by the reactions shown below.

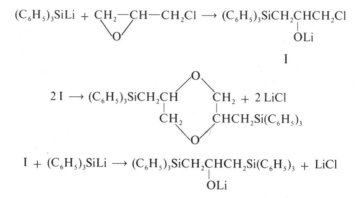

Alkyl Halides (poly). Only a few cases of reactions between aliphatic compounds containing more than one halogen and triphenylsilyllithium are known. These reactions are summarized in Table 6.4. It may be seen that in the case of methylene chloride extensive halogen-metal interconversion took place when the silylmetallic reagent was in excess throughout the reaction. None of the expected bis-(triphenylsilyl)-methane was obtained in either case. The normal increased halogen-metal interconversion for bromoalkanes is observed in these reactions (No. 10 *vs.* No. 9).

The reactions of 1,3-dichloropropene are interesting since they represent cases of a competitive type reaction between a vinyl halide and an allylic halide (Nos. 4 and 5). The normal reduced reactivity of the vinyl halide may indicate that the reaction is a simple displacement.

Reactions of 1,2-dichloropropane (Nos. 7 and 8) are significant when compared to the reaction of isopropyl chloride (No. 22 in Table 6.3). It is evident that the large yield of hexaphenyldisilane is not due to the halogen-metal interconversion of chlorine attached to the isopropyl group since isopropyl chloride itself, even under the reverse mode of addition, gave a small amount of hexaphenyldisilane. Neither is it likely that allyl

TABLE 6.4. REACTIONS OF TRIPHENYLSILYLMETALLIC COMPOUNDS WITH ALKYL HALIDES (POLY)

Number	Metal in R₃SiM	Alkyl halide	RX/R₃SiM Ratio	Ph₆Si₂ (%)	Other products (%)	Ref.
1	K	Methylene chloride[a,b]	1:2	0	Triphenylsilanol, 20; Hexaphenyldisiloxane, 50	11
2	K	Methylene chloride[a]	1:2	62	Triphenylsilanol, 11; Hexaphenyldisiloxane, 4	11
3	Li	1,2-Dichloropropene-1	1:2	61.8	1-Triphenylsilyl-propyne-1, 2	1
4	Li	1,3-Dichloropropene	1:1	10.9	1-Chloro-3-(triphenylsilyl)-propene-1, 50.4	1
5	Li	1,3-Dichloropropene	1:2	11.8	1,3-Bis-(triphenylsilyl)-propene-1, 13.8	1
6	Li	1,3-Dichloropropene	1:2	12.5	1,3-Bis-(triphenylsilyl)-propene-1, 31	1
7	Li	1,2-Dichloropropane	1:2	93		1
8	Li	1,2-Dichloropropane	1:3	87.5		1
9	Li	1,3-Dichloropropane	1:2	0	1,3-Bis-(triphenylsilyl)-propane, 73	45
10	Li	1,3-Dibromopropane	1:2	71.5		45
11	Li	1,4-Dibromobutane	1:2	74	1,4-Bis(triphenylsilyl)-butane, 3	168

[a]All reactions were carried out in tetrahydrofuran except Nos. 1 and 2, which were carried out in ether. The silylmetallic compound was added to the halide in all cases but No. 2 in which the reverse mode of addition was used.
[b]All reactions were performed at room temperature except No. 6 at 0°.

chloride was formed under the reaction conditions and that this underwent a rapid halogen-metal interconversion with part of the silylmetallic compound (See No. 14, Table 6.3).

Aromatic Halides (mono). Aromatic halides react with silylmetallic compounds in much the same manner as alkyl halides. Table 6.5 summarizes the reactions of a wide variety of aryl halides.

Reactions of the various silylmetallic compounds indicate that triphenylsilylcesium and triphenylsilylrubidium behave similarly to triphenylsilyllithium toward fluorobenzene (Nos. 1, 5 *vs.* No. 3). However, great dif-

TABLE 6.5. REACTIONS OF TRIPHENYLSILYLMETALLIC
COMPOUNDS WITH ARYL HALIDES (MONO)

Number	Metal in R_3SiM	Aryl halide	Ph_6Si_2 (%)	Other products (%)	Ref.
1	Cs	Fluorobenzene[a,b]	0	Tetraphenylsilane, 25	30
2	Li	Fluorobenzene	0	Tetraphenylsilane, 50.9	30
3	Li	Fluorobenzene[a]	0	Tetraphenylsilane, 47.4	30
4	K	Fluorobenzene	3	Tetraphenylsilane, 12 Triphenylsilanol, 31	92
5	Rb	Fluorobenzene[a]	0	Tetraphenylsilane, 39	30
6	Cs	Chlorobenzene	0	Tetraphenylsilane, 17.4 Triphenylsilanol, 27	30
7	Li	Chlorobenzene (run 1)	76.5	Tetraphenylsilane, 11.8	30
8	Li	Chlorobenzene (run 2)	73.5	Tetraphenylsilane, 12.2	30
9	K	Chlorobenzene	10	Tetraphenylsilane[d], 53	92
10	Li	Bromobenzene	66.3	Tetraphenylsilane, 17.7	30
11	Li	Bromobenzene[a]	75	Tetraphenylsilane, 16.0	30
12	K	Bromobenzene	0	Tetraphenylsilane, 55	92
13	K	Bromobenzene[a]	0	Tetraphenylsilane, 79, 55, 45	7,11, 92
14	K	Bromobenzene[a]	10	Tetraphenylsilane, 70 Triphenylsilanol, 19 Biphenyl, 10	11
15	K	Bromobenzene[a]		Tetraphenylsilane, 79	7
16	K	Bromobenzene[a]	27	Tetraphenylsilane, 55	11
17	K	Bromobenzene	0	Tetraphenylsilane, 61 Hexaphenyldisiloxane, 34 Biphenyl, 8	11
18	K	Bromobenzene[a]	22	Tetraphenylsilane, 55 Benzene, 9 Triphenylsilanol, 5 Hexaphenyldisiloxane, 4	11
19	Li	Iodobenzene (run 1)	68.5	Tetraphenylsilane, 19.9	30
20	Li	Iodobenzene (run 2)	73.5	Tetraphenylsilane, 19.5	30
21	K	Iodobenzene	4	Tetraphenylsilane, 63	92
22	Li	o-Bromotoluene	52	o-Tolyltriphenylsilane, 1.7	30
23	K	o-Bromotoluene	0	o-Tolyltriphenylsilane, 57	92
24	K	p-Iodotoluene	6	p-Tolyltriphenylsilane, 95	92
25	Li	o-Bromobenzoic acid[a]	71		31
26	Li	2-Chlorodibenzofuran	44.3	2-Triphenylsilyldibenzofuran, 19	31
27	Li	2-Bromodibenzofuran	53.8		31
28	Li	2-Bromodibenzofuran[c]	54	2-Triphenylsilyldibenzofuran, 11.8	31

TABLE 6.5. (*continued*)

Number	Metal in R_3SiM	Aryl halide	Ph_6Si_2 (%)	Other products (%)	Ref.
29	K	2-Bromodibenzothiophene	0	2-Triphenylsilyldibenzothiophene, 57	*132*
30	Li	3-Bromo-9-ethylcarbazole	57.7	3-Triphenylsilyl-9-ethylcarbazole, 27.5	*31*
31	Li	3-Bromo-9-ethylcarbazole[c]	44.3	3-Triphenylsilyl-9-ethylcarbazole, 40.7	*31*
32	K	3-Bromo-9-ethylcarbazole	0	3-Triphenylsilyl-9-ethylcarbazole, 63	*132*
33	Li	2-Chloro-10-ethylphenothiazine[c]	57.6	2-Triphenylsilyl-10-ethylphenothiazine, 28	*31*
34	Li	3-Bromo-10-ethylphenothiazine[c]	53.8	3-Triphenylsilyl-10-ethylphenothiazine, 27.8	*31*
35	Li	3-Bromo-10-ethylphenothiazine[c]	58	3-Triphenylsilyl-10-ethylphenothiazine, 23.7	*31*
36	K	3-Bromo-10-ethylphenothiazine[a,b]	10	Hexaphenyldisiloxane, 20	*139*
37	Li	4-Iodo-10-ethylphenothiazine[c]	46.3	4-Triphenylsilyl-10-ethylphenothiazine, 14.8	*31*

[a]All reactions were carried out at room temperature except No. 36 which was carried out at room temperature and reflux. The ratio of silylmetallic compound to aryl halide was 1:1 in all cases but Nos. 4, 14, and 36, 2:1; No. 25, 3:1. In all cases the silylmetallic compound was added to the halide except Nos. 3, 5, 11, 10, 15, 18, and 25 where the reverse addition was used. In 16 both reactants were added simultaneously.
[b]Tetrahydrofuran was used as solvent in all cases involving silyllithium compounds, whereas ether was used with silylpotassium compounds, except for those marked c.
[c]All these reactions were carried out in a 2:1 mixture of tetrahydrofuran to ether.
[d]From a similar reaction there was isolated hexaphenyldisilane (7%), tetraphenylsilane (52%) and biphenyl (6%): (*11*).

ferences are observed between triphenylsilyllithium and triphenylsilylpotassium in their reactions with aryl halides. With the exception of fluorobenzene, which reacted slowly with triphenylsilylpotassium, triphenylsilyllithium gave a much higher yield of hexaphenyldisilane and a lower yield of tetraphenylsilane in all cases than did triphenylsilylpotassium (8 *vs.* 9, 11 *vs.* 13, and 14 and 20 *vs.* 21, 22 *vs.* 23). This is the reverse of the observation for alkyl halides with triphenylsilylmetallic compounds and warrants further investigation.

The mode of addition seems to have only a minor effect on the product distribution (compare items Nos. 2 and 3, 12 and 13), except in the reaction between bromobenzene and triphenylsilylpotassium. Thus, if bromobenzene and triphenylsilylpotassium are added simultaneously a larger yield of hexaphenyldisilane resulted than if the bromobenzene was added to excess silylpotassium; whereas no hexaphenyldisilane resulted from the addition of the silylmetallic reagent to the aryl halide.

For any given silylmetallic compound reacting with a series of aryl halides having different halogens it may be noted that there is no progressive relationship. From reactions 8, 10 and 20, it may be seen that triphenylsilyllithium reacts with chlorobenzene, bromobenzene and iodobenzene to give approximately the same yields of tetraphenylsilane (12.2, 18, and 19.5 per cent, respectively), and hexaphenyldisilane (73, 66, and 73 per cent, respectively), although fluorobenzene behaves abnormally (No. 2). If the comparable reactions of triphenylsilylpotassium are considered (Nos. 4, 9, 12, and 21), then it appears that fluorobenzene reacts much less readily and the yields of tetraphenylsilane obtained from the other halides are of comparable magnitude (53, 55, 63 per cent) and consistently higher than those obtained from triphenylsilyllithium. It appears that fluorobenzene occupies a unique position towards triphenylsilyllithium, an observation which may be consistent with an elimination-addition reaction involving a benzyne intermediate. The difference between triphenylsilyllithium and triphenylsilylpotassium in reactions with aryl bromides is particularly pronounced with *o*-bromotoluene (23 and 22). The effect of other substituents in the aromatic nucleus has not been studied extensively, although reactions listed in Table 6.5 (23 *vs.* 12; 24 *vs.* 21; 22 *vs.* 10) show that no major difference can be noticed between a methyl group and a hydrogen atom.

From the reactions of triphenylsilyllithium with halogenated heterocycles it may be concluded that higher yields of coupling products are obtained in a mixture of tetrahydrofuran and ether than in tetrahydrofuran alone (28 *vs.* 27, and 31 *vs.* 30). In agreement with the above comparisons it was found that triphenylsilylpotassium gave better yields of the coupling product than did triphenylsilyllithium (32 *vs.* 31), and that insignificant amounts of hexaphenyldisilane were obtained from the silylpotassium reagent compared to the silyllithium reagent.

Aromatic Halides (poly). A series of polyhalogenated aromatic compounds was treated with triphenylsilyllithium. Only in a few cases was more than one triphenylsilyl group introduced.

Aromatic substances containing two like aromatic halogens on one benzene nucleus gave only hexaphenyldisilane on reaction with triphenylsilyllithium. The route to this product has not been established, but it almost certainly involved a halogen-metal interconversion of one of the halogens. When triphenylsilyllithium reacts with an aromatic compound containing two different halogens *ortho* to each other, products were isolated which

TABLE 6.6. REACTIONS OF TRIPHENYLSILYLLITHIUM WITH ARYL HALIDES (POLY)

Number	Aryl halide[a,b]	RX/R_3SiM Ratio	Ph_6Si_2 (%)	Other products (%)	Ref.
1	o-Chlorofluorobenzene	$1:2^b$	68.5	o-Fluorophenyltriphenylsilane, 28	30
2	o-Bromofluorobenzene	$1:3^b$	60	Triphenylene, 3.3 Tetraphenylsilane, 9.5	30
3	o-Dichlorobenzene	$1:2$	79.8	Tetraphenylsilane, 9.5	30
4	o-Dichlorobenzene	$1:3^b$	69.5		30
5	o-Dibromobenzene	$1:2$	71.7		30
6	o-Dibromobenzene	$1:2^b$	60.6		30
7	o-Dibromobenzene	$1:3^{a,b}$	55.9		30
8	o-Bromoiodobenzene	$1:2^b$	72.5	Triphenylene, 3.85 Tetraphenylsilane, 3.8	30
9	o-Bromoiodobenzene	$1:1^b$	68.5	Tetraphenylsilane, 2.4	30
10	m-Bromofluorobenzene	$1:1^b$	51.5		30
11	m-Bromoiodobenzene	$1:2^b$	84.5		30
12	m-Bromoiodobenzene	$1:1^b$	78		30
13	p-Dichlorobenzene	$1:3$	55		30
14	p-Dibromobenzene	$1:4$	68		30,151
15	p-Di-iodobenzene	$1:2$	65.2		30
16	p-Bromofluorobenzene	$1:2$	47.2	p-Fluorophenyltriphenylsilane, 13.6	30
17	p-Bromochlorobenzene	$1:3$	61.5		30
18	3,7-Dichloro-10-ethylphenothiazine-5,5-dioxide[a]	$1:2$	44.2	3,7-Bis-(triphenylsilyl)-10-ethylphenothiazine-5,5-dioxide, 17.5	31
19	3,7-Dibromo-10-ethylphenothiazine-5,5-dioxide[a]	$1:2$	64.2	3,7-Bis-(triphenylsilyl)-10-ethylphenothiazine-5,5-dioxide, 19	31
20	1,2,3-Trichlorobenzene	$1:3^b$	61		30
21	1,2-Dichloro-4-bromobenzene	$1:3^b$	58		30
22	1,2,4-Tribromobenzene	$1:3$	71	p-Bis-(triphenylsilyl)-benzene, 0.1	151
23	1,2,4-Tribromobenzene	$1:1$	65.7	1,3,5-Tribromobenzene, 2.9	151
24	1,3,5-Trichlorobenzene	$1:3$	71	Tetraphenylsilane, 2.2	151

TABLE 6.6 (*continued*)

Num- ber	Aryl halide[a,b]	RX/R₃SiM Ratio	Ph₆Si₂ (%)	Other products (%)	Ref.
25	1,3,5-Tribromoben- zene	1 : 3	65.3	Tetraphenylsilane, 1.1	*151*
26	1,3,5-Tribromoben- zene	1 : 3[b]	66.1		*30*

[a]All reactions were run at room temperature, except No. 7 at −65°; and tetra- hydrofuran was used as solvent throughout, except in Nos. 18 and 19 in which a 2 : 1 mixture of tetrahydrofuran and ether was used.
[b]All reactions were performed by adding triphenylsilyllithium to the polyhalide except when marked with *b* in which case reverse addition was used.

could have arisen from the transient existence of benzyne. Thus, from *o*-bromofluorobenzene there were isolated triphenylene (3.3 per cent) and tetraphenylsilane which could have been formed from an elimination-coupling or elimination-addition reaction.

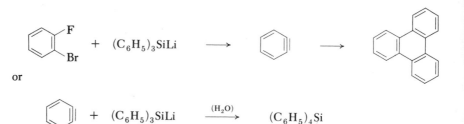

The isolation of small amounts of *o*-fluorophenyltriphenylsilane from *o*-chlorofluorobenzene seems to indicate that aryl chlorides couple more rapidly with silyllithium compounds than aryl fluorides, an observation which agrees with the formation of *p*-fluorophenyltriphenylsilane from *p*-bromofluorobenzene.

The trisubstituted benzene derivatives behave similarly to the disubstituted types with the exception of 1,2,4-tribromobenzene which on reaction with triphenylsilyllithium gave 1,3,5-tribromobenzene. This reaction product was also obtained earlier from the reaction of 1,2,4-tribromobenzene with sodium amide (*178*).

Reactions of aromatic compounds with two halogens on different benzene nuclei proceed normally to give bis-triphenylsilyl derivatives (Nos. 18 and 19). The low yields of the triphenylsilyl derivatives from sulfur-containing heterocycles may be due to sulfur-carbon bond cleavages similar to those observed for diphenyl sulfide or diphenyl sulfone (see p. 302).

Bond between Silicon and Group VI and VII Elements. There are few examples of reactions between silyllithium compounds and bonds between silicon and Group VI elements. The reaction of alkoxysilanes or siloxanes with triphenylsilyllithium will be discussed briefly in this section. Triphenylsilyllithium reacts with ethyl silicate to produce hexaphenyldisilane and triphenylsilane after hydrolysis (*165*).

$$(C_6H_5)_3SiLi + Si(OEt)_4 \xrightarrow{(H_2O)} (C_6H_5)_6Si_2 + (C_6H_5)_3SiH$$

Similarly, ethoxytriphenylsilane reacts with triphenylsilylpotassium to yield hexaphenyldisilane (*179*). An attempt to react ethoxytrimethylsilane with triphenylsilylpotassium failed to give any other product than triphenylsilanol from unreacted silylpotassium reagent (*149*). The cleavage of alkoxysilanes thus occurs mainly at the silicon to oxygen rather than at the carbon to oxygen bond. It was found that benzhydryloxydiphenylsilane reacted with triphenylsilyllithium to give hexaphenyldisilane, pentaphenyldisilane, and benzhydrol (*165*).

$$(C_6H_5)_3SiLi + (C_6H_5)_2SiHOCH(C_6H_5)_2 \xrightarrow{(H_2O)}$$

$$(C_6H_5)_6Si_2 + (C_6H_5)_2CHOH + (C_6H_5)_3SiSiH(C_6H_5)_2$$

Cleavage of the silicon-oxygen bond accounts for the formation of pentaphenyldisilane and benzhydrol.

Alkoxysilanes are likewise cleaved by organometallic compounds. Thus, ethoxytriphenylsilane reacts with *n*-butyllithium and with phenylmagnesium bromide to give high yields of tetra-substituted silanes (*179*).

$$(C_6H_5)_3SiOC_2H_5 + n\text{-}C_4H_9Li \longrightarrow n\text{-}C_4H_9Si(C_6H_5)_3 + C_2H_5OLi$$

$$(C_6H_5)_3SiOC_2H_5 + C_6H_5MgBr \longrightarrow (C_6H_5)_4Si + C_2H_5OMgBr$$

In contrast to the failure of ethoxytrimethylsilane to react with triphenylsilylpotassium, the reaction went smoothly with phenyllithium to give phenyltrimethylsilane (*149*).

Siloxanes were readily cleaved by *n*-butyllithium. Hexaphenyldisiloxane thus reacted with *n*-butyllithium to produce, on carbonation, benzoic acid and *n*-butyltriphenylsilane. It is apparent that carbon-silicon as well as silicon-oxygen cleavage occurred (*48*):

$$(C_6H_5)_3SiOSi(C_6H_5)_3 + n\text{-}C_4H_9Li \xrightarrow{(CO_2)} (C_6H_5)_3Si\text{-}n\text{-}C_4H_9 + C_6H_5COOH$$

The cleavage of various siloxanes by *n*-butyllithium, phenyllithium, and *p*-tolyllithium has been studied in some detail (*47*). Hexaphenylcyclotrisiloxane reacts with triphenylsilyllithium to form a linear compound in addition to hexaphenyldisilane (*116*):

$$[(C_6H_5)_2SiO]_3 + (C_6H_5)_3SiLi \longrightarrow (C_6H_5)_3Si[(C_6H_5)_2SiO]_3Li$$

I

$$I + (C_6H_5)_3SiLi \xrightarrow{(H_2O)} (C_6H_5)_3SiSi(C_6H_5)_3 + H[(C_6H_5)_2SiO]_3H$$

Apparently, a considerable amount of silicon-silicon cleavage occurred.

Representative examples of reactions of triphenylsilylmetallic compounds with chlorotrimethylsilane are summarized in Table 6.7.

$$(C_6H_5)_3SiM + (CH_3)_3SiCl \longrightarrow (C_6H_5)_3SiSi(CH_3)_3 + MX$$

TABLE 6.7. REACTIONS OF TRIPHENYLSILYLMETALLIC
COMPOUNDS WITH CHLOROTRIMETHYLSILANE

Number	Alkali metal in Ph_3SiM	Solvent[a]	Mode of addition	% 1,1,1-Trimethyl-2,2,2-triphenyldi-silane	Ref.
1	Li	THF[b]	Normal[c]	79	*71*
2	Li	GDME[d]	Normal	72	*15*
3	Na	GDME	Normal	68	*15*
4	K	Ether	Reverse[e]	45–75	*4,10,86,92*
5	K	n-Butyl ether	Reverse	47	*86,92*
6	K	GDME	Normal	77	*15*
7	Rb	n-Butyl ether	Reverse	48	*92*
8	Cs	Ether	Reverse	26	*92*

[a]All reactions were run at room temperature.
[b]Tetrahydrofuran.
[c]Indicates the addition of triphenylsilylmetallic compound to the chlorotrimethylsilane.
[d]Ethylene glycol dimethyl ether.
[e]Indicates the addition of the chlorosilane to the triphenylsilylmetallic compound.

From Table 6.7 it appears that the yields of 1,1,1-trimethyl-2,2,2-triphenyldisilane from triphenylsilyllithium, -sodium, and -potassium are of comparable magnitude when the reactions are carried out by adding a solution of the silylmetallic compound to the chlorosilane. The yields obtained from the silylrubidium and -cesium compounds are lower but comparable to those obtained by a similar mode of addition of triphenylsilylpotassium.

Table 6.8 includes reactions of silylmetallic compounds with Group IV-B halides other than alkyl and aryl halides. The reactions with chlorotrimethylsilane have not been included in this Table unless at least one of the organic substituents on the silylmetallic compound was different from phenyl.

Most of the entries in Table 6.8 cover the reactions of silylmetallic compounds with monohalosilanes or polyhalosilanes. It should be noted that only small yields of coupling products were obtained from the reaction of triphenylsilyllithium and trichlorosilane (No. 1), and none was obtained

TABLE 6.8. REACTIONS BETWEEN SILYLMETALLIC COMPOUNDS AND GROUP IV-B HALIDES

Number	Silylmetallic compound	Group IV-B halide	Mode of addition	Solvent	Products (%)	Ref.
1	Triphenylsilyllithium[a]	Trichlorosilane	Normal[b,c]	THF[d]	Triphenylsilane, 29.5; Hexaphenyldisilane, 20.6; Tris-(triphenylsilyl)-silane, 4.4	165
2	Triphenylsilyllithium[a]	Silicon tetrachloride	Normal	THF	Triphenylsilane, 7.5; Hexaphenyldisilane, 72.5	165
3	Triphenylsilyllithium	Dichlorodiphenylsilane	Normal[e]	THF	Pentaphenyldisilane, 24.5; Hexaphenyldisilane, 45; Octaphenyltrisilane, 9.6	165
4	Triphenylsilyllithium	Chlorotriphenylsilane	Normal	THF	Hexaphenyldisilane, 89	37
5	Triphenylsilyllithium	Chlorotriphenylsilane	Normal[c]	THF	Hexaphenyldisilane, 68	37
6	Triphenylsilyllithium	Chloropentaphenyldisilane	Normal	THF	Hexaphenyldisilane, 42.3; Octaphenyltrisilane, 25.7	165
7	Triphenylsilyllithium	Trimethyltin chloride	Reverse[f]	Liquid ammonia	Triphenylsilyltrimethyltin	122
8	Triphenylsilylpotassium	Silicon tetrachloride	Normal	Ether	Hexaphenyldisilane, 40; 1,1,1-Triphenyl-2,2,2-trichlorodisilane, 27	86,90
9	Triphenylsilylpotassium	Trichlorophenylsilane	Normal	Ether	1,1,1,2-Tetraphenyl-2,2-dichlorodisilane, 34; Hexaphenyldisilane, 16	86,90
10	Triphenylsilylpotassium[a]	Dichlorodiphenylsilane	Normal	Ether	Octaphenyltrisilane, 29	92,93
11	Triphenylsilylpotassium	Dichlorodiphenylsilane	Normal	Ether	Chloropentaphenyldisilane, 50	92,93

TABLE 6.8. (*continued*)

Number	Silylmetallic compound	Group IV-B halide	Mode of addition	Solvent	Products (%)	Ref.
12	Triphenylsilyl-potassium	Chlorotriethyl-silane	Reverse	Ether	1,1,1-Triethyl-2,2,2-tri-phenyldisilane, 37, 41, 87	7,10, 149
13	Triphenylsilyl-potassium	Chlorodimethyl-phenylsilane	Reverse	Ether	1,1-Dimethyl-1,2,2,2-tetra-phenyldisilane, 68.4	67
14	Triphenylsilyl-potassium	Chlorotriphenyl-silane	Normal	Ether	Hexaphenyldisilane, 69	11
15	Triphenylsilyl-potassium	Chloro-di-p-tolyl-phenylsilane	Normal	Ether	Hexaphenyldisiloxane, 13; *Unsym*-tetraphenyldi-p-tolyldisilane, 72	90
16	Triphenylsilyl-potassium	Chloro-p-tolyl-di-phenylsilane	Normal	Ether	Pentaphenyl-p-tolyldisilane, 77	90
17	Triphenylsilyl-potassium	Triphenylgermyl-bromide	Reverse	Ether	Triphenylsilyltriphenylger-mane, 63	58
18	Triphenylsilyl-potassium	Triphenylgermyl chloride	Reverse	Ether	Triphenylsilyltriphenylger-mane, 43	58
19	Triphenylsilyl-potassium	Triphenyltin chloride	Normal	Ether	Triphenylsilyltriphenyltin, 76	92
20	Dimethylphenyl-silyllithium	Chlorotrimethyl-silane	Normal	THF	Pentamethylphenyldisilane, 40	70
21	Dimethylphenyl-silyllithium	Chlorotriphenyl-silane	Normal	THF	1,1-Dimethyl-1,2,2,2-tetra-phenyldisilane, 32; Hexaphenyldisilane, 2.3	70
22	Dimethylphenyl-silyllithium	Chlorotriphenyl-silane	Reverse	THF	1,1,2,2-Tetramethyl-1,2-di-phenyldisilane, 58-71; Hexaphenyldisilane, 35-38	70
23	Methyldiphenyl-silyllithium	Chlorotrimethyl-silane	Normal	THF	1,1,1,2-tetramethyl-2,2-di-phenyldisilane, 57.5	70
24	Methyldiphenyl-silyllithium	Chlorotriphenyl-silane	Normal	THF	Methylpentaphenyldisilane, 52	70

25	Methyldiphenyl-silyllithium	Chlorotriphenyl-silane	Reverse	THF	Trace of Methylpentaphenyl-disilane; Trace of 1,2-Dimethyl-1,1,2,2-tetraphenyldisilane; Hexaphenyldisilane, 19–27	70
26	Diphenyl-p-tolyl-silylpotassium	Chlorophenyl-di-p-tolylsilane	Normal	Ether	1,1,2-Triphenyl-1,2,2-tri-p-tolyldisilane, 52	90
27	Tri-p-tolylsilyl-potassium	Chlorotriphenyl-silane	Normal	Ether	1,1,1-Triphenyl-2,2,2-tri-p-tolyldisilane, 26	90
28	Tris-(triphenyl-germyl)-silyl-lithium	Triphenyltin chloride	Reverse^c	Benzene	Tris-(triphenylgermyl)-tri-phenylstannylsilane, 15.5	97
29	Diphenylsilyl-lithium	Chlorotriphenyl-silane	Normal	THF	Pentaphenyldisilane, 9.5–11.3	84

[a] A molar ratio of 1:1 was used throughout except in reaction 11, 2:1; reaction 1, 3:1; and reaction 2, 4:1; of silylmetallic to halide.
[b] Indicates the addition of the organosilylmetallic compound to the group IV-B halide.
[c] The reaction was carried out at room temperature, except for Nos. 1 and 5 which were kept at −70° and No. 29 at 0°.
[d] Tetrahydrofuran.
[e] The reaction mixture was treated with lithium aluminum hydride prior to hydrolysis.
[f] Indicates the addition of the group IV-B compound to the silylmetallic compound.

with silicon tetrachloride (No. 2). Large percentages of hexaphenyldisilane were obtained, indicating either a large amount of halogen-metal interconversion or a rapid cleavage of newly formed silicon-silicon bonds by the excess silyllithium reagent:

$$(C_6H_5)_3SiLi + SiCl_4 \longrightarrow Cl_3SiSi(C_6H_5)_3$$

$$Cl_3SiSi(C_6H_5)_3 + (C_6H_5)_3SiLi \longrightarrow (C_6H_5)_3SiSi(C_6H_5)_3 + Cl_3SiLi$$

The reaction of trichlorophenylsilane with triphenylsilylpotassium gave 1,1,1,2-tetraphenyl-2,2-dichlorodisilane in addition to hexaphenyldisilane. The success of this reaction rests in the rapid consumption of the silylmetallic compound and the decreased opportunity for the interfering side-reaction of silicon-silicon bond cleavage by the excess silylmetallic compound.

$$(C_6H_5)_3SiK + C_6H_5SiCl_3 \longrightarrow (C_6H_5)_3SiSiCl_2(C_6H_5) + KCl$$

If only two halogens are attached to one silicon the yields of disilanes or trisilanes are improved. Thus octaphenyltrisilane could be obtained from a 2:1 reaction of triphenylsilylpotassium and dichlorodiphenylsilane.

$$2 (C_6H_5)_3SiK + (C_6H_5)_2SiCl_2 \longrightarrow (C_6H_5)_3SiSi(C_6H_5)_2Si(C_6H_5)_3$$

$$(C_6H_5)_3SiK + (C_6H_5)_2SiCl_2 \longrightarrow (C_6H_5)_3SiSiCl(C_6H_5)_2$$

The yield obtained with the silylpotassium reagent is higher than that obtained with the silyllithium reagent when a molar ratio of 1:1 is used. The product obtained from the reaction involving triphenylsilyllithium was reduced with lithium aluminum hydride before isolation which could account in part for the lower yield.

Silanes containing only one chlorine attached to silicon generally give good yields of coupling products. From reactions 24 and 25, it is seen that the addition of the silylmetallic compound to the chlorosilane gives by far the highest yield. This is evidently due to the cleavage of the disilanes by excess silyllithium compound present when the chlorosilane is added to the silylmetallic reagent. That such cleavages do take place can be concluded from the isolation of 1,2-dimethyl-1,1,2,2-tetraphenyldisilane in reaction 25.

$$(C_6H_5)_2CH_3SiLi + ClSi(C_6H_5)_3 \longrightarrow (C_6H_5)_2CH_3SiSi(C_6H_5)_3$$

$$(C_6H_5)_2CH_3SiSi(C_6H_5)_3 + (C_6H_5)_2CH_3SiLi \longrightarrow$$
$$(C_6H_5)_3SiLi + (C_6H_5)_2CH_3SiSiCH_3(C_6H_5)_2$$

$$(C_6H_5)_3SiLi + (C_6H_5)_3SiCl \longrightarrow (C_6H_5)_3SiSi(C_6H_5)_3$$

Reaction Nos. 21 and 22 likewise indicate the occurrence of this secondary cleavage reaction in the reverse type of addition.

$$(CH_3)_2(C_6H_5)SiLi + ClSi(C_6H_5)_3 \longrightarrow (CH_3)_2(C_6H_5)SiSi(C_6H_5)_3$$

$$(CH_3)_2C_6H_5SiLi + (CH_3)_2C_6H_5SiSi(C_6H_5)_3 \longrightarrow$$
$$(C_6H_5)_3SiLi + (CH_3)_2C_6H_5SiSi(CH_3)_2C_6H_5$$

$$(C_6H_5)_3SiLi + ClSi(C_6H_5)_3 \longrightarrow (C_6H_5)_3SiSi(C_6H_5)_3$$

Chloro-tri-*n*-hexadecylsilane couples with triphenylsilylpotassium to give a good yield of 1,1,1-tri-*n*-hexadecyl-2,2,2-triphenyldisilane (*78*). The disilane shown below is formed in good yields by either of the two routes depicted below (*136*):

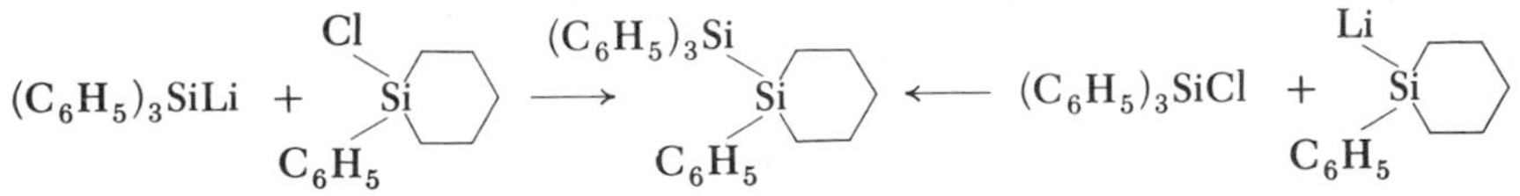

Two cases are known of reactions of silyllithium compounds with compounds which contain a silicon-silicon bond in addition to a silicon-hydrogen or a silicon-chlorine bond. These are the reactions of pentaphenyldisilane and chloropentaphenyldisilane with triphenylsilyllithium (*173*). From the former was isolated triphenylsilane and hexaphenyldisilane whereas the latter yielded octaphenyltrisilane (No. 6). It should be noticed that octaphenyltrisilane was not obtained from the reaction of triphenylsilyllithium with pentaphenyldisilane because of silicon-silicon bond cleavage.

$$(C_6H_5)_3SiLi + (C_6H_5)_3SiSiH(C_6H_5)_2 \longrightarrow (C_6H_5)_3SiSi(C_6H_5)_3$$

That this type of cleavage is of minor importance in the case of chloropentaphenyldisilane (No. 6) is due to the much faster coupling reaction with the chlorosilane.

From a combination of cleavage reactions and coupling reactions it was possible to prepare a complete series of hexa-arylated disilanes containing two different aryl groups, phenyl and *p*-tolyl. These compounds were prepared incidental to a study of the possible dissociation of hexa-aryldisilanes. All of the possible isomers have been prepared. Typical examples of some of these preparations are given in Table 6.8 (Nos. 15, 16 and 27). The symmetrical compounds were usually formed from chlorosilanes and sodium.

Chlorotrialkylsilanes react with silylmetallic compounds to give slightly lower yields of disilanes.

Examples of reactions between silylmetallic compounds and halides of germanium and tin are shown in Table 6.8 (Nos. 7, 17, 18, 19 and 28). The reaction of tris-(triphenylgermyl)-silyllithium with triphenyltin chloride gave a low yield of the compound containing a silicon-tin bond. Better yields were obtained in reactions of triphenylsilylpotassium with triphenyl-germyl chloride and bromide of which the former gave a slightly lower yield. The somewhat higher yield of triphenylsilyltriphenyltin indicates that some germanium-silicon bond cleavage may have occurred in the former case since reverse addition was involved.

$$(C_6H_5)_3SiK + (C_6H_5)_3SnCl \longrightarrow (C_6H_5)_3SnSi(C_6H_5)_3 + KCl$$

Cases of germanium-silicon cleavages by a silylmetallic compound have been discussed on p. 296.

Multiple Bonds. Silylmetallic compounds add to activated double bonds to give new carbon-silicon bonds. The reaction is by no means a general one. Table 6.9 lists the attempted reactions as well as the successful ones.

TABLE 6.9. REACTIONS OF TRIPHENYLSILYLMETALLIC
COMPOUNDS WITH OLEFINS AND ACTYLENES

No.	Metal in Ph₃SiM	Olefin or acetylene	Solvent	Products (%)	Ref.
1	K	Ethylene	Ether	Triphenylsilanol, 54	179
2	K	Cyclohexene	Ether	Triphenylsilanol, 66–87	179
3	K	1-Methyl-cyclopen-tene	Ether	Triphenylsilanol, 72	179
4	K	n-Octene-1	Ether	Triphenylsilanol, 63	179
5	K	n-Octene-1	GDME[a] /Ether	Hexaphenyldisiloxane, 22 Triphenylsilanol, 25 Tetraphenylsilane, 24	179
6	K	n-Dodecene-1	Ether	Triphenylsilanol, 78	179
7	K	n-Dodecene-1	GDME	Triphenylsilanol, 21 Tetraphenylsilane, 36 Hexaphenyldisiloxane, 20	179
8	K	n-Hexadecene-1	Ether	Triphenylsilanol, 86	179
9	K	n-Octadecene-1	Ether	Triphenylsilanol, 89	179
10	Li	Styrene	THF[b]	Triphenylsilane, 35	1
11	Li	1,1-Diphenylethyl-ene	THF	1,1-Diphenyl-2-(triphenyl-silyl)-ethane, 80	179
12	K	1,1-Diphenylethyl-ene	Ether	1,1-Diphenyl-2-(triphenyl-silyl)-ethane, 42	179
13	Li	trans-Stilbene	GDME[c]	1,2-Bis-(triphenylsilyl)-1,2-diphenylethane, 26 1-(Triphenylsilyl)-1,2,-3,4-tetraphenylbutane, 24	21
14	Li	trans-Stilbene	GDME[d]	1,2-Bis-(triphenylsilyl)-1,2-diphenylethane, 2 1-(Triphenylsilyl)-1,2-3,4-tetraphenylbutane, 16	21

TABLE 6.9. (*continued*)

No.	Metal in Ph₃SiM	Olefin or acetylene	Solvent	Products (%)	Ref.
15	K	*trans*-Stilbene	Ether	1-(Triphenylsilyl)-1,2-diphenylethane, 55	*179*
16	Li	Triphenylethylene	THF	1-(Triphenylsilyl)-1,2,2-triphenylethane, 62	*179*
17	Li	Tetraphenylethylene	THF	Triphenylsilane, 56	*179*
18	K	Tetraphenylethylene	Ether	Triphenylsilanol, 74	*179*
19	Li	1,2-Diphenylpropene-1	THF	Hexaphenyldisilane, 45	*125*
20	Li	1,4-Diphenylbutadiene-1,3	Ether	Hexaphenyldisilane, 12 Triphenylsilanol, 42	*179*
21	K	Δ$^{9,9'}$-Bifluorene	Ether	Tars	*179*
22	Li	Diphenylacetylene	GDME	1,2-Bis-(triphenylsilyl)-1,2-diphenylethane, 8	*21*
23	K	Diphenylacetylene	Ether	Tetraphenylsilane, 15	*88*
24	Li	1-Chloropropene-1	THF	Hexaphenyldisilane, 13 1,2-Bis-(triphenylsilyl)-propane, 27	*1*
25	Li	Trimethylvinylsilane	THF[e]	Tetraphenylsilane, 28	*1*
26	Li	Dimethyldivinylsilane	THF	Polymer	*1*

[a]GDME—ethylene glycol dimethyl ether.
[b]THF—tetrahydrofuran.
[c]The reaction was allowed to proceed 24 hours.
[d]The reaction was allowed to proceed 30 minutes.
[e]Phenyllithium was added.

From this Table it is apparent that no reaction occurs with linear aliphatic (Nos. 1, 4–9) or cyclic olefins (Nos. 2 and 3). Compounds containing phenyl groups attached directly to doubly bonded carbon atoms are more reactive. Styrene apparently polymerizes whereas 1,1-diphenylethylene, *trans*-stilbene, and triphenylethylene react with triphenylsilyllithium or -potassium to form the addition product. The structure of the product derived from triphenylethylene was proven by independent synthesis.

$$(C_6H_5)_2C{=}CHC_6H_5 + (C_6H_5)_3SiLi \xrightarrow{\text{(H}_2\text{O)}} (C_6H_5)_2CHCH(C_6H_5)Si(C_6H_5)_3$$

The direction of addition to 1,1-diphenylethylene is similar to that observed in the corresponding reaction with organo-alkali metal compounds (*181*). The failure of tetraphenylethylene and Δ$^{9,9'}$-bifluorene to react with the silylmetallic reagent may have been largely the result of steric factors. The absence of reaction with 1,2-diphenylpropene-1 may be attributed to the deactivating effect of the methyl group toward nucleophilic attack on the double bond. The addition of two moles of silylmetallic reagent to diphenylacetylene is unusual, unless protonation occurs after addition of the first molecule.

$$2 \ (C_6H_5)_3SiLi + C_6H_5C{\equiv}CC_6H_5 \xrightarrow{(H_2O)} (C_6H_5)_3Si-\overset{\displaystyle H}{\underset{\displaystyle C_6H_5}{C}}-\overset{\displaystyle H}{\underset{\displaystyle C_6H_5}{C}}-Si(C_6H_5)_3$$

The failure of 1,4-diphenylbutadiene-1,3 to form a mono- or di-substituted triphenylsilyl derivative is unexpected inasmuch as 1,4-diphenylbutadiene-1,3 is a vinylog of stilbene. Interfering polymerizations may have proceeded at a rapid rate and made the isolation of the expected compound difficult.

The reaction of 1-chloropropene-1 with excess triphenylsilyllithium may have occurred stepwise:

$$(C_6H_5)_3SiLi + ClCH{=}CHCH_3 \longrightarrow (C_6H_5)_3SiCH{=}CHCH_3$$

$$(C_6H_5)_3SiCH{=}CHCH_3 + (C_6H_5)_3SiLi \xrightarrow{(H_2O)} (C_6H_5)_3SiCH_2CH(CH_3)Si(C_6H_5)_3$$

The structure of the product was, however, not proven conclusively and awaits further investigation. The apparent favored position of entry has been conjectured on the basis of inductive and steric factors. It was found that triphenylsilyllithium adds smoothly to anthracene, to give 9,10-dihydro-9-lithio-10-triphenylsilylanthracene(*127*).

The reactions between azobenzene and triphenylsilylmetallic compounds paralleled the successful experiments mentioned above. It was found that both triphenylsilyllithium and triphenylsilylpotassium add to the nitrogen-nitrogen double bond to form, on hydrolysis, 1-triphenylsilyl-1,2-diphenylhydrazine in good yields (*166*).

$$(C_6H_5)_3SiLi + C_6H_5N{=}NC_6H_5 \xrightarrow{(H_2O)} C_6H_5N{-}NC_6H_5$$
$$\underset{(C_6H_5)_3Si \quad H}{}$$

This is one of the few cases where a distinctly lower yield (36 *vs.* 67 per cent) of a product was obtained from a reaction involving triphenylsilylpotassium in the presence of the excess alloy (*87,166*). The same trisubstituted hydrazine was formed when an excess of triphenylsilyllithium was added to azoxybenzene (*154*).

$$(C_6H_5)_3SiLi + \underset{\underset{O}{\downarrow}}{C_6H_5N}{=}NC_6H_5 \longrightarrow (C_6H_5)_3SiOLi + C_6H_5N{=}NC_6H_5$$

$$(C_6H_5)_3SiLi + C_6H_5N{=}NC_6H_5 \xrightarrow{(H_2O)} (C_6H_5)_3Si\underset{\displaystyle C_6H_5}{N}NHC_6H_5$$

The reaction also proceeded with methyldiphenylsilyllithium and azoxybenzene. It should be noted that no appreciable silicon-nitrogen cleavage was observed in these reactions since disilanes were not isolated.

Reactions of silylmetallic compounds with carbon-oxygen double bonds include the following types: carbon dioxide, aldehydes, ketones, acid chlorides, acid anhydrides, esters, and amides.

From the reaction between silylmetallic compounds and carbon dioxide, silanecarboxylic acids are isolated. Triphenylsilanecarboxylic acid has been obtained by carbonation of triphenylsilylpotassium (in 87 per cent yield) (10,16) and triphenylsilyllithium (in 93.4 per cent yield) (39). In a basic medium the acid is readily decomposed to carbon monoxide and triphenylsilanol (16).

$$(C_6H_5)_3SiK + CO_2 \xrightarrow{(H_2O)} (C_6H_5)_3SiCOOH \xrightarrow{(OH^-)} (C_6H_5)_3SiOH + CO$$

Recently the corresponding acids have been prepared from methyldiphenyl- and dimethylphenylsilyllithium in 66 and 35 per cent yields, respectively (158). The structures of the acids were established by preparation of the methyl esters and subsequent reduction by lithium aluminum hydride to the carbinols, which could be prepared directly from the silyllithium reagents and formaldehyde (16).

$$(C_6H_5)_3SiCOOH \xrightarrow{CH_2N_2} (C_6H_5)_3SiCOOCH_3$$

$$(C_6H_5)_3SiCOOCH_3 \xrightarrow{LiAlH_4} (C_6H_5)_3SiCH_2OH$$

$$(C_6H_5)_3SiLi + CH_2O \xrightarrow{(H_2O)} (C_6H_5)_3SiCH_2OH$$

From tri-*p*-tolylsilylpotassium there was obtained a good yield of tri-*p*-tolylsilanecarboxylic acid (18).

Several aldehydes and ketones have been treated with silylmetallic reagents to produce various carbinols or alkoxysilanes, as summarized in Table 6.10.

Aliphatic aldehydes react with triphenylsilyllithium in the normal manner to produce silylcarbinols:

$$(C_6H_5)_3SiLi + CH_3CHO \xrightarrow{(H_2O)} (C_6H_5)_3SiCHOHCH_3$$

Similar products were obtained from reactions of various silylmetallic compounds with formaldehyde and propionaldehyde. Triphenylsilyllithium very probably adds in a normal manner to the carbonyl group in benzaldehyde, then rearrangement follows to give benzyloxytriphenylsilane (174).

$$(C_6H_5)_3SiLi + C_6H_5CHO \xrightarrow{(H_2O)} C_6H_5CH_2OSi(C_6H_5)_3$$

TABLE 6.10. REACTIONS OF SILYLMETALLIC COMPOUNDS
WITH ALDEHYDES AND KETONES

No.	Silylmetallic compound	Carbonyl compound	Products (%)	Ref.
1	Triphenylsilyl-lithium[a-d]	Formaldehyde	Hydroxymethyltriphenyl-silane, 12	91
2	Dimethylphenyl-silyllithium[a]	Formaldehyde	Hydroxymethyldimethyl-phenylsilane, 45.3	158
3	Triphenylsilyl-lithium[c]	Acetaldehyde	1-(Triphenylsilyl)-ethanol, 39 Triphenylsilane, 38	169
4	Triphenylsilyl-lithium	Acetaldehyde	1-(Triphenylsilyl)-ethanol, 53	22
5	Triphenylsilyl-lithium[c]	Propionalde-hyde	1-(Triphenylsilyl)-propa-nol, 4.3 Triphenylsilane, 43.6	79
6	Triphenylsilyl-lithium[a]	Benzaldehyde	Benzyloxytriphenylsilane, 46	174
7	Triphenylsilyl-lithium	Benzaldehyde	Hexaphenyldisilane, 60 Hydrobenzoin, 49	174
8	Triphenylsilyl-lithium	Benzaldehyde	Hexaphenyldisilane, 62 Hydrobenzoin, 58 Benzyloxytriphenylsilane, 4.1	174
9	Triphenylsilyl-potassium[b,d]	Benzaldehyde	Tetraphenylsilane, 77 Hydrobenzoin, 16 Triphenylsilanol, 11	174
10	Triphenylsilyl-lithium	Acetone	2-(Triphenylsilyl)-propa-nol-2, 45	13
11	Triphenylsilyl-lithium[c]	Acetone	2-(Triphenylsilyl)-propa-nol-2, 52	72
12	Dimethylphenyl-silyllithium	Acetone	2-(Dimethylphenylsilyl)-propanol-2, 45	72
13	Methyldiphenyl-silyllithium	Acetone	2-Methyldiphenylsilylpro-panol-2, 44	72
14	Triphenylsilyl-lithium	Cyclohexanone	2-(Triphenylsilyl)-cyclo-hexanol-1, 7	72
15	Dimethylphenyl-silyllithium	Cyclohexanone	2-(Dimethylphenylsilyl)-cyclohexanol-1, 29	72
16	Triphenylsilyl-lithium	8-Pentadeca-none	8-(Triphenylsilyl)-penta-decanol-8, 26	72
17	Triphenylsilyl-lithium	3-Octadeca-none	3-(Triphenylsilyl)-octa-decanol-3, 34	72
18	Triphenylsilyl-lithium	2-Nonadeca-none	2-(Triphenylsilyl)-nona-decanol-2, 33	72
19	Triphenylsilyl-lithium	9-Nonadeca-none	2-(Triphenylsilyl)-decanol-9, 25	72

TABLE 6.10. (*continued*)

No.	Silylmetallic compound	Carbonyl compound	Products (%)	Ref.
20	Triphenylsilyl-lithium	12-Tricosanone	12-(Triphenylsilyl)-tricosanol-12, 10	*72*
21	Triphenylsilyl-lithium	Benzophenone	Benzhydryloxytriphenyl-silane, 50	*72*
22	Triphenylsilyl-potassium[b,d]	Benzophenone	Triphenylsilanol, 13 Hexaphenyldisiloxane, 54 Benzhydrol, 22 Benzhydryloxytriphenyl-silane, 25	*89*
23	Triphenylsilyl-potassium[b,d]	Benzophenone	Benzhydryloxytriphenyl-silane, 21 Benzhydrol, 18 Triphenylsilane, 41	*11*
24	Triphenylsilyl-potassium[b,d]	Benzophenone	2-(Triphenylsiloxy)-tetra-phenylethanol-1, 48 Triphenylsilanol, 4	*20*
25	Triphenylsilyl-potassium[b,d]	Benzophenone	Triphenylsiloxydiphenyl-methylpotassium, 64	*20*
26	Methyldiphenyl-silyllithium	Benzophenone	Benzopinacol, trace Benzhydryloxymethyldi-phenylsilane, 19	*71*
27	Dimethylphenyl silyllithium	Benzophenone	Denzopinacol, trace Benzhydrol, 6 Benzhydryloxydimethyl-phenylsilane, 20	*71*
28	Triphenylsilyl-potassium[b,d]	4,4'-Dimethyl-benzophe-none	Triphenylsilanol, 27 4,4'-dimethylbenzhydryl-oxytriphenylsilane, 26	*89*
29	Triphenylsilyl-lithium	Dibenzyl ketone	Triphenylsilane, 78	*72*
30	Triphenylsilyl-lithium	Xanthone	Xanthhydryloxytriphenyl-silane, 12.7	*158*
31	Triphenylsilyl-lithium	10-Thiaxan-thenone	Hexaphenyldisilane, 34.6 10-Thiaxanthhydryloxytri-phenylsilane, 12	*31*

[a]All reactions were carried out at room temperature, except No. 6 at $-70°$, No. 3 at $-20°$; and in tetrahydrofuran as the solvent unless otherwise indicated.

[b]Normal addition of the silylmetallic compound to the carbonyl compound was used in all cases except Nos. 1, 22, 23, 24, 25 and 28, in which reverse addition was employed.

[c]A 1:1 ratio was used in all cases but Nos. 3 (1:4.8), 5 (1:2), 11 (2.7:1) (carbonyl compound/silylmetallic).

[d]Ether was used as the solvent.

A like difference between aliphatic and aromatic ketones, such as acetone and benzophenone had previously been noted. It is currently considered that the addition takes place in the normal manner in both cases but that the aromatic carbonyl addition product rearranges under the experimental conditions.

$$(C_6H_5)_3SiLi + (C_6H_5)_2C{=}O \longrightarrow (C_6H_5)_3Si(C_6H_5)_2COLi \xrightarrow{(H_2O)}$$

$$(C_6H_5)_3SiOCH(C_6H_5)_2$$

It was shown that the carbinol of I prepared by an alternate route did indeed rearrange to the alkoxysilane under mildly basic conditions (*13*).

A large number of aliphatic ketones was found to react normally with triphenylsilylmetallic compounds to give the substituted triphenylsilyl-carbinols in moderate yields (Nos. 10–20). It is somewhat surprising that dibenzyl ketone did not add the silylmetallic reagent across the carbonyl group. From the reaction there was isolated a 78 per cent yield of triphenylsilane. It was assumed that an acidic hydrogen in the benzyl-group was abstracted by the silylmetallic reagent.

A series of reactions of triphenylsilylpotassium with benzophenone was carried out under varying conditions in the hope of isolating one or more intermediates (Nos. 23–27). Brook and co-workers were successful in isolating triphenylsiloxydiphenylmethylpotassium and 2-triphenylsiloxytetra-phenylethanol (*20*). From these observations and other evidence a somewhat different mechanism has been postulated for the formation of these compounds.

Xanthone (*158*) and 10-thiaxanthenone (*31*) react with triphenylsilyllithium to give xanthhydryloxytriphenylsilane and 10-thiaxanthhydryloxy-triphenylsilane, respectively, in agreement with the comparable reactions of benzophenone.

A few reactions of acid chlorides with silylmetallic compounds are known. Some acid chlorides give products which indicate that the silyl-metallic compound reacted with the carbonyl group as well as the chlorine. It is evident that the labile chlorine of benzoyl chloride reacts with triphenylsilylpotassium to give chlorotriphenylsilane which couples with excess triphenylsilylpotassium to give hexaphenyldisilane (33 per cent) (*12*). This reaction is less pronounced at very low temperatures. However, benzenesulfonyl chloride reacts even at −50° with triphenylsilyllithium to give a 69 per cent yield of hexaphenyldisilane (*173*).

Acetyl chloride reacted with triphenylsilyllithium at −50° to give a mixture of acetyltriphenylsilane (8.3 per cent), triphenyl-(1-triphenylsiloxy-ethyl)-silane (1.9 per cent), 1,1-bis-(triphenylsilyl)-ethanol (20.4 per cent), and triphenylsilane (29 per cent) (*79,169*).

$$(C_6H_5)_3SiLi + CH_3COCl \longrightarrow CH_3COSi(C_6H_5)_3 + [(C_6H_5)_3Si]_2\overset{\displaystyle |}{\underset{\displaystyle OH}{C}}CH_3 +$$

$$\text{I} \qquad\qquad\qquad \text{II}$$

$$(C_6H_5)_3Si\overset{\displaystyle |}{\underset{\displaystyle OSi(C_6H_5)_3}{C}}HCH_3 \quad + (C_6H_5)_3SiH$$

$$\text{III} \qquad\qquad\qquad \text{IV}$$

When temperatures of $-10°$ to $-20°$ were maintained throughout the reaction there was obtained only II and IV in 16.3 and 31 per cent yields, respectively. However, at room temperature only triphenyl-(1-triphenylsiloxyethyl)-silane, III (16.5 per cent), and 39 per cent of IV were isolated. The triphenylsilane may have been formed by enolization in agreement with the comparable reaction of triphenylmethylsodium (*143,144*). It further appears that acetyltriphenylsilane (which was isolated from a reaction performed at $-40°$ to $-50°$), is an intermediate in the stepwise formation of IIa which would yield IIIa by a rearrangement, similar to the one observed with aromatic ketones.

$$(C_6H_5)_3SiLi + CH_3COCl \longrightarrow CH_3COSi(C_6H_5)_3$$

$$\text{I}$$

$$(C_6H_5)_3SiLi + CH_3COSi(C_6H_5)_3 \longrightarrow CH_3\overset{\displaystyle |}{\underset{\displaystyle OLi}{C}}[Si(C_6H_5)_3]_2 \xrightarrow{(H_2O)} CH_3\overset{\displaystyle |}{\underset{\displaystyle OH}{C}}[Si(C_6H_5)_3]_2$$

$$\text{I} \qquad\qquad\qquad\qquad \text{IIa} \qquad\qquad\qquad \text{II}$$

$$CH_3\overset{\displaystyle |}{\underset{\displaystyle OLi}{C}}[Si(C_6H_5)_3]_2 \longrightarrow CH_3\overset{\displaystyle \overset{\displaystyle Li}{|}}{\underset{\displaystyle OSi(C_6H_5)_3}{C}}Si(C_6H_5)_3 \xrightarrow{(H_2O)} CH_3\overset{\displaystyle |}{\underset{\displaystyle OSi(C_6H_5)_3}{C}}HSi(C_6H_5)_3$$

$$\text{IIa} \qquad\qquad \text{IIIa} \qquad\qquad\qquad\qquad \text{III}$$

Propionyl chloride reacted similarly to give a type II compound, triphenyl-(1-triphenylsiloxypropyl)-silane, in addition to minor amounts of triphenylsilane and triphenylsilanol (*79*). Benzoyl chloride, on the other hand, yielded hexaphenyldisilane and a small amount of benzoyltriphenylsilane on treatment with triphenylsilylpotassium at $0°$ (*12*).

Only one case of a reaction between an acid anhydride and a silylmetallic compound has been reported. From triphenylsilyllithium and acetic anhydride there was isolated 1,1-bis-(triphenylsilyl)-ethanol (20.8 per cent) (*22,79*).

$$(C_6H_5)_3SiLi + (CH_3CO)_2O \longrightarrow [(C_6H_5)_3Si]_2COHCH_3$$

The reaction of ethyl acetate with triphenylsilyllithium yielded a small amount of triphenyl-(1-triphenylsiloxyethyl)-silane, the same product which had been isolated from the reaction of the silylmetallic compound with acetyl chloride. It is likely that the ethoxy group of the ester is displaced from the carbonyl carbon by the nucleophilic attack of the triphenylsilyl anion, and that the reaction proceeds further by the route outlined above for acetyl chloride. From the reaction of ethyl benzoate with triphenylsilyllithium there has been isolated, under varying experimental conditions, ethoxytriphenylsilane, benzoin, and in one case triphenyl-silanol; while in other experiments only hexaphenyldisilane and triphenyl-silanol were obtained (*158*). For a discussion of the reaction of triphenyl-silyllithium with the carbonyl group of amides, see p. 298.

It has been shown that under forcing conditions phenylmagnesium bromide reacted with benzophenone anil by a 1,4-addition (*34,68,69*), while phenyllithium reacted by a 1,2-addition (*69,74*). The respective products were *o*-phenylbenzhydrylaniline and N-(triphenylmethyl)-aniline. The product obtained from triphenylsilylpotassium or triphenylsilyllithium and benzophenone anil was shown to be N-1,1,1-tetraphenyl-N-(diphenyl-methyl)-silylamine. A possible route to this compound is shown below:

$$(C_6H_5)_3SiK \; + \; (C_6H_5)_2C{=}NC_6H_5 \; \rightarrow \; \underset{\underset{Si(C_6H_5)_3}{\overset{\overset{K}{|}}{\underset{\quad I}{}}}}{(C_6H_5)_2C{-}NC_6H_5}$$

$$\underset{\underset{Si(C_6H_5)_3}{|}}{\underset{I}{(C_6H_5)_2\overset{\overset{K}{|}}{C}{-}NC_6H_5}} \; \rightarrow \; \underset{\underset{Si(C_6H_5)_3}{|}}{\underset{II}{(C_6H_5)_2C{-}\overset{\overset{K}{|}}{N}C_6H_5}} \; \overset{H_2O}{\longrightarrow} \; \underset{\underset{Si(C_6H_5)_3}{|}}{\underset{III}{(C_6H_5)_2\overset{\overset{H}{|}}{C}{-}NC_6H_5}}$$

Compound III may have been formed by a direct "abnormal" addition of the silylmetallic compound to the azomethine linkage in much the same manner as was suggested for the addition of triphenylsilylpotassium to benzophenone. However, by analogy with benzophenone, it is more likely that a "normal" addition to the azomethine linkage occurred to give the intermediate I, which immediately rearranged to give the compound II. This type of rearrangement for phenylsubstituted α-silylcarbinols to the corresponding alkoxysilanes has been reported to occur under the influence of catalytic amounts of base (*13*) (p. 279).

Triphenylsilyllithium acted as a highly selective nucleophile in its addition to the azomethine linkage in pyridine. From the reaction of tri-phenylsilyllithium with pyridine there was isolated only 4-triphenylsilyl-pyridine after oxidation (*167*). None of the 2-triphenylsilylpyridine isomer was isolated, in contrast to the comparable reaction of organolithium (*183,184*) or Grignard reagents (*6*) which give predominantly the 2-isomer. Selective nucleophiles such as benzylmagnesium chloride (*6,161*) and allyl-magnesium bromide (*53*) give 4-substitution in low yields. A similar addition was observed with acridine (*73a*), which yielded 10-triphenylsilyl-9,10-dihydroacridine subsequent to hydrolysis.

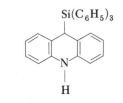

COMPARISON BETWEEN ORGANOSILYLMETALLIC
AND ORGANOGERMYLMETALLIC CHEMISTRY

In general, organogermylmetallic compounds undergo the same reactions as the analogous organosilylmetallic compounds (*106a*). The most pronounced differences have been found in the modes of formation. Hexaphenyldisilane can be cleaved readily by sodium-potassium alloy in diethyl ether to give triphenylsilylpotassium. In contrast, hexaphenyldigermane is not cleaved under these conditions unless initiated by either tetraphenylgermane, bromobenzene, or tetrahydrofuran (*55*).

Triphenylgermylmetallic compounds have been prepared from hexaphenyldigermane by various methods. Lithium in ethylene glycol dimethyl ether (*54,56*), sodium in liquid ammonia (*120*), and sodium-potassium alloy in ether (to which had been added a trace of tetrahydrofuran or tetraphenylgermane) (*55*) gave triphenylgermyllithium, -sodium, and -potassium, respectively. A wide variety of unsuccessful attempts to cleave hexaphenyldigermane have also been reported (*23,55*). Hexaethyldigermane has been cleaved by lithium and potassium in ethylamine after prolonged reaction (*119*). The trialkylgermyllithium reacted with the solvent; however, the existence of triethylgermylpotassium could be proven directly by coupling with ethyl bromide to give a nearly quantitative yield of tetraethylgermane (*119*). Later, the formation of trialkylgermyllithium was confirmed by metalation of triethylgermane with *n*-butyl and phenyllithium and subsequent derivatization (*103*).

Tetraphenylgermane is cleaved by lithium in ethylene glycol dimethyl ether (*54*) or in ether by sodium-potassium alloy (*42*). From the cleavage of β-phenethyltriphenylgermane with lithium in ethylene glycol dimethyl ether and derivatization with β-phenethyl bromide there was obtained bis-(β-phenethyl)-diphenylgermane. Di-*n*-octyldiphenylgermane was prepared by a similar route (*42*). These reactions indicate that the germanium-phenyl bond is cleaved preferentially to the germanium-alkyl bond. This is also borne out by the failure of tetraethylgermane to cleave under the conditions which caused cleavage of tetraphenylgermane (*103*).

Triphenylgermane reacted readily with lithium to give triphenylgermyllithium which on coupling with *n*-octadecyl bromide gave *n*-octadecyltriphenylgermane (*98*).

$$(C_6H_5)_3GeH + Li \longrightarrow (C_6H_5)_3GeLi + LiH$$

$$(C_6H_5)_3GeLi + RX \longrightarrow (C_6H_5)_3GeR + LiX$$

Methylgermyllithium, ethylgermyllithium, isoamylgermyllithium, and ethylisoamylgermyllithium have been prepared from the corresponding mono- or disubstituted germanes and lithium in ethylamine (96). Monogermylsodium has been reported as the product of a reaction of monogermane with sodium metal in liquid ammonia (156).

Triphenylstannyltriphenylgermane was cleaved slowly in the presence of sodium-potassium alloy as evidenced by the isolation of hexaphenyldigermane (42). Similarly triphenylmethyltriphenylgermane is cleaved by sodium-potassium alloy (13a).

$$(C_6H_5)_3GeSn(C_6H_5)_3 + 2 K \longrightarrow (C_6H_5)_3GeK + (C_6H_5)_3SnK$$

$$(C_6H_5)_3GeK + (C_6H_5)_3GeSn(C_6H_5)_3 \longrightarrow (C_6H_5)_3GeGe(C_6H_5)_3 + (C_6H_5)_3SnK$$

Germanium compounds containing hydrogen bound directly to germanium are readily metalated in contrast to similar silicon compounds. Thus triphenylgermane is readily metalated by methyllithium, n-butyllithium, and phenyllithium (57) to give, on carbonation, triphenylgermanecarboxylic acid in good yields. Only in the first case was alkylation (the dominant reaction in the organosilicon types) (76,77) to methyltriphenylgermane noticed. The corresponding alkylation reaction of triethylgermane proceeded to only a slight extent (103). Even a Grignard reagent such as allylmagnesium chloride in tetrahydrofuran was found to metalate triphenylgermane to give, on carbonation, triphenylgermanecarboxylic acid (185). Depending on conditions, triphenylgermane reacts with phenyllithium to give tetraphenylgermane or hexaphenyldigermane (106b). If an excess of triphenylgermane is present, hexaphenyldigermane is the main product. A plausible explanation is the intermediate formation of triphenylgermyllithium. If the conditions described cause the formation of triphenylgermyllithium then in this case germanium may be acting more like carbon than like silicon (106b). Triphenylgermyllithium couples readily with triphenylgermane to give hexaphenyldigermane (57). Tetraphenylsilane is the main product from the analogous reaction in the silicon series (see p. 295).

Triphenylsilyllithium metalated triphenylgermane to give triphenylsilane (76 per cent), and triphenylgermanecarboxylic acid (66.5 per cent) after carbonation (185). This marked case of metalation is consistent with the position of germanium above hydrogen in the electronegativity series (142).

$$(C_6H_5)_3SiLi + (C_6H_5)_3GeH \xrightarrow{(CO_2,H_2O)} (C_6H_5)_3GeCOOH + (C_6H_5)_3SiH$$

Germylmetallic compounds have been prepared from germyl halides. Trialkylgermyl halides react with alkali metals to form digermanes, possibly through intermediary germylmetallic compounds. Thus chlorotriethylgermane on reaction with lithium in ether gives hexaethyldigermane in a 60.2 per cent yield (*103*), whereas the yield in tetrahydrofuran was only 16.8 per cent (*103*). Hexamethyldigermane and hexaethyldigermane were prepared by heating the corresponding bromogermanes and alkali metals without solvent at 210° (*23,119,134*). When liquid ammonia was used as a solvent triethylgermylsodium could be prepared, but a rapid reaction with the solvent resulted in the formation of bis-(triethylgermyl)-amine (*119*). When ethylamine was used as the solvent both bromo- and chlorotriphenylgermane reacted with lithium to give the germylmetallic compound, whereas fluorotriphenylgermane formed hexaphenyldigermane (*119*). Bromotriphenylgermane reacted readily with lithium in tetrahydrofuran to produce triphenylgermyllithium (*40b*).

Triphenylgermylsodium reacts with oxygen in liquid ammonia to give sodium triphenylgermanolate (*120*). The reaction of bromine with triphenylgermyllithium in ethylene glycol dimethyl ether at −20° caused the formation of small amounts of bromotriphenylgermane in addition to larger amounts of hexaphenyldigermane (*60*). The hexaphenyldigermane was presumably formed from the coupling of triphenylgermyllithium with bromotriphenylgermane.

$$(C_6H_5)_3GeLi + Br_2 \longrightarrow (C_6H_5)_3GeBr + LiBr$$

$$(C_6H_5)_3GeBr + (C_6H_5)_3GeLi \longrightarrow (C_6H_5)_3GeGe(C_6H_5)_3$$

Triethylgermyllithium reacted with ammonium bromide to give triethylgermane (*119*). Addition of water to triethylgermyllithium also produced triethylgermane (*120*).

Triphenylgermyllithium was found to be a metalating agent of intermediate strength. Fluorene underwent metalation in ethylene glycol dimethyl ether to give a 69 per cent yield of 9-fluorenylcarboxylic acid subsequent to carbonation (*60*), whereas dibenzofuran was not metalated (*60*). Phenyllithium gives a 78 per cent yield of 9-fluorenylcarboxylic acid under similar conditions (*42,135*).

The cleavage of germanium-carbon bonds has been discussed in relation to the preparation of germylmetallic compounds. In addition to these cleavages by metal it was found that triphenylgermyllithium reacted with methyl triphenylgermanecarboxylate to give hexaphenyldigermane by cleavage of a germanium-carbon bond (*54*).

$$(C_6H_5)_3GeCOOCH_3 + (C_6H_5)_3GeLi \longrightarrow (C_6H_5)_3GeGe(C_6H_5)_3 + CO + CH_3OLi$$

Ethyl carbonate reacted with triphenylgermyllithium in an analogous way to give a large yield of hexaphenyldigermane.

$$(C_6H_5)_3GeLi + (C_2H_5O)_2CO \longrightarrow (C_6H_5)_3GeCOOC_2H_5 + C_2H_5OLi$$

$$(C_6H_5)_3GeLi + (C_6H_5)_3GeCOOC_2H_5 \longrightarrow (C_6H_5)_3GeGe(C_6H_5)_3 + CO + C_2H_5OLi$$

The silicon-tin bond in triphenylsilyltriphenyltin was not cleaved by triphenylgermyllithium (*104,125*).

Germylmetallic compounds react with epoxides in the same way as do silylmetallic compounds (*45*). Thus triphenylgermyllithium reacted with ethylene oxide, propylene oxide, cyclohexene oxide, and styrene oxide to give the corresponding alcohols containing *beta*-triphenylgermyl groups. Trimethylene oxide reacted with triphenylgermyllithium to give 3-triphenylgermylpropanol-1 (*42*), whereas tetrahydrofuran and 1,4-dioxane did not react under normal conditions (*42*).

Triphenylgermyllithium reacted with *n*-octadecyl bromide to give a 70 per cent yield of *n*-octadecyltriphenylgermane (*62*) and apparently no hexaphenyldigermane, indicating that little halogen-metal interconversion had occurred in contrast to the corresponding organosilyllithium type (see Table 6.3, Nos. 47 and 52). Benzyl chloride reacted with triphenylgermylpotassium to produce a low yield of benzyltriphenylgermane and a trace of tetraphenylgermane (*42*). Bromobenzene was found to enter into halogen-metal interconversion when allowed to react with triphenylgermylsodium (*120*) as evidenced by the isolation of a small amount of hexaphenyldigermane.

Chlorosilanes couple with germylmetallic reagents. Thus, from triphenylgermylsodium and trichlorosilane there was isolated tris-(triphenylgermyl)-silane (*133*).

$$3(C_6H_5)_3GeNa + HSiCl_3 \longrightarrow [(C_6H_5)_3Ge]_3SiH + 3 NaCl$$

From silicon tetrachloride and triphenylgermylsodium there were obtained hexaphenyldigermane and a compound purported to be tetrakis-(triphenylgermyl)-silicoethylene (*133*). The presence of a silicon to silicon double bond has not been rigorously established.

Triphenylsilyltriphenylgermane has been prepared from the reaction of triphenylsilylpotassium with chlorotriphenylgermane or.bromotriphenylgermane (*58*). The same compound could, however, not be obtained in satisfactory yield from the reaction of triphenylgermylpotassium with chlorotriphenylsilane (*58*). A halogen-metal interconversion reaction between triphenylchlorosilane and the germylpotassium compound may account for the failure to isolate anything but a mixture of hexaphenyldigermane and hexaphenyldisilane from the reaction. When two moles of triphenylsilyllithium are allowed to react with one mole of hexaphenyldigermane only hexaphenyldisilane and triphenylgermane were isolated (*125*). Similarly, triphenylsilyl-triphenylgermane was cleaved by triphenylsilyllithium (*37*).

$$(C_6H_5)_3GeGe(C_6H_5)_3 + (C_6H_5)_3SiLi \longrightarrow (C_6H_5)_3GeSi(C_6H_5)_3 + (C_6H_5)_3GeLi$$

$$(C_6H_5)_3GeSi(C_6H_5)_3 + (C_6H_5)_3SiLi \longrightarrow (C_6H_5)_3SiSi(C_6H_5)_3 + (C_6H_5)_3GeLi$$

Triphenylgermylpotassium and triphenylgermyllithium add to 1,1-diphenylethylene (*59*) in a manner analogous to the reaction observed for the organosilylmetallic compounds (*179*). In contrast to this it was found that the germylmetallic compounds did not add to *trans*-stilbene in the manner of triphenylsilylpotassium (*167*) or triphenylsilyllithium (*21*). Addition occurred between *n*-octadecene-1 and triphenylgermyllithium to give *n*-octadecyltriphenylgermane. However, neither triphenylgermyllithium nor triphenylsilylmetallic compounds add to octene-1 or cyclohexene (*59, 179*). Triphenylgermyllithium did add normally, however, to azoxybenzene (*154*) and azobenzene (*42*).

The reactions of triphenylgermyllithium with formaldehyde (*56*) or acetaldehyde (*42*) are analogous to the comparable reactions of triphenylsilylpotassium (*91*). Most interesting was the observation that triphenylgermyllithium reacted with benzophenone to give triphenylgermyldiphenylcarbinol (*56*), whereas triphenylsilylmetallic compounds gave exclusively the rearranged product.

$$(C_6H_5)_3GeLi + (C_6H_5)_2C{=}O \xrightarrow{(H_2O)} (C_6H_5)_3Ge(C_6H_5)_2CHOH$$

Thus in this particular reaction the germylmetallic compound reacts differently from both the carbon analog, triphenylmethylmagnesiumbromide, which gives benzopinacol (*3*); or triphenylmethylsodium which gives a ketyl (*143*); or organosilylmetallic compounds which give benzhydryloxy-triphenylsilane.

Benzophenone anil reacts with triphenylgermyllithium to give an unidentified product (*42*). The compound may be N-(triphenylgermyldiphenylmethyl)-aniline, the type of product obtained from phenyllithium and benzophenone anil (*53,69*).

$$(C_6H_5)_3GeLi + (C_6H_5)_2C{=}NC_6H_5 \xrightarrow{(H_2O)} (C_6H_5)_3Ge(C_6H_5)_2C\underset{\underset{H}{|}}{N}(C_6H_5)$$

REACTIVITY OF ORGANOSILYLMETALLIC COMPOUNDS

The high reactivity of organosilylmetallic compounds has been demonstrated throughout this chapter. Organosilylmetallic compounds are considered to be as significant for organosilicon chemistry as organometallic compounds are for carbon chemistry. Some tentative formulations concerning relative reactivities of such types have been proposed.

Cleavage of some substituted ethanes occurs more readily than the corresponding cleavages of disilanes. Hexaphenylethane is cleaved readily by metals to form the triphenylmethylmetallic compounds, whereas the comparable silicon compound, hexaphenyldisilane, requires somewhat more forcing conditions. The ease of cleavage of substituted ethane molecules by metals decreases as the number of aryl substituents decreases. For example, hexaphenylethane undergoes cleavage much more readily than sym-tetraphenylethane, and 1,2-diphenylethane is resistant towards cleavage by metals (141,182). The ease of cleavage of disilanes appears to follow a similar order. Thus, hexaphenyldisilane despite its low solubility in tetrahydrofuran (71), reacts with lithium to form triphenylsilyllithium. Sym-tetraphenyldisilane undergoes cleavage much less readily under similar conditions (151). The complete reaction of sym-dimethyltetraphenyldisilane with lithium in tetrahydrofuran appears slightly slower than the reaction of hexaphenyldisilane, and sym-tetramethyldiphenyldisilane reacts by far the slowest of the three (71). Hexamethyldisilane resisted cleavage by metals entirely (67).

The relative reactivities of the various substituted ethanes and disilanes towards alkali metals are readily rationalized if the resonance stabilities of the anions formed are considered the driving forces of these reactions. Thus, the following order of decreasing resonance stability parallels the decreasing ease with which these are formed from the respective disilanes.

$$(C_6H_5)_3Si^-, (C_6H_5)_2CH_3Si^-, C_6H_5(CH_3)_2Si^-, (CH_3)_3Si^-$$

Decreased stability often causes increased reactivity and the above series may also be looked upon as a series of ions with increasing relative reactivity. This was indeed the order of reactivity observed in the cleavage of various disilanes by different organosilylmetallic compounds (see p. 292).

Only a few attempts have been made to place triphenylsilylmetallic compounds in a proton affinity scale such as that proposed for metalations involving organometallic anions (26,128). The anions of several organoalkali compounds have been arranged in a series of decreasing proton affinity:

$$n\text{-}C_4H_9^-, C_6H_5^-, C_6H_5CH_2^-, (C_6H_5)_2CH^-, (C_6H_5)_3C^-, C_6H_5NH^-, RO^-$$

This series indicates that an anion will metalate the conjugate acid of an anion below it, but not the conjugate acid of an anion above it. For example, benzylpotassium will metalate diphenylmethane but not benzene. It has been shown that triphenylsilylpotassium metalates triphenylmethane to give triphenylmethylpotassium (*17*). Thus, the anion of the silylmetallic compound should appear above the triphenylmethyl anion. Organosilylmetallic compounds are relatively stable in ether or tetrahydrofuran which indicates a position below the butyl anion.

If one considers the anions of the other Group IV-B elements, then the relative proton affinities within the Group appear to follow the decreasing order:

$$(C_6H_5)_3Si^-, (C_6H_5)_3Ge^-, (C_6H_5)_3Sn^-, (C_6H_5)_3Pb$$

It has been found, for example, that triphenylsilyllithium metalates triphenylgermane (*185*). All the above ions abstract a proton from fluorene (*29,60,95,127,175*), indicating proton affinities above the fluorenyl anion (which is probably between the triphenylmethyl and the diphenylmethyl anion). Triphenylgermane has been metalated by *n*-butyllithium and phenyllithium which might further indicate the position of the triphenylsilyl anion between phenyl and triphenylmethyl anions on the relative proton affinity scale. However, there is an inherent difficulty in placing the silylmetallic reagent more accurately since it has not been possible to metalate triphenylsilane, the conjugate acid of the triphenylsilyl anion. Alkyl- and arylmetallic compounds couple with silanes. This coupling involves displacement of a hydride ion from the silicon atom and not the transfer of a proton (*8,94,185*). This difference between carbon and silicon chemistry may be rationalized from the position of silicon below hydrogen and carbon above hydrogen on the electronegativity scale (*142*), which would make the hydrogen-silicon bond polarized with the negative end of the dipole towards the hydrogen whereas the hydrogen-carbon bond is polarized in the opposite direction.

The relative reactivity of some organometallic and organosilylmetallic compounds has recently been demonstrated. It was observed that triphenylsilyllithium reacted faster than *n*-butyllithium with chlorotriphenylsilane in a competitive reaction (*158*). Similarly triphenylsilyllithium coupled with chlorotriphenylsilane much more readily than did phenyllithium (*171*).

However, phenyllithium reacts more readily with triphenylsilane than does triphenylsilyllithium. This order of reactivity, the reverse of that observed for chlorosilanes, was established from the reaction of a 1 : 1 mixture of phenyllithium and triphenylsilyllithium with triphenylsilane (*151*). The relative reactivity of phenyllithium and triphenylsilyllithium is thus dependent on the nature of the reactant.

Competitive reactions between silylmetallic reagents and various functional groups have been carried out in a preliminary search for a correlation between the reactivity of the silylmetallic compound and the type of reaction involved. The reaction of triphenylsilyllithium with RX compounds produces hexaphenyldisilane from a secondary coupling reaction (44). Since hexaphenyldisilane is insoluble in most organic solvents and, as a result, is very easy to isolate in excellent reproducible yields, the formation of this product from a competitive reaction of triphenylsilyllithium with a functional compound and an organic halide has been used as an indication of the relative reactivity of the functional group. A typical example is the competitive reaction of triphenylsilyllithium with chlorobenzene and benzophenone.

$$(C_6H_5)_3SiLi + C_6H_5Cl + C_6H_5COC_6H_5 \longrightarrow (C_6H_5)_4Si +$$
$$2.68\%$$

$$(C_6H_5)_6Si_2 + (C_6H_5)_2CHOSi(C_6H_5)_3$$
$$14.3\% \qquad 27.2\%$$

Chlorobenzene reacts with triphenylsilyllithium under identical conditions to give a 51–53 per cent yield of hexaphenyldisilane. From the yields indicated in the equation it may be concluded that the keto group in benzophenone reacted more readily than the chlorine atom in chlorobenzene. A number of reactions of similar nature was carried out. The results of these competitive reactions (1,11,158) indicate the following order of decreasing reactivity towards triphenylsilyllithium:

$$(CH_3)_3PO_4, C_6H_5CH\!\!-\!\!CH_2, (C_6H_5)_2C\!\!=\!\!O, C_6H_5Cl, n\text{-}C_8H_{17}F, C_6H_5OCH_3$$
$$\diagdown\!\!O\!\!\diagup$$

Thus, triphenylsilyllithium reacted with a 1 : 1 mixture of trimethyl phosphate and styrene oxide to give methyltriphenylsilane (46 per cent) and 1-phenyl-2-triphenylsilylethanol-1 (15.75 per cent) (158). From a similar reaction with chlorobenzene and styrene oxide there was isolated 1-phenyl-2-triphenylsilylethanol-1 (43.3 per cent) but no hexaphenyldisilane (158). The lower reactivity of chlorobenzene compared to trimethyl phosphate was established by a competitive reaction with triphenylsilyllithium. From this reaction there was obtained a 65.3 per cent yield of methyltriphenylsilane, but no hexaphenyldisilane. An equimolar mixture of n-octyl fluoride and chlorobenzene reacted with triphenylsilyllithium to give a mixture of hexaphenyldisilane (25 per cent), n-octyltriphenylsilane (27.4 per cent), and tetraphenylsilane (17.9 per cent) (158). From the result given in Table 6.5, No. 7, it may be concluded that chlorobenzene reacted faster than n-octyl fluoride. Triphenylsilyllithium reacted with p-chloroanisole to give hexaphenyldisilane (40.7 per cent), p-triphenylsilylanisole (5.73 per cent), and triphenylsilanol (6.5 per cent) (158). This indicates the greater reactivity of chlorine over that of methoxyl attached to phenyl. From the reaction of triphenylsilyllithium with an equimolar mixture of chlorobenzene and anisole was isolated hexaphenyldisilane (51 per cent), tetraphenylsilane (11.56 per cent), and triphenylsilanol (1.45 per cent) (*158*). Again comparing this result with those obtained from chlorobenzene (Table 6.5, Nos. 7,8) it is evident that chlorobenzene is much more reactive than is anisole.

The apparent lack of selectivity in the rapid reaction of triphenylsilyllithium with a mixture of chlorodimethylphenylsilane and chlorotriphenylsilane is evident from the isolation of both hexaphenyldisilane (33 per cent) and 1,1-dimethyl-1,2,2,2-tetraphenyldisilane (40 per cent) (*171*). The somewhat larger yield of coupling product with chlorodimethylphenylsilane may indicate a more rapid reaction with the silylmetallic reagent. A competitive reaction between chlorodimethylphenylsilane and a 1 : 1 mixture of triphenylsilyllithium and dimethylphenylsilyllithium indicates that the latter reagent reacts more readily (*71*). The interpretation of this result is obscured by the possible cleavage of the disilane by the excess silyllithium compound.

In addition reactions the following decreasing series of activity of the triphenyl-metallic derivatives of Group IV-B elements appears to agree with the experimental results:

$$(C_6H_5)_3SiM, (C_6H_5)_3GeM, (C_6H_5)_3SnM, (C_6H_5)_3PbM$$

On the basis of addition reactions to the olefinic linkage, the reactivities of the silyl- and the germylmetallic compounds seem to be comparable with that of α,α-dimethylbenzylpotassium (*181*). Steric effects as well as differences in electron-distribution in the bond between the metal and the Group IV-B element, seem to be responsible for the specific differences observed in some of their additive reactions.

Organometallic compounds containing the metal linked to a Group IV-B element react with alkyl and aryl halides by coupling or halogen-metal interconversion. Halogen-metal interconversions have been used for synthetic purposes in carbon chemistry. Alkyllithium reagents convert aryl bromides and iodides into aryllithium compounds. Aryllithium reagents show interconversions with benzyl type halides, as well as with aryl iodides. Germylmetallic compounds do not appear to enter into halogen-metal interconversion to nearly the same extent as do silylmetallic reagents even though stannylmetallic compounds have been shown to undergo halogen-metal interconversion with certain aryl iodides (*81*). Organosilylmetallic compounds, however, give interconversion products not only with aryl bromides and iodides, but also with aryl chlorides, alkyl bromides, and alkyl iodides.

The relatively high reactivity of the silylmetallic compounds may be rationalized from bond energies. Despite the fact that silicon-hydrogen and silicon-carbon bonds are slightly weaker than carbon-hydrogen and carbon-carbon bonds, silicon forms stronger bonds than carbon with electronegative elements such as O, N, F, Cl, Br, and I (*52*). It has been demonstrated that the triphenylsilyl radical readily abstracts a chlorine radical from chlorobenzene (*28*). The same tendency of silicon to combine with electronegative elements may give rise to halogen-metal interconversion when organosilylmetallic compounds are allowed to react with organic halides.

Acknowledgment

The authors are grateful for assistance from G. M. Dappen, A. W. P. Jarvie, G. D. Lichtenwalter, O. L. Marrs, W. J. Trepka, D. Wittenberg and E. A. Zuech. Part of the experimental work was supported by the U. S. Air Force under Contract AF 33(616)-3510 monitored by Materials Laboratory, Directorate of Laboratories, Wright Air Development Center, Wright-Patterson AFB, Ohio.

References

(1) Aoki, D., unpublished studies.

(2) Aylett, B. J., Ph.D. Thesis, Cambridge (1954).

(3) Bachmann, W. E., *J. Am. Chem. Soc.*, **53**, 2758 (1931).

(4) Benkeser, R. A., and Foster, D. J., *J. Am. Chem. Soc.*, **74**, 4200 (1952).

(5) Benkeser, R. A., and Foster, D. J., *J. Am. Chem. Soc.*, **74**, 5314 (1952).

(6) Benkeser, R. A., and Holton, D. S., *J. Am. Chem. Soc.*, **73**, 5861 (1951).

(7) Benkeser, R. A., Landesman, H., and Foster, D. J., *J. Am. Chem. Soc.*, **74**, 648 (1952).

(8) Benkeser, R. A., and Riel, F. J., *J. Am. Chem. Soc.*, **73**, 3472 (1951).

(9) Benkeser, R. A., Robinson, R. E., and Landesman, H., *J. Am. Chem. Soc.*, **74**, 5699 (1952).

(10) Benkeser, R. A., and Severson, R. G., *J. Am. Chem. Soc.*, **73**, 1424 (1951).

(11) Brook, A. G., *J. Am. Chem. Soc.*, **79**, 1431 (1957).

(12) Brook, A. G., *J. Am. Chem. Soc.*, **79**, 4373 (1957).

(13) Brook, A. G., *J. Am. Chem. Soc.*, **80**, 1886 (1958).

(13a) Brook, A. G., and Gilman, H., *J. Am. Chem. Soc.*, **76**, 77 (1954).

(14) Brook, A. G., and Gilman, H., *J. Am. Chem. Soc.*, **76**, 278 (1954).

(15) Brook, A. G., and Gilman, H., *J. Am. Chem. Soc.*, **76**, 2333 (1954).

(16) Brook, A. G., and Gilman, H., *J. Am. Chem. Soc.*, **77**, 2322 (1955).

(17) Brook, A. G., Gilman, H., and Miller, L. S., *J. Am. Chem. Soc.*, **75**, 4759 (1953).

(18) Brook, A. G., and Mauris, R. J., *J. Am. Chem. Soc.*, **79**, 971 (1957).

(19) Brook, A. G., and Miller, L. S., *J. Am. Chem. Soc.*, **75**, 4531 (1953).

(20) Brook, A. G., and Schwartz, N. V., *J. Am. Chem. Soc.*, **82**, 2435 (1960).

(21) Brook, A. G., Tai, K. M., and Gilman, H., *J. Am. Chem. Soc.*, **77**, 6919 (1955).

(22) Brook, A. G., Warner, C. M., and McGriskin, M. E., *J. Am. Chem. Soc.*, **81,** 981 (1959).
(23) Brown, M. P., and Fowles, G. W. A., *J. Chem. Soc.*, 2811 (1958).
(24) Bygden, A., *Ber.*, **45,** 707 (1912).
(25) Bygden, A., *Ber.*, **48,** 1236 (1915).
(26) Conant, J. B., and Wheland, G. W., *J. Am. Chem. Soc.*, **54,** 1212 (1932).
(27) Cristol, S. J., Douglass, J. R., and Meek, J. S., *J. Am. Chem. Soc.*, **73,** 816 (1951).
(28) Curtice, J., Gilman, H., and Hammond, G. S., *J. Am. Chem. Soc.*, **79,** 4754 (1957).
(29) D'Ans, J., Zimmer, H., Endrulat, E., and Lübke, K., *Naturwissenschaften*, **39,** 450 (1952).
(30) Dappen, G. M., unpublished studies.
(31) Diehl, J. W., unpublished studies.
(32) Eaborn, C., *J. Chem. Soc.,* 2755 (1949).
(33) Emeléus, H. J., Maddock, A. G., and Reid, C., *J. Chem. Soc.,* 353 (1941).
(34) Fuson, R. C., Lokken, R. J., and Pedrotti, R. L., *J. Am. Chem. Soc.*, **78,** 6064 (1956).
(35) Gaj, B. J., unpublished studies.
(36) Gaylord, N. G., and Becker, E. I., *Chem. Reviews*, **49,** 413 (1951).
(37) George, M. V., unpublished studies.
(38) George, M. V., Gaj, B. J., and Gilman, H., *J. Org. Chem.*, **24,** 624 (1959).
(39) George, M. V., and Gilman, H., *J. Am. Chem. Soc.*, **81,** 3288 (1959).
(40a) George, M. V., Lichtenwalter, G. D., and Gilman, H., *J. Am. Chem. Soc.*, **81,** 978 (1959).
(40b) George, M. V., Peterson, D. J., and Gilman, H., *J. Am. Chem. Soc.*, **82,** 403 (1960).
(41) George, M. V., Wittenberg, D., and Gilman, H., *J. Am. Chem. Soc.*, **81,** 361 (1959).
(42) Gerow, C. W., unpublished studies.
(43) Gerow, C. W., and Hughes, M. B., unpublished studies.
(44) Gilman, H., and Aoki, D., *J. Org. Chem.*, **24,** 426 (1959).
(45) Gilman, H., Aoki, D., and Wittenberg, D., *J. Am. Chem. Soc.*, **81,** 1107 (1959).
(46) Gilman, H., Beel, J. A., Brannen, C. G., Bullock, M. W., Dunn, G. E., and Miller, L. S., *J. Am. Chem. Soc.,* **71,** 1499 (1949); see also Beel, J. A., *et al., J. Org. Chem.,* **24,** 2036 (1959).
(47) Gilman, H., Benedict, H. N., Hartzfeld, H., *J. Org. Chem.*, **19,** 419 (1954).
(48) Gilman, H., Benkeser, R. A., and Dunn, G. E., *J. Am. Chem. Soc.*, **72,** 1689 (1950).
(49) Gilman, H., and Brook, A. G., *J. Am. Chem. Soc.*, **76,** 2338 (1954).
(50) Gilman, H., Brown, G. E., Webb, F. J., and Spatz, S. M., *J. Am. Chem. Soc.*, **62,** 977 (1940).
(51) Gilman, H., and Dunn, G. E., *J. Am. Chem. Soc.*, **73,** 5077 (1951).
(52) Gilman, H., and Dunn, G. E., *Chem. Reviews*, **52,** 77 (1953).
(53) Gilman, H., Eisch, J., and Soddy, T. S., *J. Am. Chem. Soc.*, **79,** 1245 (1957).
(54) Gilman, H., and Gerow, C. W., *J. Am. Chem. Soc.,* **77,** 4675 (1955).

(55) Gilman, H., and Gerow, C. W., *J. Am. Chem. Soc.*, **77,** 5509 (1955).

(56) Gilman, H., and Gerow, C. W., *J. Am. Chem. Soc.*, **77,** 5740 (1955).

(57) Gilman, H., and Gerow, C. W., *J. Am. Chem. Soc.*, **78,** 5435 (1956).

(58) Gilman, H., and Gerow, C. W., *J. Am. Chem. Soc.*, **78,** 5823 (1956).

(59) Gilman, H., and Gerow, C. W., *J. Am. Chem. Soc.*, **79,** 342 (1957).

(60) Gilman, H., and Gerow, C. W., *J. Org. Chem.*, **23,** 1582 (1958).

(61) Gilman, H., and Goodman, J. J., *J. Am. Chem. Soc.*, **75,** 1250 (1953).

(62) Gilman, H., and Gorsich, R. D., *J. Am. Chem. Soc.*, **80,** 3243 (1958).

(63) Gilman, H., and Hartzfeld, H., *J. Am. Chem. Soc.*, **73,** 5878 (1951).

(64) Gilman, H., and Haubein, A. H., *J. Am. Chem. Soc.*, **66,** 1515 (1944).

(65) Gilman, H., Hofferth, B., and Honeycutt, J. B., *J. Am. Chem. Soc.*, **74,** 1594 (1952).

(66) Gilman, H., Hofferth, B., Melvin, H. W., and Dunn, G. E., *J. Am. Chem. Soc.*, **72,** 5767 (1950).

(67) Gilman, H., Ingham, R. K., and Smith, A. G., *J. Org. Chem.*, **18,** 1743 (1953).

(68) Gilman, H., Kirby, J. E., and Kinney, C. R., *J. Am. Chem. Soc.*, **51,** 2252 (1929).

(69) Gilman, H., and Kirby, R. H., *J. Am. Chem. Soc.*, **55,** 1265 (1933).

(70) Gilman, H., and Lichtenwalter, G. D., *J. Am. Chem. Soc.*, **80,** 607 (1958).

(71) Gilman, H., and Lichtenwalter, G. D., *J. Am. Chem. Soc.*, **80,** 608 (1958).

(72) Gilman. H., and Lichtenwalter, G. D., *J. Am. Chem. Soc.*, **80,** 2680 (1958).

(73) (a) Gilman, H., and Lichtenwalter, G. D., *J. Org. Chem.*, **23,** 1586 (1958); (b) *J. Org. Chem.*, **24,** 1588 (1959); (c) *J. Am. Chem. Soc.*, **81,** 5320 (1959).

(74) Gilman, H., and Massie, S. P., *J. Am. Chem. Soc.*, **68,** 1128 (1946).

(75) Gilman, H., McNinch, H. A., and Wittenberg, D., *J. Org. Chem.*, **23,** 2044 (1958).

(76) Gilman, H., and Melvin, H. W., *J. Am. Chem. Soc.*, **71,** 4050 (1949).

(77) Gilman, H., and Melvin, H. W., *J. Am. Chem. Soc.*, **72,** 995 (1950).

(78) Gilman, H., Miles, D. H., Moore, L. O., and Gerow, C. W., *J. Org. Chem.*, **24,** 219 (1959).

(79) Gilman, H., and Peterson, D. J., *J. Org. Chem.*, **23,** 1895 (1958).

(80) Gilman, H., Peterson, D. J., and Wittenberg, D., *Chemistry & Industry*, 1479 (1958).

(81) Gilman, H., and Rosenberg, S. D., *J. Org. Chem.*, **18,** 680 (1953).

(82) Gilman, H., and Schulze, F., *J. Am. Chem. Soc.*, **47,** 2002 (1925).

(83) Gilman, H., and Smart, G. N. R., *J. Org. Chem.*, **15,** 720 (1950).

(84) Gilman, H., and Steudel, W., *Chemistry & Industry*, 1094 (1959).

(85a) Gilman, H., and Swiss, J., *J. Am. Chem. Soc.*, **62,** 1847 (1940).

(85b) Gilman, H., and Tomasi, R. A., *J. Am. Chem. Soc.*, **81,** 137 (1959).

(86) Gilman, H., and Wu, T. C., *J. Am. Chem. Soc.*, **73,** 4031 (1951).

(87) Gilman, H., and Wu, T. C., *J. Am. Chem. Soc.*, **75,** 234 (1953).

(88) Gilman, H., and Wu, T. C., *J. Am. Chem. Soc.*, **75,** 2509 (1953).

(89) Gilman, H., and Wu, T. C., *J. Am. Chem. Soc.*, **75,** 2935 (1953).

(90) Gilman, H., and Wu, T. C., *J. Am. Chem. Soc.*, **75,** 3762 (1953).

(91) Gilman, H., and Wu, T. C., *J. Am. Chem. Soc.*, **76,** 2502 (1954).

(92) Gilman, H., and Wu, T. C., *J. Org. Chem.*, **18,** 753 (1953).

(93) Gilman, H., Wu, T. C., Hartzfeld, H. A., Guter, G. A., Smith, A. G., Goodman, J. J., and Eidt, S. H., *J. Am. Chem. Soc.,* **74,** 561 (1952).

(94) Gilman, H., and Zuech, E. A., *J. Am. Chem. Soc.,* **79,** 4560 (1957); *ibid.,* **81,** 5925 (1959).

(95) Gist, L. A., unpublished studies.

(96) Glarum, S. N., and Kraus, C. A., *J. Am. Chem. Soc.,* **72,** 5398 (1950).

(97) Goodman, J. J., unpublished studies.

(98) Gorsich, R. D., unpublished studies.

(99) Harvey, M. C., Nebergall, W. H., and Peake, J. S., *J. Am. Chem. Soc.,* **79,** 1437 (1957).

(100) Haubein, A. H., *Iowa State College J. Sci.,* **18,** 48 (1943).

(101) Hauser, C. R., and Hance, C. R., *J. Am. Chem. Soc.,* **73,** 5846 (1951).

(102) Hofferth, B. F., *Iowa State College J. Sci.,* **26,** 219 (1952).

(103) Hughes, M. B., unpublished studies.

(104) Ingham, R. K., Rosenberg, S. D., and Gilman, H., *Chem. Reviews,* **60,** in press (1960).

(105) Ivanoff, M. D., *Bull. soc. chim. France,* **39,** 47 (1926).

(106a) Johnson, O. H., *Chem. Reviews,* **48,** 259 (1951).

(106b) Johnson, O. H., and Harris, D. H., *J. Am. Chem. Soc.,* **72,** 5566 (1950).

(107) Kipping, F. S., *J. Chem. Soc.,* **119,** 647 (1921).

(108) Kipping, F. S., *J. Chem. Soc.,* **123,** 2590, 2598 (1923).

(109) Kipping, F. S., *J. Chem. Soc.,* **125,** 2291 (1924).

(110) Kipping, F. S., *J. Chem. Soc.,* 2728 (1927).

(111) Kipping, F. S., *Proc. Roy. Soc.,* **A159,** 139 (1937).

(112) Kipping, F. S., and Sands, J. F., *J. Chem. Soc.,* **119,** 830 (1921).

(113) Kipping, F. S., and Short, J. F., *J. Chem. Soc.,* 1029 (1930).

(114) Kipping, F. S., and Steele, A. R., *J. Chem. Soc.,* 1431 (1928).

(115) Knoth, W. H., and Lindsey, R. V., *J. Org. Chem.,* **23,** 1392 (1958).

(116) Krämer, J., unpublished studies.

(117) Kraus, C. A., and Eatough, H., *J. Am. Chem. Soc.,* **55,** 5008 (1933).

(118) Kraus, C. A., and Eatough, H., *J. Am. Chem. Soc.,* **55,** 5014 (1933).

(119) Kraus, C. A., and Flood, F. A., *J. Am. Chem. Soc.,* **54,** 1635 (1932).

(120) Kraus, C. A., and Foster, L. S., *J. Am. Chem. Soc.,* **49,** 457 (1927).

(121) Kraus, C. A., and Kawamura, T., *J. Am. Chem. Soc.,* **45,** 2756 (1923).

(122) Kraus, C. A., and Nelson, W. K., *J. Am. Chem. Soc.,* **56,** 195 (1924).

(123) Kraus, C. A., and Rosen, R., *J. Am. Chem. Soc.,* **47,** 2739 (1925).

(124) Kraus, C. A., and Sessions, W. V., *J. Am. Chem. Soc.,* **47,** 2361 (1925).

(125) Lichtenwalter, G. D., unpublished studies.

(126) MacDiarmid, A. G., *Quart. Reviews,* **10,** 208 (1956).

(127) Marrs, O. L., unpublished studies.

(128) McEwen, W. K., *J. Am. Chem. Soc.,* **58,** 1124 (1936).

(129) McNinch, H. A., unpublished studies.

(130) Meals, R. N., *J. Am. Chem. Soc.,* **68,** 1128 (1946).

(131) Meals, R. N., *J. Am. Chem. Soc.,* **68,** 1880 (1946).

(132) Meen, R. H., and Gilman, H., *J. Org. Chem.,* **20,** 73 (1955).

(133) Milligan, J. G., and Kraus, C. A., *J. Am. Chem. Soc.,* **72,** 5297 (1950).

(134) Morgan, G. T., and Drew, H. D. K., *J. Chem. Soc.*, **127,** 1760 (1925).
(135) Morton, J. W., unpublished studies.
(136) Peterson, D. J., unpublished studies.
(137) Piper, T. S., and Lemal, D., *Naturwissenschaften*, **43,** 129 (1956).
(138) Polis, A., *Ber.*, **18,** 1540 (1885).
(139) Ranck, R., unpublished studies.
(140) Reynolds, H. H., Bigelow, L. A., and Kraus, C. A., *J. Am. Chem. Soc.*, **51,** 3067 (1929).
(141) Runge, F., "Organo-Metallverbindungen," p. 45, Stuttgart, Wissenschaftliche Verlagsges., 1944.
(142) Sanderson, R. T., *J. Chem. Ed.*, **32,** 140 (1955).
(143) Schlenk, W., and Ochs, R., *Ber.*, **49,** 608 (1916).
(144) Schlenk, W., Renning, J., and Racky, G., *Ber.*, **44,** 1178 (1911).
(144a) Schmitz-DuMont, O., and Bungard, G., *Ber.*, **92,** 2399 (1959).
(145) Schumb, W. C., Ackermann, J., and Saffer, C. M., *J. Am. Chem. Soc.*, **60,** 2486 (1938).
(146) Schumb, W. C., and Saffer, C. M., *J. Am. Chem. Soc.*, **61,** 363 (1939).
(147) Schumb, W. C., and Saffer, C. M., *J. Am. Chem. Soc.*, **63,** 93 (1941).
(148) Selin, T. G., and West, R., *Tetrahedron*, **5,** 97 (1959).
(149) Smith, A. G., unpublished studies.
(150) Steele, A. R., and Kipping, F. S., *J. Chem. Soc.*, 1431 (1928).
(151) Steudel, W., unpublished studies.
(152) Stock, A., and Somieski, C., *Ber.*, **52,** 695 (1919).
(153) Tai, K., unpublished studies.
(154) Talukdar, P. B., unpublished studies.
(155) Taurke, F., *Ber.*, **38,** 1661 (1905).
(156) Teal, G. K., and Kraus, C. A., *J. Am. Chem. Soc.*, **72,** 4706 (1950).
(157) Thompson, R. A., and Kipping, F. S., *J. Chem. Soc.*, 1176 (1929).
(158) Trepka, W. J., unpublished studies.
(159) Tushaus, L., unpublished studies.
(160) VanArtsdalen, E. R., and Gavis, J., *J. Am. Chem. Soc.*, **74,** 3196 (1952).
(161) Veer, W. L. C., and Goldschmidt, S., *Rec. trav. chim.*, **65,** 793 (1946).
(162) Walling, C., and Buckler, S. A., *J. Am. Chem. Soc.*, **77,** 6032 (1955).
(163) Winkler, H. J. S., unpublished studies.
(164) Wittenberg, D., Aoki, D., and Gilman, H., *J. Am. Chem. Soc.*, **80,** 5933 (1958).
(165) Wittenberg, D., George, M. V., and Gilman, H., *J. Am. Chem. Soc.*, **81,** 4812 (1959).
(166) Wittenberg, D., George, M. V., Wu, T. C., Miles, D. H., and Gilman, H., *J. Am. Chem. Soc.*, **80,** 4532 (1958).
(167) Wittenberg, D., and Gilman, H., *Chemistry & Industry*, 390 (1958).
(168) Wittenberg, D., and Gilman, H., *J. Am. Chem. Soc.*, **80,** 2677 (1958).
(169) Wittenberg, D., and Gilman, H., *J. Am. Chem. Soc.*, **80,** 4529 (1958).
(170) Wittenberg, D., and Gilman, H., *Quart. Reviews*, **13,** 116 (1959).
(171) Wittenberg, D., and Gilman, H., unpublished studies.

(172) Wittenberg, D., McNinch, H. A., and Gilman, H., *J. Am. Chem. Soc.*, **80,** 5418 (1958).
(173) Wittenberg, D., Wu, T. C., and Gilman, H., *J. Org. Chem.*, **23,** 1898 (1958).
(174) Wittenberg, D., Wu, T. C., and Gilman, H., *J. Org. Chem.*, **24,** 1349 (1959).
(175) Wittig, G., and Löhmann, L., *Ann.*, **550,** 260 (1942).
(176) Wittig, G., and Pohmer, L., *Ber.*, **89,** 1334 (1956).
(177) Wittig, G., and Stahnecker, E., *Ann.*, **605,** 69 (1957).
(178) Wotiz, J. H., and Huba, F., *J. Org. Chem.*, **24,** 595 (1959).
(179) Wu, T. C., unpublished studies.
(180) Wu, T. C., and Gilman, H., *J. Org. Chem.*, **23,** 913 (1958).
(181) Ziegler, K., and Bähr, K., *Ber.*, **61,** 253 (1928).
(182) Ziegler, K., and Thielmann, F., *Ber.*, **56,** 1740 (1923).
(183) Ziegler, K., and Zeiser, A., *Ber.*, **63,** 1847 (1930).
(184) Ziegler, K., and Zeiser, H., *Ann.*, **485,** 174 (1931).
(185) Zuech, E. A., unpublished studies.

7. CYCLOPENTADIENYL METAL COMPOUNDS

P. L. Pauson

Royal College of Science and Technology, Glasgow, Scotland

INTRODUCTION

Hydrocarbon derivatives of transition metals are of two types. Those in which the hydrocarbon is the only ligand and those in which there are other groups directly attached to the metal. Complexes containing carbonyl groups, which are formed by a wide variety of hydrocarbons, are included in Chapter 10. Most others contain aromatic systems; of these, the present chapter deals only with the cyclopentadienyl group which has hitherto been studied most extensively and the following chapter deals with all others. There have been a number of earlier reviews, notably references: (*24,27, 31,115,144,145,179* and *216*).

COMPOUNDS WITH TWO HYDROCARBON LIGANDS

The first of these substances, dicyclopentadienyliron or "ferrocene," (*222*) $(C_5H_5)_2Fe$, was discovered (*87,102*) in 1951 and many analogs have been described since. It is readily obtained from ferrous ion and cyclopentadienide ions. Since the latter contain six π-electrons, ferrocene may be regarded as isoelectronic with bis-benzenechromium. Like the latter (*210*) it possesses a centrosymmetrical structure with the two rings disposed in parallel planes about the central iron atom. Ferrocene crystallizes in the monoclinic space-group $P2_{1/c}$ with two molecules in the unit cell (*23,50*). Hence the metal atom lies at a center of symmetry both within the unit cell and within the molecule (*50,220*). The chromium atom in the cubic crystals of bis-benzenechromium must also constitute a molecular center of symmetry. This leads to the opposed conformation of the rings in the latter (I) and to the staggered conformation (II) in ferrocene, but the analogous dicyclopentadienylruthenium (*75*) (III), and dicyclopentadienylosmium (*83*) have the opposed conformation in their orthorhombic crystals. One reason

I   II   III

for this difference from ferrocene may be the larger size of ruthenium and osmium which reduces the repulsion between hydrogen atoms attached to different rings. In the second and third transition series only these elements (ruthenium (210) and osmium (34)) in the same group as iron have yielded compounds of the type $(C_5H_5)_2M$. In the first transition series such products have been described for all metals from titanium to nickel inclusive and most of these have the same melting point, 173°, as ferrocene and form a series of isomorphous crystals (206–209). With the exception of manganese, whose complex is ionic in character, having a paramagnetic susceptibility corresponding to five unpaired electrons (48,51,95,200,217), they must all be regarded as being bonded like ferrocene. That even the ionic complexes of magnesium and manganese have the same geometrical arrangement is suggested by X-ray data (206,207).

The following are the first row complexes with the number of unpaired electrons (48,51) in each:

$(C_5H_5)_2Ti$ (26)	$(C_5H_5)_2V$ (36)	$(C_5H_5)_2Cr$ (35,212)	$(C_5H_5)_2Mn$ (217)
0(?)	3	2	5

$(C_5H_5)_2Fe$ (220)	$(C_5H_5)_2Co$ (44,218)	$(C_5H_5)_2Ni$ (43,218)
0	1	2

The tendency to acquire a closed inert gas shell of electrons finds expression in the formation of more stable complexes in other valency states by most of these elements. Nevertheless even ferrocene may be oxidized to the ferricinium ion (50,220), $(C_5H_5)_2Fe^+$, which has one unpaired electron and though much less stable than the parent compound, retains stability to air and water. Cobalt can attain inert gas configuration of electrons in the analogous dicyclopentadienylcobalt(III) ion (42,211), $(C_5H_5)_2Co^+$, and the redox potential of −1.16V of this ion reflects the strong tendency of the metal atom to remain in this favored state. This "cobalticinium ion" is thus isoelectronic with ferrocene and at least as stable. Rhodium and iridium form analogous ions (20). Attempts to reduce the cobalticinium ion back to the neutral compound, e.g., with sodium borohydride, lead instead to another type of substance, cyclopentadienylcobalt(I)-cyclopentadiene (IV; M = Co; R = H), by addition of hydride to one of the rings (67). Here only one of the rings retains its symmetrical (and aromatic) character, the other being linked to cobalt by dative π-bonds from the two conjugated double bonds; but the E.A.N. of krypton is retained in this complex. The related (67) trichloromethyl derivative (IV; M = Co; R = CCl_3) is formed (85) in a remarkable reaction between dicyclopentadienylcobalt(II) and carbon tetrachloride:

$$(C_5H_5)_2Co + CCl_4 \longrightarrow C_5H_5CoC_5H_5CCl_3 + (C_5H_5)_2Co^+Cl^-.$$

The rhodium and iridium analogs, $C_5H_5RhC_5H_6$ (IV; M = Rh; R = H) and $C_5H_5IrC_5H_6$ (IV; M = Ir; R = H) have been obtained (62) directly from the metal(III) chlorides and cyclopentadienylsodium; they react with acids to give hydrogen and dicyclopentadienylrhodium(III), viz. iridium-(III) salts. The closely related cyclopentadienylrhodium-cyclooctadiene, (V), was prepared from di[cyclooctadienerhodium chloride] with cyclopentadienylsodium (16,17).

An intermediate type of complex is represented by the cyclopentadienyl-cobalt-cyclopentadienone type (VI) which must be regarded as a resonance hybrid of a structure analogous to (IV) and the ionic form whose conjugate acid is a hydroxycobalticinium ion (99).

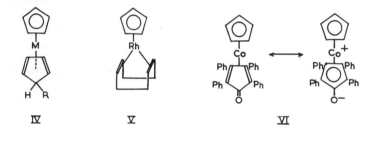

Dicyclopentadienylnickel, in which, as in the cobalt analog, the unpaired electrons are in excess of the E.A.N. of krypton, can likewise be oxidized, but again only to a unipositive cation, $C_{10}H_{10}Ni^+$, which still retains one unpaired electron (43,218). The only related diamagnetic purely hydrocarbon nickel complexes known are dicyclopentadienenickel, (VII), analogous to and isoelectronic with (IV), and obtained directly from cyclopentadiene and nickel carbonyl under mild conditions (60), and the dimeric cyclopentadienylnickel acetylene complexes, e.g., (VIII), obtained from dicyclopentadienylnickel (22a) or from di(cyclopentadienylnickel carbonyl (195) (p. 351). The bonding of the acetylene in this compound (VIII) is believed to be analogous to that in dicobalt hexacarbonyl-acetylene.

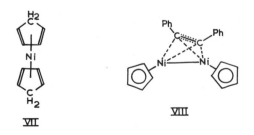

The elements preceding iron give dicyclopentadienyl derivatives which do not quite reach the ideal E.A.N. They may however be able to attain it by addition of further ligands.

The manganese dicyclopentadienyl, though ionic, would only be one electron short of an inert gas shell if covalent. Although such covalent dicyclopentadienyl manganese derivatives are unknown, a single covalently bonded cyclopentadiene gives stable complexes with Mn(I) if other ligands supply six electrons as in methylcyclopentadienyl-benzene-manganese (*cf.* Chapter 8) and in cyclopentadienylmanganese tricarbonyl, (XIX). By reaction with cyclopentadienylsodium, rhenium salts do not form an analog of dicyclopentadienylmanganese, but afford instead the hydride, (IX), thus attaining a stable diamagnetic structure (*215*). This compound (IX) behaves neither as a hydride capable of yielding hydride ions nor (like the carbonyl hydrides) as an acid (*66,215*). It does, however, behave as a base, reacting with acids to give the more symmetrical protonated ion (IXa). Treatment of the hydride (IX) with carbon monoxide (*61*) results in

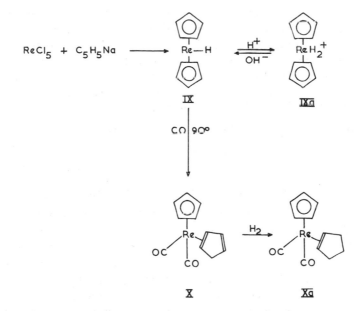

transfer of the hydrogen atom to one of the rings which is bonded only through one double bond to the metal in the product (X). The chief evidence for this structure (*69*) comes from nuclear magnetic resonance data and from hydrogenation to the dihydro derivative (Xa).

In Group VI, molybdenum, but not chromium, can form stable diamagnetic dicyclopentadienyl dihalides (*21*) with closed outer electron shells,

$(C_5H_5)_2MoX_2$ (X = halogen), and the corresponding dihydrides of molybdenum (X = H) and tungsten, analogous to (IX) have recently been described (41a,68).

Niobium(V) and tantalum similarly form the trihalides, $(C_5H_5)_2NbX_3$ and $(C_5H_5)_2TaX_3$, although vanadium only reaches oxidation state four in $(C_5H_5)_2VCl_2$ with one unpaired electron (214). Titanium also forms very stable halides, $(C_5H_5)_2TiX_2$, and zirconium forms the analogous $(C_5H_5)_2$-$ZrCl_2$ (214). Though having only 34 electrons around the titanium or zirconium atom the electrons in the outer shell are all bonding electrons, so that these compounds are necessarily diamagnetic; moreover the metal is in its preferred oxidation state, four. A less stable dicyclopentadienyltitanium(III) chloride has been described (107).*

The mixed benzene and cycloheptatrienyl- cyclopentadienyl complexes, e.g., $C_5H_5CrC_6H_6$ and $CH_3C_5H_4MnC_6H_6$ are dealt with in Chapter 8.

COMPOUNDS WITH ONE HYDROCARBON LIGAND

The cyclopentadienyl metal halides should be intermediate in the formation of the dicyclopentadienyl derivatives from cyclopentadienylsodium and the metal halide. Only in the cases of titanium and zirconium has this been demonstrated (183) by isolation of $C_5H_5TiCl_3$, viz. $C_5H_5ZrCl_3$. A more practicable synthesis (64) is achieved by carrying the reaction to completion with two equivalents of cyclopentadienylsodium and then heating the resultant dihalide with titanium tetrachloride:

$$(C_5H_5)_2TiCl_2 + TiCl_4 \longrightarrow 2 C_5H_5TiCl_3$$

Related compounds have been obtained starting, for example, from dibutoxytitanium dichloride (82):

$$(BuO)_2TiCl_2 + C_5H_5{}^- \longrightarrow C_5H_5Ti(OBu)_2Cl$$

Chromium has yielded a compound (191) of the formula, $C_5H_5Cr(CH_3-COCHCOCH_3)Br$, by the reaction of chromium acetylacetonate with one mole of cyclopentadienylsodium followed by hydrogen bromide. Treatment of the crude reaction mixture from cyclopentadienylsodium and chromic chloride with nitric oxide affords cyclopentadienylchromiumdinitrosochloride, (XI) (158). It has not been established with what immediate precursor the nitric oxide reacts. The most likely intermediates would appear to be cyclopentadienylchromium(II) chloride or dicyclopentadienylchromium(III) chloride. If the latter is involved, a displacement of one of the cyclopentadienyl residues occurs. Such a reaction with dicyclopentadienylnickel leads to cyclopentadienyl nickel nitrosyl (29,148)

---

*The corresponding tricyclopentadienyl $(C_5H_5)_3Ti$ has now been obtained as a green, paramagnetic, sublimable solid (48a).

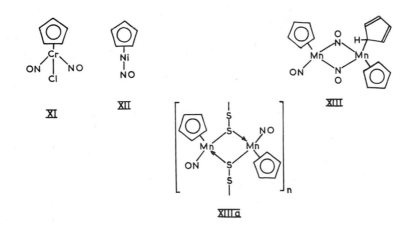

(XII), and dicyclopentadienylmanganese affords a product for which a formulation such as (XIII) has been suggested (*153*) and which is converted by sulfur to a cyclopentadienylmanganese nitrosyl disulfide polymer formulated as (XIIIa) (*155*).

Carbon monoxide replaces one cyclopentadiene group similarly from the dicyclopentadienyls of vanadium, chromium, manganese and cobalt. Ferrocene is too stable to react in this fashion, but all the iron carbonyls react readily with cyclopentadiene at 135° and the mixed dicyclopentadienyldi-iron tetracarbonyl (XXI) so formed (*73,148*) reacts further to give ferrocene only near 200°. The cyclopentadienylcobalt- and chromium carbonyls are likewise accessible from the metal carbonyl. Table 7.1 lists the mixed carbonyl complexes obtained by such methods. The manganese compound (*45,148*), (XIX), is the most stable of these and although it can be formed from dicyclopentadienylmanganese or (less readily) from manganese carbonyl (*25*) with carbon monoxide or cyclopentadiene, respectively, it does not appear to react further with either of these reagents. On the other hand, for cobalt we can write the complete series of equilibria:

$$Co_2(CO)_8 \underset{CO}{\overset{C_5H_6}{\rightleftarrows}} C_5H_5Co(CO)_2 \underset{CO}{\overset{C_5H_6}{\rightleftarrows}} (C_5H_5)_2Co$$
$$XXII$$

A similar situation applies to chromium. The hydrogen atoms eliminated from cyclopentadiene are not evolved as such, but reduce part of this hydrocarbon to cyclopentene (*cf.* Chapter 10). The dicyclopentadienyldinickel dicarbonyl (XXIII) is obtained (*49*) by refluxing nickel carbonyl with dicyclopentadienylnickel in benzene solution:

$$Ni(CO)_4 + (C_5H_5)_2Ni \rightarrow 2\,CO + [C_5H_5Ni(CO)]_2 \rightarrow CO + (C_5H_5)_3Ni_3(CO)_2$$
$$XXIII \qquad\qquad XXIIIa$$

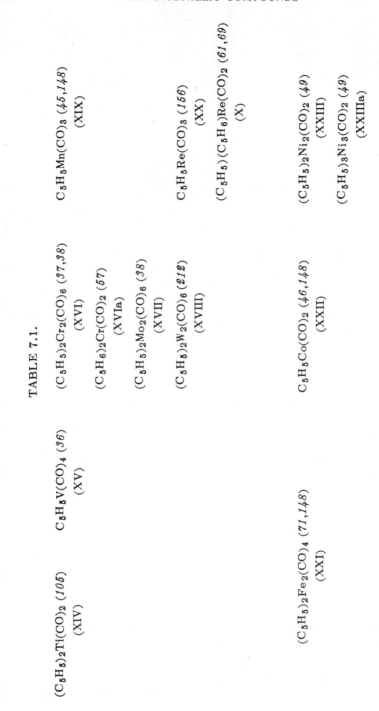

TABLE 7.1.

$(C_5H_5)_2Ti(CO)_2$ *(105)* (XIV)

$C_5H_5V(CO)_4$ *(36)* (XV)

$(C_5H_5)_2Cr_2(CO)_6$ *(37,38)* (XVI)

$(C_5H_6)_2Cr(CO)_2$ *(57)* (XVIa)

$(C_5H_5)_2Mo_2(CO)_6$ *(38)* (XVII)

$(C_5H_5)_2W_2(CO)_6$ *(212)* (XVIII)

$C_5H_5Mn(CO)_3$ *(45,148)* (XIX)

$C_5H_5Re(CO)_3$ *(156)* (XX)

$(C_5H_5)(C_5H_6)Re(CO)_2$ *(61,69)* (X)

$(C_5H_5)_2Fe_2(CO)_4$ *(71,148)* (XXI)

$C_5H_5Co(CO)_2$ *(46,148)* (XXII)

$(C_5H_5)_2Ni_2(CO)_2$ *(49)* (XXIII)

$(C_5H_5)_3Ni_3(CO)_2$ *(49)* (XXIIIa)

This is the only product (*194*) when short reaction times are employed, but prolonged reaction (*49*) leads to a mixture of this and the trinuclear complex (XXIIIa; *cf.* Chapter 10). The molybdenum and tungsten compounds were the first to be described, as the reaction of the corresponding carbonyls with cyclopentadiene, carried out (*212*) in the attempt to prepare dicyclopentadienyls of molybdenum and tungsten, stopped at this point, even under vigorous conditions. They have also been obtained by the reaction sequence:

$$M(CO)_6 + C_5H_5Li \longrightarrow \underset{XXIV}{C_5H_5M(CO)_3Li} \overset{H^+}{\longrightarrow} \underset{XXV}{C_5H_5M(CO)_3H} \overset{}{\underset{H_2}{\longrightarrow}} \underset{XVI\text{-}XVIII}{(C_5H_5)_2M_2(CO)_6}$$

The intermediate hydrides (*37,38*) (XXV; M = Cr, Mo or W) and their reactions are discussed more fully in Chapter 10 as typical examples of metal carbonyl hydrides. They resemble manganese hydrocarbonyl most closely in stability and reactivity. The formation of the cyclopentadienylchromium carbonyl from dicyclopentadienylchromium involves a further intermediate $(C_5H_5)_3Cr_2(CO)_3$ which is regarded (*47*) as being essentially $[(C_5H_5)_2Cr]^+$ $[C_5H_5Cr(CO)_3]^-$ on the basis of its infrared spectrum and its paramagnetism with three unpaired electrons as expected. The cation has also been obtained (*47*) as the iodide from dicyclopentadienylchromium and iodine. In the presence of hydrogen the action of carbon monoxide on dicyclopentadienylchromium leads to a mixture of the hydride (XXV; M = Cr) and dicyclopentadiene chromium dicarbonyl (XVIa) analogous to dicyclopentadiene nickel, (VII) (*57*).

The reduction of the dimeric carbonyls leads to monomeric singly charged anions. It proceeds readily with the compounds of the Group VI metals and has also been accomplished with the iron (*30*) but not with the nickel compound. Similar reduction of the monomeric compounds must proceed with loss of carbon monoxide. Thus cyclopentadienylvanadium tetracarbonyl (XV) yields salts of the ion (XXIV) (*59*). On oxidation in presence of hydrogen chloride this carbonyl (XV) affords the oxychloride (XXV) (*58*). The E.A.N. of the metal remains unchanged in these reductions of the cyclopentadienyl carbonyls to the corresponding

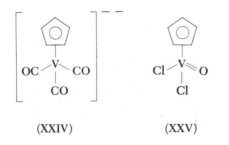

(XXIV)　　　　(XXV)

anions. The cations derivable by oxidation of the dimeric carbonyls would be two electrons short, but can attain the same E.A.N. by adding a further ligand. Hence the iodides (XXVI-XXVIII) obtainable by oxidation of the corresponding binuclear carbonyls or their mercury salts with iodine behave as covalent compounds as does the analogous nitrosyl halide (XI).

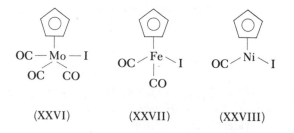

(XXVI)   (XXVII)   (XXVIII)

The chloride and bromide corresponding to (XXVII) have been obtained similarly, but the chloride corresponding to (XXVI) has only been obtained by reaction of the cyclopentadienylmolybdenum tricarbonyl hydride with carbon tetrachloride. Oxidation of the dicyclopentadienyl di-iron tetracarbonyl (XXI) in aqueous acid probably affords initially the aquo-cation $[C_5H_5Fe(CO)_2H_2O]^+$ (73). The halides (XXVI and XXVII) as well as the related cyclopentadienylchromium dinitrosyl chloride (XI) react with alkyl- or aryl-lithium or Grignard reagents to afford the corresponding alkyls $C_5H_5Mo(CO)_3R$ (38,150), $C_5H_5Fe(CO)_2R$ (72,149,152) and $C_5H_5Cr(NO)_2R$ (151) including the cyclopentadienyls (72,151) (R = C_5H_5) in which only one of the cyclopentadienyl groups is π-bonded to the metal (73,151,152,154). The iron compound, π-$C_5H_5Fe(CO)_2$-σ-C_5H_5, decomposes slowly at room temperature with evolution of carbon monoxide to yield ferrocene and if one of the cyclopentadienyl groups is substituted, an unsymmetrically substituted ferrocene derivative will result (73). The same derivative may be obtained in one step from (XXI) by heating with a substituted cyclopentadiene, although the tetracarbonyl (XXI) affords ferrocene on heating alone under comparable conditions.

The only cyclopentadienyl metal carbonyl of which numerous substitution products have been prepared is the manganese compound (XIX). The indenyl derivative (13) (XXIX) and a few others have been obtained from the substituted dicyclopentadienyl manganese with carbon monoxide, but the majority by substitution reactions of (XIX) (cf. p. 364). Reaction of indene with iron carbonyl affords (XXX) analogous to (XXI) (74). This compound, (XXX), absorbs 4 molecules of hydrogen over a platinum catalyst to afford the octahydro derivative (XXXI). The latter has also been obtained (74) by treating iron pentacarbonyl with $\Delta^{2,4}$-bicyclo-[4,4]-

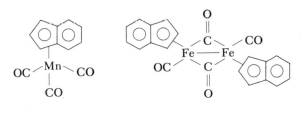

(XXIX)   (XXX)

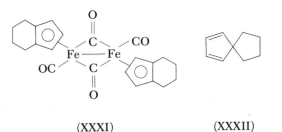

(XXXI)   (XXXII)

nonadiene (**XXXII**), a reaction which involves enlargement of the saturated ring of the initial spiran (**XXXII**).

PREPARATION OF DICYCLOPENTADIENYLMETAL DERIVATIVES

The formation of dicyclopentadienyl metal derivatives has been carried out by two basic methods which comprise high temperature reactions involving cyclopentadiene itself and reactions involving cyclopentadienide ions.

The reactions between metal carbonyls and cyclopentadiene lead directly to the dicyclopentadienylmetal compounds, $(C_5H_5)_2M$, when carried out under more vigorous conditions than those required for preparation of the cyclopentadienylmetal carbonyls discussed in the previous section. The method was used in early preparations of chromium and cobalt derivatives of this type and has been shown to be applicable to iron and nickel; it appears now of little preparative importance. The related method of heating the metal itself with cyclopentadiene, used in the original preparation of ferrocene by Miller et al. (*102*) has not been extended to other metals (except magnesium (*3*)). It has, however, been developed into an apparently practicable technical method by employing iron oxide and hydrogen to supply the free metal at the same rate at which it reacts with the hydrocarbon (*23a*). The use of specially prepared oxide without hydrogen has also been covered by a patent (*23a,164*). The reaction may then be written as:

$$FeO + 2 C_5H_6 \longrightarrow (C_5H_5)_2Fe + H_2O$$

The only similar use of a metal oxide is that of copper oxide in the reaction (*219*):

$$Cu_2O + 2 C_5H_6 + 2 PEt_3 \longrightarrow 2 C_5H_5Cu\,PEt_3 + H_2O$$

The cyclopentadiene ring in the resultant copper complex is regarded as essentially σ-bonded to the metal. Since these metal oxides are basic, these reactions may be thought of as intermediate in character between the thermal method using the metal and methods using metal salts and cyclopentadienide ions. Indeed the latter may be replaced by use of the hydrocarbon in presence of sodium ethoxide or amines (*7*)—bases which are not strong enough to convert more than a small proportion (if any) of the hydrocarbon to the anion. The amine method has been developed into a convenient laboratory method for preparing ferrocene (*213*) and has also been used in preparing dicyclopentadienyl cobalt and nickel, and both mono- and dicyclopentadienyltitanium halides (*7,104a*). It can be developed into a method for producing ferrocene from metallic iron and cyclopentadiene by using the successive steps:

$$Fe + 2 R_3N \cdot HCl \longrightarrow FeCl_2 + 2 R_3N + H_2$$

$$FeCl_2 + 2 C_5H_6 + 2 R_3N \longrightarrow Fe(C_5H_5)_2 + 2 R_3N \cdot HCl$$

net reaction: $Fe + 2 C_5H_6 \longrightarrow Fe(C_5H_5)_2 + H_2$

By far the most general preparative technique, however, is the use of the anion, $C_5H_5{}^-$, as the Grignard reagent, or as an alkali metal salt. Originally ferric chloride was used and the Grignard reagent acted simultaneously as reducing agent; but ferrous chloride is now generally preferred. Reduction is involved in many other cases but to varying extents. Thus chromic chloride (*217*) yields dicyclopentadienylchromium(II) while the molybdenum(V) and tungsten(VI) chlorides afford $[(C_5H_5)_2MoCl]^+$ and $[(C_5H_5)_2WCl_2]^+$, respectively (*21*). More extensive reduction is involved in the formation of the products (IV; M = Rh, R = H) and (IX) from the trichlorides of rhodium and rhenium, while no reduction occurs in the reactions of the group IV and V halides, although in all these cases only two halogens are replaced by cyclopentadienyl groups.

The actual choice of metal salt and the choice of cyclopentadiene derivative are to some extent interrelated. The Grignard reagent is relatively unreactive and the transition metal must be introduced in a soluble form, e.g., as the acetylacetone complex. Solutions of cyclopentadienylsodium in tetrahydrofuran or similar solvents react smoothly even with the insoluble metal chlorides and hence are of widest use. In liquid ammonia as medium cyclopentadienylsodium has been shown to react (*35,43,44*) with complex ammines of Cr, Mn, Fe, Co and Ni to give ionic cyclopentadienides:

e.g., $2 C_5H_5Na + [Co(NH_3)_6] (SCN)_2 \rightarrow 2 NaSCN + [Co(NH_3)_6]^{++}[C_5H_5^{-}]_2$

On warming, the ammine complex decomposes to yield the dicyclopentadienyl metal derivative:

$$[(Co(NH_3)_6] (C_5H_5)_2 \rightarrow 6 NH_3 + Co(C_5H_5)_2$$

The intermediate ammine complex need not be isolated and variants of this technique may be useful. Thus tetrapyridine-nickel chloride reacts more efficiently with cyclopentadienylsodium in tetrahydrofuran to give dicyclopentadienylnickel, than either anhydrous nickel chloride or nickel acetylacetonate.

A variety of substituted cyclopentadienes can be used in the above methods (143,160,165,203). Apart from numerous simple alkyl and aryl derivatives, indene has been employed to afford the di-indenyl derivatives of manganese (13), iron (54,147), cobalt (56,147), and nickel (56). In other cases substituted cyclopentadienyl anions are prepared as lithium or sodium salts without isolation of the free cyclopentadiene. This method is applicable in some instances, where the neutral compound dimerizes too rapidly to permit its isolation, or is impossible to prepare for other reasons.

The most notable example is the preparation of "hydroxymetallocenes" by Benson and Lindsey (5). They showed that methylcyclopentenone is converted by excess sodium amide in liquid ammonia into the doubly charged anion (XXXIII). This reacts with ferrous chloride giving the two stereoisomeric anions (XXXIV and XXXV) of dihydroxydimethylferrocene, separated in the form of the corresponding benzoates. Use of cobaltous chloride led to the related dihydroxycobalticinium salts (XXXVI). Reaction of cyclopentadienylsodium with methyl chloroformate yields methyl cyclopentadienecarboxylate. This may be isolated, but dimerizes rapidly. For preparation of the corresponding ferrocene it is more convenient to conduct the reaction in presence of free sodium, when the corresponding anion (XXXVI) is formed, which, on addition of ferrous chloride, yields dimethyl ferrocenedicarboxylate directly (142,146).

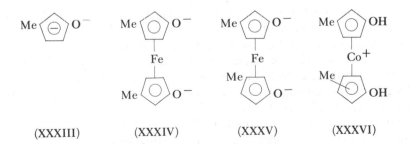

(XXXIII)   (XXXIV)   (XXXV)   (XXXVI)

Cyclopentadiene derivatives which cannot be obtained directly from cyclopentadiene can sometimes be obtained *via* the corresponding ferrocene, making use of the decomposition reaction (*196*):

$$(C_5H_5)_2Fe + 2\,Li + (EtNH_2) \longrightarrow 2\,C_5H_5{}^-Li^+ + Fe$$

Thus dimethylaminomethylferrocene, $C_5H_5FeC_5H_4CH_2NMe_2$ may be obtained quantitatively from ferrocene. Its decomposition with lithium and ethylamine must yield the lithium salt (XXXVIII) together with cyclo-

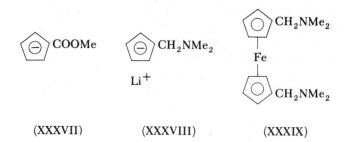

(XXXVII)   (XXXVIII)   (XXXIX)

pentadienyllithium. Free dimethylaminomethylcyclopentadiene could not be isolated from this reaction mixture, but when ferrous chloride was added to it, the original amine, ferrocene, and the diamine (XXXIX) were produced approximately in the statistical ratio (*142,146*).

Conversion of dialkylfulvenes to secondary and tertiary-alkyl-cyclopentadienes is effected readily by addition, respectively, of lithium aluminium hydride and lithium alkyls (*90,91*):

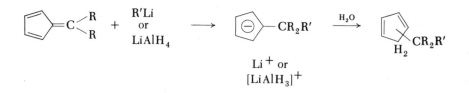

Here again it is advantageous to use the intermediate lithium salt directly in reactions with metal halides, e.g. $FeCl_2$, $CoCl_2$, $Ni(C_5H_5N)_4Cl_2$ or $TiCl_4$. The mono-alkyl or arylfulvenes may be used similarly (*90,146*). Azulene also behaves as a fulvene in this reaction and after addition of lithium aluminium hydride to form the salt (XL), treatment with ferrous chloride yields the corresponding ferrocene, obtained crystalline in one of its stereo-isomeric forms (XLI) or (XLII).

When fulvenes, e.g., 6,6-dimethylfulvene, are treated with sodamide in liquid ammonia, they behave as acids yielding such anions as (XLIII)

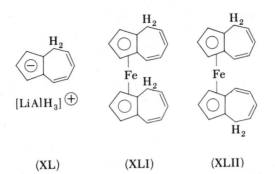

(XL)   (XLI)   (XLII)

from which the corresponding ferrocene and the cobalt(III) derivative (XLIV) have been obtained (89). Diazocyclopentadiene adds alkyl- or aryl lithium in similar fashion to the fulvenes yielding anions (XLV) which

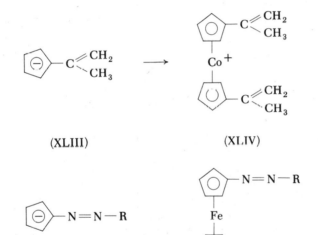

(XLIII)   (XLIV)

(XLV) 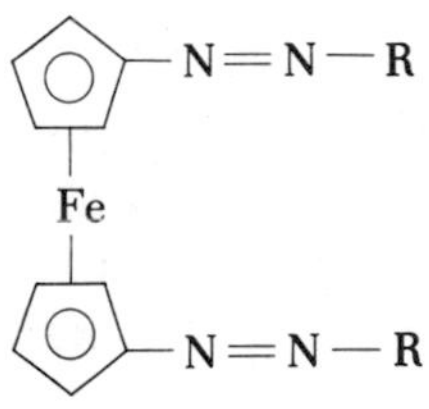   (XLVI)

afford di-(alkyl- or arylazo)ferrocenes (XLVI) on treatment with ferrous chloride (88). Mono-phenylazoferrocene has been obtained similarly by mixing (XLV; R = Ph) with C_5H_5Li before adding ferrous chloride (88).

SOME PROPERTIES AND STRUCTURES

The dicyclopentadienyl compounds of transition metals vary widely in stability. In general, when the metal attains inert-gas configuration of electrons and is in an oxidation state in which it is normally stable, the compound will be stable both thermally and to air. Compounds in lower valency states are rapidly oxidized by air and may be hydrolyzed by water. Such hydrolysis occurs not only with the completely ionic manganese compound, but also with others which can at most have slight ionic character. Attempts to distinguish between π-, σ- and ionic bonding by reaction with ferrous chloride (to yield ferrocene) or with maleic anhydride have not yielded conclusive results (*217*). Where available, X-ray data favor ferrocene-like geometry even for compounds of undoubtedly ionic character, and infrared data suggest a gradation from the covalent ferrocene-like to the fully ionic type rather than a sudden change (*63*). These spectra reflect the symmetry of the ferrocene-like molecules in their simplicity, being made up of only five intense bands, the C—H stretching (3075 cm^{-1}), two C—H bending (811 and 1002 cm^{-1}), an antisymmetrical ring breathing (1108 cm^{-1}) and an antisymmetrical C—C stretching mode (1411 cm^{-1}) in the usual infrared range. The appearance of these bands depends on the symmetry of the individual rings rather than the molecule as a whole, and the presence of the bands near 1005 and 1110 cm^{-1} has been found to be so characteristic of the presence of an unsubstituted cyclopentadienyl ring, that it has been widely used to determine the substitution pattern in ferrocene derivatives (*86,110,173,176*). The similarity of their infrared spectra to those of the transition metal derivatives rather than those of the typically ionic (alkali metal) or σ-bonded (Hg, etc.) derivatives has led to the assignment of similar structures to the dicyclopentadienyls of Sn and Pb, although the rings must here be inclined to each other to account for the marked dipole moments (*22,32,33,53a,63,205*). The numbers and types of C—H stretching bands present led to the recognition (*151*) that π- and σ-bonded cyclopentadienyl groups coexist in the compounds, $(C_5H_5)_2Cr(NO)_2$ and $(C_5H_5)_2Fe(CO)_2$, a fact for which chemical proof has been secured in the latter case (*73*). Curiously neither this iron compound nor dicyclopentadienyl mercury (*219*) (XLVII) shows more than a single peak due to

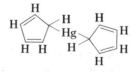

(XLVII)

the σ-bonded rings in its nuclear spin resonance spectrum (*154,185*). Since all other information indicates such σ-bonding in these cases, and even the position of the nuclear spin resonance peak is closer to those of $C_5H_5SiMe_3$

(which shows 3 as expected for σ-bonded rings) than to those of typical π-bonded cyclopentadienyl groups, it has been suggested that the apparent discrepancy is due to a rotation of the σ-bonded rings about their centers. This would eliminate the differences between the hydrogen atoms by allowing each carbon atom in turn to be attached to the metal.*

Electron diffraction and X-ray methods have been employed for detailed structural elucidation of ferrocene (23,181), dibenzoylferrocene, (XLVIII), (186,187,188), di-indenyliron (XLIX), (197), dicyclopentadienyldi-iron tetracarbonyl (103), dicyclopentadienylruthenium (75), dicyclopentadienyl-dimolybdenum hexacarbonyl (221), cyclopentadienylnickel nitrosyl (144), and tricyclopentadienyl trinickel dicarbonyl (104). Typical metal-ring carbon distances are Fe—C: 2.045–2.11 Å; Ru—C: 2.208 ± 0.02 Å; Ni—C: 2.107 ± 0.001 Å and all carbon-carbon distances are within the range 1.40–1.43 Å. Incomplete data are also available for two of the com-

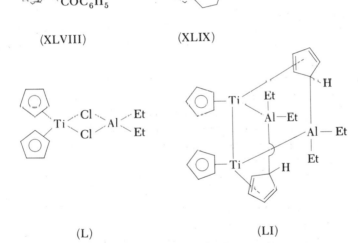

(XLVIII)   (XLIX)

(L)   (LI)

plexes obtainable (109) from dicyclopentadienyl titanium dichloride and triethylaluminium. In dicyclopentadienyltitanium dichloro diethylaluminium (106), (L), the rings are inclined to each other in agreement with the dipole moments (190a) of several simpler compounds of the type,

*This explanation was put forward for the iron compound by Professor G. Wilkinson during a lecture to the Liverpool section of the Chemical Society in February, 1957. It was independently suggested to the author by Dr. G. V. D. Tiers to explain the data for dicyclopentadienylmercury.

$(C_5H_5)_2TiX_2$. The chlorine-free product, $(C_5H_5)_4Ti_2Al_2Et_4$, has the structure (LI) with direct Ti—Ti and Ti—Al bonds and two different types of rings, one being symmetrical and symmetrically bonded to titanium, the other σ-bonded to aluminium and π-bonded through two fixed double bonds to titanium (108).

Two interesting compounds having more than two cyclopentadienyl groups per metal atom have been reported. Reaction of dicyclopentadienyl-cobalt bromide with cyclopentadienyllithium affords pentacyclopentadienyldicobalt, $(C_5H_5)_5Co_2$ (28). Its exact structure is unknown, but its zero dipole moment suggests a symmetrical formulation.

The tricyclopentadienyluranium cation, obtained as the chloride, $(C_5H_5)_3UCl$, is regarded as having all three rings π-bonded to the metal (159). The size of the central metal atom undoubtedly makes such a formulation plausible and its stability contrasts sharply with the ease of hydrolysis of the lanthanide (8), indium (39) and bismuth (53) derivatives, $(C_5H_5)_3M$, which are regarded as largely ionic. It is believed that these as well as other ionic cyclopentadienides will be found to resemble π- rather than σ- bonded cyclopentadienyl compounds in geometrical arrangement. These considerations apply *inter al.* to the monocyclopentadienides of thallium (19,101), indium (39) and the alkali metals, and to the dicyclopentadienides of manganese, zinc (41) and the alkali earths, but experimental confirmation is available only in the cases of magnesium, manganese and thallium. The latter is estimated to have a Tl—C distance of 2.7 Å (198). Dicyclopentadienylberyllium differs from the magnesium compound in having a dipole moment of $2.46 \pm 0.06D$ and possible structures include formulations with *one* of the two rings σ-bonded (40). Apart from the Cu and Hg compounds mentioned earlier, σ-bonding has also been suggested (184) for the polymeric C_5H_5PdCl.

Freedom of the two rings to rotate relative to each other has been investigated in ferrocene derivatives. There is no theoretical reason to expect a large energy barrier hindering such rotation and both chemical (176) and physical evidence is in agreement with substantially "free" rotation in solution. Several dipole measurements (163,182,190a), on disubstituted ferrocenes have given values corresponding approximately with those expected if free rotation obtains. A deviation in the direction of greater separation of the substituents in the case of the dinitrile, $(C_5H_4CN)_2Fe$, may be explained as resulting from repulsion between these substituent groups (190a). In the solid state, the staggered configuration is preferred not only in the parent compound, but also in dibenzoylferrocene (XLVIII) and dibenzoferrocene (di-indenyliron) (XLIX) which have the configurations shown. An upper limit for the ring rotational barrier of 3.9 kcal/mole has been suggested for di(cyclopentadienylmolybdenum tricarbonyl) on the basis of proton resonance studies (*202*).

The disruption of the metal-ring bond has not been extensively studied, although several such reactions of the ferrocene system are known. Only in the reaction with lithium and ethylamine (p. 358) is the cyclopentadiene ring preserved as such. Catalytic hydrogenation only occurs under extreme conditions, e.g., near 350° using Raney nickel, and yields cyclopentane and iron (*122*). Many substituents including benzene rings may be reduced preferentially (*55,90,139*). Bromination (*122,132*) decomposes ferrocene to pentabromocyclopentane and ferric bromide, and the formation of the former has been employed as a test of the presence of an unsubstituted ring in polysubstituted ferrocenes. It may be assumed that this and other oxidative degradations proceed *via* the easily disrupted ferricinium ion. Cyclopentadienyl compounds of other metals have not been studied in these reactions, but the dicyclopentadienylcobalt(III) ion is known to be stable both to bromine (which merely precipitates it as the tribromide) and to ozone (*27*). Iodine, unlike bromine, merely oxidizes ferrocene to the ferricinium ion and the kinetics of this process have been investigated (*177*).

Reactions not involving the Cyclopentadienyl Group

The behavior of the covalently bound halogen atoms in $(C_5H_5)_2TiX_2$ and related compounds has been studied in a variety of reactions. The exchange for Cl^- occurs by a dissociative mechanism (*84*).

Hydrolysis with water readily affords $(C_5H_5)_2Ti(OH)Cl$ (*214*) while $C_5H_5TiCl_3$ behaves more like titanium tetrachloride in yielding $(C_5H_5-TiCl_2)_2O$. The latter compound is remarkable in having a linear arrangement of the atoms Ti—O—Ti with very short bond distances, implying some degree of double bonding between titanium and oxygen (*18*). In neither case has further replacement of the halogens been reported, nor has attempted alcoholysis with sodium alkoxides yielded crystalline products. On the other hand, reaction with phenylmagnesium bromide and related reagents proceeds smoothly according to

$$2\,PhMgBr + (C_5H_5)_2TiCl_2 \longrightarrow (C_5H_5)_2Ti(C_6H_5)_2$$

The resulting diaryl derivatives (*189,190*) and also dimethyl dicyclopentadienyltitanium (*154*) $(C_5H_5)_2Ti(CH_3)_2$, are stable compounds which are unaffected by brief exposure to air or moisture. Their considerable thermal stability compared to tetramethyltitanium or to the mixed alkyltitanium halides demonstrates the stabilizing effect which the cyclopentadienyl group exerts on the Ti-carbon σ-bond and which is similar to the effect of carbonyl groups. Vanadium affords the analogous $(C_5H_5)_2VC_6H_5$, but although stable thermally, this is a derivative of vanadium in the low oxidation state of three and hence ignites spontaneously in air (96). Reduction of dicyclopentadienyltitanium dichloride with a Jones reductor (214) yields the dicyclopentadienyl titanium(III) cation and the same oxidation state is reached in its reaction with triethylaluminum to give the complex (L). Several other mixed titanium-aluminum complexes have been described by Natta and others, including the remarkable (LI) (106–109). Some of these mixed complexes show a promising degree of activity when used in place of $TiCl_4$-$AlEt_3$ as catalysts for the polymerization of olefins (9,107). Other uses of cyclopentadienyl compounds include that of cyclopentadienyl manganese tricarbonyl and especially its methyl derivative as an antiknock compound, while alkylferrocenes are claimed to be of value as anti-anaemic drugs.

AROMATIC SUBSTITUTION REACTIONS

Only ferrocene (222) dicyclopentadienylruthenium, dicyclopentadienylosmium (157,158) and cyclopentadienylmanganese tricarbonyl (92) have been shown to undergo electrophilic (and free radical) substitution reactions, although all the other π-cyclopentadienyl derivatives must be regarded as aromatic (145). Most of these others however cannot readily be substituted directly on grounds of instability or nuclear charge.

The Friedel-Crafts alkylation and acylation and the sulfonation reactions are the only direct substitutions which have been reported (14a,52,92) with cyclopentadienyl manganese tricarbonyl, while in addition to these reactions, ferrocene has been shown to undergo metalation, arylation, formylation by the Vilsmeier reaction as well as various condensations with aldehydes. In both cases nitration and halogenation are prevented by oxidation, which in the case of ferrocene yields the ferricinium ion, unreactive towards electrophiles, whereas the manganese complex is destroyed completely. These difficulties have been overcome in the case of ferrocene by use of indirect routes to the nitro and halogen derivatives described below. The oxidation of ferrocene is facilitated by electron donating and hindered by electron withdrawing substituents. Hence nitroferrocene is stable even in presence of acid, although ferrocene itself is oxidized by nitrobenzene, for example, under such conditions. Another consequence is that acylferrocenes, especially the mono- and diacetyl derivatives may be oxidized to the corresponding acids without extensive oxidation to ferricinium salts.

The monocarboxylic acid resembles benzoic acid in having a $pK_a =$ 6.29. This value is raised by electron donating and lowered by electron withdrawing substituents, even when these are attached to the second ring, showing that such effects are transmitted across the metal atom (*136,137*).

The ferrocene and cyclopentadienylmanganese tricarbonyl derivatives obtained from these primary substitutions have been subjected to many transformations by methods which closely parallel well-known reactions of the corresponding benzene derivatives. No attempt will be made to cover such reactions exhaustively, but the following discussion will emphasize methods which have proved most adaptable to these organometallic systems and any results of special interest.

Friedel-Crafts Acylation

This reaction has been studied more extensively than any other in this field. It has provided the means of comparing reactivity showing, for example (*157,158*), that ferrocene is most, and dicyclopentadienylosmium least, reactive of the Fe, Ru, and Os compounds. Competitive experiments lead to the order (*92*): Ferrocene >> anisole > methylcyclopentadienyl-manganese tricarbonyl > cyclopentadienylmanganese tricarbonyl > benzene. The very high reactivity of ferrocene was further demonstrated by the mild conditions (*11,65,76,203*), e.g., the use of acetic anhydride in presence of phosphoric acid, which suffice to effect acetylation in this case.

The deactivating effect of the first substituent is sufficiently effective not only on the same ring, but also on the unsubstituted ring, to prevent di-substitution under these mild conditions. With aluminum chloride, however, ferrocene itself can form an unreactive complex (*175*) and the uncom-plexed portion will become disubstituted, even with one equivalent of acid chloride, when the catalyst is present in excess. Such diacylation yields the 1,1'-isomer (LII) as expected from the deactivating effect of the first acyl group on the ring to which it is attached (*143,222*).

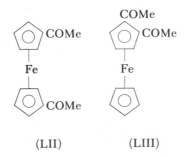

(LII)   (LIII)

A very small amount of the 1,2-diacetyl derivative (*161*) (LIII) has been isolated together with the symmetrical isomer (LII). Although failure to obtain the 1,3-isomer in comparably small amount may not be regarded as conclusive, it at least suggests that the 3 (or β-)position is more strongly deactivated than the 2(or α-)position. Various alkyl and aryl derivatives have been acetylated (*171,174*) and the ratios of 2:3-isomer for 1,1′-di-methyl, 1,1′-di-isopropyl, and 1,1′-diphenyl ferrocenes are estimated to be: 1:2.3, 1:4.3, and 1:1, respectively. These results are in agreement with the conclusion, as a corollary to the above, that the 3 position is the more strongly activated of the two; but steric effects are clearly important and could be wholly responsible. Acylation of methylcyclopentadienylmanganese tricarbonyl has also been shown (*92*) to give both expected isomers, but evidence to distinguish between them has not been presented. Diacetylation of methylferrocenes has been studied (*170*) and shown to give the expected mixture, each of the position isomers (2,2′-), (2,3′-) and (3,3′-) being capable of existing in two geometrically isomeric forms, e.g., (LIV) and (LV). It has not been demonstrated which is which, but in principle such pairs as (LIV) and (LV) should be distinguishable by the resolvability of the latter, whereas the former is a "meso" form. Optical activity arises in homoannularly disubstituted ferrocenes of the type (LVI) provided X

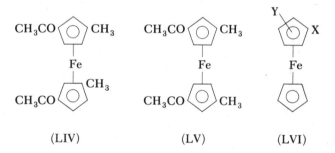

(LIV)   (LV)   (LVI)

and Y differ and has been demonstrated (*192*) in the case of the cyclic ketone (LVIII; n = 3). This and the next higher homolog (LVIII; n = 4) may be obtained (*134,135,167*) by polyphosphoric acid or trifluoroacetic acid catalyzed cyclization of the corresponding acids (LVII; n = 3 or 4),

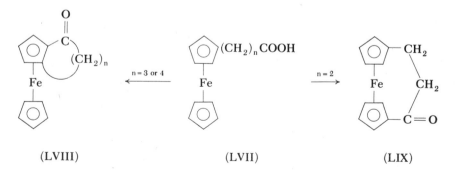

(LVIII)   (LVII)   (LIX)

while the lower homolog (LVII; n = 2) cyclizes heteroannulàrly (*167*) to give the bridged ketone (LIX). Besides this compound several other bridged ferrocenes have been obtained (*98,180*), most successfully by acyloin condensation of esters of acids, $Fe[C_5H_4(CH_2)_nCOOH]_2$. These and the acids (LVII) are obtained by Clemmensen or catalytic reduction of the corresponding keto acids, $C_5H_5FeC_5H_4CO(CH_2)_{n-1}COOH$, viz., $Fe[C_5H_4CO-(CH_2)_{n-1}COOH]_2$, which are formed from ferrocene by appropriate Friedel-Crafts reactions (*134,135,168,193*).

Similar reduction of other acyl derivatives of ferrocene has been commonly used to prepare the corresponding alkyl derivatives, as direct Friedel-Crafts alkylation has only met with moderate success (*111,112,113, 133,199*). By contrast, alkylation of cyclopentadienyl manganese tricarbonyl proceeds quite smoothly (*92*).

Sulfonation

Both cyclopentadienylmanganese tricarbonyl (*14a*) and ferrocene as well as ferrocenecarboxylic acid (*137*) have been sulfonated in high yield. In the ferrocene series both mono- and disubstitution products may be obtained under appropriate conditions (*89,119,203*). The sodium salt of the disulfonic acid is cleaved to ferrous ion and cyclopentadienesulfonic acid (dimer) on treating with base, so that it cannot serve as a source of dihydroxyferrocene (*166*). Both the manganese and iron derivatives have been converted to the corresponding sulfonyl chlorides (*14a,89,118*). In the former series this chloride has in turn served as the source of the corresponding sulfinic acid and a series of sulfones, while the ferrocene sulfonyl chlorides have been reduced both to sulfinic acids and mercaptans. Ferrocenyl mercaptan is so readily oxidized that it was only isolated in the form of the corresponding disulfide or other derivatives (*89,118*). Its methyl ether as well as 1,1'-di(methylthio)ferrocene have been subjected to the aminomethylation reaction (*cf.* below), but contrary to expectation based on the behavior of thioanisole, the methylthio group appears to be devoid of activating influence when attached to ferrocene nuclei (*90a*). Indeed, the results suggest possibly a slight deactivating effect and the observed preference for attack at the 2 rather than the 3 position may be connected with this, although more detailed study is required before such a conclusion would be justified.

Mercuration

Like other substitutions this reaction proceeds with ferrocene under conditions which would be too mild in the case of benzene (*121*). Mono- and disubstitution occur together, but the two mercurichlorides differ sufficiently in their solubility characteristics to be readily separated. Similar results have been obtained with the ruthenium compound (*158*). Chloromercurycyclopentadienylmanganese tricarbonyl has been obtained from the sulfinic acid but has not been reported from direct substitution. The two ferrocene derivatives have served as a source of bromo- and iodoferrocenes (*125,126*). The mono-mercurichloride has also been reduced to diferrocenyl mercury (**LX**) and this in turn converted to diferrocenyl (**LXI**) and to various other products shown, though mostly in poor yields (*126, 138*).

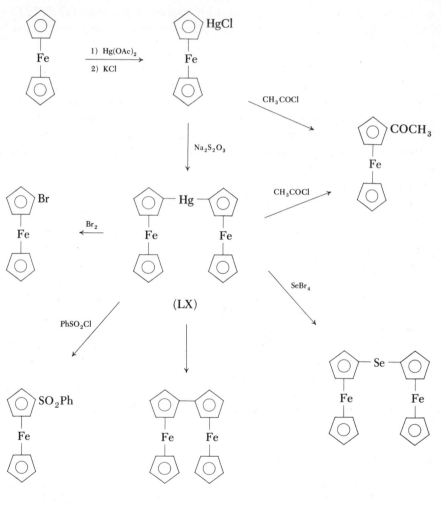

Arylation

The smooth arylation which ferrocene undergoes with diazonium salts, under a wide variety of conditions, was discovered independently by three groups of workers (12,120,121,123,204). Some of the conditions used are typical of those leading to free radical arylation in the benzene series. Nevertheless disubstitution follows closely the pattern of electrophilic substitution with a deactivating substituent as discussed in the case of acylation, above. It leads to 1,1'-diarylferrocenes, accompanied by a very small proportion of 1,2-isomer (12). An attempt to effect the same reaction between diacetyl ferrocene and p-nitrophenyldiazonium salt led to complete disruption of the molecule giving an unidentified product, $C_{13}H_{11}O_3N_3$ (124).

Condensation with Formaldehyde

Ferrocene, like highly reactive benzene derivatives will condense with formaldehyde, both in presence of acids and of amines. With the latter it yields (97) smoothly the typical "Mannich bases," $C_{10}H_9FeCH_2NR_2$, which are discussed further in the next subsection. In presence of sulfuric (114) or hydrofluoric acids (203) it affords $(C_{10}H_9FeCH_2)_2$ via the intermediate cation, $C_{10}H_9FeCH_2^+$, and, presumably, its tautomeric diradical form, $C_{10}H_9F\dot{e}—CH_2$, a mode of reaction which can find no parallel in ordinary aromatic chemistry (169). The exceptional stability and hence ease of formation of ions of the type, $C_{10}H_9FeCHR^+$, has been demonstrated in several investigations (6,14), most convincingly by a study of the solvolysis rates of a series of acetates (162).

Aldehydes

Cyclopentadienylmanganese tricarbonyl has been converted to the aldehyde, $OCHC_5H_4Mn(CO)_3$, via the corresponding acid and acid chloride (15). Ferrocene is sufficiently reactive to afford ferrocenecarboxyaldehyde (LXII) by direct substitution either using the Vilsmeier reaction (10,11, 65,172), preferably with N-methylformanilide rather than dimethylformamide, and phosphorus oxychloride, or using dichloromethyl ethyl ether under Friedel-Crafts conditions (201). The same aldehyde as well as the symmetrical dialdehyde have been obtained by manganese dioxide oxidation of the corresponding alcohols (77,142). Since ferrocenylcarbinol is available, not only by lithium aluminium hydride reduction of ferrocenecarboxylic acid (178), but more readily by alkaline hydrolysis of ferrocenylmethyl trimethylammonium iodide (LXIII), this provides a route to the aldehyde from the above Mannich bases (77,97). An alternative but

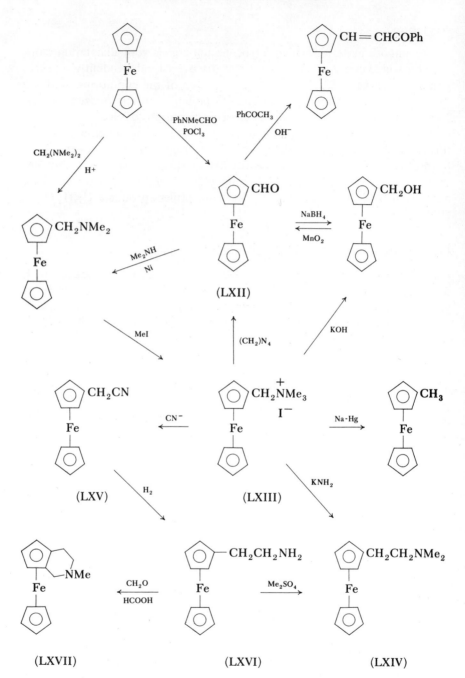

inferior route is to heat the quaternary salt with hexamethylenetetramine (10), while the reverse conversion of the aldehyde to the amine has been effected by the Leuckart method (78). Both the quaternary salt (LXIII) and the aldehyde have been used as starting materials for the preparation of a miscellany of other compounds. They undergo reactions comparable to those of benzyltrimethylammonium iodide and benzaldehyde respectively (11,78,79,93,97,127,139,178). Curiously the bisquaternary salt derived from the diamine (XXXIX) does not show comparable reactivity (142).

By contrast to the *ortho* rearrangement undergone by benzyltrimethylammonium iodide under these conditions, the salt (LXIII) suffers a Stevens rearrangement on treatment with potassamide yielding (LXIV) (77,80). The latter has also been formed (140) by the alternative route shown *via* the cyanide (LXV) and primary amine (LXVI). Attempted methylation of the latter with formaldehyde-formic acid afforded instead of (LXIV) the cyclic amine (LXVII) (93,94,141).

Metalation

Metalation other than mercuration has been effected on ferrocene with *n*-butyllithium (4,100,121) and with *n*-amyl- or phenylsodium (116,117). Carbonation of the products shows that mono- and disubstitution products are formed together in the case of lithiation, whereas sodiation yields predominantly the latter. Nevertheless only the former method has been widely used. The wide range of derivatives available *via* these metal-substituted intermediates may be seen from the following chart showing products derived from the monolithium compound (LXVIII).

The direct conversion (1,123) to the amine (LXIX) provides the best route to that substance, which has also been obtained by the more tedious Curtius degradation of the acid (LXX), from chloro- or bromoferrocene *via* phthalimidoferrocene and from phenylazoferrocene by reduction. Although this amine gives typical derivatives of a primary amine it cannot be diazotized owing to its instability to oxidation. The 1,1'-diamine was not isolated from the mixed lithium salts and has hitherto been obtained only from the di-phenylazo derivative (LXV; R = Ph). Nitro and nitroso derivatives have only been obtained (70,81,166) by the route shown and again only monosubstitution products were isolated. Both should of course afford the same amine (LXIX) on reduction. The boronic acid (LXXI) obtained (128) together with the diboronic acid, $[(HO)_2BC_5H_4]_2Fe$, affords routes to the halogen substituted ferrocenes and to diferrocenyl (LXI) which are superior to those *via* chloromercuriferrocene (128,129,130). The conversions (129,130,131) of this boronic acid or the derived chloro- or

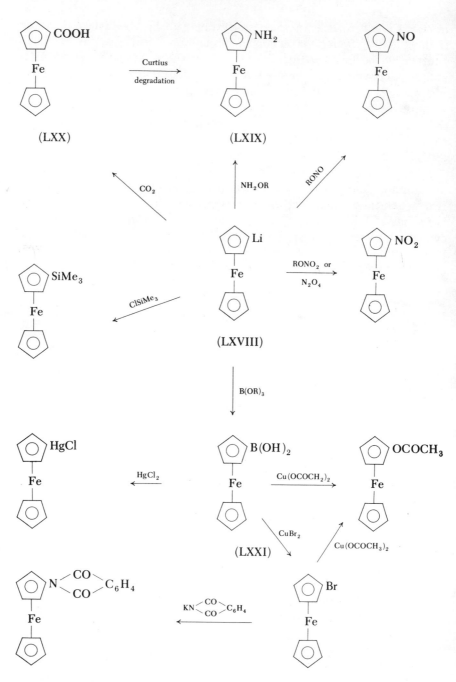

bromoferrocenes with copper acetate to ferrocenyl acetate and hence to hydroxyferrocene, provide at present the only routes to this important compound, whose more detailed study will be awaited with much interest.

References

(1) Acton, E. M., and Silverstein, R. M., *J. Org. Chem.*, **24**, 1487 (1959).

(2) Arimoto, F. S., and Haven, A. C., *J. Am. Chem. Soc.*, **77**, 6295 (1955).

(3) Barber, W. A., *J. Inorg. Nucl. Chem.*, **4**, 373 (1957).

(4) Benkeser, R. A., Goggin, D., and Schroll, G., *J. Am. Chem. Soc.*, **76**, 4025 (1954).

(5) Benson, R. E., and Lindsey, R. V., Jr., *J. Am. Chem. Soc.*, **79**, 5471 (1957).

(6) Berger, A., Kleinberg, J., and McEwen, W. E., *Chemistry and Industry*, 204 (1960).

(7) Birmingham, J. M., Seyferth, D., and Wilkinson, G., *J. Am. Chem. Soc.*, **76**, 4179 (1954).

(8) Birmingham, J. M., and Wilkinson, G., *J. Am. Chem. Soc.*, **78**, 42 (1956).

(9) Breslow, D. S., and Newburg, N. R., *J. Am. Chem. Soc.*, **79**, 5072 (1957).

(10) Broadhead, G. D., Osgerby, J. M., and Pauson, P. L., *Chemistry and Industry*, 209 (1957).

(11) Broadhead, G. D., Osgerby, J. M., and Pauson, P. L., *J. Chem. Soc.*, 650 (1958).

(12) Broadhead, G. D., and Pauson, P. I., *J. Chem. Soc.*, 367 (1955).

(13) Brown, J. E., and Shapiro, H., (to Ethyl Corp.), U. S. 2,818,417 (Dec. 31, 1957); *C.A.*, **52**, 8535 (1958).

(14) Buell, G. R., McEwen, W. E., and Kleinberg, J., *Tetrahedron Letters*, **No. 5**, 16 (1959).

(14a) Cais, M., and Kozikowski, J., Abstracts, 136th Am. Chem. Soc. Meeting, 1959, p. 112P.

(15) Cais, M., and Modiano, A., *Chemistry and Industry*, 202 (1960).

(16) Chatt, J., and Venanzi, L. M., *Nature*, **177**, 853 (1956).

(17) Chatt, J., and Venanzi, L. M., *J. Chem. Soc.*, 4735 (1957).

(18) Corradini, P., and Allegra, G., *J. Am. Chem. Soc.*, **81**, 5510 (1959).

(19) Cotton, F. A., and Reynolds, L. T., *J. Am. Chem. Soc.*, **80**, 269 (1958).

(20) Cotton, F. A., Whipple, R. O., and Wilkinson, G., *J. Am. Chem. Soc.*, **75**, 3586 (1953).

(21) Cotton, F. A., and Wilkinson, G., *Z. Naturforsch.*, **9b**, 417 (1954).

(22) Dave, L. D., Evans, D. F., and Wilkinson, G., *J. Chem. Soc.*, 3684 (1959).

(22a) Dubeck, M., *J. Am. Chem. Soc.*, **82**, 502 (1960).

(23) Dunitz, J. D., Orgel, L. E., and Rich, A., *Acta Cryst.*, **9**, 373 (1956).

(23a) duPont, E. I. de Nemours, British Patent 737,780 (Sept. 28, 1955); British Patent 764,058 (Dec. 19, 1956); Arimoto, F. S. (to duPont) U. S. Patent 2,804,468 (Aug. 27, 1957); California Research Corp., British Patent 744,450 (Feb. 8, 1956); British Patent 767,298 (Jan. 30, 1957).

(24) Dyatkina, M. E., *Uspekhi Khim.*, **27**, 57 (1958); *C. A.*, **52**, 14579 (1958).
(25) Ethyl Corporation, British Patent 782,738, (Sept. 11, 1957); *C.A.*, **52**, 3851 (1958).
(26) Fischer, A. K., and Wilkinson, G., *J. Inorg. Nucl. Chem.*, **2**, 149 (1956).
(27) Fischer, E. O., *Angew. Chem.*, **67**, 475 (1955).
(28) Fischer, E. O., *Tagungsbericht der Chemischen Gesellschaft in der Deutschen Demokratischen Republik*, 132 (1955).
(29) Fischer, E. O., Beckert, O., Hafner, W., and Stahl, H.-O., *Z. Naturforsch.*, **10b**, 598 (1955).
(30) Fischer, E. O., and Böttcher, R., *Z. Naturforsch.*, **10b**, 600 (1955).
(31) Fischer, E. O., and Fritz, H. P., "Advances in Inorganic and Radiochemistry," Vol. 1, p. 55, New York, Academic Press, 1959.
(32) Fischer, E. O., and Grubert, H., *Z. anorg. Chem.*, **286**, 237 (1956).
(33) Fischer, E. O., and Grubert, H., *Z. Naturforsch.*, **11b**, 423 (1956).
(34) Fischer, E. O., and Grubert, H., *Chem. Ber.*, **92**, 2302 (1959).
(35) Fischer, E. O., and Hafner, W., *Z. Naturforsch.*, **8b**, 444 (1953).
(36) Fischer, E. O., and Hafner, W., *Z. Naturforsch.*, **9b**, 503 (1954).
(37) Fischer, E. O., and Hafner, W., *Z. Naturforsch.*, **10b**, 140 (1955).
(38) Fischer, E. O., Hafner, W., and Stahl, H.-O., *Z. anorg. Chem.*, **282**, 47 (1955).
(39) Fischer, E. O., and Hofmann, H. P., *Angew. Chem.*, **69**, 639 (1957).
(40) Fischer, E. O., and Hofmann, H. P., *Chem. Ber.*, **92**, 482 (1959).
(41) Fischer, E. O., Hofmann, H. P., and Treiber, A., *Z. Naturforsch.*, **14b**, 599 (1959).
(41a) Fischer, E. O., and Hristidu, Y., *Z. Naturforsch.*, **15b**, 135 (1960).
(42) Fischer, E. O., and Jira, R., *Z. Naturforsch.*, **8b**, 1 (1953).
(43) Fischer, E. O., and Jira, R., *Z. Naturforsch.*, **8b**, 217 (1953).
(44) Fischer, E. O., and Jira, R., *Z. Naturforsch.*, **8b**, 327 (1953).
(45) Fischer, E. O., and Jira, R., *Z. Naturforsch.*, **9b**, 618 (1954).
(46) Fischer, E. O., and Jira, R., *Z. Naturforsch.*, **10b**, 355 (1955).
(47) Fischer, E. O., and Kögler, H. P., *Angew. Chem.*, **68**, 462 (1956).
(48) Fischer, E. O., and Leipfinger, H., *Z. Naturforsch.*, **10b**, 353 (1955).
(48a) Fischer, E. O., and Löchner, A., *Z. Naturforsch.*, **15b**, 266 (1960).
(49) Fischer, E. O., and Palm, C., *Chem. Ber.*, **91**, 1725 (1958).
(50) Fischer, E. O., and Pfab, W., *Z. Naturforsch.*, **7b**, 377 (1952).
(51) Fischer, E. O., and Piesbergen, U., *Z. Naturforsch.*, **11b**, 758 (1956).
(52) Fischer, E. O., and Pleszke, K., *Chem. Ber.*, **91**, 2719 (1958).
(53) Fischer, E. O., and Schreiner, S., *Angew. Chem.*, **69**, 205 (1957).
(53a) Fischer, E. O., and Schreiner, S., *Chem. Ber.*, **92**, 938 (1959).
(54) Fischer, E. O., and Seus, D., *Z. Naturforsch.*, **8b**, 694 (1953).
(55) Fischer, E. O., and Seus, D., *Z. Naturforsch.*, **9b**, 386 (1954).
(56) Fischer, E. O., Seus, D., and Jira, R., *Z. Naturforsch.*, **8b**, 692 (1953).
(57) Fischer, E. O., and Ulm, K., *Z. Naturforsch.*, **15b**, 59 (1960).
(58) Fischer, E. O., and Vigoureux, S., *Chem. Ber.*, **91**, 1342 (1958).
(59) Fischer, E. O., and Vigoureux, S., *Chem. Ber.*, **91**, 2205 (1958).
(60) Fischer, E. O., and Werner, H., *Chem. Ber.*, **92**, 1423 (1959).
(61) Fischer, E. O., and Wirzmüller, A., *Z. Naturforsch.*, **12b**, 737 (1957).

(62) Fischer, E. O., Zahn, U., and Baumgärtner, F., Z. Naturforsch., **14b**, 133 (1959); *Chem. Ber.*, **92**, 1624 (1959).

(63) Fritz, H. P., *Chem. Ber.*, **92**, 780 (1959).

(64) Gorsich, R. D., *J. Am. Chem. Soc.*, **80**, 4744 (1958).

(65) Graham, P. J., Lindsey, R. V., Jr., Parshall, G. W., Peterson, M. L., and Whitman, G. M., *J. Am. Chem. Soc.*, **79**, 3416 (1957).

(66) Green, M. L. H., Pratt, L., and Wilkinson, G., *J. Chem. Soc.*, 3916 (1958).

(67) Green, M. L. H., Pratt, L., and Wilkinson, G., *J. Chem. Soc.*, 3753 (1959).

(68) Green, M. L. H., Street, C. N., and Wilkinson, G., Z. Naturforsch., **14b**, 738 (1959).

(69) Green, M. L. H., and Wilkinson, G., *J. Chem. Soc.*, 4314 (1958).

(70) Grubert, H., and Rinehart, K. L., Jr., *Tetrahedron Letters*, No. 12, 16 (1959).

(71) Hallam, B. F., Mills, O. S., and Pauson, P. L., *J. Inorg. Nucl. Chem.*, **1**, 313 (1955).

(72) Hallam, B. F., and Pauson, P. L., *Chemistry and Industry*, 653 (1955).

(73) Hallam, B. F., and Pauson, P. L., *J. Chem. Soc.*, 3030 (1956).

(74) Hallam, B. F., and Pauson, P. L., *J. Chem. Soc.*, 646 (1958).

(75) Hardgrove, G. L., and Templeton, D. H., *Acta Cryst.*, **12**, 28 (1959).

(76) Hauser, C. R., and Lindsay, J. K., *J. Org. Chem.*, **22**, 482 (1957).

(77) Hauser, C. R., Lindsay, J. K., Lednicer, D., and Cain, C. E., *J. Org. Chem.*, **22**, 717 (1957).

(78) Hauser, C. R., and Lindsay, J. K., *J. Org. Chem.*, **22**, 906 (1957).

(79) Hauser, C. R., and Lindsay, J. K., *J. Org. Chem.*, **22**, 1246 (1957).

(80) Hauser, C. R., Lindsay, J. K., and Lednicer, D., *J. Org. Chem.*, **23**, 358 (1958).

(81) Helling, J. F., and Schechter, L., *Chemistry and Industry*, 1157 (1959).

(82) Herman, D. F., and Weil, R. M., (to National Lead Co.), U. S. Patent 2,898,355 (Aug. 4, 1959), *C. A.*, **53**, 17926 (1959).

(83) Jellinek, F., Z. Naturforsch., **14b**, 737 (1959).

(84) Jensen, A., and Basolo, F., *J. Am. Chem. Soc.*, **81**, 3813 (1959).

(85) Katz, S., Weiher, J. F., and Voigt, A. F., *J. Am. Chem. Soc.*, **80**, 6459 (1958).

(86) Kazitsyna, L. A., Lokshin, B. V., and Nesmeyanov, A. N., *Doklady Akad. Nauk*, **127**, 333 (1959).

(87) Kealy, T. J., and Pauson, P. L., *Nature*, **168**, 1039 (1951).

(88) Knox, G. R., *Proc. Chem. Soc.*, 56 (1959).

(89) Knox, G. R., and Pauson, P. L., *J. Chem. Soc.*, 692 (1958).

(90) Knox, G. R., and Pauson, P. L., *Proc. Chem. Soc.*, 289 (1958).

(90a) Knox, G. R., Pauson, P. L., and Tiers, G. V. D., *Chemistry and Industry*, 1046 (1959).

(91) Koestler, R. C., and Little, W. F., *Chemistry and Industry*, 1589 (1958).

(92) Kozikowski, J., Maginn, R. E., and Klove, M. S., *J. Am. Chem. Soc.*, **81**, 2995 (1959).

(93) Lednicer, D., Lindsay, J. K., and Hauser, C. R., *J. Org. Chem.*, **23**, 653 (1958).

(94) Lednicer, D., and Hauser, C. R., *J. Org. Chem.*, **24**, 43 (1959).

(95) Leipfinger, H., Z. Naturforsch., **13b**, 53 (1958).

(96) Liefde Meijer, H. J. de, Janssen, M. J., and van der Kerk, G. J. M., *Chemistry and Industry*, 119 (1960).

(97) Lindsay, J. K., and Hauser, C. R., *J. Org. Chem.*, **22**, 355 (1957).

(98) Lüttringhaus, A., and Kullick, W., *Angew. Chem.*, **70**, 438 (1958).

(99) Markby, R., Sternberg, H. W., and Wender, I., *Chemistry and Industry*, 1381 (1959).

(100) Mayo, D. W., Shaw, P. D., and Rausch, M. D., *Chemistry and Industry*, 1388 (1957).

(101) Meister, H., *Angew. Chem.*, **69**, 533 (1957).

(102) Miller, S. A.. Tebboth, J. A., and Tremaine, J. F., *J. Chem. Soc.*, 632 (1952).

(103) Mills, O. S., *Acta Cryst.*, **11**, 620 (1958).

(104) Mills, O. S., Hock, A. A., and Robinson, G., XVIIth *Intern. Congr. Pure and Appl. Chem.* Munich, (1959), (Abstr. A. 143).

(104a) Morehouse, E. L. (to Union Carbide Corp.), British Patent 797,151 (June 25, 1958).

(105) Murray, J. G., *J. Am. Chem. Soc.*, **81**, 752 (1959).

(106) Natta, G., Corradini, P., and Bassi, I. W., *J. Am. Chem. Soc.*, **80**, 755 (1958).

(107) Natta, G., Dall'asta, G., Mazzanti, G., Giannini, U., and Cesca, S., *Angew. Chem.*, **71**, 205 (1959).

(108) Natta, G., and Mazzanti, G., *Tetrahedron*, **8**, 86 (1960).

(109) Natta, G., Pino, P., Mazzanti, G., and Giannini, U., *J. Inorg. Nucl. Chem.*, **8**, 612 (1958).

(110) Nesmeyanov, A. N., Kazitsyna, L. A., Lokshin, B. V., and Kritskaya, I. I., *Doklady Akad. Nauk S.S.S.R.*, **117**, 433 (1957).

(111) Nesmeyanov, A. N., and Kochetkova, N. S., *Doklady Akad. Nauk S.S.S.R.*, **109**, 543 (1956).

(112) Nesmeyanov, A. N., and Kochetkova, N. S., *Doklady Akad. Nauk S.S.S.R.*, **114**, 800 (1957).

(113) Nesmeyanov, A. N., and Kochetkova, N. S., *Doklady Akad. Nauk S.S.S.R.*, **117**, 92 (1957).

(114) Nesmeyanov, A. N., and Kritskaya, I. I., *Izvest. Akad. Nauk S.S.S.R., Otdel. khim. Nauk*, 253 (1956).

(115) Nesmeyanov, A. N., and Perevalova, E. G., *Uspekhi Khim.*, **27**, 3 (1958).

(116) Nesmeyanov, A. N., Perevalova, E. G., and Beinoravichute, Z. A., *Doklady Akad. Nauk S.S.S.R.*, **112**, 439 (1957).

(117) Nesmeyanov, A. N., Perevalova, E. G., Beinovarichute, Z. A., and Malygina, I. L., *Doklady Akad. Nauk S.S.S.R.*, **120**, 1263 (1958); *C. A.*, **53**, 1293 (1959).

(118) Nesmeyanov, A. N., Perevalova, E. G., Churanov, S. S., and Nesmeyanova, O. A., *Doklady Akad. Nauk S.S.S.R.*, **119**, 949 (1958); *C. A.*, **52**, 17225 (1958).

(119) Nesmeyanov, A. N., Perevalova, E. G., and Churanov, S. S., *Doklady Akad. Nauk S.S.S.R.*, **114**, 335 (1957).

(120) Nesmeyanov, A. N., Perevalova, E. G., and Golovnya, R. V., *Doklady Akad. Nauk S.S.S.R.*, **99**, 539 (1954).

(121) Nesmeyanov, A. N., Perevalova, E. G., Golovnya, R. V., and Nesmeyanova, O. A., *Doklady Akad. Nauk S.S.S.R.*, **97**, 459 (1954).

(122) Nesmeyanov, A. N., Perevalova, E. G., Golovnya, R. V., Nikitina, T. V., and Simukova, N. A., *Izvest. Akad. Nauk S. S. S. R., Otdel. khim. Nauk*, 739 (1956).

(123) Nesmeyanov, A. N., Perevalova, E. G., Golovnya, R. V., and Shilovtseva, L. S., *Doklady Akad. Nauk, S.S.S.R.,* **102,** 535 (1955).
(124) Nesmeyanov, A. N., Perevalova, E. G., Golovnya, R. V., Simukova, N. A., and Starovsky, O. V., *Izvest. Akad. Nauk S.S.S.R., Otdel. khim. Nauk,* 638 (1957).
(125) Nesmeyanov, A. N., Perevalova, E. G., and Nesmeyanova, O. A., *Doklady Akad. Nauk S.S.S.R.,* **100,** 1099 (1955).
(126) Nesmeyanov, A. N., Perevalova, E. G., and Nesmeyanova, O. A., *Doklady Akad. Nauk S.S.S.R.,* **119,** 288 (1958); *C. A.,* **52,** 14579 (1958).
(127) Nesmeyanov, A. N., Perevalova, E. G., Shilovtseva, L. S., and Ustyniuk, Yu. A., *Doklady Akad. Nauk, S.S.S.R.,* **124,** 331 (1959); *C. A.,* **53,** 11332 (1959).
(128) Nesmeyanov, A. N., Sazonova, V. A., and Drozd, V. N., *Doklady Akad. Nauk, S.S.S.R.,* **126,** 1004 (1959).
(129) Nesmeyanov, A. N., Sazonova, V. A., and Drozd, V. N., *Tetrahedron Letters,* **No. 17,** 13 (1959).
(130) Nesmeyanov, A. N., Sazonova, V. A., and Drozd, V. N., *Doklady Akad. Nauk. S.S.S.R.,* **129,** 1060 (1959).
(131) Nesmeyanov, A. N., Sazonova, V. A., and Drozd, V. N., *Doklady Akad. Nauk. S.S.S.R.,* **130,** 1030 (1960).
(132) Nesmeyanov, A. N., and Vol'kenau, N. A., *Doklady Akad. Nauk S.S.S.R.,* **111,** 605 (1956).
(133) Nesmeyanov, A. N., and Vol'kenau, N. A., *Doklady Akad. Nauk S.S.S.R.,* **107,** 262 (1956).
(134) Nesmeyanov, A. N., Vol'kenau, N. A., and Vil'chevskaya, V. D., *Doklady Akad. Nauk S.S.S.R.,* **111,** 362 (1956).
(135) Nesmeyanov, A. N., Vol'kenau, N. A., and Vil'chevskaya, V. D., *Doklady Akad. Nauk S.S.S.R.,* **118,** 512 (1958); *C. A.,* **52,** 11019 (1958).
(136) Nesmeyanov, N. A., and Reutov, O. A., *Doklady Akad. Nauk S.S.S.R.,* **115,** 518 (1957).
(137) Nesmeyanov, N. A., and Reutov, O. A., *Izvest. Akad. Nauk S.S.S.R., Otdel khim. Nauk,* 926 (1959).
(138) Nesmeyanova, O. A., and Perevalova, E. G., *Doklady Akad. Nauk S.S.S.R.,* **126,** 1007 (1959).
(139) Osgerby, J. M., and Pauson, P. L., *J. Chem. Soc.,* 656 (1958).
(140) Osgerby, J. M., and Pauson, P. L., *Chemistry and Industry,* 196 (1958).
(141) Osgerby, J. M., and Pauson, P. L., *Chemistry and Industry,* 1144 (1958).
(142) Osgerby, J. M., and Pauson, P. L., unpublished observations.
(143) Pauson, P. L., *J. Am. Chem. Soc.,* **76,** 2187 (1954).
(144) Pauson, P. L., *Quart. Reviews,* **9,** 391 (1955).
(145) Pauson, P. L., "Non-Benzenoid Aromatic Compounds," Ed. by D. Ginsburg, New York, Interscience Publishers, 1959.
(146) Pauson, P. L., Knox, G. R., Munro, J. D., and Osgerby, J. M., *Angew. Chem.,* **72,** 37 (1960).
(147) Pauson, P. L., and Wilkinson, G., *J. Am. Chem. Soc.,* **76,** 2024 (1954).
(148) Piper, T. S., Cotton, F. A., and Wilkinson, G., *J. Inorg. Nucl. Chem.,* **1,** 165 (1955).

378 ORGANOMETALLIC COMPOUNDS

(149) Piper, T. S., Lemal, D., and Wilkinson, G., *Naturwissenschaften*, **43**, 129 (1956).
(150) Piper, T. S., and Wilkinson, G., *Naturwissenschaften*, **42**, 625 (1955).
(151) Piper, T. S., and Wilkinson, G., *Chemistry and Industry*, 1296 (1955).
(152) Piper, T. S., and Wilkinson, G., *Naturwissenschaften*, **43**, 15 (1956).
(153) Piper, T. S., and Wilkinson, G., *J. Inorg. Nucl. Chem.*, **2**, 38 (1956).
(154) Piper, T. S., and Wilkinson, G., *J. Inorg. Nucl. Chem.*, **3**, 104 (1956).
(155) Piper, T. S., and Wilkinson, G., *J. Am. Chem. Soc.*, **78**, 900 (1956).
(156) Pruett, R. L., and Morehouse, E. L., *Chemistry and Industry*, 980 (1958).
(157) Rausch, M. D., Fischer, E. O., and Grubert, H., *Chemistry and Industry*, 756 (1958).
(158) Rausch, M. D., Fischer, E. O., and Grubert, H., *J. Am. Chem. Soc.*, **82**, 76 (1960).
(159) Reynolds, L. T., and Wilkinson, G., *J. Inorg. Nucl. Chem.*, **2**, 246 (1956).
(160) Reynolds, L. T., and Wilkinson. G., *J. Inorg. Nucl. Chem.*, **9**, 86 (1959).
(161) Richards, J. H., and Curphey, T. J., *Chemistry and Industry*, 1456 (1956).
(162) Richards, J. H., and Hill, E. A., *J. Am. Chem. Soc.*, **81**, 3484 (1959).
(163) Richmond, H. H., and Freiser, H., *J. Am. Chem. Soc.*, **77**, 2022, (1955).
(164) Riemschneider, R., and Helm, D., *Z. Naturforsch*, **14b**, 811 (1959).
(165) Riemschneider, R., and Nehring, R., *Monatsh.*, **90**, 568 (1959).
(166) Rinehart, K. L., Jr., presented at *XVIIth International Congress of Pure and Applied Chemistry*, Munich, 1959.
(167) Rinehart, K. L., Jr., and Curby, R. J., Jr., *J. Am. Chem. Soc.*, **79**, 3290 (1957).
(168) Rinehart, K. L., Jr., Curby, R. J., Jr., and Sokol, P. E., *J. Am. Chem. Soc.*, **79**, 3420 (1957).
(169) Rinehart, K. L., Jr., Michejda, C. J., and Kittle, P. A., *J. Am. Chem. Soc.*, **81**, 3162 (1959).
(170) Rinehart, K. L., Jr., and Motz, K. L., *Chemistry and Industry*, 1150 (1957).
(171) Rinehart, K. L., Jr., Motz, K. L., and Moon, S., *J. Am. Chem. Soc.*, **79**, 2749 (1957).
(172) Rosenblum, M., *Chemistry and Industry*, 72 (1957).
(173) Rosenblum, M., *Chemistry and Industry*, 953 (1958).
(174) Rosenblum, M., *J. Am. Chem. Soc.*, **81**, 4530 (1959).
(175) Rosenblum, M., and Santer, J. O., *J. Am. Chem. Soc.*, **81**, 5517 (1959).
(176) Rosenblum, M., and Woodward, R. B., *J. Am. Chem. Soc.*, **80**, 5443 (1958).
(177) Savitsky, A. V., and Syrkin, Ia. K., *Doklady Akad. Nauk S.S.S.R.*, **120**, 119 (1958).
(178) Schlögl, K., *Monatsh.*, **88**, 601 (1957).
(179) Schlögl, K., *Osterr. Chemiker Ztg.*, **59**, 93 (1958).
(180) Schlögl, K., and Seiler, H., *Monatsh.*, **91**, 79 (1960).
(181) Seibold, E. A., and Sutton, L. E., *J. Chem. Phys.*, **23**, 1967 (1955).
(182) Semenow, D. A., and Roberts, J. D., *J. Am. Chem. Soc.*, **79**, 2741 (1957).
(183) Sloan, C. L., and Barber, W. A., *J. Am. Chem. Soc.*, **81**, 1364 (1959).
(184) Smidt, J., and Jira, R., *Angew. Chem.*, **71**, 651 (1959).
(185) Strohmeier, W., and Lemmon, R., *Z. Naturforsch.*, **14a**, 109 (1959).
(186) Struchkov, Yu. T., *Doklady Akad. Nauk S.S.S.R.*, **110**, 67 (1956); *C. A.*, **52**, 4282 (1958).

(187) Struchkov, Yu. T., *Zhur. Obshchei Khim.*, **27**, 2039 (1957); *C. A.*, **52**, 6326 (1958).
(188) Struchkov, Yu. T., and Khotsyanova, T. L., *Kristallografiya*, **2**, 382 (1957); *C. A.*, **52**, 3457 (1958).
(189) Summers, L., and Uloth, R. H., *J. Am. Chem. Soc.*, **76**, 2278 (1954).
(190) Summers, L., Uloth, R. H., and Holmes, A., *J. Am. Chem. Soc.*, **77**, 3604 (1955).
(190a) Sutton, L. E., personal communication.
(191) Thomas, J. C., *Chemistry and Industry*, 1388 (1956).
(192) Thomson, J. B., *Tetrahedron Letters*, **No. 6**, 26 (1959).
(193) Thomson, J. B., *Chemistry and Industry*, 1122 (1959).
(194) Tilney-Bassett, J. F., personal communication.
(195) Tilney-Bassett, J. F., and Mills, O. S., *J. Am. Chem. Soc.*, **81**, 4757 (1959).
(196) Trifan, D. S., and Nicholas, L., *J. Am. Chem. Soc.*, **79**, 2746 (1957).
(197) Trotter, J., *Acta Cryst.*, **11**, 355 (1958).
(198) Tyler, J. K., Cox, A. P., and Sheridan, J., *Nature*, **183**, 1182 (1959).
(199) Vogel, M. Rausch, M. D., and Rosenberg, H., *J. Org. Chem.*, **22**, 1016 (1957).
(200) Voitländer, J., and Schimitschek, E., *Z. Elektrochem.*, **61**, 941 (1957).
(201) Watts, W. E., and Pauson, P. L., unpublished observations.
(202) Waugh, J. S., Loehlin, J. H., Cotton, F. A., and Shoemaker, D. P., *J. Chem. Phys.*, **31**, 1434 (1959).
(203) Weinmayr, V., *J. Am. Chem. Soc.*, **77**, 3009 (1955).
(204) Weinmayr, V., *J. Am. Chem. Soc.*, **77**, 3012 (1955).
(205) Weiss, E., *Z. anorg. Chem.*, **287**, 236 (1956).
(206) Weiss, E., and Fischer, E. O., *Z. Naturforsch*, **10b**, 58 (1955).
(207) Weiss, E., and Fischer, E. O., *Z. anorg. Chem.*, **278**, 219 (1955).
(208) Weiss, E., and Fischer, E. O., *Z. anorg. Chem.*, **284**, 69 (1956).
(209) Weiss, E., and Fischer, E. O., *Z. anorg. Chem.*, **286**, 142 (1956).
(210) Wilkinson, G., *J. Am. Chem. Soc.*, **74**, 6146 (1952).
(211) Wilkinson, G., *J. Am. Chem. Soc.*, **74**, 6148 (1952).
(212) Wilkinson, G., *J. Am. Chem. Soc.*, **76**, 209 (1954).
(213) Wilkinson, G., *Org. Syntheses*, **36**, 31 (1956).
(214) Wilkinson, G., and Birmingham, J. M., *J. Am. Chem. Soc.*, **76**, 4281 (1954).
(215) Wilkinson, G., and Birmingham, J. M., *J. Am. Chem. Soc.*, **77**, 3421 (1955).
(216) Wilkinson, G., and Cotton, F. A., "Progress in Inorganic Chemistry," Vol. 1, Ed. by F. A. Cotton, p. 1, New York, Interscience Publishers, 1959.
(217) Wilkinson, G., Cotton, F. A., and Birmingham, J. M., *J. Inorg. Nucl. Chem.*, **2**, 95 (1956).
(218) Wilkinson, G., Pauson, P. L., and Cotton, F. A., *J. Am. Chem. Soc.*, **76**, 1970 (1954).
(219) Wilkinson, G., and Piper, T. S., *J. Inorg. Nucl. Chem.*, **2**, 32 (1956).
(220) Wilkinson, G., Rosenblum, M., Whiting, M. C., and Woodward, R. B., *J. Am. Chem. Soc.*, **74**, 2125 (1952).
(221) Wilson, F. C., and Shoemaker, D. P., *J. Chem. Phys.*, **27**, 809 (1957).
(222) Woodward, R. B., Rosenblum, M., and Whiting, M. C., *J. Am. Chem. Soc.*, **74**, 3458 (1952).

8. ARENE COMPLEXES OF THE TRANSITION METALS

H. Zeiss

Monsanto Chemical Company, Dayton, Ohio

INTRODUCTION

The chemical literature has often contained thoughts and experiences which were recorded before their significance was fully comprehended either by the authors or their readers. Some of these instances have been dramatic in reëmergence, such as the Kekulé-Thiele benzene structures, von Baeyer's description of a carbonium ion in 1902, Merling's preparation of tropylium bromide almost seventy years ago, and Willstätter's synthesis of cycloöctatetraene. The intervention of years, even decades, is sometimes necessary before the whole import of such events is realized; and this realization is usually followed by periods of intense activity. The subject of this chapter is the history of the origin and development of a contemporary literature discovery.

Immediately following the preparation of organomagnesium halides by V. Grignard in 1900, there ensued a broad program of preparation of organometallic derivatives in many laboratories. This was in fact a most fruitful period of research activity, the results of which served to establish useful methods of metallorganic synthesis according to the general equation,

$$RMgX + MX_n \longrightarrow R_nM + MgX_2.$$

The reaction of metallic halides, such as those of boron, mercury and lead, with alkyl and aryl Grignard derivatives is still the method of choice in a number of instances. However, some metallic halides, notably those of the transition metals, react with Grignard reagents to give either a coupling product,

$$2\,RMgX + MX_n \longrightarrow R_2 + MX_{n-2} + 2\,MgX_2$$

or unstable organometallic compounds which decompose before isolation into coupling product and metal, e.g.,

$$R_2M \longrightarrow R_2 + M^0.$$

These latter processes have not been well understood, as Kharasch and Reinmuth have written in their treatise on the Grignard reaction (*73*).

Difficulty with reactions between the transition metal halides and Grignard reagents arose early. Sand and Singer (*94*) in reacting chromyl chloride with phenylmagnesium bromide in 1903 observed the formation of an unstable organochromium intermediate which hydrolyzed quickly during hydrolysis. In another attempt to secure a stable organic derivative of chromium, i.e., triphenylchromium, Bennett and Turner (*2*) employed a slurry of solid chromium trichloride with phenylmagnesium bromide in diethyl ether but achieved instead a satisfactory yield of biphenyl. The process was formulated as one of oxidation-reduction, and the reduction step was accounted for in terms of $Cr^{III} \longrightarrow Cr^{II}$.

$$2\,CrCl_3 + 2\,C_6H_5MgBr \longrightarrow (C_6H_5)_2 + 2\,CrCl_2 + MgBr_2 + MgCl_2$$

Had the authors chosen to carry out this reaction at a reduced temperature, the discovery of organochromium compounds by Fr. Hein four years later might have been anticipated. However, the redox process was to receive considerable attention at the hands of Kharasch and his students at Chicago where much effort was devoted to the study of the effects of the metallic halides on Grignard reactions (*73*).

HEIN'S POLYPHENYLCHROMIUM CHEMISTRY

The first successful preparation of an organochromium compound was reported by Hein (*37*) at Leipzig in 1919. He found that when a chromium trichloride-phenylmagnesium bromide slurry in ether was kept in an ice-bath during reaction, an amorphous, hygroscopic organochromium material could be recovered after hydrolysis of the mixture. This dark brown solid was not readily purified and was designated as a "raw bromide," corresponding to "$(C_6H_5)_5Cr \cdot Br$." On treatment with alkali, however, it was converted into an orange, crystalline substance, formulated as a hydrate of "pentaphenylchromium hydroxide, $(C_6H_5)_5Cr \cdot OH \cdot 4H_2O$." While there was little doubt that the latter was a homogeneous substance, its chemical properties were not altogether consistent with this formulation; and in fact much of Hein's subsequent work (*38–64*) in polyphenylchromium chemistry was concerned with these inconsistencies.

The Hein reaction in equation form expressed the same

$$5\,C_6H_5MgBr + 4\,CrCl_3 \longrightarrow \text{"}(C_6H_5)_5Cr \cdot Br\text{"} + 2\,MgBr_2 + 3\,MgCl_2 + 3\,CrCl_2$$

reduction process ($Cr^{III} \longrightarrow Cr^{II}$) suggested by Bennett and Turner but differed greatly in that Cr^{III} was promoted to Cr^{VI} in the oxidation step. Some years later Klemm and Neuber undertook the magnetic susceptibility measurements of "pentaphenylchromium hydroxide" and a number of polyphenylchromium compounds derived from it with the singular and astonishing result that *all* exhibited paramagnetism to the same degree, namely, $1.7 \pm 5\%$ Bohr magnetons (74). This clearly was not consistent with formulations containing the chromium atom in a hexavalent state. These authors suggested the pentavalent level for chromium in these substances; but little came from this proposal.

The strangest of the anomalies associated with "pentaphenylchromium hydroxide" was its reaction with potassium iodide to give "tetraphenylchromium" iodide, "$(C_6H_5)_4Cr$" · I, and phenol!

$$\text{"}(C_6H_5)_5Cr \cdot OH\text{"} + KI \xrightarrow{H_2O} \text{"}(C_6H_5)_4Cr\text{"} \cdot I + C_6H_5OH + KOH + H$$

Since hydrogen was not evolved or iodine liberated, it was difficult to conceive of a path by which Cr^{VI} was reduced to Cr^{V} with concurrent loss of a phenyl radical and reappearance in the form of phenol (39,62). The apparent loss of phenyl group recurred in a number of "acid-base" reactions between the "hydroxide" and organic or inorganic acids (61) which provided upwards of fifty salts of the "tetraphenylchromium" cation. On the other hand, a few of these salts had to be formulated in the "pentaphenyl" form as simple, metathetical products on the basis of rather unsatisfactory analyses.

Yet a third valency series arose when a somewhat water-soluble "triphenylchromium" cation was isolated as the iodide from the alkaline hydrolysis of the "raw bromide" after removal of "pentaphenylchromium hydroxide" (38,40,52). As in the case of its predecessor, the one electron paramagnetism of "triphenylchromium" iodide, "$(C_6H_5)_3Cr$" · I (74), was inconsistent with the tetravalent state of chromium in this formula. However, the isolation of the partially water-soluble "triphenylchromium" cation might have led, as it later did, to a search for an even more water-soluble "diphenylchromium" cation which, in the hydrolysis step, would have been lost in the discarded aqueous washing of the "raw bromide."

Another curious relationship between the "pentaphenyl- and tetraphenyl-chromium" series was uncovered (47,52). Electrolysis of the anhydrous form of "pentaphenylchromium hydroxide" and of "tetraphenylchromium" iodide in liquid ammonia gave the *same* reduction product, "tetraphenylchromium." This substance, likewise orange in color, was sensitive to air and was oxidized in the presence of water to "tetraphenylchromium" hydroxide. This hydroxide was different from that of the "pentaphenylchromium" cation. A loss of phenyl group from "pentaphenylchromium hydroxide" had occurred again during the electrolysis.

Another very puzzling feature of the polyphenylchromium compounds was that they all exhibited approximately the same visible and ultraviolet absorption. The salts of "pentaphenyl-, tetraphenyl-, and triphenyl-chromium" ranged from orange to yellow in color and exhibited a common absorption band near 350 mμ. This uniformity in spectral characteristics supported the Klemm-Neuber deduction that all of the polyphenylchromium compounds contained the chromium atom in the same valence state. Since the pentavalent level appeared to be the only state for the chromium phenyl compounds which could be reasonably supported at that time, the three series of polyphenylchromium compounds were reformulated (see Table 8.1) in 1936 by the latter authors to fit the limitations of structure imposed by this valency.

TABLE 8.1. STRUCTURAL FORMULATIONS OF POLYPHENYLCHROMIUM COMPOUNDS (1936)

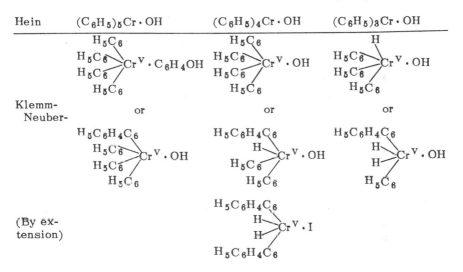

Hein	$(C_6H_5)_5Cr \cdot OH$	$(C_6H_5)_4Cr \cdot OH$ $(C_6H_5)_3Cr \cdot OH$

ORIGIN OF THE π-BIS-ARENE CONCEPT

Experimental Basis

The inconclusive status of the structures of the polyphenylchromium compounds continued for another seventeen years. In 1953 the Hein compounds became the subject of a doctoral investigation by one of the author's graduate students at Yale (*100*). Despite inordinate experimental difficulties M. Tsutsui was successful in obtaining small amounts of the "raw bromide" from which the key compounds in Hein's series, "pentaphenylchromium hydroxide," "tetraphenylchromium" iodide and "triphenylchromium" iodide, could be prepared. At the outset of this new work it was clear from infrared spectral records that the amorphous "raw bromide, $(C_6H_5)_3Cr \cdot Br$," was a complex mixture and that very little information could be derived from this material. On the other hand, the other polyphenylchromium compounds were crystalline, considerably more tractable and possessed exactly the properties described for them. There was no doubt that the newly prepared substances were identical with those of Hein's. However, meager yields, obtained at great expense of time and effort, forced the reinvestigation of the polyphenylchromium compounds into a direction which led to a maximum of information with a minimum loss of material, namely, reductive degradation of the polyphenylchromium compounds with lithium aluminum hydride.

The reductive cleavage of "tetraphenylchromium" iodide by aluminum hydride ion in ether, according to the Hein or the Klemm-Neuber formulations, required the formation of benzene from one or more of the phenyl groups bonded to chromium. Yet none was detected in the product, spectroscopically or otherwise. The *sole* organic product was biphenyl, two molar equivalents of which were produced for each mole of the iodide

$$\text{``}(C_6H_5)_4Cr\text{''} \cdot I \xrightarrow{\text{LiAlH}_4} 2 \ (C_6H_5)_2$$

consumed. The Klemm-Neuber formulations permitted the liberation of biphenyl from chromium, but also required the production of benzene. However, by the simple expedient of extending their structural proposal to one having two biphenyl groups and two hydrogen atoms attached to chromium (Table 8.1) this experiment result was accommodated.

The possibility of the formation of phenyl radicals followed by recombination to biphenyl during the hydride reduction was eliminated by the demonstration that diphenylmercury on reduction with lithium aluminum hydride in ether gave benzene as the sole organic product. This conclusion was based, however, on the assumption that the phenyl-to-chromium bonding in the Hein and Klemm-Neuber formulations was essentially of the same kind as that in diphenylmercury. In any event, these two experimental facts rendered inadmissible all of these formulations for "tetraphenylchromium" iodide, except the "di-biphenyl-dihydro-chromium(V)" structure (*cf.* Table 8.1).

Similar reduction of "triphenylchromium" iodide produced both *benzene* and biphenyl in a 1 : 1 ratio. It was thus certain that benzene could

$$\text{``}(C_6H_5)_3Cr\text{''} \cdot I \xrightarrow{\text{LiAlH}_4} C_6H_6 + (C_6H_5)_2$$

be detected when present in the reduction product even in minute quantities. Since biphenyl was also a product, the Hein formulation was clearly incorrect; but one of the Klemm-Neuber structures, "phenyl-biphenyl-dihydro-chromium(V)" (Table 8.1) was consistent with this result.

The reductive degradation of "pentaphenylchromium hydroxide" at once disposed of the chief anomaly existing in polyphenylchromium chemistry, namely, the convertibility of "pentaphenylchromium" compounds to the "tetraphenylchromium" series and phenol either by "acid-base" reaction or by electrolytic reduction. This "hydroxide" was reduced by aluminum hydride ion in ether to a mixture of biphenyl and that ubiquitous product, *phenol*. No benzene was detected. It then became clear that

$$\text{``}(C_6H_5)_5Cr \cdot OH\text{''} \xrightarrow{\text{LiAlH}_4} 2(C_6H_5)_2 + C_6H_5OH$$

"pentaphenylchromium hydroxide" was in fact a member of the so-called "tetraphenylchromium" series and that its anion was not "hydroxide" but rather *phenoxide*. It followed, regardless of the structure of the "tetraphenylchromium" cation, that the "acid-base" reaction which had led to the preparation of some fifty salts were in actuality simple *metathetical* reactions:

$$\text{``}(C_6H_5)_4Cr\text{''} \cdot OC_6H_5 + HX \longrightarrow \text{``}(C_6H_5)_4Cr\text{''} \cdot X + HO \cdot C_6H_5$$

The corollary to these deductions was the rejection of all of the previous formulations of the "pentaphenylchromium" structure.

The "raw bromide," as expected, revealed itself as a complex mixture in giving benzene, biphenyl, terphenyl, and a mixture of high boiling aromatic products on hydride reduction. This complexity in part accounted for the difficulties and low yields experienced in isolating the "hydroxide" from it.

More recently, Razuvaev and co-workers (*88*) in Russia have repeated the degradation of Hein's polyphenylchromium compounds by photochemical means. Their results and conclusions agree with those described here.

Two annoying inconsistencies of the foregoing experimental results and the Klemm-Neuber formulations of the "triphenylchromium," $(C_6H_5C_6H_4)$-$(C_6H_5)Cr^VH_2$, and (by extension) "tetraphenylchromium," $(C_6H_5C_6H_4)_2$-Cr^VH_2, cations, still remained unresolved. In an effort to confirm or deny the reality of the pentavalent chromium hydride structures, a sample of the latter iodide was reduced with lithium aluminum hydride in ether, and the reduction product was then solvolyzed with deuterium oxide. This experiment was performed under the assumption of a Klemm-Neuber structure and that aluminum hydride ions would effect nucleophilic displacement of biphenyl anions from chromium. These anions should then be neutralized by one atom of deuterium each on solvolysis and should contain when isolated 10 atom per cent of deuterium, or one atom of deuterium for each mole of biphenyl. In the event, deuterium was *not* found in the product biphenyl; and so it was clear that either the mechanistic assumption or the structural formulation (or both) was incorrect. When, however, a sample of "tetraphenylchromium" iodide was reduced with lithium aluminum *deuteride* in ether, the biphenyl isolated was found to have incorporated 5 atom per cent of deuterium in the course of reduction, or only one-half of the amount anticipated in terms of the chromium(V) hydride structure. The decomposition of the iodide by reduction, therefore, must have involved attack by aluminum deuteride ion on carbon rather than on chromium. In this process, deuterium was introduced into the arene ring.

The aluminum deuteride ion reduction of "triphenylchromium" iodide gave biphenyl containing 6.6 atom per cent of deuterium, or about two-thirds of the value predicted in the foregoing discussion.* Although this and the previous isotopic result did not unequivocally dispose of the hydride formulations, they did not support them either. Moreover, the chemical stability of the polyphenylchromium compounds toward mildly acidic or basic aqueous conditions did not argue for a chromium hydride structure.

Thus, at the conclusion of this stage of the experimental work, several anomalies associated with the polyphenylchromium compounds had been removed. But, in invalidating the earlier structural proposals for Hein's organochromium compounds, we had created a void which could not be left unattended.

Onsager's Proposal

In early 1954 Lars Onsager at Yale became interested in the structural problem posed by the results which had accumulated from our work with the Hein compounds. This interest was the basis for a number of stimulating discussions. The advent of the discovery and structural elucidation of bis-cyclopentadienyl-iron(II), or ferrocene, several years earlier (see Chapter 7), together with his own searching analysis of the experimental data now available, led Onsager to propose a biconoidal ("sandwich") structure for the "tetraphenylchromium" cation (110). The isoelectronic resemblance between the bis-cyclopentadienyl-ferricinium ion and the bis-biphenyl-chromium(I) cation (Fig. 8.1) now under consideration supported, at least on theoretical grounds, this most tempting hypothesis. The bis-arene π-complexed structure, in which chromium is permitted to achieve its familiar octahedral coördination geometry by d^2sp^3 bonding with two aromatic rings, instantly removed the anomalies still remaining in the polyphenyl-chromium literature. The bis-biphenyl-chromium(I) structure, in which chromium is one electron short of the inert gas, or krypton, configuration, should be paramagnetic to the extent of 1.72 Bohr magnetons as had been found for the entire series of the Hein compounds. The fact that the "pentaphenyl- and tetraphenyl-chromium" series all exhibited nearly the

---

*The limited amount of sample available precluded isotopic examination of the benzene produced.

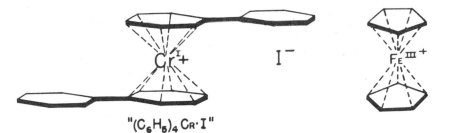

"$(C_6H_5)_4 C_R \cdot I$"

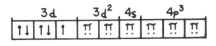

Fig. 8.1

same spectral as well as magnetic properties became understandable, and the metathetical exchange of anions, as in the conversion of phenoxide to iodide with liberation of phenol, was now clear. Furthermore, the electrolytic reduction of the common cation to bis-biphenylchromium(0), a substance in which chromium is now isoelectronic with iron in bis-cyclopentadienyl-iron(II), was no longer incongruous (Fig. 8.2).

The new concept of the bis-arene complex structure was easily extended to the reformulation of the "triphenylchromium" cation. The products of its reduction by lithium aluminum hydride, benzene, and biphenyl, supported a mixed bis-arene complex, i.e., benzene-biphenyl-chromium(I). As has been mentioned before, the possible or actual existence of a third bis-

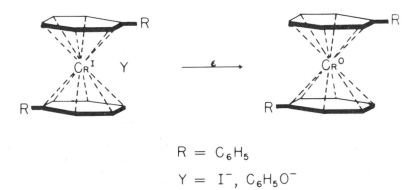

R = C_6H_5

Y = I^-, $C_6H_5O^-$

Fig. 8.2

Fig. 8.3

arene complex in this series, the bis-benzene-chromium(I) cations, was a reasonable deduction (Fig. 8.3).

The skepticism which these first proposals (*5,111,112,121*) attracted was not surprising in view of the reluctance of organic chemists, in particular, to permit an aromatic system, particularly benzene, to lose its familiar resonance energy in coördinating with an inorganic nucleus. However, the weight of conclusive evidence now increased rapidly, and further resistence to the concept became unreasonable.

BIS-ARENE CHROMIUM

It was fortuitous in a sense that most of the fundamental work leading up to the origin of the concept of the bis-arene complex was concerned with the chromium halides. The advantage in the selection of chromium from the list of the transition metals lay in the great capacity of this element to form stable, octahedral complexes. Consequently, one could have done no better than to have chosen a chromium trihalide for the next step in the development of this chemistry, namely, a direct assault on the bis-arene complex structure. The success of this attempt in the latter part of 1955 represented a major advance in the chemistry of these complexes in that the π-bis-arene concept was placed on the solid foundation of rational synthesis.

Fischer-Hafner Synthesis

In Munich, E. O. Fischer and his student, W. Hafner, discovered that when chromium trichloride was reduced by aluminum powder at 150° in the presence of benzene and aluminum trichloride, the parent bis-arene complex, bis-benzene-chromium* was formed (*17,18*). As Hein had found in the case of "tetraphenylchromium" iodide, or bis-biphenyl-chromium(I)

---

*The term "bis-" is used in the nomenclature of metallarene complexes in which both arene complements plating the transition metal are the same. This terminology is phonetically better suited to the English language than the German use of "di-".

(47,52), the cation of bis-benzene-chromium(I) could be reduced to bis-benzene-chromium(0). In air the zerovalent complex was readily oxidized back to the cation.

In rapid order Fischer and his co-workers reported the synthesis of bis-toluene, bis-p-xylene, bis-cumene-, bis-tetralin-, bis-mesitylene-, and bis-hexamethylbenzene-chromium(0) by the same method. These complexes as well as that of bis-benzene-chromium(0) were uniformly diamagnetic as the molecular orbital arrangement previously drawn for the cationic form of a bis-arene-chromium complex in Fig. 8.1 would require them to be. The method of synthesis was extended then to molybdenum pentachloride and benzene from which the diamagnetic bis-benzene-molybdenum(0), in which the metal atom has achieved a xenon-like configuration, was obtained (33). It should be noted that Hein was able to prepare organic derivatives of molybdenum (43) and tungsten (54) by his Grignard method also, but these were less well characterized than those of chromium.

The direct synthesis of the bis-biphenyl-chromium complex from biphenyl and chromium trichloride by Fischer and Seus (32) confirmed the structure which had been proposed for Hein's "tetraphenylchromium" compounds. Hein and Eisfeld (46), employing a mixture of benzene and biphenyl as the aromatic components in the Fischer-Hafner synthesis, isolated the benzene-biphenyl-chromium(I) cation in the form of its iodide from the other expected products, bis-benzene- and bis-biphenyl-chromium(I), and found it to be indistinguishable from "triphenylchromium" iodide.

Properties of Bis-Benzene-Chromium

Physical. Bis-Benzene-chromium, in both its zerovalent and cationic forms, has now been studied in much detail, chiefly by Fischer and his colleagues. The diamagnetic (29) neutral complex is a thermodynamically stable substance (although less so than bis-cyclopentadienyl-iron(II)), melting between 283–285° and decomposing with increasing rapidity above this temperature into benzene and chromium mirror. It is a rather insoluble, dark brown, feathery crystalline compound which can be sublimed under reduced pressure. In its oxidized or cationic form, the complex forms a water-soluble hydroxide, chloride and bromide and is precipitated quantitatively from aqueous solution by the tetraphenylboron ion. Other salts of limited water solubility are its Reineckate, picrate, perchlorate and iodide.

The hexagonal prismatic structure of the bis-benzene-chromium complex has been unequivocally established. It has a dipole moment of zero in its zerovalent form (31,101) and a centrosymmetric molecular structure as determined by X-ray analysis (102). The latter study, although somewhat preliminary, confirms the parallel planar positions of the two benzene rings. Bond distances of 1.38 ± 0.05 Å for C—C, 2.19 ± 0.1 Å for Cr—C and ~ 1.69 Å for Cr—C_6H_6 are reported. Further confirmation of the "sandwich" structure is to be derived from electron spin resonance studies (*3,67,89,90*) of the bis-benzene-chromium(I) cation in aqueous solution. Since it is found that the unpaired electron is not localized on chromium but interacts equally with all twelve hydrogens of the two benzene rings, the biconoidal structure is well established.

The insolubility of bis-benzene-chromium(0) precluded the measurement of its proton magnetic resonance spectrum in solution. However, Mulay and Rochow (*79*) were able to obtain its solid state spectrum over a broad range of temperatures. The narrow line width of about 3.0 gauss at room temperature given by bis-benzene-chromium(0) is taken as evidence that there is motion in the crystalline complex similar to that also found in bis-cyclopentadienyl-iron(II). However, since this motion is completely "frozen out" at $-196°$, at a higher temperature than that recorded for ferrocene, the chromium complex is considerably more rigid than that of ferrocene. The nature of this motion in the solid state is probably due to rotation of the molecule as a whole within its crystalline lattice rather than to rotational motions of the rings within the complex itself. However, in solution the arene rings appear to be rotating freely, since the dipole moments of substituted bis-arene complexes, e.g., bis-toluene and -xylenes, are also zero (*31*).

The heat of combustion of bis-benzene-chromium(0), determined calorimetrically at $20°$, is 1724 kcal/mole (*30*). From this, its calculated heat of formation from the constituent elements is $+51.0$ kcal/mole and from benzene and chromium is $+28.6$ kcal/mole. In the vapor phase this heat amounts to -58.3 kcal/mole. The latter value is less than half of that (-147 kcal/mole) obtained for the formation of ferrocene from cyclopentadiene and iron. Fischer and Schreiner point out that this difference is consistent with the greater thermal stability ($470°$) of the latter complex.

The question of the type of chemical bonding in the bis-arene-chromium complexes has proved as troublesome as that involved in the metallocenes (see Chapter 1). It is only mentioned here that Ruch (*93*) in particular has argued for a three-fold symmetrical structure arising from covalent bonding between chromium and the three sets of π-electrons available from each arene ring. As experimental support for this "Dreiersymmetrie" hypothesis Fischer and Böttcher (*13*) attribute the fact that bis-mesitylene-iron(II) is chemically more stable than bis-benzene-iron(II), to the additional three-fold symmetry already existing in the mesitylene ligands. However, this view is not tenable, since bis-durene- and bis-hexamethylbenzene-iron(II) are found to be increasingly more stable* than bis-mesitylene-iron(II) in that order (*122*). More recently, the "Dreiersymmetrie" hypothesis has been questioned also by Randall and Sutton (*87*) on the basis of a series of measurements of the electric dipole moments of arene-tricarbonyl-chromium (0) complexes. They do not find any special effects of symmetry on the magnitude of these values or evidence of unique behavior associated with a three-fold symmetry in the aromatic component in the arene complexes which might be expected from the "Dreiersymmetrie" hypothesis. It is clear that the matter is unsettled and must await further study.

Chemical. The chemical properties of bis-arene-chromium(0) compounds presently known are largely of a negative sort. Despite a number of attempts to prepare functional derivatives of the complex by substitution methods which are effective with benzene and ferrocene, either failure or decomposition of the complex has resulted. Fritz and Fischer (*15*) tried a series of electrophilic, free radical, and nucleophilic reactions, all to no avail. This lack of aromatic behavior of the arene rings attached to chromium must be due to the preoccupation of their π-electrons with the d^2sp^3 orbitals of chromium and their consequent unavailability for chemical reactions. This may also be inferred from infrared spectra of bis-arene-chromium(0) compounds. These are characterized and also differentiated from benzene and other corresponding aromatic systems by two intense bonds, one between 1410–1430 cm^{-1} and the other between 1120–1140 cm^{-1}, in the region of C—C stretching, and three to five similar bands, between 955–1000 cm^{-1} (2–3) and 740–790 cm^{-1} (1–2), in the region of C—H deformation frequencies. The C—H stretching frequency of bis-arene-chromium complexes between 3010–3160 cm^{-1} is also less characteristic than that of free aromatic systems (3030 cm^{-1}). Consequently, the arene complexes are no more "aromatic" in their spectral properties than they are in their chemical behavior. This difference also distinguishes them chemically from the metallocenes. While in the latter compounds cyclopentadienyl-metal π-bonding confers "aromaticity" on the cyclopentadienyl rings, this property is weakened by the metal in the bis-arenes.

An almost completely reversible oxidation-reduction system consisting of bis-benzene-chromium(0) and its cation in methanol-benzene solutions was constructed by Furlani (*36*). The half-wave reduction potential of this system was determined polarigraphically to be –0.81 volts. This value, in comparison with that measured for Cd^{++} (–0.705) and Zn^{++} (–1.320) in

---

*The word "stable" is used here in the sense of resistance of the complex to decomposition by chemical reagents.

the same solvents, permits the conclusion that the bis-benzene-chromium structure is stable and that the metal ion character of the monovalent chromium cation is intermediate between that of cadmium and zinc. Razuvaev and co-workers (91) have measured the reducing half-wave potentials of the series, bis-benzene-, toluene-, mesitylene-, biphenyl-, cumene-, and cyclohexylbenzene-chromium(I). Little variation in the potential required was observed with change in substituent except in the case of the biphenyl complex. The phenyl substituent in this compound caused a sharp reduction of potential to –0.66 v from that (–0.97 v) measured for the unsubstituted complex. No conclusions were drawn from this exception.

Grignard Synthesis

The water solubility of the bis-benzene-chromium cation confirmed our prediction regarding this property of the complex and with this knowledge, the Grignard reaction between phenylmagnesium bromide and chromium trichloride under the Hein conditions was reinvestigated. The aqueous hydrolysis layer was indeed found to contain the bis-benzene-chromium(I) cation as a major product (113). Taking advantage of the partial solubilities of the benzene-biphenyl-chromium(I) cation in water and chloroform and of the solubility of bis-biphenyl-chromium(I) cation in chloroform only, a complete separation was achieved (114).* It then became clear that the latter complex was in fact the minor product of the Grignard reaction and that the first two benzene complexes were the major, being formed in about equal amounts although in a relatively low, total yield of about 30 per cent. However, the Grignard method leads directly to the complexes in the zerovalent state if the reaction and its hydrolysis are performed in the absence of air or other oxidizing agents.

The unusual sequence of chemical events by which chromium(III) is reduced to chromium(0) and the phenyl group of phenylmagnesium bromide is transformed into the π-complexed benzene and biphenyl ring systems within the bis-arene complexes led us to examine the metal halide-Grignard system in detail. The formation of intermediates in the reaction leading to the π-complexes seemed probable; and it was hoped that one or more of these could be intercepted and isolated.

Triphenylchromium Synthesis

The reaction of chromium trichloride and phenylmagnesium bromide was found by W. Herwig to exhibit a completely different physical appear-

*These separations have also been performed by the chromatographic method (48,53).

ance when conducted in tetrahydrofuran (*115,118*). Whereas in diethyl ether the precipitation of a black, pyrophoric solid was observed as reaction progressed, in tetrahydrofuran the reaction mixtures became brown-red in color and deposited a red crystalline solid.

$$CrCl_3 + 3 C_6H_5MgBr \xrightarrow{THF} (C_6H_5)_3Cr^{III} \cdot 3 THF + 3 MgBrCl$$

These crystals proved to be the organochromium compound sought earlier, triphenylchromium, in the form of its tri-tetrahydrofuranate. Subsequently, it has been described also in combination with phenyllithium (*65,66*).

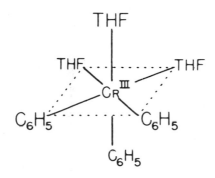

Fig. 8.4

This organochromium compound melts at 85° (dec) and may be stored for days without rapid decomposition in tetrahydrofuran solution in the absence of air and moisture. It is strongly paramagnetic, which value of 3.89 Bohr magnetons compares with that of 3.87 for inorganic chromium(III) compounds. Triphenylchromium in tetrahydrofuran is cleaved quantitatively by mercuric chloride into exactly 3 mole equivalents of phenylmercuric chloride and the violet crystalline tri-tetrahydrofuranate of chromium trichloride (*117*). This cleavage provides an accurate method of determining the concentration of triphenylchromium solutions in tetrahydrofuran:

$$(C_6H_5)_3Cr \cdot 3 THF + 3 HgCl_2 \longrightarrow 3 C_6H_5HgCl + CrCl_3 \cdot 3 THF$$

Tetrahydrofuran can be removed from the crystalline triphenylchromium solvate in various ways. On warming its tetrahydrofuranate above 60° at atmospheric pressure, or by reducing pressure on it at room temperature, or simply by washing the red solid *with diethyl ether*, its coördinated tetrahydrofuran was lost in an amount of 3 mole equivalents and the substance was transformed concurrently into a black, pyrophoric and

strongly paramagnetic solid. Solution of the black material in tetrahydrofuran did not restore the red color of the tetrahydrofuranate of triphenylchromium. These results provide the explanations for several questions.

The failure to isolate triphenylchromium from diethyl ether solution appears to be due to the instability of its trietherate which in turn is related
to the weak basicity, or ligand properties, of diethyl ether. Tetrahydrofuran, being considerably more basic than ether, is capable of forming a
moderately strong ligand bond with chromium(III) and thereby stabilizes
the triphenylchromium entity in an octahedral, hexacoördinate form. Diethyl does not coördinate effectively and in effect destroys the solid tetrahydrofuranate form by a leaching action. Tetrahydrofuran solutions of triphenylchromium, however, are more stable, tolerating considerable dilution with diethyl ether without appreciable decomposition.

The black, pyrophoric solid observed earlier as an intermediate in the
Hein experiments was the same as that resulting from the collapse of tri-
phenylchromium(III) tetrahydrofuranate described above. In both cases,
hydrolysis of the paramagnetic material under nitrogen gave the zerovalent
bis-benzene-, benzene-biphenyl-, and bis-biphenyl-chromium complexes in
the same ratio and yield.

Hydrolysis of the black material, either as solid or in tetrahydrofuran
solution, produced the bis-arene complexes. However, an attempt to sub-
lime the complexes in their zerovalent form from the solid *before* hydrolysis resulted only in thermal decomposition to biphenyl. The black solid is
therefore considered to be a mixture of bis-arene π-complexed *intermediates* which must undergo further reaction in order to produce the final
products. While the black mixture is estimated to be composed of approximately equal parts of bis-benzene- and benzene-biphenyl-chromium intermediates (and traces of the bis-biphenyl-chromium complex), its chemical
composition is more complicated. Since the solid is strongly paramagnetic,
it is regarded as having free radical structure. Further, since its magnetic
susceptibility increases abnormally with decreasing temperature, i.e., χ (T-
Δ)$\neq$ const., it may be formulated, partially at least, in terms of a bi-
radical structure (Fig. 8.5).

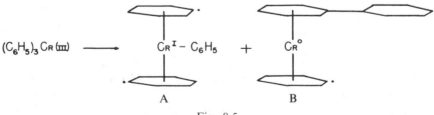

Fig. 8.5

Chemical evidence supporting the π-complex character of the black material was obtained (*114*). When the Grignard reaction was performed in diethyl ether and the product solvolyzed with deuterium oxide instead of water, one deuterium atom was incorporated into the benzene rings but none into the biphenyl structures, i.e., bis-monodeuterobenzene-, mono-deutero-biphenyl-, and bis-biphenylchromium cations were the products. These results have led to the proposal of the formalized radical structures, (A) and (B), as the π-complexed intermediates formed by the collapse of triphenylchromium(III). The small amounts of bis-biphenyl-chromium formed may arise by a phenyl radical abstraction by (B) from another intermediate.

The hydrolysis step, by which the black intermediates are converted into final product, is not clear. However, the loss of phenyl group attached to Cr^I in (A) would account for the production of sufficient phenol in the Hein reaction to result in the isolation of bis-biphenyl-chromium(I) as the phenoxide. Also, the evolution of a gas, presumably hydrogen, which was observed during hydrolysis of the black material, is to be expected from these intermediates together with the production of hydrogen peroxide. Then, too, the experimentally observed instability of both the zerovalent and cationic forms of the bis-arene-chromium complexes to the latter oxidizing agent could account for the consistently low yields ($\sim$30 per cent) of chromium complexes synthesized by the Grignard method. In this connection, it is mentioned that a striking analogy exists between the formation of the bis-arene-chromium(0) complexes and the preparation of hexacarbonyl-chromium(0) by the Job Cassal reaction which is discussed in the last section of this chapter.

Chromous(II) chloride also underwent reaction with phenylmagnesium bromide in diethyl ether or tetrahydrofuran to yield the bis-benzene- and benzene-biphenyl-chromium(0) complexes, the former in a preponderance of $3:2$, in an inert atmosphere (*123*). The total yield again was about 30 per cent. The failure of this reaction to stop at the diphenylchromium(II) stage, even in tetrahydrofuran, is related perhaps to the ease of proceeding from $Cr^{II} \longrightarrow Cr^0$ by the internal oxidation-reduction rearrangement described above and to the weaker coördinating ability of Cr^{II}. However, the former factor appears to be a dominant one, since it was possible to isolate dimesitylchromium(II) tetrahydrofuranate as a violet crystalline compound. In this case and also with the blue trimesitylchromium(III), attempts to rearrange the organochromium compounds to the bis-arene complexes failed, and only decomposition to bimesityl resulted when forcing conditions were used (*125*). These results support the argument for close bonding (σ) between chromium and carbon in these organochromium compounds and for internal rearrangement in the π-complexing step

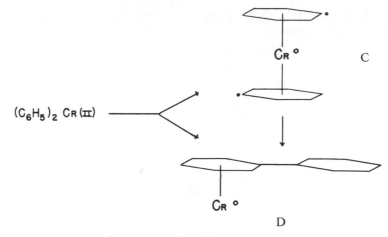

C

D

Fig. 8.6

to the intermediates, (C) and (D). The intermediate (D) must add a molecule of phenylmagnesium bromide to complete the bis-arene structure, or decompose to biphenyl and nascent chromium. Here, as above, the intermediates are drawn to express the evidence available and are therefore only tentative forms.

The catalytic effect of transition metal halides in promoting the synthesis of biaryls from aryl Grignard reagents (*73*), e.g., biphenyl from phenylmagnesium bromide, finds an explanation in terms of these internal rearrangements. The most effective of these, cobaltous(II) chloride, can be compared with chromous(II) chloride in this respect. Chromous chloride is readily reduced by phenylmagnesium bromide *via* diphenylchromium(II) and then stabilized in the π-complex form by redox rearrangement. As a consequence, chromous chloride is not a particularly good catalyst in Grignard coupling reactions. The analogous reaction of cobaltous chloride with phenylmagnesium bromide is also considered to form diphenyl-cobalt(II) (*125*) which after redox rearrangement to a "sandwich" or "half-sandwich" structure would possess one electronic feature uncommon to chromium and to most of the other transition metals in similar reaction. That is to say, cobalt, in the zerovalent state (atomic no. 27) which it would attain by this rearrangement is incapable of forming either a bis-arene complex or a stable "half-sandwich." In the former case, the electron configuration of krypton is exceeded by three; and in the latter there is a deficiency of the same number. Therefore, the decomposition of diphenyl-cobalt is pictured as leading quantitatively to biphenyl and nascent (not colloidal) cobalt. The element in this state must undergo instant oxidation by loss of electrons to neighboring solvent or reactant molecules, becoming available in its divalent form for reduction by phenylmagnesium bromide once again. Present knowledge of the reaction of metallic halides with Grignard reagents, therefore, does not support the mechanism proposed earlier by Kharasch (*73*) according to which metal subhalides, e.g., $CoCl \cdot$, are the effective reducing agents in such systems.

BIS-ARENE METAL COMPLEXES

The Fischer-Hafner synthesis of the bis-arene chromium, molybdenum, and tungsten complexes has been useful in the preparation of similar complexes of many of the remaining groups of the transition metals. The method apparently has not been adaptable to the synthesis of the manganese and technetium bis-arene complexes. The physical properties of arene organometallic compounds are compiled in Table 8.2.

Arene Complexes of V and Fe

In the preparation of bis-benzene-vanadium from vanadium tetrachloride and benzene Fischer and Kögler (*22*) found that the complex obtained on hydrolysis contained the vanadium atom in its zerovalent form, this being isoelectronic with chromium(I) in the bis-benzene-chromium cation. The reaction was formulated as taking place in two steps: the first being the reduction of $V^{IV} \rightarrow V^{I}$,

$$VCl_4 + Al + 2C_6H_6 \xrightarrow{AlCl_3} ([C_6H_6]_2V^I) AlCl_4,$$

and then the hydrolysis resulting in the further reduction of $V^I \rightarrow V^0$, by disproportionation of $V^I \rightarrow V^V$,

$$5[C_6H_6]_2V^I \rightarrow 4[C_6H_6]_2V^0 + V^V + 2C_6H_6.$$

There are several factors about this mechanism which are inconsistent. It is not clear why the reduction of vanadium by aluminum stops at the V^I stage, thus requiring a hydrolytic disproportionation to reach the final product. In view of the categorical statement that the synthesis *does* stop at the Cr^I stage according to

$$3CrCl_3 + 2Al + AlCl_3 + 6C_6H_6 \rightarrow 3([C_6H_6]_2Cr) AlCl_4$$

and that a second, independent reduction step,

$$2[C_6H_6]_2Cr^I + S_2O_4^= + 4OH^- \rightarrow 2[C_6H_6]_2Cr^0 + 2SO_3^= + 2H_2O,$$

is necessary in order to obtain the zerovalent complex, it is puzzling why hydrolytic disproportion does not occur in the chromium case also. This is even more surprising since the bis-benzene complexes of the other members of the Group Vb metals, molybdenum(0) and tungsten(0), are reported to

TABLE 8.2. ARENE COMPLEXES OF THE TRANSITION METALS

Isoelectronic Species No. 23
V°, Cr^I, Mo^I, W^I

	M.P.	Color	μ^*_{eff} (↑)	IR	UV	Ref.
BIS-ARENE						
[C$_6$H$_6$]$_2$ V°	277–78	Red-brown	1.73 (20,22)			22
[C$_6$H$_6$]$_2$ Cr^I	–	Yellow	1.73 (20,29)	109,114	109	18,21,46,113,114
[C$_6$H$_5$D]$_2$ Cr^I	–	Yellow		114		114
[C$_6$H$_6$] [(C$_6$H$_5$)$_2$] Cr^I	–	Yellow-orange	1.80 (74)			46,114
[(C$_6$H$_5$)$_2$]$_2$ Cr^I	I⁻, 157	Orange	1.75 (32)	32	32	32,46,114
[C$_6$H$_6$]$_2$ Mo^I	–	Brown	1.73 (20)			33
[C$_6$H$_6$]$_2$ W^I	–	Orange-yellow				128
MIXED ARENE						
[C$_6$H$_6$] [C$_5$H$_5$] Cr^I	227–29	Orange	1.70 (23)	23	23	23

Isoelectronic Species No. 24
Cr°, Mo°, W°, Mn^I, Re^I, Fe^{II}, Ru^{II}, Os^{II}, Co^{III}, Rh^{III}, Ir^{III}

	M.P.	Color	μ^*_{eff} (↑↓)	IR	UV	Ref.
BIS-ARENE						
[C$_6$H$_6$]$_2$ Cr°	282–84	Dark brown	0 (17,29)	17	77	18,113,114
[C$_6$H$_6$] [(C$_6$H$_5$)$_2$] Cr°	120–21	Yellow-brown	–			52
[(C$_6$H$_5$)$_2$]$_2$ Cr°	~112	Orange-brown	0 (29)			32,52

Compound	M.p.	Color			References
[C₆H₆]₂ Mo°	~115 dec	Green	0 (*29,33*)		*33*
[C₆H₆]₂ W°	110 dec	Yellow-green			*128*
[C₆(CH₃)₆]₂ Mn I	—	Pink	0 (*125*)		*125*
[C₆H₆]₂ Re I	—	Yellow	0 (*20*)		*35*
[*sym*-C₆H₃(CH₃)₃]₂ Re I	—	Red-brown			*35*
[C₆H₆]₂ Fe II	—	Yellow			*122*
[C₆H₅CH₃]₂ Fe II	—	Yellow-orange			*122*
[*o,m,p*-xylene]₂ Fe II	—	Orange			*122*
[tetralin]₂ Fe II	—	Orange			*122*
[*sym*-C₆H₃(CH₃)₃]₂ Fe II	—	Orange-red	0 (*13,29*)		*13,122*
[durene]₂ Fe II	—	Red-orange			*122*
[C₆(CH₃)₆]₂ Fe II	—	Red			*122*
[*sym*-C₆H₃(CH₃)₃]₂ Ru II	—	Red-brown	0 (*14*)		*14*
[*sym*-C₆H₃(CH₃)₃]₂ Os II	—	Yellow			*128*
[*sym*-C₆H₃(CH₃)₃]₂ Co III	—	Red-brown			*128*
[*sym*-C₆H₃(CH₃)₃]₂ Rh III	—	Light brown			*128*
[*sym*-C₆H₃(CH₃)₃]₂ Ir III	—	Brown-yellow			*128*
MIXED ARENE					
[C₆H₆] (CO)₃Cr°	161.5–163 (165.5–66.5)	Yellow	0 (*25*)	*24,36a,103* *11*	*25,27,28,80,103, 103a*
-acetamino	133–134 (134–35.5 dec.)	Yellow			*103,103a*
-acetoxy	94–95.5	Yellow			*28,103*
-chloro	102–3 (98)	Yellow		*36a*	*27,80,103*
-fluoro	122.5–24	Yellow		*36a*	*103*
-*tert*-butyl	83.5–84.5	Yellow			*103*

TABLE 8.2. (*continued*)

	M.P.	Color	μ_{eff}^{*} ($\uparrow\downarrow$)	IR	UV	Ref.
-hexamethyl	211–13 dec (232)	Yellow		*36a*		*27,28,103*
[C₆H₅CH₃] (CO)₃Cr°	80–81 (82.5–83.5)	Yellow		*36a*	*103*	*27,28,80,103,103a*
[C₆H₄(CH₃)₂] (CO)₃Cr° *o-*	98.5–99 (90–91.5) (88–90)	Yellow		*36a*		*27,28,80,103,103a*
m-	103–5 (107–8.5)	Yellow		*36a*		*27,28,80,103*
p-	97–98 (97–100)	Yellow		*36a*		*27,28,80,103*
[*sym*-C₆H₃(CH₃)₃] (CO)₃Cr°	172–174 (177.5–78) (165)			*36a*	*103*	*27,28,80,103,103a*
[tetralin] (CO)₃Cr°	114–15 (116–17.5)				*103*	*80,103,103a*
[naphthalene] (CO)₃Cr°	150 dec	Yellow		*24,36a*	*24*	*27,28*
[(C₆H₅)₂] (CO)₃Cr°	87			*36a*		*24*
[anthracene] (CO)₃Cr°	175–6	Black-red		*24,36a*	*24*	*24*
[9,10-dihydroanthracene] (CO)₃Cr°	143–4	Yellow		*36a*		*24*
[phenanthrene] (CO)₃Cr°	157–60 dec	Red		*24,36a*	*24*	*24*
[chrysene] (CO)₃Cr°	129–30 dec	Dark red		*24,36a*	*24*	*24*

Compound	m.p. (°C)	Color		Ref.	References
$[C_6H_5OH] (CO)_3Cr°$	113–115 (114)		36a		27,28,103,103a
$[C_6H_5CH_2OH] (CO)_3Cr°$	95.5–96.5	Orange	36a		80,103
$[C_6H_5OCH_3] (CO)_3Cr°$	83–84 (86–87) (84)	Yellow			27,28,80,103,103a
$[CH_3C_6H_4OCH_3] (CO)_3Cr°$ o-	75–77				103
p-	52–53.5				103
$[C_6H_5COCH_3] (CO)_3Cr°$	91–92.5	Yellow			10,92,103
$[hydroquinone] (CO)_3Cr°$	impure				103
$[C_6H_5COOH] (CO)_3Cr°$	194 dec	Orange	36a		27,28,103
$[C_6H_5CH_2COOH] (CO)_3Cr°$	134–35.5			103	103
$[C_6H_5COOCH_3] (CO)_3Cr°$	95.5–96 (97.5–98.5) (95)	Orange	36a	103	27,28,103,103a
$[C_6H_5OCOCH_3] (CO)_3Cr°$	94–95.5			103	103
$[C_6H_5CH_2COOC_2H_5] (CO)_3Cr°$	liquid 161–162				103
$[C_6H_5NH_2] (CO)_3Cr°$	(173–75 dec) (161)	Yellow	36a	103	103,103a
-N-methyl	127.5–128	Yellow			103
-N,N-dimethyl	145–146 (146.0–46.5)	Yellow	36a	103	103,103a

TABLE 8.2. (continued)

		M.P.	Color	μ^*_{eff} (↑↓)	IR	UV	Ref.
[CH₃C₆H₄NH₂] (CO)₃Cr° -N,N-dimethyl	o-	130–132	Yellow				103
	m-	76.5–78	Yellow				103
	p-	137–39	Yellow				103
		156–57.5	Yellow				103
[C₆H₆] (CO)₃Mo°		120–25 dec	Green-yellow		36a		27,28
[sym-C₆H₃(CH₃)₃] (CO)₃Mo°		130–40 dec (150 dec)	Yellow		36a		27,28,103
[C₆H₆] (CO)₃W°		140–45 dec					27,28
[sym-C₆H₃(CH₃)₃] (CO)₃W°		160					27,28
[sym-C₆H₃(CH₃)₃] (CO)₃Mnᴵ		–	Yellow	0 (4)	4	4	4
[C₆H₆] [CH₃C₅H₄] Mnᴵ		116–18	Red	0 (4)		4	4
[sym-C₆H₃(CH₃)₃] (C₅H₅] Feᴵᴵ		–	Ivory	0 (4)		4	4
NONBENZENOID							
[C₇H₇]⁺ (CO)₃Mo°	BF₄⁻, ~270 dec		Orange		8	8	8
HETEROCYCLIC							
[C₄H₄S] (CO)₃Cr°		–	Red	0 (26)	26,36a	26	26
[2,2'-dipyridyl]₃ Cr°		–	Black				68

Compound		Form	Color	Value	Ref.	Ref.
[Hexahydrotriazine] (CO)$_3$Cr^0						
-N,N,N-trimethyl		Crystalline	Yellow		76	76
-N,N,N-triethyl		Crystalline	Orange		76	76
-N,N,N-tricyclohexyl		Crystalline	Yellow		76	76
[C$_5$H$_5\overset{+}{N}$CH$_3$] (CO)$_3$Mo^0	I$^-$,	120 dec	Yellow			108
[Hexahydrotriazine] (CO)$_3$Mo^0						
-N,N,N-trimethyl		Crystalline	Yellow		76	76
-N,N,N-triethyl		Crystalline	Yellow		76	76
-N,N,N-tricyclohexyl		Crystalline	Yellow		76	76

Isoelectronic Species No. 25
(none reported)

Isoelectronic Species No. 26
Fe^0, Co^I, Ni^{II}, Pd^{II}, Pt^{II}

BIS-, MIXED, NONBENZENOID AND PSEUDO-ARENE

Compound	MP	Color	Value	Ref.	Ref.
[C$_4$H$_4$S] (CO)$_2$Fe^0	51	Red		107	98
[C$_8$H$_8$] (CO)$_3$Fe^0	92–93.5	Red		98	98
[C$_8$H$_8$] (CO)$_6$Fe$_2$	~190 dec	Yellow		98	98
[C$_8$H$_8$] (CO)$_7$Fe$_2^0$	~220 dec	Black		98	98
[C$_6$(CH$_3$)$_6$]$_2$ Co^I	ϕ_4B$^-$, 205–208 picrate, 210 dec	Dark red	0 (125)		125

TABLE 8.2. (*continued*)

	M.P.	Color	μ_{eff}^{*} (↑↓)	IR	UV	Ref.
$[(CH_3)_2C_4(CH_3)_2]$ Ni^{II} $Cl_2^{=}$	dec	Red-violet	7	7	7	7
$[(C_6H_5)_2C_4(C_6H_5)_2]$ Pd^{II} $Cl_2^{=}$	–					78
$[C_7H_7]$ Pt^{II} $Br_3^{\equiv}$,	154.5–155	Orange	16	16	16	16
Isoelectronic Species No. 27 (none reported)						
Isoelectronic Species No. 28 Ni°, Ag^{I}, Hg^{II}						
$[C_5H_5]_2$ Ni°	41–42	Deep red	0 (*34*)		*34*	*34*
$[C_4H_4]$ Ag^{I} NO_3^{-}	140	Colorless			*82,83*	*82,83*
$[C_4H_4]$ Hg^{II}	Unstable				*82,83*	*82,83*

*Room temperature

be formed in the neutral state under similar conditions (22). In our hands (125) the Fischer-Hafner synthesis of the bis-benzene-chromium complex, according to the method described in the literature (18), *does* result in the zerovalent complex if strongly alkaline hydrolysis and oxygen-free conditions are used. Part of the explanation may lie in our finding that bis-benzene-chromium(0) can act as a Lewis base and as such is instantly precipitated from benzene solution by aluminum trichloride (or triphenylboron). Alkaline hydrolysis of this salt regenerates the zerovalent complex. Whether this salt is similar to that described in the equation above as $([C_6H_6]_2Cr^I)AlCl_4$,* has not been ascertained, since the experimental details concerning the latter substance have not yet appeared. Meanwhile, it is suggested that the reduction of Cr^{III} by aluminum may possibly proceed directly to the zerovalent state,

$$CrCl_3 + Al + 2 C_6H_6 \longrightarrow [C_6H_6]_2Cr^{+} \rightarrow \bar{A}lCl_3$$

where it is coördinated with aluminum trichloride until hydrolysis. Very recently the preparation of hexacarbonylchromium(0) by the Fischer-Hafner method (19) has been formulated in the same way. Here, as before,

$$CrCl_3 + Al + 6 CO \longrightarrow (CO)_6Cr^0 + AlCl_3$$

reduction of $Cr^{III} \longrightarrow Cr^0$ by $Al^0 \longrightarrow Al^{III}$ seems most logical.

The preparation of bis-arene iron complexes proceeds directly from the ferrous state into the Fe^{II} complex,

$$FeBr_2 + 2 Ar \xrightarrow{AlCl_3} [Ar]_2 Fe^{II} Br_2.$$

Whereas the *o-*, *m-*, *p*-xylene, mesityene-, durene-, and hexamethylbenzene complexes of iron are not particularly difficult to isolate, bis-benzene- and bis-toluene-iron(II) are best hydrolyzed in the presence of tetraphenylboron ion in order to isolate the salts before extensive hydrolytic decomposition of the complex has occurred (122).

Bis-Arene Complexes of Re, Ru, Os, Co, Rh, and Ir

The reducing action of aluminum in the presence of aluminum trichloride on the halides of rhenium,

$$3 ReCl_3 + 4 Al + 6 Ar \xrightarrow{AlCl_3} 3([Ar]_2Re^I)AlCl_4 + AlCl_3,$$

and ruthenium,

$$3 RuCl_3 + Al + 6 Ar + 5 AlCl_3 \longrightarrow 3([Ar]_2Ru^{II}) (AlCl_4)_2,$$

*In a later publication Fischer, Hafner and Öfele (19) reformulate this as $([C_6H_6]_2Cr^I)AlCl_4 \cdot AlCl_3$.

is also effective in the preparation of the bis-arene complexes of these metals (14,35). However, in these cases further reduction of Re^I or Ru^{II} on hydrolysis was not observed for the reason that, being isoelectronic with chromium(0), their complexes are in their most stable state. The osmium^{II}, cobalt^{III}, rhodium^{III}, iridium^{III} (127,128) bis-arenes (see Table 8.2) are likewise accessible by this method.

Acetylenic Synthesis of Cr, Mn, and Co Bis-Arene Complexes

Triphenylchromium has now been found to undergo reaction with acetylenes, presumably by way of an initial exchange of its coördinating ligands, tetrahydrofuran, with the acetylenic π-electron system. The unisolated acetylenic chromium complex intermediates condense immediately into aromatic systems (see later discussion of **Acetylenic Metal Complexes**) and bis-arene complexes of chromium. Thus, 2-butyne has been cyclized into hexamethylbenzene, 1,2,3,4-tetramethylnaphthalene and the bis-arene complexes of these hydrocarbons with chromium (116,119). The method is effective with other transition metals, particularly in the preparation of the previously unknown bis-arene complexes of manganese(I) and cobalt(I).

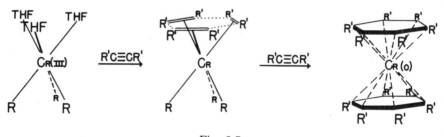

Fig. 8.7

When tetrahydrofuran solutions of dimesitylcobalt(II) and diphenylmanganese(II) are reacted with 2-butyne (dilution of the latter solution with diethyl ether or the use of ether alone is required for reaction), the pink, diamagnetic tetraphenylboron salt of bis-hexamethylbenzene-manganese(I) is obtained from the latter reaction and the burgundy red, diamagnetic tetraphenylboron salt of bis-hexamethylbenzene-cobalt(I) in the former (125). Whereas the electron complement of the manganese complex conforms to the inert gas configuration, that of the cobalt compound is unusual in that the krypton configuration is exceeded. Since the complex is diamagnetic, the excess electron pair is put into the 5s orbital. However, the octahedral geometry assumed in this structural assignment has not been verified, and so the electronic arrangement must be considered only as a possibility.

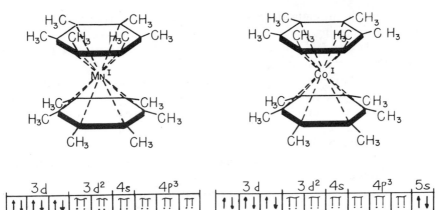

Fig. 8.8

Mixed Arene and Arene-Carbonyl Metal Complexes

Ingenious use has been made of the Grignard and Friedel-Crafts type reactions in preparing mixed arene complexes. Metallocene and metallarene systems have been joined by Coffield, Sandel, and Closson (*4*). Methylcyclopentadienyl-benzene-manganese(I) was synthesized by allowing phenylmagnesium bromide to react with methylcyclopentadienyl-manganese chloride or bis-methylcyclopentadienyl-manganese in tetrahydrofuran. Then, by treatment of cyclopentadienyl-dicarbonyl-iron dichloride with aluminum chloride in refluxing mesitylene, cyclopentadienyl-mesitylene iron iodide was obtained.

Metal carbonyl and metallarene chemistry have been merged most successfully by independent efforts. Fischer and Öfele (*25*) discovered that benzene-tricarbonyl-chromium(0) is formed by reaction between bis-benzene-chromium(0) and hexacarbonylchromium(0). More generally, these authors (*27*) as well as Natta and his colleagues (*80*) in Italy and Whiting and Nicholls (*103*) in England have found that the metal carbonyls react readily with aromatic systems either in autoclave or under reflux with partial liberation of carbon monoxide and formation of a mixed arene complex, e.g.,

$$(CO)_6Cr^0 + C_6H_6 \rightleftarrows [C_6H_6](CO)_3Cr^0 + 3\,CO.$$

The aromatic reactant in this synthesis may contain functional groups or may even be a part of another ring system, as in the paracyclophanes (*5a*). As a consequence, the number of the tricarbonylchromium, molybdenum, and tungsten derivatives (*28,81,103*; also *9,12*) has now become quite large (see Table 8.2). The limitations of the method encountered to this date have been due to the substituents, —COOH, —CHO, —CN and

—NO$_2$, which promote decomposition of hexacarbonylchromium(0) before the complexing reaction becomes predominant. However, the benzoic and phenylacetic acid complexes are obtained by hydrolysis of their corresponding ester complexes.

The dissociation constants of benzoic acid-, phenol- and phenylacetic acid-tricarbonyl-chromium(0) have been compared with the pK$_a$ values of the free aromatic compounds (28,103). In each case the acidity has been strengthened by the tricarbonylchromium(0) π-bonding to the arene ring. Conversely, the basicity of aniline in the complex is weakened. This withdrawal of π-electrons from the arene ring by the carbonyl groups through chromium is also clearly shown by an increase in dipole moment, μ (31,87), as the inductive effect of methyl (or methoxy, anilino, etc.) groups strengthens the π-bond between arene and chromium, e.g., benzene- (4.92) vs hexamethylbenzene- (6.22) tricarbonyl-chromium(0). On the other hand, an electron withdrawing arene group, e.g., methylbenzoate- (4.47), decreases the electric moment. However, in spite of these results and the reported inertness of arene-tricarbonyl-chromium(0) compounds toward electrophilic reagents, the Friedel-Crafts acylation of benzene-tricarbonyl-chromium(0) has been accomplished independently in two laboratories (10,92). Conversion of chlorobenzene-tricarbonyl-chromium(0) to the anisole complex by nucleophilic substitution proceeds readily and in high yield (103).

The arene-tricarbonyls all show two strong C—O stretching vibrations at 1980 and 1895 cm^{-1} (103). Ercoli and Mangini (11) have recorded the ultraviolet spectra of a series of these compounds and find three characteristic absorption areas: 315–325 mμ (log $\epsilon \sim 4$), 250–270 mμ (log ϵ = 3.7–4.0) and 220–230 (log ϵ = 4.3–4.8).

Non-Benzenoid Arene Metal Complexes

It was certain, particularly in view of the great interest in non-benzenoid aromatic systems, such as the tropylium ion and the cyclobutadiene molecule, that attempts to prepare the metal complexes of these structures would be made. Wilkinson (104,105) in England initiated the drive for a tropylium complex by synthesizing 1,3,5-cycloheptatriene-tricarbonyl-molybdenum(0) from the cycloheptatriene and hexacarbonylmolybdenum(0). But it remained for Dauben and Honnen (8) to complete the synthesis of the tropylium (or tropenium) ring in this complex by a hydride ion abstraction using trityl carbonium ion (Fig. 8.9). The tropylium-tricarbonyl-molybdenum(0) ion was separated as its tetrafluoroboron salt. The tropylium bromide complex of platinum is reported to arise from the reaction of cycloheptatriene with platinum tetrabromide or bromoplatinic acid (16).

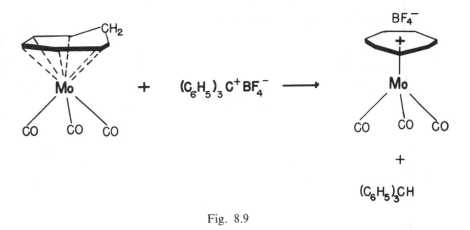

Fig. 8.9

The atomic number of nickel (*28*) seemed at the outset to have given it a particular advantage over the other transition metals in serving as the metal nucleus for the eventual capture of the elusive cyclobutadiene (*75, 121*). Indeed, some of the work now reported has involved this approach. In spite of what appeared to be a promising lead, there is still no conclusive proof available of the *independent* existence of this four-membered "aromatic" ring.

Criegee and Schröder (*6,7*) have described a nickel complex of tetramethylcyclobutadiene which they obtained by reduction of 1,2-dichloro-1,2,3,4-tetramethylcyclo-3-butene with tetracarbonylnickel. However, at-

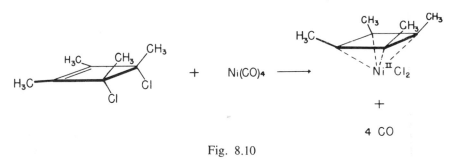

Fig. 8.10

tempts to isolate the free cyclobutadiene derivative by removal of nickel resulted in the formation of octamethyl-cycloöctatetraene and other products as well. Nenitzescu and his co-workers (*82,83*) have claimed the capture of cyclobutadiene itself in the form of its silver nitrate complex. The ring system is reported to be formed by the action of lithium amalgam on 1,2-dichlorocyclo-3-butene. Confirmatory evidence, however, is not yet available.

Our own efforts to synthesize either bis-tetraphenylcyclobutadiene or its nickel complex by acetylenic synthesis from diphenylacetylene and di-phenylnickel(II) are inconclusive. Although the stoichiometry of the reaction and the diphenylacetylene-nickel polymeric product, together with the concurrent synthesis of hexaphenylbenzene, strongly indicates a cyclobuta-diene-type intermediate, the molecule or its nickel complex has not been isolated (*125*, cf. *96*).

Fischer and Werner (*34*) more recently have obtained bis-cyclopenta-diene-nickel(0) from cyclopentadiene and tetracarbonylnickel(0). A palladium dichloride complex of tetraphenylcyclobutadiene is now reported also (*78*).

It is well to remember in considering these aspects of the cyclobuta-diene problem that even though metal complexes of cyclobutadiene deriva-tives exist, the chemistry of cyclobutadiene, or perhaps more sensibly, sub-stituted cyclobutadienes, still remains unknown. In fact, the stability of these metal complexes now has created another problem of its own.

Heterocyclic Metal Complexes

Pseudo-arene metal complexes have now been prepared, illustrating the variety of organic molecules and ions which can be used in constructing new complexes. In rapid succession, thiophene (*26,107*), the pyridinium ion (*108*), cycloöctatetraene (*98*), 2,2-dipyridyl (*68*) and the hexahydrotriazine

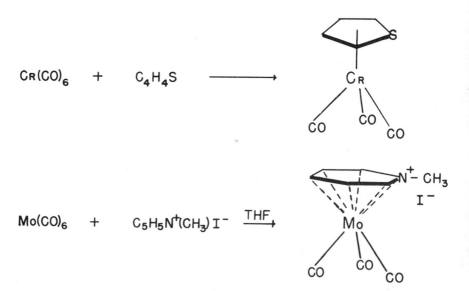

Fig. 8.11

(76) ring systems have been brought to face metal atoms in these complexes. Thiophene was treated directly with hexacarbonyl-chromium(0) in preparing thiophene-tricarbonyl-chromium(0). The other syntheses follow the same pattern of reaction of metal carbonyl with the organic moiety.

ACETYLENIC METAL COMPLEXES

The concept of a hexacoördinated organochromium(III) complex containing replaceable tetrahydrofuran ligands, was introduced in the section dealing with the properties of triphenylchromium tetrahydrofuranate. The development of this idea has led to experiments with π-electron systems which would not only serve as the replacing ligands on chromium but which would also be expected to react further within the confines of the hexacoördinated complex. Thus, acetylenic systems have been used to displace the tetrahydrofuran, after which the acetylene molecules, now positioned favorably within the octahedral complex, may condense into cyclic arrangements. The synthesis of bis-arene metal complexes from the acetylene, 2-butyne, described earlier represented one of the first fruits of this approach. However, the method is capable of considerably broader application to organic synthesis.

Cyclic Condensation on Chromium

Triphenylchromium in tetrahydrofuran is decomposed rapidly by either the acidic hydrogen of acetylene or a monosubstituted acetylene, and the acetylene is polymerized. The sensitivity of organochromium(III) compounds, in general, toward acidic hydrogen is similar to that of the Grignard reagents. Disubstituted alkyl- or aryl-acetylenes, however, are cyclized by the organochromium(III) compounds along reaction paths which may be varied by stoichiometric control (*116,119*).

Addition of 2-butyne to triphenylchromium in tetrahydrofuran solution produced an exothermic reaction whose onset was either delayed or hastened by reactant ratio as shown in Table 8.3. The most striking feature observed in this reaction, however, was the product and the product ratio. The primary product is **1,2,3,4-tetramethylnaphthalene** and its π-complex. Only when quantities of 2-butyne exceeding four mole equivalents were used did triphenylchromium promote the formation of hexamethylbenzene

TABLE 8.3. REACTION OF TRIPHENYLCHROMIUM AND 2-BUTYNE

Mole ratio $(C_6H_5)_3Cr$: 2-Butyne	1:1	1:2	1:3	1:5	1:20
Start of Exothermic Reaction, Min.	330	280	90	50	15
Yield of $(CH_3)_6 C_6$, %	–	–	–	25	55
Yield of 1,2,3,4-Tetramethylnaphthalene, %	13	31	40	36	38

in appreciable amounts. Since the π-complexes of these hydrocarbons were only formed when an excess of the butyne is employed, these complexes were not intermediates in the hydrocarbon synthesis.

The dependence of the course of reaction between 2-butyne and triphenylchromium on reactant stoichiometry has thus been demonstrated. A step-wise replacement of the coördinating tetrahydrofuran ligands and participation of the phenyl groups bonded to chromium is supported by this variation of product. In Fig. 8.12 the reaction scheme is illustrated.

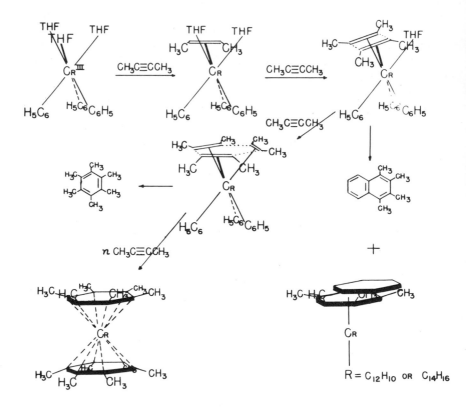

Fig. 8.12

The synthesis of 1,2,3,4-tetramethylnaphthalene requires a transition assembly, composed of one phenyl group and two moles of 2-butyne, which is expressed as the second intermediate in the diagram, i.e., a "tetramethylcyclobutadiene"-metal complex intermediate. The fact that this naphthalene is always produced in this reaction, regardless of the amount of 2-butyne used, supports, but of course does not prove, this formulation of a highly reactive intermediate. The evidence available (see following section) strongly indicates that the chromium atom is responsible for the abstraction of *ortho*-substituted hydrogen from the phenyl group, facilitating ring closure at that position to the polynuclear structure. The latter conclusion may be interpreted in terms of a "benzyne" intermediate forming *within* the complex, as hydrogen is removed from a phenyl group, followed by an internal Diels-Alder reaction between "benzyne-" and "tetramethylcyclobutadiene."

When sufficient 2-butyne is present in the reaction system, the "tetramethylcyclobutadiene"-metal complex may either lose its remaining tetrahydrofuran in favor of a third mole of the acetylene or undergo an external Diels-Alder addition with 2-butyne to produce hexamethylbenzene. Saturation of the reaction system with 2-butyne is favorable to reaction of the third intermediate in the diagram to yield small amounts of the bis-arene complexes *via* mechanism proposed for the Job-Cassal reaction on pp. 417–421 of this chapter.

The condensation of 2-butyne by triethylchromium in tetrahydrofuran gave hexamethylbenzene in somewhat higher yield than that obtained using triphenylchromium. Again, hexamethylbenzene was the only condensation product isolated when a triarylchromium having blocked *ortho*-positions, e.g., trimesitylchromium, was used as the cyclizing agent.

The generality of these condensation reactions is illustrated further by the cyclization of diphenylacetylene by triphenylchromium to hexaphenylbenzene and 1,2,3,4-tetraphenylnaphthalene and by the one-step synthesis of **1,2,3,4-tetramethylphenanthrene** plus hexamethylbenzene from tri-α-naphthylchromium and 2-butyne (Fig. 8.13). The condensation of the same acetylene with tri-β-naphthylchromium also was performed in order to detect any unusual directive influence during ring closure. However, both **1,2,3,4-tetramethylanthracene** and 1,2,3,4-tetramethylphenanthrene were formed, the latter in the greater amount.

The conclusion that the chromium atom in organochromium compounds is a powerful hydrogen acceptor was substantiated by several unique syntheses. For example, triethylchromium not only cyclized diphenylacetylene to hexaphenylbenzene, but also contributed an ethyl group in a mixed condensation with this acetylene to yield **1,2,3,4-tetraphenylbenzene** (*124*). In this case, chromium has not only abstracted a hydrogen atom from a methyl group of its ethyl substituent (ethylene-metal complex) but has also dehydrogenated the resulting dihydrotetraphenylbenzene to the aromatic product. Trimethylchromium, on the other hand, contributed a methyl group (methylene-metal complex) in a mixed condensation with two molecules of diphenylacetylene to form **1,2,3,4-tetraphenylcyclopentadiene** (*124*). The formidable oxidizing power of Cr^{III} when bonded to carbon aryl

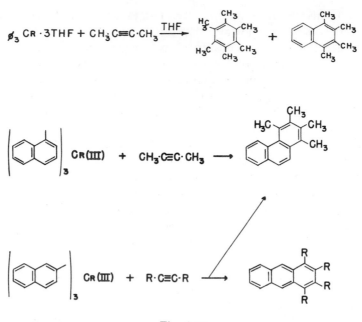

Fig. 8.13

and alkyl groups is a new property of this element which has yet to be exploited.

Cyclic Condensation on Nickel

Tetrahydrofuran solutions of dialkyl and diaryl-nickel(II) derivatives are relatively unstable unless maintained at low temperatures. However, these organometallics are capable of cyclizing acetylenes but with distinguishing differences from the organochromium compounds (*125*). Dimesitylnickel, for example, condensed diphenylacetylene to hexaphenylbenzene and to an intractable polymeric material whose composition approximates that of a tetrameric form of diphenylacetylene containing one atom of nickel. The critical effect of reactant ratio on product ratio again indicates a highly reactive intermediate similar to that deduced from the acetylene condensations on chromium. Thus, the preparation of one mole of dimesitylnickel from one mole of nickelous bromide and two moles of phenylmagnesium bromide in tetrahydrofuran and its reaction with four moles of diphenylacetylene gave only 0.1 mole of hexaphenylbenzene and a large amount of the diphenyl-acetylene-nickel polymer. However, if the mole ratio of organonickel to tolane was increased from 1 : 4 to only 1 : 6, the yield of hexaphenylbenzene rose sharply to 1.7 moles and that of the polymer fell to trace amounts. Further increases in the ratio did not significantly raise the yield of the benzene derivative. This sharp reversal in product yields is interpreted in terms of a bis-tetramethylcyclobutadiene-nickel reaction intermediate described in Fig. 8.14. According to this picture the formation

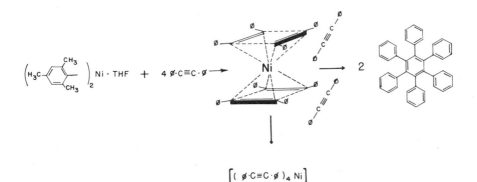

Fig. 8.14

of the intermediate requires four moles of tolane; and this nickel complex undergoes intermolecular Diels-Alder condensations to polymer. If, however, excess tolane is available, the intermediate reacts by external addition with the acetylene, giving rise to a theoretical yield of just two moles of hexaphenylbenzene. This reaction scheme is also strengthened by the observation that bis-arene nickel compounds have resisted preparation by any of the methods available. These hypothetical complexes, in which nickel possessed either the zero-, mono-, or di-valent states, would, of course, require an electron complement exceeding that of the inert gas configuration.

It is further noted that, in contradistinction to the acetylene condensation on chromium, diphenylnickel does not form substituted naphthalenes. *In its capacity for abstracting ortho-substituted hydrogen from its aromatic groups, chromium is unique among the transition metals.* However, diethyl nickel, in condensing tolane to hexaphenylbenzene, does contribute an ethyl group in mixed condensation but is unable to dehydrogenate the product, **1,2,3,4-tetraphenyl-1,3-cyclohexadiene** (*124*).

Cyclic Condensation on Cobalt

Diphenylcobalt possesses a singular position among the organo-transition metal compounds in several respects. The first, already mentioned, is the apparent violation of the inert gas configuration "rule" by its bis-hexamethylbenzene complex electron complement. Yet it is conceivable that this inconsistency provides the source of the second singularity, namely, its catalytic power in acetylene condensations. Whereas the cyclic condensations on organo-chromium, -nickel, -manganese, etc., proceed in stoichiometric ratios between the metal atom and the acetylene, the cobalt atom is effective in continuing the condensation beyond the stoichiometric limit. This behavior is reflected in Table 8.4 which contains the results of

TABLE 8.4. CYCLIC CONDENSATION OF 2-BUTYNE
WITH DIMESITYLCOBALT

2-Butyne (mole)	6	8	10	20	40
$CoCl_2$ (mole)	1	1	1	1	1
Yield of HMB,[a] % (based on cobalt)	50	153	200	480	1000
π-Complex	20	20	30	20	20

[a] Hexamethylbenzene

reactions between diphenylcobalt and 2-butyne in tetrahydrofuran. It is seen that the amount of hexamethylbenzene produced rose at a catalytic rate with the increase in concentration of 2-butyne, while the yield of its cobalt complex remained essentially constant.

Addition Reactions

In the reaction scheme presented in Figure 8.12 the stepwise replacement of tetrahydrofuran ligands of triphenylchromium gives, as the first intermediate, a structure in which only one acetylene molecule has been π-complexed to chromium. Since the existence of second and third π-complexed intermediates in this diagram is based on the products and their hypothetical paths of formation, an analogous interaction of the aryl substituents of chromium with lone acetylene π-complexed to chromium in the initial intermediate might be expected. This has in fact been realized (*120*). By using trimesitylchromium in order to avoid polynuclear condensation and π-complex formation, and by keeping the initial reactant ratio low, 1:1, the addition of mesityl group to 2-butyne to form 2-mesityl-2-butene was accomplished in addition to the expected cyclic condensation to hexamethylbenzene.

A second example of this type of reaction involves the addition of two aryl groups from the arylchromium reagent to an acetylenic bond. Dimethyl acetylenedicarboxylate and triphenylchromium in tetrahydrofuran interacted exothermally to produce *cis-dimethyl diphenylmaleate*. The *cis* geometry of the product indicates a firm bonding of the π-electron system of this acetylene to chromium at the time of the stereo-specific addition of the aryl groups. In this instance, no cyclic condensation of the acetylene was observed.

The mechanism of these additions is not clear. The fact that they do occur supports the view of a stepwise displacement of tetrahydrofuran from the triarylchromium molecule in that solvent. The effects of the stoichiometric ratio of reactants and of the π-electron density in the acetylenic bond are undoubtedly important factors; but a detailed discussion of the addition reaction is not now possible. However, the addition of one and two aryl groups to the acetylenic bond does have an important analogy. In fact, the resemblance between the products of the Job-Cassal reaction and those described in this section merits discussion since they are probably related mechanistically.

THE JOB-CASSAL REACTION

In 1926, some seven years after Hein first reported his preparation of an organochromium derivative, Job and Cassal (72) described the first preparation of hexacarbonyl-chromium(0) by passing carbon monoxide into a *reacting* mixture of chromium trichloride and phenylmagnesium bromide and diethyl ether and then hydrolyzing the reaction solution. In addition to the zerovalent chromium compound a highly diversified mixture of organic compounds, including those of the organo-carbonyl type, was isolated and separated. The organocarbonyl mixture contained benzaldehyde, benzophenone, benzil, benzoin, and diphenylacetophenone. In addition, *phenol*, biphenyl, a large quantity of benzpinacol, and other reduction products, benzhydrol, triphenylvinyl alcohol, triphenylcarbinol, and triphenylmethane were also identified. The organochromium residue described by Hein was also observed.

Two significant results arising from the Job-Cassal reaction now to be considered arc the reduction of the chromium(III) to its zerovalent state and the synthesis of organocarbonyl functions by the interaction of carbon monoxide with the phenyl group of the *reacting* Grignard system. Although the latter system had been shown to produce organochromium compounds of uncertain structure, the relationship of the Job-Cassal products to the Hein polyphenylchromium compounds was not then apparent. The elucidation of the structures of the Hein compounds and the behavior of triphenylchromium in the presence of acetylene now permit a rationalization of the formation of the Job-Cassal products.

The instability of triphenylchromium tri-tetrahydrofuranate in diethyl ether has been ascribed to the leaching effect and the weak coordination of ether in the chromium compound. The collapse of the triphenylchromium

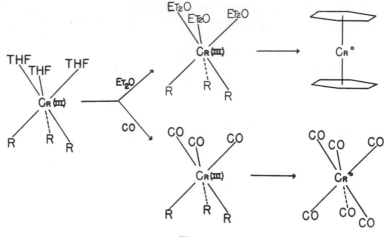

Fig. 8.15

etherate to bis-arene complex follows (Fig. 8.15). The reaction of chromium trichloride and phenylmagnesium bromide in ether, that is, under the conditions of the Job-Cassal reaction, must therefore result in the same unstable form of triphenylchromium. This intermediate, if undisturbed, rearranges to the π-complex intermediates. However, if carbon monoxide is made available at the moment of the triphenylchromium etherate synthesis, the intermediate may undergo an exchange of its ether ligands with carbon monoxide, in much the same way as acetylene molecules are considered to exchange with tetrahydrofuran ligands. However, the polar character of carbon monoxide, $:\overset{-}{C}\equiv\overset{+}{O}:$, must result in a linear coordination of the molecule to chromium rather than the edge-on position described for the acetylene. By this argument, the first step in the Job-Cassal reaction is considered to involve replacement of the weakly coordinating diethyl ether molecules which surround triphenylchromium(II) at the moment of its synthesis in that solvent by carbon monoxide and formation of an intermediate triphenylchromium carbonyl, such as I in Figure 8.16.

Rearrangement of I in the presence of carbon monoxide by the internal oxidation-reduction process previously described for π-complex formation from triphenylchromium(III) (see p. 394) to the hexacarbonylchromium(I) structure is the second; and subsequent hydrolytic reduction of the cation to hexacarbonylchromium(0) is the third. Direct replacement of the phenyl groups on chromium and expulsion of biphenyl by carbon monoxide without a biphenyl-tricarbonylchromium(I) intermediate of course remains a possibility.

Hieber and Romberg (*69*) have studied the Job-Cassal reaction in some detail and concluded that carbon monoxide *must* be introduced into the *reacting* chromium halide-Grignard system in order to obtain the hexacarbonyl. Furthermore, they found that the hydrolysis step was required also for the formation of hexacarbonylchromium(0), for none could be sublimed from the reaction mixture *prior* to it. These experimental facts are consistent with the interpretation of the Job-Cassal reaction presented in Fig. 8.16. According to this scheme, too, the hydrolytic step requires the liberation of hydrogen gas and the production of *phenol* which are observed experimentally.

In other studies of the Job-Cassal reaction, the dependence of the reaction equilibrium and consequent product yield on carbon monoxide concentration has been clearly demonstrated (*1,84a*) by subjecting the reacting chromium trichloride-phenylmagnesium bromide mixture to increased pressure with consequent rise (→67 per cent) in the amount of hexacarbonylchromium formed. This evidence too is consistent with the course of reaction proposed here.

More recently, it has been shown that benzene-tricarbonylchromium(0) may be reversibly converted into hexacarbonylchromium(0) by employ-

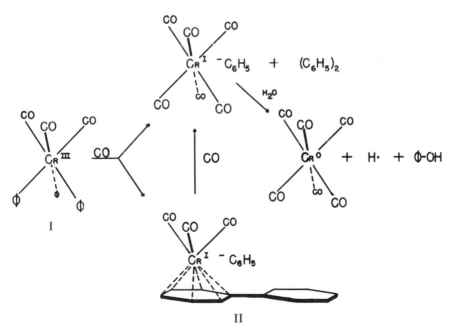

Fig. 8.16

ing carbon monoxide in excess in the forward direction of the reaction and by allowing it to escape from a free system containing benzene in the reverse (*25,27,80,103*). This relatively facile interchange of carbon monoxide and arene groups apparently occurs in the Job-Cassal reaction also.

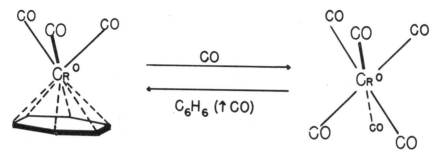

Fig. 8.17

However, hexacarbonylchromium(0) is the minor product (∼14 per cent) of the Job-Cassal reaction under normal Grignard conditions. The major products are listed among the organic compounds above. An explanation of their synthesis is to be found in an oxidative-reductive rearrangement similar to that proposed in the coupling of two phenyl groups to form the biphenyl-arene ring, as in the conversion of I to II in Fig. 8.16, or in obtaining the benzene-biphenylchromium complex from triphenylchromium. An analogous interaction between a phenyl and a carbonyl group within the intermediate I would produce the reactive benzoylonium ion whose reactions with its chemical environment provide the experimentally observed products (Fig. 8.18). The benzaldehyde present in the product mixture results from abstraction of hydrogen by the ion from solvent. Reaction of the cation with neighboring phenyl or carbonyl groups in the complex leads to the synthesis of benzophenone or the phenylglyoxylium ion which in turn may capture a phenyl group to yield benzil. The remainder of the products isolated by Job and Cassal are accountable by subsequent action of the Grignard system on benzaldehyde, benzophenone and benzil (*73*).

The Job-Cassal reaction apparently is another example of the capacity of the organic ligands to undergo reaction within the geometrical confines of the organotransition metal complexes. This phenomenon, together with the inverse process of reaction of metal carbonyls with organic π-electron systems such as those of the acetylenes (*4a,70,70a,95,97,99*), nitriles (*84, 95*), dienes (*11,71,85,86*), and aromatic groups (*25,27,80,103,106*) provides a new dimension of unknown potentialities to chemical synthesis. However,

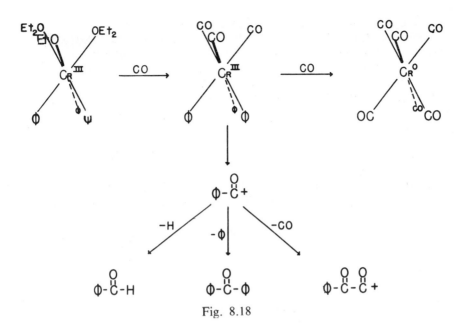

Fig. 8.18

it may already be safely predicted that organic synthesis by way of the metal complexes will yield new structural systems which until now have been inaccessible by more prosaic methods.

Acknowledgment. The author particularly wishes to acknowledge his indebtedness to Dr. Earl W. Gluesenkamp under whose aegis the research described in the latter sections of this chapter was performed. Best thanks also go to his coworkers, Drs. T. Burger, W. Herwig, W. Metlesics and M. Tsutsui, upon whose broad shoulders this work has moved forward. Professor Marshall Gates has greatly improved the readibility of this chapter by his very kind assumption of the task of reading and correcting the manuscript.

References

(1) Anisimov, K. N., and Nesmeyanov, A. N., *Compt. rend. acad. sci. USSR*, **26,** 58 (1940).

(2) Bennett, G. M., and Turner, E. E., *J. Chem. Soc.*, **105,** 1057 (1914).

(3) Calvin, M., Feltham, R. D., and Sogo, P., *J. Chem. Phys.*, **25,** 1354 (1957).

(4) Coffield, T. H., Sandel, V., and Closson, R. D., *J. Am. Chem. Soc.*, **79,** 5826 (1957).

(4a) Coffield, T. H., Ihrman, K. G., and Burns, W., *J. Am. Chem. Soc.*, **82,** in press (1960).

(5) Cotton, F. A., *Chem. Reviews*, **55,** 551 (1955).

(5a) Cram, D. J., and Wilkinson, D. I., *J. Am. Chem. Soc.*, in press.

(6) Criegee, R., and Louis, G., *Chem. Ber.*, **90.** 417 (1957).

(7) Criegee, R., and Schröder, G., *Ann.*, **623**, 1 (1959).
(8) Dauben, H. J., Jr., and Honnen, L. R., *J. Am. Chem. Soc.*, **80**, 5570 (1958).
(9) Ercoli, R., Calderazzo, F., and Alberola, A., *Chim. e Ind.*, **41**, 975 (1959).
(10) Ercoli, R., Calderazzo, F., and Mantica, E., *Chim. e Ind.*, **41**, 404 (1959).
(11) Ercoli, R., and Mangini, A., *Ricerca sci.*, **28**, 2135 (1958).
(12) Fischer, E. O., and Beckert, O., *Angew. Chem.*, **70**, 744 (1958).
(13) Fischer, E. O., and Böttcher, R., *Chem. Ber.*, **89**, 2397 (1956).
(14) Fischer, E. O., and Böttcher, R., *Z. anorg. Chem.*, **291**, 305 (1957).
(15) Fischer, E. O., and Fritz, H. P., *Z. Naturforsch.*, **12b**, 67 (1957).
(16) Fischer, E. O., and Fritz, H. P., *Z. physikal. Chem.*, **17**, 132 (1958).
(17) Fischer, E. O., and Hafner, W., *Z. Naturforsch.*, **10b**, 655 (1955).
(18) Fischer, E. O., and Hafner, W., *Z. anorg. Chem.*, **286**, 146 (1956).
(19) Fischer, E. O., Hafner, W., and Öfele, K., *Chem. Ber.*, **92**, 3050 (1959).
(20) Fischer, E. O., Joos, G., and Meer, W., *Z. Naturforsch.*, **13b**, 456 (1958).
(21) Fischer, E. O., and Kögler, H. P., *Angew. Chem.*, **68**, 462 (1956).
(22) Fischer, E. O., and Kögler, H. P., *Chem. Ber.*, **90**, 250 (1957).
(23) Fischer, E. O., and Kögler, H. P., *Z. Naturforsch.*, **13b**, 197 (1958).
(24) Fischer, E. O., Kriebitsch, N., and Fischer, R. D., *Chem. Ber.*, **92**, 3214 (1959).
(25) Fischer, E. O., and Öfele, K., *Chem. Ber.*, **90**, 2532 (1957).
(26) Fischer, E. O., and Öfele, K., *Chem. Ber.*, **91**, 2395 (1958).
(27) Fischer, E. O., Öfele, K., Essler, H., Fröhlich, W., Mortensen, J. P., and Semmlinger, W., *Z. Naturforsch.*, **13b**, 458 (1958).
(28) Fischer, E. O., Öfele, K., Essler, H., Fröhlich, W., Mortensen, J. P., and Semmlinger, W., *Chem. Ber.*, **91**, 2763 (1958).
(29) Fischer, E. O., and Piesbergen, U., *Z. Naturforsch.*, **11b**, 758 (1956).
(30) Fischer, E. O., and Schreiner, S., *Chem. Ber.*, **91**, 2213 (1958).
(31) Fischer, E. O., and Schreiner, S., *Chem. Ber.*, **92**, 938 (1959).
(32) Fischer, E. O., and Seus, D., *Chem. Ber.*, **89**, 1816 (1956).
(33) Fischer, E. O., and Stahl, H.-O., *Chem. Ber.*, **89**, 1805 (1956).
(34) Fischer, E. O., and Werner, H., *Chem. Ber.*, **92**, 1423 (1959).
(35) Fischer, E. O., and Wirzmüller, A., *Chem. Ber.*, **90**, 1725 (1957).
(36) Fischer, E. O., and Furlani, C., *Z. Elektrochem.*, **61**, 481 (1957).
(36a) Fischer, R. D., *Chem. Ber.*, **93**, 165 (1960).
(37) Hein, F., *Ber.*, **52**, 195 (1919).
(38) Hein, F., *Ber.*, **54**, 1905 (1921).
(39) Hein, F., *Ber.*, **54**, 2708 (1921).
(40) Hein, F., *Ber.*, **54**, 2727 (1921).
(41) Hein, F., *J. prakt. Chem.*, **132**, 59 (1931).
(42) Hein, F., *Z. anorg. Chem.*, **227**, 272 (1936).
(43) Hein, F., *Angew. Chem.*, **51**, 503 (1938).
(44) Hein, F., *Chem. Ber.*, **89**, 1816 (1956).
(45) Hein, F., and Bähr, G., *Chem. Ber.*, **86**, 1171 (1953).
(46) Hein, F., and Eisfeld, K., *Z. anorg. Chem.*, **292**, 162 (1957).
(47) Hein, F., and Eissner, W., *Ber.*, **59**, 362 (1926).
(48) Hein, F., and Fischer, K. W., *Z. anorg. Chem.*, **288**, 279 (1956).
(49) Hein, F., and Herzog, S., *Z. anorg. Chem.*, **267**, 337 (1952).

(50) Hein, F., Kleinert, P., and Kurras, E., Z. anorg. Chem., **289**, 229 (1957).
(51) Hein, F., and Kurras, E., Z. anorg. Chem., **290**, 179 (1957).
(52) Hein, F., and Markert, E., Ber., **61**, 2255 (1928).
(53) Hein, F., and Müller, H., Chem. Ber., **89**, 2722 (1956).
(54) Hein, F., and Nebe, E., Naturwissenschaften, **28**, 93 (1940).
(55) Hein, F., and Pauling, H., Z. anorg. Chem., **273**, 209 (1953).
(56) Hein, F., and Pintus, F., Ber., **60**, 2388 (1927).
(57) Hein, F., Reschke, J., and Pintus, F., Ber., **60**, 679 (1927).
(58) Hein, F., Reschke, J., and Pintus, F., Ber., **60**, 749 (1927).
(59) Hein, F., and Retter, W., Z. physikal. Chem., **156**, 81 (1931).
(60) Hein, F., and Schwartzkopff, O., Ber., **57**, 8 (1924).
(61) Hein, F., Schwartzkopff, O., Hoyer, K., Klar, K., Eissner, W., and Clauss, W., Ber., **61**, 730 (1928).
(62) Hein, F., Schwartzkopff, O., Hoyer, K., Klar, K., Eissner, W., Clauss, W., and Just, W., Ber., **62**, 1151 (1929).
(63) Hein, F., and Späte, R., Ber., **57**, 899 (1924).
(64) Hein, F., and Späte, R., Ber., **59**, 751 (1926).
(65) Hein, F., and Weiss, R., Z. anorg. Chem., **295**, 145 (1958).
(66) Hein, F., and Weiss, R., Naturwissenschaften, **46**, 321 (1959).
(67) Herzog, S., and Elschner, B., Z. Naturforsch., **12a**, 860 (1957).
(68) Herzog, S., and Renner, K.-C., Chem. Ber., **92**, 872 (1959).
(69) Hieber, W., and Romberg, E., Z. anorg. Chem., **221**, 321 (1935).
(70) Hübel, W., Braye, E. H., Clauss, A., Weiss, E. H., Krüerke, U., Brown, D. A., King, G. S. D., and Hoogzand, C., J. Inorg. Nucl. Chem., **9**, 204 (1959).
(70a) Hübel, W., and Braye, E. H., J. Inorg. Nucl. Chem, **10**, 250 (1959).
(71) Hübel, W., and Weiss, E. H., J. Inorg. Nucl. Chem., **11**, 42 (1959).
(72) Job, A., and Cassal, A., Compt. rend., **183**, 58 (1926); ibid., 392; Bull. soc. chim., **41**, 814 (1927); ibid., 1041.
(73) Kharasch, M. S., and Reinmuth, O., "Grignard Reactions of Nonmetallic Substances," New York, Prentice-Hall, 1954.
(74) Klemm, W., and Neuber, A., Z. anorg. Chem., **227**, 261 (1936).
(75) Longuet-Higgins, H. C., and Orgel, L. E., J. Chem. Soc., 1969 (1956).
(76) Lüttringhaus, A., and Kullick, W., Tetrahedron Letters, **No. 10**, 13 (1959).
(77) McConnell, H. M., Porterfield, W. W., and Robertson, R. E., J. Chem. Phys., **30**, 442 (1959).
(78) Maletesta, L., Santarella, G., Vallerino, L., and Zingales, F., Angew. Chem., **72**, 34 (1960).
(79) Mulay, L. N., Rochow, E. G., and Fischer, E. O., J. Inorg. and Nucl. Chem., **4**, 231 (1957).
(80) Natta, G., Ercoli, R., and Calderazzo, F., Chim. e Ind., **40**, 287 (1958).
(81) Natta, G., Ercoli, R., Calderazzo, F., and Santambrogio, F., Chim. e Ind., **40**, 1003 (1958).
(82) Nenitzescu, C. D., Avram, M., and Marica, E., Chem. Ber., **92**, 1088 (1959).
(83) Nenitzescu, C. D., Avram, M., Marica, E., and Pogany, J., Angew. Chem., **71**, 626 (1959).
(84) Orgel, L. E., and Kettle, S. F. A., Proc. Chem. Soc., 307 (1959).

(84a) Owen, B. B., English, J., Jr., Cassidy, H. G., and Dundon, C. V., *J. Am. Chem. Soc.*, **69**, 1723 (1947).

(85) Pauson, P. L., and Hallam, B. F., *J. Chem. Soc.*, 642 (1958).

(86) Pettit, R., *J. Am. Chem. Soc.*, **81**, 1266 (1959).

(87) Randall, E. W., and Sutton, L. E., *Proc. Chem. Soc.*, 93 (1959).

(88) Razuvaev, G. A., Sorokin, Yu. A., and Domrachev, G. A., *Doklady Acad. Nauk USSR*, **111**, 1264 (1956).

(89) Razuvaev, G. A., Sorokin, Yu. A., Domrachev, G. A., Petrukhov, G. G., Tsvetkov, Yu. D., and Molin, Yu. N., *Doklady Acad. Nauk USSR*, **113**, 1293 (1957).

(90) Razuvaev, G. A., Tsvetkov, Yu. D., Voevodsky, V. V., Sorokin, Yu. V., and Domrachev, G. A., *Doklady Acad. Nauk USSR*, **115**, 118 (1957).

(91) Razuvaev, G. A., Korshunov, I. A., Vertiulina, L. N., Sorokin, and Yu. A., Domrachev, G. A., *Proc. Acad. Sci. USSR*, **122**, 769 (1958).

(92) Riemschneider, R., Becker, O., and Franz, K., *Monatsh.*, **90**, 571 (1959).

(93) Ruch, E., "Electronentheorie der homopolaren Bindung," p. 125, Berlin, Akademie-Verlag, 1956.

(94) Sand, J., and Singer, F., *Ann.*, **329**, 190 (1903).

(95) Schrauzer, G. N., *J. Am. Chem. Soc.*, **81**, 5307 (1959); *Chemistry and Industry*, 1403 (1958).

(96) Schrauzer, G. N., *J. Am. Chem. Soc.*, **81**, 5310 (1959).

(97) Sternberg, H. W., Markby, R., and Wender, I, *J. Am. Chem. Soc.*, **80**, 1009 (1958).

(98) Stone, F. G. A., and Manuel, T. A., *J. Am. Chem. Soc.*, **82**, 366 (1960); *Proc. Chem. Soc.*, 90 (1959).

(99) Tilney-Bassett, J. F., and Mills, O. S., *J. Am. Chem. Soc.*, **81**, 4757 (1959).

(100) Tsutsui, M., *Dissertation*, Yale University, 1954.

(101) Weiss, E., *Z. anorg. Chem.*, **287**, 236 (1956).

(102) Weiss, E., and Fischer, E. O., *Z. anorg. Chem.*, **286**, 142 (1956).

(103) Whiting, M. C., and Nicholls, B., *Proc. Chem. Soc.*, 152 (1958); *J. Chem. Soc.*, 551 (1959).

(103a) Whiting, M. C., Nicholls, B., and Jackson, W. R., *J. Chem. Soc.*, 469 (1960).

(104) Wilkinson, G., Abel, E. W., and Bennett, M. A., *Proc. Chem. Soc.*, 152 (1958).

(105) Wilkinson, G., Abel, E. W., Bennett, M. A., and Burton, R., *J. Chem. Soc.*, 4559 (1958).

(106) Wilkinson, G., Abel, E. W., and Singh, A., *J. Chem. Soc.*, 3097 (1959).

(107) Wilkinson, G., Burton, R., Green, M. L. H., and Abel, E. W., *Chemistry and Industry*, 1592 (1958).

(108) Wilkinson, G., and Moore, B., *Proc. Chem. Soc.*, 61 (1959).

(109) Yamada, S., Nakamura, H., and Tsuchida, R., *Bull. Chem. Soc. Japan*, **30**, 647 (1957).

(110) Zeiss, H., Tsutsui, M., and Onsager, L., *Abstr., 126th Meeting, Amer. Chem. Soc.*, New York, N. Y., 1954, p. 29–0; *Angew. Chem.*, **67**, 282 (1955).

(111) Zeiss, H., *Yale Sci. Mag.*, **29**, 14 (1955).

(112) Zeiss, H., *Handbook, XIVth International Congress of Pure and Applied Chemistry*, Zürich, 1955, p. 262.

(113) Zeiss, H., and Herwig, W., *J. Am. Chem. Soc.,* **78,** 5959 (1956).
(114) Zeiss, H., and Herwig, W., *Ann.,* **606,** 209 (1957).
(115) Zeiss, H., and Herwig, W., *J. Am. Chem. Soc.,* **79,** 6561 (1957).
(116) Zeiss, H., and Herwig, W., *J. Am. Chem. Soc.,* **80,** 2913 (1958).
(117) Zeiss, H., and Herwig, W., *J. Org. Chem.,* **23,** 1404 (1958).
(118) Zeiss, H., and Herwig, W., *J. Am. Chem. Soc.,* **81,** 4798 (1959).
(119) Zeiss, H., Herwig, W., and Metlesics, W., *J. Am. Chem. Soc.,* **81,** 6203 (1959).
(120) Zeiss, H., and Metlesics, W., *J. Am. Chem. Soc.,* **81,** 4117 (1959).
(121) Zeiss, H., and Tsutsui, M., *J. Am. Chem. Soc.,* **79,** 3062 (1957).
(122) Zeiss, H., and Tsutsui, M., *Naturwissenschaften,* **44,** 420 (1957).
(123) Zeiss, H., and Tsutsui, M., *J. Am. Chem. Soc.,* **81,** 1367 (1959).
(124) Zeiss, H., and Tsutsui, M., *J. Am. Chem. Soc.,* **81,** 6090 (1959).
(125) Zeiss, H., and Tsutsui, M., unpublished results.

Reviews

(126) Cotton, F. A., "Progress in Inorganic Chemistry," Vol. 1, Chapter 1, New York, Academic Press, 1959.
(127) Fischer, E. O., "International Conference on Coördination Chemistry," Special Publ. No. 13, pp. 73–92, London, The Chemical Society, 1959.
(128) Emeléus, H. J., and Sharpe, A. G., "Advances in Inorganic Chemistry and Radiochemistry," Vol. I, pp. 97–115, New York, Academic Press, 1959.

9. TRANSITION METAL ALKYLS AND ARYLS

G. E. Coates and F. Glockling

The University, Durham, England

INTRODUCTION

With the exception of platinum(IV) and gold(III), *stable* σ-bonded organic derivatives of the transition metals are of recent development, many of the most striking advances having been made since 1955. Although most transition metals react with, for example, alkyl and aryl Grignard or organolithium reagents, under normal conditions isolable organometallic products are frequently not obtained. Indeed the reaction between various transition metal halides and aryl Grignard reagents has been commonly applied to the preparation of biaryls. It is well known that an attempt to apply this reaction to the preparation of bi-cyclopentadienyl from cyclopentadienylmagnesium bromide and ferric chloride led to one of the two independent discoveries of ferrocene.

The major successes in the preparation of sigma bonded transition metal alkyls and aryls have mostly resulted from close attention to experimental conditions (e.g., low temperature reactions in the preparation of titanium alkyls) or, more commonly, from a realization of certain electronic conditions for stability. The most important general rule requires that in order to form stable organic derivatives a transition metal should attain the electronic structure of the next inert gas, or two electrons short of this number. For example, the most stable sigma bonded organic compounds of the Group VII metals are those in which the metal is bound to a cyclopentadienyl ring, which contributes five electrons, or several carbonyl or nitrosyl groups, each of which contributes two and three electrons respectively. Examples are tricarbonylcyclopentadienylmethyltungsten, π-$(C_5H_5)(CO)_3W$-(σ-CH_3), and pentacarbonylmethylmanganese, $(CO)_5Mn(\sigma$-$CH_3)$.

Near the end of the transition series the elements have more electrons and organic derivatives are obtained from complexes in which the metal atoms are bound to a *small* number of donor molecules. For example, nickel, palladium and platinum form sigma bonded organic compounds derived from sixteen-electron tertiary phosphine complexes: $(Et_3P)_2Ni$-(mesityl)Cl, $(Ph_3P)_2PtMe_2$.

More experimental data are needed before a really clear statement can be made of the rules governing the stabilities of transition metal organic compounds. Some of the factors, for example the importance of the relative energies of electrons in non-bonding and anti-bonding orbitals, are considered later in this chapter in connection with the nickel, palladium, platinum triad. The essential distinction between organic groups as ligands which are attached to metal atoms by metal-to-carbon covalent bonds, and the more familiar ligands of transition metal chemistry is as follows. Dissociation of the more familiar ligands results in the formation of ions (such as Cl^-, NO_3^-) or of neutral molecules (such as H_2O, NH_3, Et_3P, CO) all of which are stable: dissociation of these ligands from a complex is therefore likely to be *reversible*.

In contrast, the dissociation of a metal-to-carbon bond is very likely to result in the formation of a reactive product, such as a free radical or—less probably—a carbanion. Thus the dissociation of metal-to-carbon bonds in organic compounds of transition metals is, in general, *irreversible*.

The nickel complex, $(Et_3P)_2NiBr_2$, could dissociate reversibly in several ways,

$$(Et_3P)_2NiBr_2 \rightleftharpoons (Et_3P)_2NiBr^+ + Br^-$$

$$(Et_3P)_2NiBr_2 \rightleftharpoons (Et_3P)NiBr_2 + Et_3P$$

and its solutions in fact smell of triethylphosphine. Solutions of the dimesityl complex, $(Et_3P)_2Ni(mesityl)_2$, do *not* smell of triethylphosphine, so there is no appreciable dissociation of the type,

$$(Et_3P)_2Ni(mesityl)_2 \rightleftharpoons (Et_3P)Ni(mesityl)_2 + Et_3P.$$

Dissociation of a nickel-to-mesityl bond, being irreversible, would lead to complete decomposition of the complex and this does not occur (at least in solution at room temperature).

$$(Et_3P)_2Ni(mesityl)_2 \longrightarrow (Et_3P)_2Ni \ mesityl + mesityl \ (free \ radical),$$

$$mesityl \ (free \ radical) + solvent \longrightarrow mesitylene + etc.$$

In this chapter the transition elements are discussed according to their position in the Periodic Table, from Group III to Group VIII and ending with copper, silver and gold (Group IB). Compounds containing carbonyl groups are, in general, omitted, since these are treated in other chapters. Olefin and acetylene complexes are considered as separate classes rather than alongside the other organic compounds of the metal concerned.

GROUP III

The reported formation of alkyl scandium and yttrium compounds is almost certainly incorrect (*30*), and the only genuine organo-derivatives of these metals and of the rare earths so far reported are cyclopentadienyl compounds. These have been obtained from the anhydrous metal halides and cyclopentadienyl sodium as crystalline compounds, many of which are strongly colored.

$$3\,C_5H_5Na\,+\,MCl_3\,\xrightarrow{\text{Tetrahydrofuran}}\,M(C_5H_5)_3$$

Unlike so many transition metal cyclopentadienyls, their properties suggest that they are essentially *ionic* like biscyclopentadienylmagnesium. Thus they are insoluble in nonpolar solvents and react with ferrous chloride to give ferrocene. They are air and water sensitive, and may be sublimed *in vacuo* at about 200° (*112*).

GROUP IV

The organotitanium compounds so far known are all derivatives of titanium(IV) in which, with one exception, the metal is also σ-bonded to electronegative ligands or π-bonded to cyclopentadienyl rings.

Titanium tetrahalides are alkylated by a number of reactive organometallic compounds. The best characterized products are methyltitanium trichloride and tribromide, and dimethyltitanium dichloride. If trimethylaluminum is added slowly to an excess of titanium tetrachloride in hexane at room temperature, and the mixture subsequently distilled *in vacuo* a dark violet crystalline material—methyltitanium trichloride—may be isolated in a cooled receiver. At room temperature it is a liquid.

$$TiCl_4 + (CH_3)_3Al \longrightarrow CH_3TiCl_3 + (CH_3)_2AlCl$$

$$TiCl_4 + (CH_3)_2AlCl \longrightarrow CH_3TiCl_3 + CH_3AlCl_2 \text{ (incomplete)}$$

The corresponding bromide, CH_3TiBr_3, has also been isolated from the reaction between titanium tetrabromide and dimethylzinc in boiling hexane solution. Using zinc or cadmium alkyls as alkylating agents temperatures even as high as 150° may be employed to effect the reaction. Dimethyltitanium dichloride, $(CH_3)_2TiCl_2$, has been obtained from the reaction between titanium tetrachloride and trimethylaluminum at –80°. It forms dark violet crystals and is much less stable than the mono-alkyl compound (*7,8*).

Ethyltitanium trichloride is also a violet solid which melts at room temperature to a red liquid, and is soluble in organic solvents. It has been prepared (*5*) by the alkylation of titanium tetrachloride (present in excess) by tetraethyllead at –80°. It appears to be decidely less stable than the methyl compound since on standing at room temperature for 24 hours it is decomposed to ethane, butane and titanium trichloride.

Under normal conditions attempts to alkylate titanium tetrahalides using organolithium or Grignard reagents result in reduction of the titanium(IV) to lower valency states. However, methyllithium at –80° reacts with a suspension of the titanium tetrachloride-diethyl ether complex in ether to yield the volatile but unstable tetramethyltitanium as a yellow substance which has not yet been obtained free from ether. This preparation is only successful if the entire apparatus used in the distillation is kept below –10°. Tetramethyltitanium decomposes at room temperature and is hydrolyzed by water. It shows a fairly high degree of reactivity since it reacts with aldehydes and ketones, and gives a strong color reaction with Michler's ketone. Its reaction with iodine is quantitative.

$$(CH_3)_4Ti + 4I_2 = TiI_4 + 4CH_3I$$

In the aromatic series an impure phenyltitanium tri-isopropoxide, $PhTi(OPr^i)_3$, having a melting point of 88–90° has been isolated from the reaction between phenyllithium and isopropyltitanate (60). It is remarkable that this compound should be colorless whereas the mono-alkyls are violet.

The π-bonded cyclopentadienyltitanium compounds are treated elsewhere in this book (Chapter 7), but it is relevant to note that π-bonded cyclopentadienyl groups have a most pronounced stabilizing effect on the formation of σ-type carbon-titanium bonds. Thus bis-cyclopentadienyltitanium dichloride will react with a number of aryl-lithium compounds (phenyl, p-tolyl, p-dimethylaminophenyl) giving the mixed π- and σ-bonded organotitanium derivatives (109)

$$\pi(C_5H_5)_2TiCl_2 + 2\,ArLi \longrightarrow \pi(C_5H_5)_2Ti(\sigma)Ar_2.$$

Diphenylbis-cyclopentadienyltitanium is a monomeric orange crystalline solid which decomposes slowly at room temperature and rapidly at 100°. Electron releasing groups in the *para* positions diminish the stabilities of these compounds, which decrease in the order $Ar = p\text{-}CF_3C_6H_4- >$ $C_6H_5 > p\text{-}(CH_3)_2NC_6H_4-$. The rather unstable dimethyl compound, $\pi\text{-}(C_5H_5)_2Ti(CH_3)_2$, has been isolated in 1% yield from the analogous reaction using methylmagnesium iodide in tetrahydrofuran (115).

The bonding involved in these organotitanium compounds is probably rather complex. The first excited, d^3s, state of titanium would lead to a tetrahedral bond distribution; but d^3s hybridized orbitals are symmetrical with respect to inversion through the nucleus (having g symmetry) and are therefore not so suitable for covalent bonding (poorer overlap) as, for example, are the unsymmetrical sp^3 orbitals. Calculations indicate (105) that admixture of quite a small proportion of sp^3 with d^3s results in another set of tetrahedral orbitals likely to give much greater overlap with orbitals derived from carbon than the simple d^3s hybrids. A very substantial improvement in bonding power, related to overlap, results from a small admixture of sp^3 requiring a relatively small amount of $d \rightarrow p$ promotion energy.

GROUP V

Vanadium, Niobium and Tantalum

Various halides of all three metals react vigorously with Grignard reagents, but in no case has a definite compound been isolated (30). The only recent study of niobium and tantalum compounds leads to the conclusion that these metals do not form organometallic compounds other than π-complexes (121).

GROUP VI

Chromium, Molybdenum and Tungsten

The work of Hein and co-workers on polyphenylchromium complexes has been clarified and extended, and the whole range of compounds described by Hein is now considered to involve π-bonding between chromium and aromatic six-membered rings (122). Quite apart from this class of *arene complexes* which are analogous to the transition metal cyclopentadienyls, several examples of σ-bonded chromium-carbon compounds are known in addition to the chromium carbonyls and their isocyanide analogs.

The effect of π-bonded cyclopentadienyl groups in stabilizing σ-bonds to carbon has already been mentioned in connection with titanium. In the case of chromium, this is illustrated by the isolation of a number of mixed cyclopentadienyl nitrosyl derivatives (II) formed by reaction of the corresponding sodio compound (I) with an alkyl or aryl halide:

$$\pi\text{-}C_5H_5Cr(NO)_2Br \longrightarrow \pi\text{-}C_5H_5Cr(NO)_2Na \xrightarrow{RX} \pi\text{-}C_5H_5Cr(NO)_2R.$$
$$\text{I} \qquad\qquad\qquad\qquad \text{II}$$

In this way the σ-bonded methyl, ethyl, phenyl and cyclopentadienyl derivatives of II have been prepared (115).

A remarkable blood-red crystalline σ-triphenylchromium(III) complex, Ph_3Cr (tetrahydrofuran)$_3$, has been isolated from the reaction between chromic chloride and phenylmagnesium bromide in tetrahydrofuran solution at $-20°$. The complex is readily hydrolyzed to the green chromic ion, $[Cr(H_2O)_6]^{3+}$, and undergoes a quantitative cleavage reaction with mercuric chloride (119,120).

$$Ph_3Cr(THF)_3 + 3\ HgCl_2 \xrightarrow{THF} 3\ PhHgCl + CrCl_3$$

A related magnesium halide-tetrahydrofuran complex, $Ph_3Cr(THF)_3$-$[MgBrCl\text{-}THF]_3$ has a paramagnetism of $3 \cdot 89$ B.M. as required for a complex of chromium(III). This Grignard reaction in tetrahydrofuran solution (120) is very closely akin to the method of preparing the phenylchromium π-complexes and in ether solution (ether being a weaker donor than tetrahydrofuran) the σ-Ph_3Cr complexes rearrange to the π-bonded chromium(0) derivatives. Heating either of these tetrahydrofuran complexes *in vacuo* causes loss of all the tetrahydrofuran and formation of a black solid which, after hydrolysis in the absence of oxygen, gives bis-

$$Ph_3Cr(THF)_3 \xrightarrow[\text{2. } H_2O]{\text{1. heat}} \pi\text{-}(C_6H_6)_2Cr + \pi\text{-}C_6H_6Cr(C_6H_5 \cdot C_6H_5)$$

benzenechromium(0) and benzene-biphenylchromium(0). Sigma trialkyl derivatives of chromium(III) and of nickel(II) have also been prepared *in tetrahydrofuran solution*; they are of particular interest in their catalysis probably *via* π-complexes, of the formation of aromatic compounds from disubstituted acetylenes (*122a*).

σ-Bonded mesitylchromium complexes are more stable than the phenyl compound and both dimesitylchromium(II) and trimesitylchromium(III) complexes have been described which are decomposed to bimesityl and not to π-complexes on heating (*120*).

The hexaphenylchromium(III) compound has been obtained as a red, water and air sensitive, solid by the reaction:

$$CrCl_3 + 6\,PhLi \xrightarrow{Et_2O} (C_6H_5)_6Cr \cdot 3\,LiC_6H_5 \cdot 2.5Et_2O$$

This complex salt undergoes a remarkable reaction with hydrogen at atmospheric pressure forming the pentaphenyl hydride, $Li_3[Ph_5CrH]3Et_2O$, as a bright red crystalline solid. The further action of hydrogen leads to complex products (*58,59*).

Evidence for the existence of a benzylpentaaquochromium ion, $[PhCH_2\text{-}Cr(H_2O)_5]^{2+}$, has been obtained by a study of the reduction of benzylchloride by chromous perchlorate in dilute perchloric acid solution (*4*). Separation of the ionic species by counter current distribution and ion exchange chromatography yields a colored solution (yellow to reddish brown depending on the concentration) believed to contain the ion $[PhCH_2Cr\text{-}(H_2O)_5]^{2+}$. These solutions give benzaldehyde when exposed to air, whilst decomposition in the absence of air (half life about 1.5 days at room temperature) results in the formation of dibenzyl. The reaction with mercuric chloride is rapid, giving benzyl mercuric chloride and the chromic ion without any change in the pH of the solution.

$$[PhCH_2Cr(H_2O)_5]^{2+} + HgCl_2 + H_2O \longrightarrow PhCH_2HgCl + [Cr(H_2O)_6]^{3+} + Cl^-$$

If the reduction of benzyl chloride is carried out in hydrochloric acid solution, then toluene is produced and not the organochromium(III) cation, but reduction of chloroform by chromium(II) perchlorate evidently gives an organochromium compound (*3*).

$$CHCl_3 + 2[Cr(H_2O)_6]^{2+} = [Cr(H_2O)_5Cl]^{2+} + [CHCl_2Cr(H_2O)_5]^{2+} + 2 H_2O$$

A π-cyclopentadienyl-σ-methylmolybdenum tricarbonyl and an analogous tungsten compound of considerable stability have been obtained from the corresponding hydrides by reaction with diazomethane.

$$\pi\text{-}C_5H_5Mo(CO)_3H + CH_2N_2 \longrightarrow \pi\text{-}C_5H_5Mo(CO)_3CH_3 + N_2$$

There are reports that both molybdenum (56) and tungsten (57) halides react with phenyllithium to give compounds analogous to the chromium arene complexes, though of lower stability.

GROUP VII

Manganese and Rhenium

Both dimethyl- and diphenyl-manganese have been isolated from reactions between manganese(II) iodide and the appropriate organolithium compound in ether solution.

$$MnI_2 + 2 CH_3Li \longrightarrow [(CH_3)_2Mn]_n$$

$$MnI_2 + 2 PhLi \longrightarrow (Ph_2Mn)_n$$

Dimethylmanganese is obtained as a yellow, and evidently polymeric explosive powder which takes fire in air and is virtually insoluble in ether. It dissolves in excess methyl lithium forming a complex salt, $Li[Mn(CH_3)_3]$, and with manganese(II) iodide it gives methylmanganese iodide as a heavy liquid.

$$(CH_3)_2Mn + MnI_2 \longrightarrow 2 CH_3MnI$$

Diphenylmanganese is likewise evidently polymeric, but may be crystallized from tetrahydrofuran (8). Impure mixtures of phenylmanganese(II) compounds are apparently formed from phenylmagnesium halides and manganese(II) iodide as chocolate-brown precipitates which are oxidized by air (43,46).

Manganese forms stable σ-bonded organic compounds when the metal is also in combination with "double bonding" donor groups (24). In this way methyl, benzyl, acetyl, and other manganese pentacarbonyls have been obtained by the reaction

$$NaMn(CO)_5 + RX \longrightarrow RMn(CO)_5$$

The methyl compound (m.p. 95°) may also be obtained by the action of diazomethane on the carbonyl hydride

$$HMn(CO)_5 + CH_2N_2 \longrightarrow CH_3Mn(CO)_5 + N_2.$$

It is diamagnetic (63), may be sublimed at room temperature, and is stable to air and water.

Acyl manganese compounds are similarly prepared from acyl halides and NaMn(CO)$_5$. Both the acetyl and benzoyl compounds are colorless and may be sublimed (*24*). These acyl derivatives undergo a most remarkable and reversible decarbonylation reaction when heated.

$$CH_3COMn(CO)_5 \rightleftharpoons CH_3Mn(CO)_5 + CO$$

A report that rhenium trichloride and methylmagnesium iodide react vigorously to give trimethylrhenium (*34*) as a liquid boiling at 60° could not be substantiated (*44*). Rhenium does, however, form a methyl penta-carbonyl complex, CH$_3$Re(CO)$_5$ analogous to the manganese compound (*61*).

GROUP VIII

Iron, Ruthenium and Osmium

In contrast to the extensive chemistry of π-bonded organoiron compounds there are but few examples of σ-bonding between iron and carbon (except the carbon of a carbonyl, cyanide, or isocyanide group). These are all complexes in which the iron is also bonded to cyclopentadienyl or carbonyl groups which effectively stabilize σ bonds to carbon (*115*), giving the iron atom a share in eighteen electrons.

$$[\pi\text{-}C_5H_5Fe(CO)_2]^-Na^+ + RI \longrightarrow (\pi\text{-}C_5H_5)(\sigma\text{-}R)Fe(CO)_2$$

$$\pi\text{-}C_5H_5Fe(CO)_2I + RMgI \longrightarrow (\pi\text{-}C_5H_5)(\sigma\text{-}R)Fe(CO)_2$$

By using cyclopentadienyl sodium a complex having both a π- and σ-bonded cyclopentadienyl group has been obtained, viz., $(\pi\text{-}C_5H_5)Fe(CO)_2$-$(\sigma\text{-}C_5H_5)$.

Several ruthenium alkyls (*16*) have been obtained by alkylation of the chelated ruthenium chloride (III) with aluminium methyl, ethyl or *n*-propyl. In this way one chlorine atom may be substituted by an alkyl group. Reduction of the resulting alkyl halide (IV) with lithium aluminum hydride gives the corresponding alkyl hydride (V).

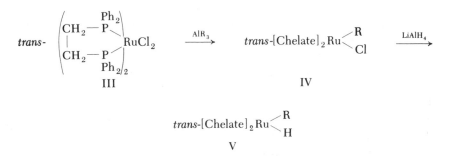

Cobalt, Rhodium and Iridium

Only recently have any σ-bonded organocobalt compounds been described, and these are less stable than their nickel analogs (*19*). The mesityl and 1-(β-methyl naphthyl) cobalt complexes $(PhPEt_2)_2Co(mesityl)_2$ and $(PhPEt_2)_2Co(C_{11}H_{10})_2$, both have small or zero dipole moments consistent with their formulation as planar *trans* complexes. It appears that aryl cobalt complexes are only stable when the aryl groups carry bulky substituents which effectively prevent the rings becoming co-planar with the bonds (dsp^2) from the cobalt atom. The electronic interpretation of this "*ortho*" effect is discussed below in connection with similar compounds of nickel. A methyl cobalt carbonyl has been prepared which is of very low stability (*62*).

$$Na[Co(CO)_4] + CH_3I \longrightarrow CH_3Co(CO)_4$$

The salt, $K[Co(CO)_4]$, reacts with butadiene in acetic acid solution to give a brown-red diamagnetic liquid (b.p. $\sim35°/1$ mm) having the molecular formula, $C_4H_7Co(CO)_3$ (*67*). Its infrared and ultraviolet spectra both show the absence of a conjugated diene and suggest that the complex contains a *cis* mono-olefin grouping. This, and proton magnetic resonance data have led to the suggested structure (VI). The bond between cobalt and the olefin is considered to be of the type discussed in detail in connection with platinum-olefin complexes.

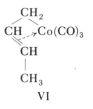

VI

Nickel, Palladium and Platinum

The effect of certain types of ligands, notably tertiary phosphines, in stabilizing σ-bonds between carbon and transition metals has already been noted in connection with various metals. For nickel, palladium and platinum in their divalent states this effect is most striking. All three metals form square planar complexes of the types, $(ligand)_2M(R)X$ and $(ligand)_2MR_2$, the stability being greatest with platinum and least with nickel.

It is proposed to describe the probable reasons for the instability of the simple organo derivatives of these metals in their divalent states, and the stabilizing effect of ligands which are capable of partial double bonding to the metal (*19,20*). The complexes of nickel and palladium are then discussed jointly whilst platinum, because of the greater range of compounds which it forms is treated separately.

The properties which characterize transition metals are largely ascribable to the small energy difference which exists between the partially filled d-orbitals and the next highest s- and p-orbitals. For the square planar complexes of nickel, palladium and platinum of the type, (ligand)$_2$MR$_2$, the metal utilizes hybrid σ-orbitals ($d_{x^2-y^2}$, s, p_x and p_y). It is suggested that the primary process leading to irreversible decomposition of the metal-carbon bonds is the promotion of a nonbonding electron to an antibonding orbital. Clearly the smaller the energy difference between the two the greater will be the probability of the transfer taking place. The result of such a transfer is effectively to weaken the σ-bonds; this naturally facilitates the separation of a radical R which may then react with a neighboring molecule with resultant *irreversible* decomposition of the complex. It seems reasonable that any effect which will *increase* the energy difference between the highest occupied orbital and the lowest vacant orbital (which is, in fact, an antibonding orbital) will result in an increase in the stability of the metal-carbon bond.

For a complex of the type, (Et$_3$P)$_2$MR$_2$, there are four possible combinations of ligand orbitals (two being sp^3 orbitals of carbon and two sp^3 orbitals of phosphorus) which have the correct symmetries to combine with metal orbitals. These are labelled (Fig. 9.1) a_g, $e_u^\pm$ (one of a conjugate pair

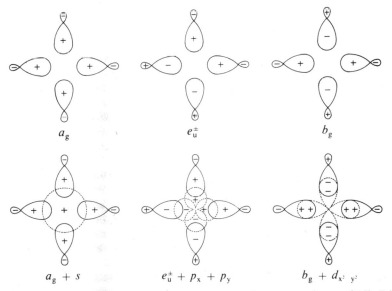

Fig. 9.1. Ligand and metal orbitals in square planar complexes of Ni, Pd and Pt. [Reproduced from "Organo-Metallic Compounds," by G. E. Coates (2nd Ed.), by courtesy of Methuen's Press].

$e_u^\pm$) and b_g. The lower row of diagrams (Fig. 9.1) shows the metal orbitals (as dotted lines) which are of appropriate symmetries to combine with the ligand orbitals. The four *bonding* combinations of metal and ligand orbitals are:

$$a_g + s$$
$$e_u^\pm + p_x + p_y$$
$$b_g + d_{x^2-y^2}$$

Four *antibonding* orbitals are produced by reversing the signs of the metal or ligand orbitals. Thus for nickel, palladium and platinum only one of the five *d*-orbitals is used in σ-bond formation. The energies of the four non-bonding *d*-orbitals in relation to the bonding and antibonding molecular orbitals are shown qualitatively in Fig. 9.2. If the four bonding orbitals

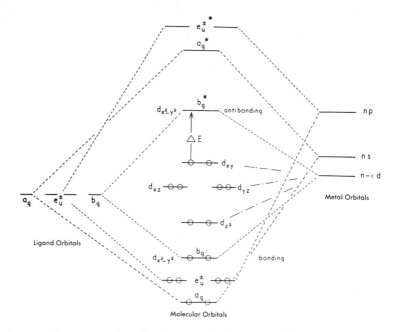

Fig. 9.2. Bonding and antibonding molecular orbitals in square planar complexes of Ni, Pd and Pt. [Reproduced from "Organo-Metallic Compounds" by G. E. Coates (2nd Ed.), by courtesy of Methuen's Press].

are taken as lying along the *xy* axes then the energies of the nonbonding *d*-orbitals will depend on their positions relative to these regions of high electron density. Clearly electrostatic repulsion will be least for the d_{z^2} orbital, which is directed away from the xy plane, and greatest for the d_{xy} which lies in the xy plane. The energies of the d_{xz} and d_{yz} orbitals occupy intermediate positions.

For these square planar complexes the energy difference between the highest occupied orbital, d_{xy}, and the lowest antibonding orbital is ΔE (Fig. 9.2), and for stable bonding between the metal and carbon this energy difference should be as large as possible. The way in which ΔE may be increased is by the use of ligands which are capable of forming π bonds with the d_{xy} orbital, and preferably also with the d_{xz} and d_{yz}, thereby reducing the energies of these orbitals. Suitable π-bonding ligands include phosphines, arsines and sulphides and of these tertiary phosphines, which combine strong donor character and π-bonding tendency have yielded the most striking examples of nickel, palladium and platinum complexes of the type $(R_3P)_2MR_2$. Of these three metals the platinum complexes are much more stable than those of nickel, with palladium occupying an intermediate position. This is the order one might expect since increase of atomic weight increases the d orbital splitting for a given set of ligands (*92a*).

Alkyl nickel complexes are apparently too unstable to be isolated, though evidence has been obtained for their formation in solution. In the aryl series the stability varies widely according to the nature of the aryl group. The most striking feature is the *low stability* of phenyl and *meta-* and *para*-substituted phenyl derivatives, as compared with *ortho*-substituted phenyl or other aryl groups. For example the diphenyl bisphosphine complex, $(Et_3P)_2NiPh_2$, decomposes rapidly in ethanol solution and melts with decomposition at 125–130°. In contrast the dimesityl derivative, $(Et_3P)_2$-Ni(mesityl)$_2$, is much more stable and melts at 148–150°. Compounds of this type and the organo halides [e.g., $(Et_3P)_2Ni(mesityl)Br$] are prepared from the bisphosphine nickel halide, $(R_3P)_2NiX_2$, and an organolithium or Grignard reagent (*21*). A selection of such compounds is given in Table 9.1.

The effect of *ortho*-substituents is clearly a steric effect since the stability is not greatly influenced by the electronic nature of the substituent. The effect of bulky (chloride, methyl or larger) *ortho*-substituents is to prevent

TABLE 9.1. ORGANONICKEL(II) COMPLEXES

Compound	M.P.	Color
$(Et_3P)_2Ni(phenyl)_2$	125–130 (dec)	Pale yellow
$(Et_3P)_2Ni(mesityl)_2$	148–150 (slight dec)	Pale yellow
$(Et_3P)_2Ni(o\text{-tolyl})_2$	146–148 (dec)	Pale yellow
$(Et_3P)_2Ni(o\text{-tolyl})Cl$	114–117	Orange-brown
$(Et_3P)_2Ni(C_6Cl_5)Cl$	156–158	Brown
$(Et_3P)_2Ni(mesityl)Br$	159–160	Brown
$(Et_3P)_2Ni(1\text{-naphthyl})Br$	150–152.5 (dec)	Brown

free rotation of the aryl groups about the nickel-carbon bonds and, if the *ortho*-substituents are large enough, to make the plane of the aromatic rings roughly perpendicular to the dsp^2 nickel bonds. Under these conditions the π-electron systems of the aromatic rings will interact exclusively with the d_{xy} orbital of nickel (Fig. 9.3), thereby lowering the energy of this orbital:

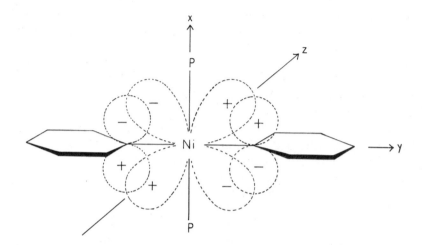

Fig. 9.3. Interaction of the nickel (d_{xy}) orbital with an aromatic π-electrons system in *ortho*-substituted phenyl derivatives. [Reproduced from "Organo-Metallic Compounds" by G. E. Coates (2nd Ed.), by courtesy of Methuen's Press].

The relative energies of the various orbitals for the different types of organonickel complexes are shown in Fig. 9.4. For aryl nickel complexes in which free rotation about the nickel-carbon bonds is possible the energies of the d_{xy}, d_{xz} and d_{yz} nickel orbitals will all be lowered from the values which would obtain in analogous (as yet unknown) alkyl complexes. Thus the energy difference between the d_{xy} orbital and the lowest antibonding state is increased from ΔE to $\Delta E'$. In *ortho*-substituted aryl complexes it is suggested (*21*) that the π-electrons of the aromatic ring interact exclusively with the d_{xy} orbital or nickel, thereby increasing this energy difference to $\Delta E''$. Of necessity the energies of the d_{xz} and d_{yz} orbitals will increase in the ortho-substituted phenyl derivatives since there will no longer by any interaction between these orbitals and the aromatic π-electrons.

It is interesting that palladium (II) which forms analogous square planar complexes does not show any pronounced "ortho" effect. The stability in this case is rather more affected by the electronic nature of the aryl group: electron attracting groups ($-CF_3$, $-\overset{+}{N}(CH_3)_3I$) stabilize the complex

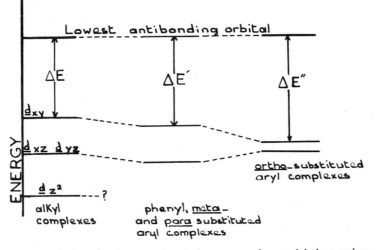

Fig. 9.4. Relative metal energy levels in square planar nickel complexes. [Reproduced in modified form by courtesy of Dr. J. Chatt and the editor of the *Journal of the Chemical Society*].

whilst, for example, the *p*-dimethylaminophenyl group (electron-releasing) gives a complex which is less stable than the phenylpalladium compound, $(R_3P)_2PdPh_2$. All the aryl palladium complexes so far isolated, both of the type $(donor)_2PdRX$ and $(donor)_2PdR_2$, are in the *trans* series, and attempts to prepare *cis*-aryl compounds have so far resulted in complete decomposition. The Grignard reaction usually leads to the mixed complex:

$$(Et_3P)_2PdX_2 + RMgX \longrightarrow trans\text{-}(Et_3P)_2Pd(R)X$$

whilst the more reactive organolithium reagents give the fully alkyl or arylated complexes.

$$(Et_3P)_2PdX_2 + 2\ RLi \longrightarrow trans\text{-}(Et_3P)_2PdR_2$$

Most of these compounds are unstable in solution, though they show a reasonable stability (towards air) in the crystalline state. The methyl complex, $(Et_3P)_2Pd(CH_3)_2$ can be sublimed in vacuum, but decomposes when its solutions in organic solvents are warmed. The binuclear complex (VII) is among the most stable organopalladium compounds (*26*).

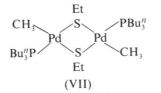

(VII)

Chelated dimethylpalladium compounds such as VIII melt with decomposition and are relatively unstable. Unlike most of these palladium(II) compounds which are colorless, the 2,2'-dipyridyl complex (IX) is bright orange.

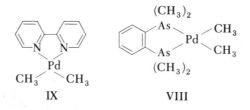

IX   VIII

A cyclopentadienylpalladium chloride has been described in a preliminary communication. It is formed, in a quantitative reaction, as a dark brown solid by the reaction between palladium(II) chloride and cyclopentadiene in aqueous solution.

$$PdCl_2 + C_5H_6 \longrightarrow C_5H_5PdCl + HCl$$

It is insoluble in the usual organic solvents, but dissolves in aqueous, alcoholic or liquid ammonia from which it may be recovered unchanged. It is diamagnetic and a polymeric halogen-bridged structure has been suggested which, in ammonia solution, undergoes a reversible depolymerization (*108*).

Alkyl and aryl organoplatinum compounds fall into two distinct classes: those derived from platinum(II) in which the metal is *four*-covalent (dsp^2 bonding), and those derived from platinum(IV) in most, if not all, of which it appears to be six-covalent. The latter have been known for over fifty years and will be treated first; the organic derivatives of platinum(II) are a comparatively new development.

Alkyls and Aryls of Platinum(IV). The earliest experiments (*94,95*) on the reaction between platinum(IV) chloride and methylmagnesium iodide resulted in the isolation of a yellow crystalline compound, trimethylplatinum iodide,

$$3 CH_3MgI + PtCl_4 \longrightarrow (CH_3)_3PtI + MgI_2 + 2 MgCl_2.$$

A closer investigation of this reaction (*47,48*) showed that other methylplatinum compounds were also formed, though in small yield, including compounds formulated as: CH_3PtI_3, $(CH_3)_2PtI_2$, $(CH_3)_4Pt$ and a black material which appeared to be CH_3PtI_5.

Trimethylplatinum iodide is the parent compound for the preparation of a wide range of methyl platinum derivatives, and is itself most conveniently obtained (*40*) from *cis*-dipyridinetetrachloroplatinum(IV) and methylmagnesium iodide in a mixture of benzene and ether. The immediate product is a pyridine complex, $[(CH_3)_3PtI \cdot py]_2$, from which trimethyl-platinum iodide may be obtained in an overall yield of about 60 per cent by conversion to the ethylene diamine complex, $\{[(CH_3)_3PtI]_2 \cdot en\}$, followed by decomposition with hydriodic acid. The iodine in trimethylplatinum iodide is readily replaced by a variety of other groups (*95*) such as chloride, sulfate, nitrate and hydroxyl. Treatment with methylsodium gives tetra-methylplatinum in almost 50 per cent yield (*48*), whilst reduction using potassium in boiling benzene converts it into hexamethyldiplatinum:

$$(CH_3)_4Pt \xleftarrow{CH_3Na} (CH_3)_3PtI \xrightarrow{K} (CH_3)_6Pt_2$$

Both tetramethylplatinum and hexamethyldiplatinum are colorless solids soluble in benzene.

A number of coordination compounds of trimethylplatinum iodide with oxygen (*81,82,84*) and nitrogen donors have been studied. Most of these substances seem to require an octahedral covalency of six for platinum. Pyridine (*40*) forms a dimeric and a monomeric complex:

$$[(CH_3)_3PtI]_4 \xrightarrow{py} [(CH_3)_3PtI,py], \xrightarrow{py} [(CH_3)_3PtI,py_2].$$

Ethylene diamine and dipyridyl also form similar complexes (*83*) for example, $[(CH_3)_3PtI,en]$ and $[(CH_3)_3PtI,dipy]$.

An X-ray examination of two chelated complexes derived from aceto-acetic ester, $(CH_3)_3Pt(CH_3COCH_2CO_2Et)$, and dibutyrylmethane, $(CH_3)_3\text{-}Pt[(CH_3CH_2CH_2CO)_2CH_2]$, shows a most unexpected structural aspect (*110*). In the solid state both complexes are dimeric and have a center of symmetry. Each platinum atom is octahedrally coördinated (Fig. 9.5) and

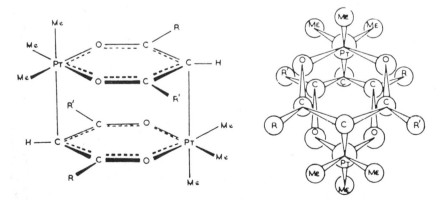

Fig. 9.5. The dimeric molecule formed by a complex between trimethylplatinum (IV) and a β-diketone ($RCOCH_2COR'$). [Reproduced by courtesy of Dr. M. R. Truter and the editor of *Chemistry and Industry*].

the structure requires inter-ring platinum-carbon bonds. The structural interpretation of these platinum-to-"active methylene" bonds is probably similar to that involved in the tetrameric tetramethylplatinum and other related compounds which are discussed below.

Only a few aromatic platinum(IV) compounds are known. Platinum(IV) chloride reacts vigorously with phenylmagnesium bromide (*78*), and only gives a positive Gilman color test after ten equivalents of Grignard reagent have been added. There is evidence that a mixture of phenylplatinum compounds results, though none has been isolated in a pure state.

Dimethylplatinum(IV) complexes having two molecules of a tertiary phosphine co-ordinated to platinum have been described (*20*), and are prepared from the corresponding stable platinum(II) complexes (see pp. 444–5). For example *cis* or *trans*-bis(triethylphosphine)iodo(methyl)-platinum, $[(Et_3P)_2PtI(CH_3)]$, adds methyl iodide at 100° giving the platinum(IV) complex(X).

$$[(Et_3P)_2PtI_2(CH_3)_2] \qquad\qquad [(Et_3P)_2PtCl_2(CH_3)_2]$$
$$\text{X} \qquad\qquad\qquad\qquad\qquad \text{XI}$$

The dipole moment of the product (X) is 5.8 D which is compatible with either XII or XIII.

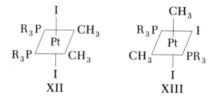

$$\text{XII} \qquad\qquad\qquad \text{XIII}$$

Likewise chlorine oxidizes *cis*-$[(Et_3P)_2Pt(CH_3)_2]$ to the platinum(IV) derivative (XI). Six stereoisomers (*a–f*) are possible for these compounds, two of which (*d* and *e*) are enantiomorphs. The estimated dipole moments are given for each structure; both the iodide (X) and the chloride (XI) have moments between 5 and 6 Debye units, and are therefore likely to have either structure (*b*) or (*c*).

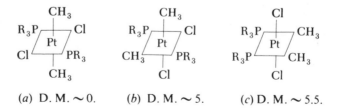

(*a*) D. M. ∼ 0.   (*b*) D. M. ∼ 5.   (*c*) D. M. ∼ 5.5.

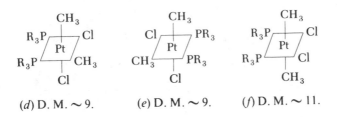

(d) D. M. ~ 9.   (e) D. M. ~ 9.   (f) D. M. ~ 11.

In the aryl series it has proved possible on the basis of dipole moment measurements to ascribe the unique structure (XIV) to the platinum(IV)

$$
\begin{array}{c}
\text{Ph} \\
\text{Et}_3\text{P} \diagdown \quad \diagup \text{Cl(I)} \\
\text{Pt} \\
\text{Ph} \diagup \quad \diagdown \text{PEt}_3 \\
\text{Cl(I)}
\end{array}
$$

XIV

complex obtained by the reaction of either chlorine or iodine on cis- or trans-[(Et₃P)₂PtPh₂].

Structure of Platinum(IV) Complexes. Trimethylplatinum chloride has been shown by X-ray analysis to have a *tetrameric* structure in which the Pt—Pt distance of 3.73 Å is too great for appreciable metal-metal bonding. The distribution of groups about the platinum atoms is roughly octahedral; the molecule having bridging chlorine atoms and terminal methyl groups. (Fig. 9.6). Essentially the same geometrical arrangement is found for tetramethylplatinum, which is also tetrameric. In this case there are four bridging methyl groups, each bridging carbon atom apparently forming six bonds (three to hydrogen and three to platinum (*102*). Other examples of the formation of methyl bridges between metal atoms are known; both dimethylberyllium (*101*) and trimethylaluminum (*100*) associate in this way, and it is possible that these platinum compounds are somewhat similar. Certainly for trimethylplatinum chloride the Pt—Cl distance of 2.48 Å is greater than the sum of the covalent radii (2.30 Å) as would be expected for bridging bonds with an order less than unity.

Hexamethyldiplatinum has also been studied by X-ray methods (*99*), but without providing a unique structure. Molecular weight measurements in freezing benzene (*47*) are in good agreement with the monomeric structure, (CH₃)₃Pt—Pt(CH₃)₃, but whether this involves a Pt—Pt bond or bridging methyl groups is not known. It is worth noting that *if* hexamethyldiplati-

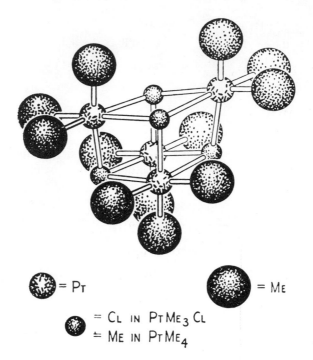

= P$_T$

= M$_E$

= C$_L$ IN P$_T$M$_E_3$C$_L$
= M$_E$ IN P$_T$M$_E_4$

Fig. 9.6. X-ray structure of trimethylplatinum chloride and tetramethylplatinum. [Reproduced by courtesy of Professor R. E. Rundle and the editor of the *Journal of the Americal Chemical Society*].

num has the structure $(CH_3)_3Pt$—$Pt(CH_3)_3$ it would be the only platinum(IV) compound without an octahedral group of ligands about the metal atom.

Alkyl and Aryl Derivatives of Platinum(II). Direct attempts to alkylate platinum(II) halides have only led to the isolation of ill-defined compounds (*78*). The realization that coördination of the metal with ligands capable of forming strong dative π-bonds would give the best chance of obtaining stable organoplatinum(II) compounds has resulted in experiments on the alkylation of platinous halides coördinated to tertiary phosphines, arsines, and dialkyl sulfides (*20*).

Cis- or *trans-*trialkyl (or aryl) phosphine dihaloplatinum (XV) reacts with methylmagnesium halides, giving a mixture of the *trans*-mono and *cis*-dimethyl derivatives (XVI) and (XVII)

$$[(R_3P)_2PtX_2] + CH_3MgX \longrightarrow trans\text{-}[(R_3P)_2PtX(CH_3)] + cis\text{-}[(R_3P)_2Pt(CH_3)_2]$$
XV   XVI   XVII

Using methyllithium complete replacement of halogen can be achieved:

$$cis\text{-}[(R_3P)_2PtCl_2] + 2\,CH_3Li \longrightarrow cis\text{-}[(R_3P)_2Pt(CH_3)_2]\ 88\%$$

In the same way chelated complexes such as (XVIII) and (XIX) may be prepared which necessarily have a *cis* configuration.

XVIII   XIX

The triphenylphosphine complex, $[(Ph_3P)_2Pt(CH_3)I]$, is best made by the reaction (*79*):

$$(Ph_3P)_3Pt + 2\,CH_3I \longrightarrow [(Ph_3P)_2Pt(CH_3)I] + [Ph_3P\cdot CH_3]^+I^-.$$

Methylplatinum(II) compounds stabilized in this way are colorless, crystalline, and mostly very stable; they are soluble in common organic solvents and some may even be distilled *in vacuo*. The halogen atom in the mixed methyl halides is readily replaced by other atoms or groups. For example:

$$trans\text{-}[(Et_3P)_2Pt(CH_3)Cl] + LiBr \longrightarrow trans\text{-}[(Et_3P)_2Pt(CH_3)Br]$$

$$trans\text{-}[(Et_3P)_2Pt(CH_3)I] + KSCN \longrightarrow trans\text{-}[(Et_3P)_2Pt(CH_3)SCN]$$

Various reactions lead to the loss of one or both methyl groups from the dimethylplatinum compounds:

$$cis\text{-}[(Et_3P)_2Pt(CH_3)_2] \xrightarrow{\text{MgI}_2} trans\text{-}[(Et_3P)_2PtI_2] + trans\text{-}[(Et_3P)_2Pt(CH_3)I]$$

$$cis\text{-}[(Et_3P)_2Pt(CH_3)_2] \xrightarrow[\text{Et}_2O]{\text{HCl}} CH_4 + cis\text{-}[(Et_3P)_2Pt(CH_3)Cl] \xrightarrow{\text{HCl}} CH_4 +$$

$$cis\text{-}[(Et_3P)_2PtCl_2]$$

Infra-red bands due to platinum (*21a*) and palladium (*26*) to carbon stretching have been identified and discussed. They lie in the 20μ region.

In addition to methyl groups ethyl, phenyl and benzyl also form stable platinum(II) complexes of these types, but in the alkyl series stability diminishes with increasing chain length. This effect is even more pronounced with the palladium alkyls.

Analogous series of aryl platinum(II) complexes are known; these are in general more readily prepared and more stable than the aliphatic compounds. Their greater stability is attributed to conjugation between the metal and the aryl groups. Dipole moment measurements indicate some electron flow in the direction metal-to-aryl. *o*-Substituted phenyl derivatives are particularly stable, presumably for the same reason that has been discussed under nickel. In contrast to both nickel and cobalt it has not proved possible to obtain the dimesityl complex, [(Et₃P)₂Pt(mesityl)₂], though the *cis*-monomesityl compound, *cis*-[(Et₃P)₂Pt(mesityl)Br], is readily prepared. A selection of organoplatinum(II) compounds are given in Table 9.2.

TABLE 9.2. ORGANOPLATINUM(II) COMPLEXES

Compound	M.p.	Dipole Moment, Debye Units
cis-(Et₃P)₂Pt(CH₃)₂	82	5.6
cis-(Et₃P)₂PtPh₂	154	7.2
trans-(Et₃P)₂PtPh₂	180	~0
cis-(Et₃P)₂Pt(CH₃)Cl	113–116 (dec)	8.4
trans-(Et₃P)₂Pt(CH₃)Cl	100	3.4

GROUP Ib

Alkyl and aryl derivatives of all three elements, copper, silver and gold, are known, although detailed structural information is for the most part lacking, due mainly to the low thermal stability of the compounds. A close similarity exists between organocopper(I) and silver compounds; with gold both the aurous and auric compounds are known. Both series of organogold compounds are formed only when the metal is coördinated to a suitable donor molecule: the coördination number is *two* for the gold(I) and *four* for the gold(III) derivatives. No organocopper(II) compounds are known: the interaction of a copper(II) salt and a Grignard or similar reagent always involved reduction to the copper(I) state as the primary reaction.

Copper

Copper(I) methyl, ethyl and phenyl have all been described. Of these the phenyl is the most stable whilst, as is so commonly the case, the methyl is more stable than the ethyl. The only satisfactory preparative method available is the reaction between a copper(I) halide and an organolithium or Grignard reagent. In this way *methylcopper* (45) may be obtained as a yellow solid from the reaction between copper(I) iodide and methyllithium at −15°. The dry solid is highly shock sensitive and decomposes in boiling ether with the formation of copper, methane and ethane. A yellow ether suspension of methylcopper dissolves on addition of a further mole of methyllithium forming an almost colorless solution which probably contains the solvated salt, $Li^+[(CH_3)_2Cu]^-$. *Phenylcopper (49)* may be obtained as a grey powder which decomposes rapidly at about 80° to copper and biphenyl. Although insoluble in most organic solvents it dissolves in pyridine, and is hydrolyzed to copper(I) oxide and benzene. It is apparently quite involatile, and is sufficiently reactive to form benzophenone from benzoyl chloride.

Methylcopper is also formed by the action of methyl chloride on copper at 250–300°. This has been demonstrated by essentially the Paneth technique in which a stream of methyl chloride is found to remove a copper mirror deposited on glass and to redeposit the copper some distance along the tube. From these and related experiments the half-life of methylcopper has been calculated as 2×10^{-3} sec at 250° (98)

$$CH_3Cl + 2\,Cu \longrightarrow CH_3Cu + CuCl$$

$$CH_3Cu \longrightarrow Cu + CH_3{}^\cdot$$

The interaction of copper(II) salts and tetramethyllead also leads to the formation of methylcopper (6) in a two-stage reaction:

$$Cu^{2+} + (CH_3)_4Pb \longrightarrow (CH_3)_3Pb^+ + Cu^+ + CH_3{}^\cdot,$$

$$Cu^+ + (CH_3)_4Pb \longrightarrow (CH_3)_3Pb^+ + CH_3Cu.$$

The reaction takes place in ethanol solution at –45° with the separation of methylcopper as a primrose solid.

There is some evidence for the existence of a highly unstable *ethylcopper* both from the reaction of ethyl chloride with copper and silicon, and from the reaction between tetraethyllead and copper(II) salts.

The most stable organocopper compound is the cyclopentadienyl triethylphosphine complex, $Et_3P \cdot Cu \cdot C_5H_5$ (114), which is formed by the addition of triethylphosphine to a suspension of copper(I) oxide in cyclopentadiene and petroleum ether. Its infrared spectrum and the observation that it reacts rapidly with ferrous chloride to give ferrocene suggests that the copper-carbon bond is of the σ- rather than the π-type.

Silver

The reaction between a reactive organometallic compound (Et_2Zn) and a silver halide (AgCl) was reported in 1859, when it was observed that silver and gaseous products were formed (10). By using similar reactions under more controlled conditions a number of compounds has been isolated which certainly contain silver-carbon bonds. The earliest described substances appear to be complex salts of the type $(ArAg)_2 \cdot AgNO_3$ (Ar =

phenyl or *o*-tolyl) which are formed by the action of alcoholic silver nitrate on various organolead, tin or bismuth compounds, e.g., Ph_3PbEt (*76*). These complexes are yellow to orange solids which decompose readily to silver when warmed. Nothing is known of their structure.

The known alkyl and aryl compounds of silver are all colored solids (yellow, orange or brown) of low thermal stability. There is no information on the structure of the solids or the nature of the bonding involved. They are generally prepared by the interaction of a tetraalkyl or aryllead compound with silver nitrate, usually in ethanol solution, at a suitably low temperature (*6,104*).

$$R_4Pb + Ag^+ \longrightarrow R_3Pb^+ + RAg$$

The stability of the organosilver compound is partly determined by the nature of the radical, R: the greater the stability of the radical, the lower the stability of the organosilver compound (*52*). Thus phenylsilver is *comparatively* stable whilst benzylsilver has only a transitory existence above $-100°$. Methyl, ethyl and *n*-propyl silver, probably as silver nitrate complexes, $(RAg)_2 \cdot AgNO_3$ (*30a*), have been obtained using this reaction as yellow solids which decompose about $-60°$. There seems to be some increase in thermal stability with compounds of the type, $RCH:CH \cdot Ag$ (*51,52*), for example, isobut-1-enylsilver, $(CH_3)_2C:CHAg$, is stable to about $-30°$ whilst styrylsilver is reasonably stable even at $0°$. Phenylsilver has also been isolated in an impure state from the reaction of silver halides with cooled solutions of phenylmagnesium bromide. It is explosive in the dry state and decomposes at about $-18°$ to silver and biphenyl (*49,97,77*).

In general the decomposition of organosilver compounds results in the formation of silver and a free radical, $R\cdot$. If the radical is fairly stable (e.g., benzyl, methallyl) then the dimer, R_2, is almost the exclusive product. More reactive radicals disproportionate and also undergo hydrogen abstraction reactions involving the solvent.

$$AgR \longrightarrow Ag + R\cdot$$

$$2\,R\cdot \longrightarrow R_2 \qquad 2\,R\cdot \longrightarrow alkane + alkene$$

$$R\cdot + solvent \longrightarrow RH + solvent\ radical$$

The methylsilver-silver nitrate complex, $(CH_3Ag)_2 \cdot AgNO_3$, decomposes above $-60°$ to give exclusively ethane and silver (*30a*, see also *6*).

Silver iodide-phosphine complexes such as $PhPEt_2 \cdot AgI$ are remarkably unreactive towards both Grignard and organolithium compounds, and the conditions necessary for reaction to occur result in decomposition to silver (*51a*).

Gold

In striking contrast to most transition metals organo-derivatives of gold(III), all of which appear to be four-covalent, have been known since the beginning of this century; many of these compounds have been prepared and in some cases detailed structural studies have been carried out. Early investigations on the reaction between aliphatic Grignard reagents and gold(III) halides (AuX_3) led to two series of compounds, $(RAuX_2)_2$ and $(R_2AuX)_2$. Trimethyl gold, almost certainly an etherate, $(CH_3)_3Au \cdot OEt_2$, is the only fully alkylated auric derivative so far described in any detail. It is formed when methyllithium is added to gold(III) bromide at $-65°$. Although stable at $-65°$ it decomposes at about $-35°$ to a mixture of methane and ethane. Addition of amines, which coördinate more strongly than ethers, has enabled crystalline coördination compounds of trimethylgold to be isolated. For example, the ethylene diamine complex,

$$[(CH_3)_3Au \cdot NH_2CH_2CH_2NH_2 \cdot Au(CH_3)_3],$$

forms colorless needles decomposing about $95°$ (*50*).

Our knowledge of the dialkylgold halides and alkylgold dihalides is due largely to the work of C. S. Gibson (*41*). Auric bromide reacts readily with aliphatic Grignard reagents to give dialkylgold bromides, e.g.,

$$AuBr_3 + EtMgBr \longrightarrow (Et_2AuBr),$$

Diethylgold bromide forms colorless needles, m.p. $58°$, which may be sublimed *in vacuo*, and decompose explosively at about $70°$. It is dimeric in solution and the halogen-bridged structure (XX) is in agreement with X-ray studies (*38*).

The corresponding ethylgold dibromide may be obtained by the reaction:

$$Et_2AuBr + Br_2 \text{ (in } CHCl_3) \longrightarrow EtAuBr_2$$

as ruby-red crystals which decompose without melting when heated. Again molecular weight measurements require a dimeric structure and in this case the planar configuration of tetracovalent (dsp^2) gold allows the possibility of *cis-trans* isomers, and also the unsymmetrical structure (XXI). The high dipole moment of the propyl analog, $(PrAuBr_2)_2$, is consistent with the unsymmetrical structure. The reaction of ethylgold dibromide with ethylene diamine yields two products: $[Auen_2]Br_3$ and $[Et_2Auen]Br$, again suggestive of the unsymmetrical structure. This reaction with electron-donor molecules is general for mono- and di-alkylgold halides and gives products in which the halogen bridge bonds are broken without altering the four-covalency of gold.

$$(Et_2AuBr)_2 + NH_3 \longrightarrow 2\, Et_2Au(Br)\cdot NH_3$$

Oxygen and sulphur can likewise function as donor atoms as in the acetyl-acetonate (XXII) and the sulphide (XXIII) derivative (*37,42*).

XXII   XXIII

Organogold cyanides (*39*) form a remarkable series of compounds. Treatment of a dialkylgold halide with silver cyanide gives the corresponding cyano-gold derivative, R_2AuCN. Molecular weight determinations in solution correspond to a *tetrameric* structure. This is in keeping with the stereochemical requirements both of the square planar configuration for gold(III) and the colinear bonds of the cyanide group, leading to the planar twelve-membered ring structure (XXIV).

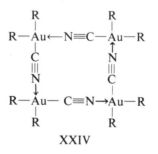

XXIV

An X-ray analysis of dipropylgold cyanide confirmed this structure (*96*). The dialkylgold cyanides are unstable in solution (*39*), the reaction product being insoluble in benzene or chloroform and clearly highly polymeric.

$$\tfrac{1}{2}(R_2AuCN)_4 \longrightarrow 2\, RAuCN + R_2$$

In boiling solvents the polymeric alkylgold cyanides decompose to gold(I) cyanide (which, of course, is also polymeric):

$$2\, RAuCN \longrightarrow 2\, AuCN + R_2$$

Much less is known of the arylgold compounds; aryl Grignard reagents apparently do not react with gold(III) halides, and the use of aryllithium compounds does not appear to have been studied. Arylgold halides may, however, be obtained by direct reaction between an aromatic hydrocarbon (benzene, toluene, biphenyl) and gold(III) chloride (*72,73*). The reactions are vigorous and hydrogen chloride is evolved. If the reaction with benzene is allowed to proceed to completion the only isolable products are gold(I) chloride, 1,2,4,5-tetrachlorobenzene and hydrogen chloride. However, by stopping the reaction when a brown precipitate appears, by the addition of ether or ethyl acetate, it is possible to isolate phenylgold dichloride as a yellow crystalline compound which decomposes at 73–75°.

Aurous alkyls and aryls in which the gold is also coördinated to a tertiary phosphine have been obtained by the reaction:

$$Et_3P \cdot AuCl + RLi \longrightarrow Et_3P \cdot Au \cdot R$$

They are white solids which are slightly associated in benzene solution but are monomeric in nitrobenzene (*27*); some of them are listed below.

TABLE 9.3. ORGANOGOLD(I) COMPOUNDS

Compound	M.p.	Dipole moment (benzene solution, 25°)
Et_3PAuCH_3	62°	5.5 D
Ph_3PAuCH_3	175° (dec)	6.6
Et_3PAuPh	67–68°	6.2
Ph_3PAuPh	152° (dec)	6.2
$Et_3PAuC\vdots CPh$	83–85°	6.6

TRANSITION METAL OLEFIN-COMPLEXES

The formation of olefin complexes appears to be confined to those transition metals which have their *d*-electron shells filled or almost filled; the most striking examples are provided by Cu(I), Ag(I), Rh(I), Ni(II), Pd(II), Pt(II), Ru(II). Of these the platinum(II) compounds are by far the most stable and thoroughly investigated. In all these complexes the olefin behaves as an unchanged ligand which retains its essential structure, in contrast to some types of acetylene complexes.

In 1827 Zeise (*118*) found that boiling platinum(IV) chloride with ethanol and adding potassium chloride resulted in the formation of a compound having the composition, $KCl, PtCl_2, C_2H_4, H_2O$, (Zeise's salt). Thermal decomposition of this salt, potassium ethylene trichloroplatinate(II), $K[C_2H_4PtCl_3]H_2O$, was subsequently shown to liberate at least some ethylene, whilst hydrolysis proceeded essentially according to the equation (*1*):

$$K[C_2H_4PtCl_3] + H_2O = CH_3CHO + Pt + 2HCl + KCl.$$

That this is a true olefin complex of platinum was further confirmed by a variety of experiments. For example, Zeise's salt may be synthesized by shaking an acid solution of platinum(II) chloride with ethylene followed by the addition of potassium chloride (9). Other olefins such as propylene, styrene and cyclohexene form analogous compounds (2). The olefin in these complexes may be quantitatively liberated by stronger donor groups such as cyanide (1), and it is possible to replace one olefin by another.

The simplest of the nonionic complexes, ethylene-platinum(II) chloride, $[C_2H_4PtCl_2]_2$ has been obtained as a rose colored solid, decomposing at 165°, by shaking an acid solution of K_2PtCl_4 in an atmosphere of ethylene for 10 days (14). It is dimeric, and has the halogen-bridged structure (XXV). At low temperatures (−70°) it will combine with a further molecule of ethylene forming the unstable *trans* complex (XXVI) (23a). There is evidence that an unsymmetrical olefin

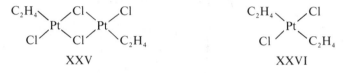

XXV   XXVI

retains its original configuration on complex formation. Thus *cis*- and *trans*-but-2-ene form crystalline complexes having the composition $[PtCl_2, C_4H_8]_2$ which differ in melting point and infrared spectra. Moreover the butenes can be recovered unchanged by displacement with aqueous cyanide (69). Reduction of olefin complexes by molecular hydrogen takes place rapidly and quantitatively even at room temperature:

$$(C_2H_4, PtCl_2)_2 + 4H_2 = 2Pt + 2C_2H_6 + 4HCl$$

The use of palladium-olefin complexes as catalysts in the conversion of olefins to aldehydes and ketones is of some interest. For example, ethylene-palladium chloride is rapidly hydrolyzed at room temperature to acetaldehyde and finely divided palladium:

$$[C_2H_4PdCl_2]_2 + H_2O = 2CH_3CHO + 2Pd + 2HCl$$

The latter may be reoxidized by air and an oxygen carrier:

$$2CuCl_2 + Pd = 2CuCl + PdCl_2$$

$$4CuCl + 4HCl + O_2 = 4CuCl_2 + 2H_2O$$

The reaction appears to be of general application; for example, but-1-ene gives ethylmethylketone and allylbenzene yields benzylmethylketone (106).

Among platinum complexes with mono-olefins the stability is greatest for ethylene, there being a general steric effect for substituted olefins. With palladium, however, cyclohexene has given the most stable mono-olefin complexes; stability decreases in the order cyclohexene > styrene > ethylene > isobutene (*74*).

Probably the most stable olefin complexes (*22*) are those formed by cyclo-octa-1,5-diene (XXVII); the palladium complex, $C_8H_{12}PdCl_2$, decomposes above 200°. Towards both palladium and platinum the diene behaves

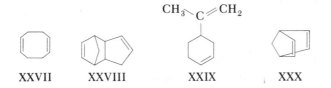

| XXVII | XXVIII | XXIX | XXX |

as a chelating group giving mononuclear complexes, [diene PtX_2]. The corresponding rhodium(I) complex is dimeric and a nonelectrolyte (*23*). The halogen-bridged structure (XXXI) is supported by its reaction with amines (e.g., piperidine) which results in cleavage of the halogen bridges and formation of mononuclear complexes.

$$\text{(XXXI)} \qquad + \quad 2 \text{ amine} \quad \longrightarrow \quad 2\,[C_8H_{12}, \text{amine, Rh, X}]$$

XXXI

Other dienes such as dicyclopentadiene (XXVIII) and dipentene (XXIX) also give very stable complexes with platinum and palladium (*68*). Dicyclopentadiene-platinum chloride is the earliest known of the chelated olefin complexes (*64*). Norbornadiene (XXX) likewise yields isolable complexes with silver(I), copper(I), palladium(II), platinum(II), rhodium(I) and ruthenium(II) salts (*111b,4a*).

A reëxamination of these chelated complexes of platinum and palladium led to the formulation of a number of compounds of previously unknown constitution as an interesting series of alkoxy derivatives (*22*) formed by the reaction:

$$2[\text{diene } PtX_2] + 2\,ROH + 2\,Na_2CO_3 \longrightarrow$$

$$[(\text{diene, OR})_2Pt_2X_2] + 2\,NaX + NaHCO_3$$

The available evidence leads to the structure (XXXII) for the cyclo-octa-1,5-diene compound.

(XXXII)

The compounds are dimeric nonelectrolytes in which the halogen is readily replaced by those anions (e.g., I^-, SCN^-) which have a high affinity for platinum and palladium, thus suggesting direct bonding between the metal and halogen. On the other hand the alkoxy, RO, group is completely unaffected by such anions (even by SEt^-, which is the strongest bridging group known in platinum(II) chemistry); it therefore seems unlikely that the alkoxy group is directly bonded to the metal. Structure (XXXII) involves addition of ClPt, OR across one double bond of each diene, the other olefinic group remaining coördinated to the metal. Infrared spectra are compatible with this formulation.

Ruthenium halides also yield complexes with cyclo-octa-1,5-diene having the formula $C_8H_{12}RuX_2$ (X = Cl, Br, I). These compounds are almost insoluble in organic solvents, and are probably polymeric involving halogen bridges, and a coördination number of *six* for ruthenium. The reaction with *p*-toluidine results in cleavage of the halogen bridges with the formation of a dark yellow crystalline complex, [diene, (*p*-toluidine)RuCl₂] (*111a*).

Butadiene also forms complexes with Cu(I), Pd(II) and Pt(II) by displacement and also by direct reactions between the metal salt and liquid butadiene (*53,70*). The palladium compound has been assigned a structure involving terminal halogen atoms and bridging butadiene molecules, (XXXIII), whilst in the case of platinum two different structural types have been proposed, (XXXIV) and (XXXV).

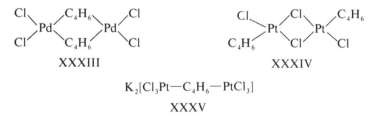

$$K_2[Cl_3Pt—C_4H_6—PtCl_3]$$

XXXV

Molecular weight measurements have not been reported for any of these three compounds and the structures may well require revision when more experimental data become available.

The mono-olefin compounds of palladium are generally prepared in anhydrous media since they are decomposed by water. Two methods have been used: direct combination, e.g., passing isobutene into a solution of palladium chloride in acetic acid gives the complex, $[(CH_3)_2C:CH_2PdCl_2]_2$. The alternative displacement method is illustrated by the reaction (*74*):

$$2 \text{ cyclohexene} + 2(PhCN)_2PdCl_2 \longrightarrow [\text{cyclohexene-}PdCl_2]_2 + 2 PhCN$$

Three remarkable olefin palladium complexes have been described (*65*,

66,107) which involve bonding between palladium and *allyl* or substituted allyl radicals. The yellow complex, $(C_3H_5PdCl)_2$, results from the reaction between allyl alcohol and palladium chloride, whilst the methallyl analog, $(C_4H_7PdCl)_2$, is obtained by decomposition of the isobutene complex, $[(CH_3)_2C:CH_2PdCl_2]_2$, with boiling water. Similarly the α-methylstyrene-palladium chloride complex yields the phenylallyl compound, $(C_9H_9PdCl)_2$, on boiling with aqueous sodium acetate. Hydrolysis of these compounds results in complete breakdown, e.g.,

$$(C_3H_5PdCl)_2 + H_2O = CH_2:CHCHO + CH_3CH:CH_2 + 2\,HCl + Pd.$$

Structurally these compounds are probably related to the metal-arene complexes, as they could be formulated as π-complexes of allyl radicals.

A nickel diene complex, bicyclopentadiene nickel(0), $(C_5H_6)_2Ni$, has been prepared from cyclopentadiene and nickel carbonyl in an inert solvent:

$$Ni(CO)_4 + 2\,C_5H_6 \rightarrow (C_5H_6)_2Ni + 4\,CO$$

It forms a red crystalline solid, m.p. 41–42°, which is *diamagnetic* and unstable in air (*35a*). In this complex, the cyclopentadiene functions in one sense as a chelating donor though, being a conjugated diene, the double bonds will not interact separately with the nickel atom, (XXXVI).

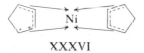

XXXVI

The same compound results from the reduction of di-cyclopentadienyl nickel by sodium amalgam (*116*).

Copper(I) and silver mono-olefinic complexes are all comparatively unstable. The absorption of ethylene by solid copper(I) chloride, usually under pressure, has resulted in the isolation of a complex, $(CuCl,C_2H_4)$. In the case of silver a wide range of olefinic compounds forms 1:1 complexes; these are mostly too unstable to be isolated, and the evidence for their existence, though completely adequate, is derived largely from distribution studies on solutions (*28*). The cyclo-octadiene-silver complexes form an interesting series: the *chelating* 1,5-diene, C_8H_{12}, $AgNO_3$, forms colorless needles melting at 135° and is stable to 90–100°. The 1,3 and 1,4 complexes having the composition $C_8H_{12} \cdot 2\,AgNO_3$ are considerably less stable and readily evolve the diene on warming (*71*). There is little doubt that the stability of the olefin-silver complexes depends mainly on steric factors, and to some extent on the presence of electropositive or electronegative groups conjugated with the double bond.

Structure of Metal-Olefin Complexes

Many structures have been proposed for the platinum-olefin complexes. The ethylene-bridged structure (XXXVII) may be excluded since many olefin complexes such as (XXXVIII) and (XXXIX) are monomeric. The isolation of *cis* and *trans* isomers (*54*) of the type (XLIII) and (XLIV) requires

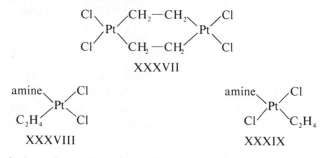

XXXVII

XXXVIII   XXXIX

a planar, dsp^2 configuration about the central platinum atom, and the dimeric complexes are all considered to have the halogen-bridged structure (XL).

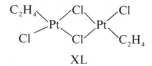

XL

There have been many speculations on the nature of the bonding between platinum and the olefin; structures such as (XLI) and (XLII) have been proposed for the anion of Zeise's salt (*13,33*).

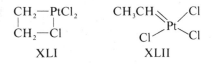

XLI   XLII

The current interpretation of the structure of the platinum- and palladium-olefin complexes is based on X-ray data (as well as infrared evidence) and the observation of the very strong *trans effect* of olefins (*12*) which is indicative, as in the case of the metal carbonyls, of pronounced double bond character between the metal and the olefinic ligand.

Infrared spectra (*14*) of a series of compounds, for example, $K[CH_3 \cdot CH:CH_2 \cdot PtCl_3]H_2O$ and $[CH_3CH:CH_2 \cdot PtCl_2]_2$, show strong olefinic C—H absorption bands (above 3000 cm^{-1}); hence the olefinic bond is not destroyed by complex formation. Strong absorption near 1500 cm^{-1} can be ascribed to the C=C stretching frequency for complexes derived from *unsymmetrical* olefins. Ethylene-platinous chloride (XLV) also shows *weak* absorption at 1506 cm⁻¹, whilst for Zeise's salt any absorption in this region is too weak to be observed. Hence the existence of a band at 1506 cm⁻¹ suggests loss of a center of symmetry by the ethylene, but the extreme weakness of the band indicates that coördination to the metal atom does not profoundly affect the symmetry. These observations are compatible with the olefin being *symmetrically coördinated to the platinum* atom. Dipole moment measurements are difficult to interpret because of uncertainty in the contribution of atom polarisation, but the moment of the C_2H_4—Pt bond appears to be about 4D. This low value may be attributed to a back drift of electrons from platinum to the olefin, resulting in the formation of a π-type bond.

The above summarized evidence led Chatt (*14*) to propose a detailed picture (Fig. 9.7) of the orbitals involved in the formation of olefin-platinum complexes.

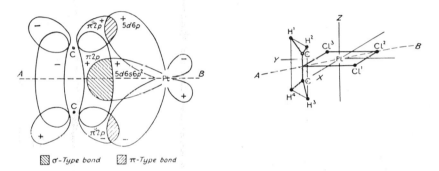

⧄ σ-*Type bond*   ⧄ π-*Type bond*

Fig. 9.7. Orbitals used in the combination of ethylene with platinum and the special arrangement of atoms in $[C_2H_4PtCl_3]^-$ [Reproduced by courtesy of Dr. J. Chatt and the editor of the *Journal of the Chemical Society*].

This structural interpretation requires the formation of a σ-type bond between a platinum dsp^2 orbital and the *bonding* π orbital of the olefin, together with a π-type bond between a platinum dp orbital and the antibonding π^* orbital of the olefin. The symmetry properties of the orbitals are correct for these combinations, and the total platinum-olefin bond order is estimated at ⁴/₃. The same interpretation holds good for the palladium(II) and rhodium(I) complexes whilst for the silver(I) and copper(I) complexes the σ-type bond involves a vacant s or sp orbital of the metal, and the π-type bond a filled d orbital of the metal atom (*31*).

The infrared evidence on which this structure of the platinum olefin complexes is largely based has recently been criticized (*36*). The similarity of the various C—H vibrations in Zeise's salt to those observed in strained three-membered ring systems (ethylene oxide, cyclopropane,

ethylene imine) is interpreted in favor of there being a carbon-carbon single
bond in the platinum-ethylene complex (XLIII). However, these points
have been met (*21b*).

XLIII

X-ray analyses of several olefin-platinum and palladium chlorides are in
agreement with the olefin being symmetrically bonded to the metal (*32,117*).
For the compound (XLIV) X-ray analysis shows that the Pt—Cl and

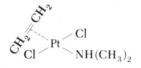

XLIV

Pt—N bonds have the values expected for single bonds, and that the
ethylene is symmetrically bonded to platinum. Thus although the amine is
labile, being *trans* to ethylene, the platinum-nitrogen bond length is unaffected (*93*).

ACETYLENIC DERIVATIVES OF TRANSITION METALS

The range of transition metal-acetylene complexes has increased greatly
over the past ten years, and it is now possible to distinguish three markedly different types:

(a) Those involving essentially normal σ-type bonding between the metal
and the acetylene: $M \cdot C \vdots C \cdot R$, e.g., $K_2Ni(C \vdots CPh)_4$, $(Et_3P)_2Ni(C \vdots CPh)_2$.

(b) Complexes, usually of disubstituted acetylenes, $R \cdot C \vdots C \cdot R$, in which
the triple bond is not greatly altered. These seem to be essentially similar to
the olefin complexes, e.g., $(Bu^tC \vdots CBu^tPtCl_2)_2$.

(c) Complexes, probably of platinum(II), in which the acetylenes behave
as chelating ligands, e.g., $(Ph_3P)_2Pt(PhC \vdots CPh)$.

The following discussion does not include the many and various compounds derived from reaction between acetylenes and metal carbonyls,
since these are considered in Chapter 10.

Acetylene Derivatives of Type (a)

Acetylene and monosubstituted acetylenes react rapidly with ammoniacal solutions of copper(I) or silver salts. From copper(I) and acetylene a red amorphous precipitate (*75*) is formed quantitatively having the composition, $Cu_2C_2 \cdot H_2O$ (*103*), from which the anhydrous and explosive cuprous acetylide is readily obtained. This reaction may be used to detect trace quantities of acetylene. At low temperatures it is possible to isolate the orange *mono*-copper(I) acetylide, CuC_2H, from the reaction between copper(I) iodide and potassium acetylide in anhydrous ammonia solution. Above –45° it decomposes into acetylene and black crystalline copper(I) acetylide (*89*)

$$CuI + KC_2H \xrightarrow[-78°]{NH_3} Cu \cdot C : CH \xrightarrow{-45°} Cu_2C_2 + C_2H_2$$

Silver acetylide, Ag_2C_2, is likewise prepared from acetylene and ammoniacal silver nitrate solution. It is highly shock sensitive and explodes at 120–140°. Gold(I) acetylide is said to be like the copper and silver compounds (*80*). It is interesting that although copper and silver are the earliest known of the transition metal acetylides, their structures and those of the monosubstituted acetylides, $R \cdot C : C \cdot M$, still remain obscure. Most of them are evidently polymeric, being highly insoluble and quite nonvolatile up to their decomposition temperatures.

Though much used as intermediates in the preparation of di from mono-acetylenes, the mono-acetylides of copper and silver (*111*) have themselves received comparatively little study due mainly to their insolubility and the difficulty of obtaining single crystals suitable for crystallographic work. One exception is *t*-butylcopper(I) acetylide (*35*) of which red and yellow forms, decomposing about 150°, have been isolated. Both are associated in solution and have been obtained in a crystalline state.

A number of coördination complexes of these mono-acetylides of copper, silver and gold (*25*) have been described. Ammonia forms a very unstable complex with phenylethynylcopper(I) (*88*). Preliminary experiments (*25*) indicate that more stable complexes are formed using tertiary phosphines and arsines as donor molecules. Thus $Ph \cdot C : C \cdot Cu$ dissolves in a benzene solution of triethylphosphine to give the yellow coördination compound, $PhC : CCu \cdot PEt_3$ which is associated in solution (2–4 times). The analogous silver compounds, $PhC : CAg \cdot PEt_3$ and $PhC : CAg \cdot AsEt_3$, are colorless, crystalline and reasonably stable in air. Even the highly insoluble propynylcopper(I) forms a polymeric, but soluble and crystalline phosphine complex, $CH_3C : C \cdot CuPEt_3$, which readily dissociates. Gold forms a colorless *monomeric* complex, $PhC : CAu \cdot PEt_3$.

An interesting series of complex anionic acetylides have been reported for the metals, Cu (*88,89*), Cr (*90*), Mn (*85*), Fe (*91*), Co (*87*) and Ni (*86,92*). The most general preparative method involves the reaction between an alkali metal acetylide and, preferably, a *soluble* metal salt (thio-cyanate or nitrate) in anhydrous ammonia solution. For example:

$$[(NH_3)_6Cr[(NO_3)_3 + KC_2H \xrightarrow{NH_3} K_3[Cr(C_2H)_6]$$

The complex acetylides are highly insoluble, and may be purified by washing with liquid ammonia. They are all highly sensitive to moisture; some such as $M_4[Fe(C\vdots CR)_6]$ decompose in the course of a few hours even in an inert atmosphere. In the case of manganese, the initially formed manganese(II) acetylide may be oxidized to the explosive manganese(III) compound.

$$K \cdot C_2H + Mn(SCN)_2 \xrightarrow{NH_3} K_2[Mn(C_2H)_4] \xrightarrow{O_2} K_3[Mn(C_2H)_6]$$

Similarly two series of iron and cobalt acetylides have been isolated, e.g., $Na_4[Fe(C_2H)_6]$ and $Na_3[Fe(C_2H)_6]$. The immediate product from the reaction using nickel(II) salts is $K_2[Ni(C\vdots CR)_4]$ which may be *reduced* by the use of excess alkali metal to the pyrophoric derivative of nickel(0).

$$K_2[Ni(C\vdots CR)_4] + 2K \longrightarrow K_4[Ni(C\vdots CR)_4]$$

This is a diamagnetic spin-paired sp^3 complex which is isoelectronic with $[Ni(CN)_4]^{4-}$, $[Ni(CNR)_4]$ and $[Ni(CO)_4]$. A binuclear nickel(I) complex has also been obtained by the reaction:

$$K_4[Ni_2(CN)_6(CO)_2] + 8KC\vdots CR \xrightarrow{NH_3} K_6[Ni_2(C\vdots CR)_8] + 2CO + 6KCN$$

The copper(I) complex is formed *via* the monoacetylide:

$$CuC_2H + 2KC_2H \longrightarrow K_2[Cu(C_2H)_3]$$

In the case of copper, two series of complexes; $K_2[Cu(C_2H)_3]$ and $K[Cu(C_2H)_2]$, have been obtained.

One of the main features of interest in these anionic acetylenic complexes is the metal-carbon bond order. As with the metal carbonyls a single σ-bonded structure implies that the metal atom bears a considerable negative charge. In the case of the nickel compounds, $K_4[Ni(\overset{\bullet\bullet}{C}\vdots CR)_4]$, such a formulation suggests that the nickel atom carries *four* units of negative charge, but it is highly likely that this unfavorable charge distribution is relieved by partial double bonding involving electron flow *from* the d-orbitals of the transition metal atoms *to* the π_g antibonding orbitals of the ethynyl groups. In this way, which itself implies an increase in the metal-to-carbon bond order and a decrease in the C—C bond order, the negative charge on the metal could be considerably reduced.

Many transition metals form σ-bonded acetylene complexes of quite high stability if the metal is simultaneously bonded to a suitable ligand. The basic reason for this has already been discussed in connection with platinum. Nickel (*21*), palladium (*26*) and platinum (*20*) all form stable complexes of the type (XLV) in which the metal forms four dsp^2 planar bonds. In

$$(R_3P)_2MX_2 + 2 R'C \vdots CLi \longrightarrow \begin{array}{c} R'C \vdots C \diagdown \quad \diagup PR_3 \\ M \\ R_3P \diagup \quad \diagdown C \vdots CR' \end{array}$$

XLV

each case the *trans* compound having zero dipole moment is obtained. The stability is greatest for platinum and least for nickel: the golden yellow nickel complex, *trans*-$(Et_3P)_2Ni(C \vdots CPh)_2$, decomposes at 150°. With platinum the intermediate compounds in which only one halogen atom has been replaced by an acetylene, $[(Et_3P)_2Pt(X)C \vdots CR]$, may be isolated if an acetylenic Grignard reagent, rather than the more reactive lithium derivative, is used. Moreover the use of the *cis*-phosphine complex, $(Et_3P)_2PtCl_2$, favors conversion to the *bis*-acetylene derivative. In all of these compounds the characteristic $C{\equiv}C$ stretching frequency can be observed at about $2100 \ cm^{-1}$.

If the nickel complex, *trans*-$[(PhPEt_2)_2Ni(1\text{-naphthyl})Br]$, is treated with sodium phenylacetylide the *trans*-bisacetylene complex $[(PhPEt_2)_2Ni(C \vdots CPh)_2]$, is obtained and not the expected "mixed" product. Nickel is also unusual in that it seems to form a 5-coördinate complex phosphine acetylide(XLVI) which is probably monomeric. Although treatment of *trans*-$[(PhPEt_2)_2NiBr_2]$ with sodium phenylacetylide gives mainly the yellow complex, $[(PhPEt_2)_2Ni(C \vdots CPh)_2]$, the deep red soluble compound (XLVI) is also obtained.

$$trans\text{-}[(PhPEt_2)_2Ni(C \vdots CPh)_2] + PhPEt_2 \rightleftharpoons [(PhPEt_2)_3Ni(C \vdots CPh)_2]$$

XLVI

Physical measurements on this compound are rendered difficult due to its reversible dissociation in solution.

Acetylene Complexes of Type (b)

The evidence for compounds of this type is derived largely from infrared or Raman studies which show the presence in the complex of the $C{\equiv}C$ stretching frequency, usually lowered by some $50–250 \ cm^{-1}$. Platinum, copper and silver are so far known to form this type of complex, and a necessary condition appears to be the presence of at least one tertiary carbon atom adjacent to the triple bond, at least in the case of platinum.

Di-tertiarybutyl acetylene reacts with sodium chloroplatinate(II), Na_2PtCl_4, in ethanol solution to give a halogen-bridged complex (XLVII) from which an unstable Zeise-type of salt, $K[C_{10}H_{18}PtCl_3]$, may be obtained but this reverts to the bridged compound in aqueous solution (*15*).

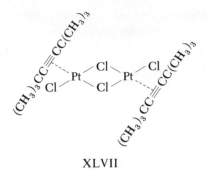

XLVII

The halogen bridge in this complex may be broken by amines giving, for example, trans-[(CH$_3$)$_3$CC : CC(CH$_3$)$_3$ piperidine, PtCl$_2$]. Simpler diacetylenes do not appear to give platinum complexes of this type, although stable Zeise-type salts are formed from the dihydroxy acetylene, (CH$_3$)$_2$-C(OH)C : CC(OH)(CH$_3$)$_2$, and its dimethyl ether. (See ref. *15* for a summary of the earlier literature). The platinum-acetylene bonding in these compounds may well be analogous to that in the olefin complexes involving overlap between the antibonding orbitals of the acetylene and *dp* hybrid orbitals of platinum. There are as yet insufficient data on these compounds, although an X-ray examination of the copper(I) chloride-but-2-yne complex shows that the copper atom lies on the perpendicular bisector of the acetylenic bond (*11*). The silver complexes are formed by a number of disubstituted acetylenes. But-2-yne and pent-2-yne both give colorless solid complexes having the composition [acetylene · AgNO$_3$] from which the acetylene is rapidly evolved on warming (*55*). With hex-3-yne and powdered silver nitrate the reaction is quantitative after eight weeks (*29*).

Acetylene Complexes of Type (c)

These, so far, are all derivatives of platinum which are formed (*17,18*) by the reduction of a bis-tertiary phosphine-platinum halide in the presence of an acetylene.

$$2\ cis\text{-}(Ph_3P)_2PtCl_2 + N_2H_4 + 2\ C_2R_2 \longrightarrow 2(Ph_3P)_2PtC_2R_2 + N_2 + 4\ HCl$$

A wide range of acetylenes react in this way, one of the most stable complexes being formed by di-*p*-nitrophenylacetylene. Acetylenes will displace one another from the complexes; the stability is least for acetylene itself, and increases with the electron attracting character of the acetylene. Acetylenes are also displaced from these complexes by a reaction with methyl iodide in which a platinum-to-methyl bond is established:

$$(Ph_3P)_2PtC_2R_2 + CH_3I \longrightarrow (Ph_3P)_2Pt(CH_3)I + C_2R_2$$

Preliminary X-ray data on the *p*-bromphenylacetylene complex are consistent with a square planar configuration about the platinum. The infrared spectra of a series of these complexes show a fairly strong band near 1700 cm⁻¹, (more consistent with an olefinic than an acetylenic C—C frequency), and have no absorption in the 2000 cm⁻¹ range which could be ascribed to an acetylenic stretching frequency. Further structural evidence comes from dipole moment measurements which are fairly large, and very strongly influenced by *para*-substituents in diphenylacetylene derivatives as might be expected on the basis of structure (XLVIII) where the aryl groups are not colinear. In this structure the platinum(II) is considered

XLVIII   XLIX

to make use of four dsp^2 square planar bonds. The bonds to carbon may then be considered as involving overlap with two sp^2 orbitals of the *cis* ethylene grouping resulting in a bent molecular orbital (XLIX). As with the acetylene complexes of type (b), much work remains to be done before detailed structures can be assigned with any degree of certainty.

Acetylene will react with cooled solutions of potassium cobaltocyanide (*113*) to yield a crystalline complex, $K_6[Co_2(CN)_{10}C_2H_2]\cdot 4\,H_2O$. Its proton magnetic resonance spectrum shows a single proton resonance in the C—H region, and this, combined with the strong absorption band in its infrared spectrum at 1615 cm⁻¹ which is indicative of an olefinic double bond, has led to the formulation (L).

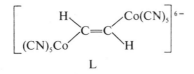

L

References

(1) Anderson, J. S., *J. Chem. Soc.,* 971 (1934).
(2) Anderson, J. S., *J. Chem. Soc.,* 1042 (1936).
(3) Anet, F. A. L., *Can. J. Chem.,* **37,** 58 (1959).
(4) Anet, F. A. L., and Leblanc, E., *J. Am. Chem. Soc.,* **79,** 2649 (1957).
(4a) Baenziger, N. C., Alexander, R. A., Carpenter, C., and Doyle, J. R., *J. Am. Chem. Soc.,* **82,** 535 (1960).
(5) Bawn, C. E. H., and Gladstone, J., *Proc. Chem. Soc.,* 227 (1959).
(6) Bawn, C. E. H., and Whitby, F., *Discuss. Faraday Soc.,* **1,** 228 (1947).

464 ORGANOMETALLIC COMPOUNDS

(7) Beermann, C., and Bestian, H., *Angew. Chem.,* **71,** 618 (1959).
(8) Beermann, C., and Clauss, K., *Angew. Chem.,* **71,** 627 (1959).
(9) Birnbaum, K., *Ann.,* **145,** 67 (1869).
(10) Buckton, G., *Ann.,* **109,** 225 (1859).
(11) Carter, F. L., and Hughes, E. W., *Acta Cryst.,* **10,** 801 (1957).
(12) Chatt, J., *Nature.,* **165,** 637 (1950).
(13) Chatt, J., *Research.,* **4,** 180 (1951).
(14) Chatt, J., and Duncanson, L. A., *J. Chem. Soc.,* 2939 (1953); see also "Inorganic Syntheses," **5,** 210.
(15) Chatt, J., Duncanson, L. A., and Guy, R. G., *Chemistry and Industry,* 430 (1959).
(16) Chatt, J., and Hayter, R. G., *Proc. Chem. Soc.,* 153 (1959).
(17) Chatt, J., and Rowe, G. A., Special Publ. No. 13, p. 117, London, The Chemical Society, 1959. (Int. Conf. Coörd. Chem.).
(18) Chatt, J., Rowe, G. A., and Williams, A. A., *Proc. Chem. Soc.,* 208 (1957).
(19) Chatt, J., and Shaw, B. L., *Chemistry and Industry,* 675 (1959).
(20) Chatt, J., and Shaw, B. L., *J. Chem. Soc.,* 705, 4020 (1959)
(21) Chatt, J., and Shaw, B. L., *J. Chem. Soc.,* 1718 (1960).
(21a) Chatt, J., Adams, D. M., and Shaw, B. L., *J. Chem. Soc.,* 2047 (1960).
(21b) Chatt, J., and Adams, D. M., *Chemistry and Industry,* 149 (1960).
(22) Chatt, J., Vallarino, L. M., and Venanzi, L. M., *J. Chem. Soc.,* 3413 (1957).
(23) Chatt, J., and Venanzi, L. M., *J. Chem. Soc.,* 4735 (1957).
(23a) Chatt, J., and Wilkins, R. G., *J. Chem. Soc.,* 2622 (1952).
(24) Closson, R. D., Kozikowski, J., and Coffield, T. H., *J. Org. Chem.,* **22,** 598 (1957).
(25) Coates, G. E., Blake, D., and Calvin, G., *Proc. Chem. Soc.,* 396 (1959).
(26) Coates, G. E., and Calvin, G., *J. Chem. Soc.,* 2008 (1960).
(27) Coates, G. E., Calvin, G., and Dixon, P. S., *Chemistry and Industry,* 1628 (1959).
(28) Comyns, A. E., and Lucas, H. J., *J. Am. Chem. Soc.,* **79,** 4339 (1957).
(29) Comyns, A. E., and Lucas, H. J., *J. Am. Chem. Soc.,* **79,** 4341 (1957).
(30) Cotton, F. A., *Chem. Reviews,* **55,** 551 (1955).
(30a) Costa, G., and Camus, A., *Gazz. chim. ital.,* **86,** 77 (1956).
(31) Dewar, M. J. S., *Bull. soc. chim. France,* **18,** C79 (1951).
(32) Dempsey, J. N., and Baenziger, N. C., *J. Am. Chem. Soc.,* **77,** 4984, 4987 (1955).
(33) Drew, H. D. K., Pinkard, F. W., Wardlaw, W., and Cox, E. G., *J. Chem. Soc.,* 988, 1895 (1932).
(34) Druce, J. G. F., *J. Chem. Soc.,* 1129 (1934).
(35) Favorsky, A., and Morev, L., *J. Russ. Phys. Chem. Soc.,* **50,** 571 (1920).
(35a) Fischer, E. O., and Werner, H., *Chem. Ber.,* **92,** 1423 (1959).
(36) Gel'man, A. D., Babushkin, A. A., and Gribov, L. A., *Russ. J. Inorg. Chem.,* **4,** 695 (1959).
(37) Gibson, C. S., and Brain, F. H., *J. Chem. Soc.,* 762 (1939).
(38) Gibson, C. S., Burawoy, A., Hampson, G. C., and Powell, H. M., *J. Chem. Soc.,* 1690 (1937).

(39) Gibson, C. S., Burawoy, A., and Holt, S., *J. Chem. Soc.,* 1024 (1935).

(40) Gibson, C. S., and Foss, M. E., *J. Chem. Soc.,* 299 (1951).

(41) Gibson, C. S., and Pope, W. J., *J. Chem. Soc.,* 2061 (1907).

(42) Gibson, C. S., and Simonsen, J. L., *J. Chem. Soc.,* 2531 (1930).

(43) Gilman, H., and Bailie, J. C., *J. Org. Chem.,* **2,** 87 (1937).

(44) Gilman, H., Jones, R. G., Moore, F. W., and Kolbezen, M. J., *J. Am. Chem. Soc.,* **63,** 2525 (1941).

(45) Gilman, H., Jones, R. G., and Woods, L. A., *J. Org. Chem.,* **17,** 1630 (1952).

(46) Gilman, H., and Kirby, R. H., *J. Am. Chem. Soc.,* **63,** 2046 (1941).

(47) Gilman, H., and Lichtenwalter, M., *J. Am. Chem. Soc.,* **60,** 3085 (1938).

(48) Gilman, H., Lichtenwalter, M., and Benkeser, R. A., *J. Am. Chem. Soc.,* **75,** 2063 (1953).

(49) Gilman, H., and Straley, J. M., *Rec. trav. chim.,* **55,** 821 (1936).

(50) Gilman, H., and Woods, L. A., *J. Am. Chem. Soc.,* **70,** 550 (1948).

(51) Glockling, F., *J. Chem. Soc.,* 716, (1955); *ibid.,* 3640 (1956).

(51a) Glockling F., and Jewitt, M., unpublished observations.

(52) Glockling, F., and Kingston, D., *J. Chem. Soc.,* 3001 (1959).

(53) Hel′man, A. D., *Compt. rend. Acad. Sci. U.S.S.R.,* **23,** 532 (1939).

(54) Hel′man, A. D., and Chernyaev, I. I., *Compt. rend. Acad. Sci. U.S.S.R.,* **4,** 181 (1936).

(55) Helmkamp, G. K., Carter, F. L., and Lucas, H. J., *J. Am. Chem. Soc.,* **79,** 1306 (1957).

(56) Hein, F., *Z. anorg. Chem.,* **51,** 503 (1938).

(57) Hein, F., and Nebe, E., *Naturwissenschaften.,* **28,** 93 (1940).

(58) Hein, F., and Weiss, R., *Z. anorg. Chem.,* **295,** 145 (1958).

(59) Hein, F., and Weiss, R., *Naturwissenschaften.,* **46,** 321 (1959).

(60) Herman, D. F., and Nelson, W. K., *J. Am. Chem. Soc.,* **75,** 3877, 3882 (1953).

(61) Hieber, W., and Braun, G., *Z. Naturforsch.,* **14b,** 132 (1959).

(62) Hieber, W., Vohler, O., and Braun, G., *Z. Naturforsch.,* **13b,** 192 (1958).

(63) Hieber, W., and Wagner, G., *Z. Naturforsch.,* **12b,** 478 (1957).

(64) Hofmann, K. A., and Narbutt, J. von., *Ber.,* **41,** 1625 (1908).

(65) Hüttel, R., and Bechter, M., *Angew. Chem.,* **71,** 456 (1959).

(66) Hüttel, R., and Kratzer, J., *Angew. Chem.,* **71,** 456 (1959).

(67) Jonassen, H. B., Aldridge, C. L., and Pulkkinen, E., *Chemistry and Industry,* 374 (1960).

(68) Jonassen, H. B., and Doyle, J. R., *J. Am. Chem. Soc.,* **78,** 3965 (1956).

(69) Jonassen, H. B., and Kirsch, W. B., *J. Am. Chem. Soc.,* **79,** 1279 (1957).

(70) Jonassen, H. B., and Slade, P. E., *J. Am. Chem. Soc.,* **79,** 1277 (1957).

(71) Jones, W. O., *J. Chem. Soc.,* 312 (1954).

(72) Kharasch, M. S., and Isbell, H. S., *J. Am. Chem. Soc.,* **53,** 2701 (1931).

(73) Kharasch, M. S., and Isbell, H. S., *J. Am. Chem. Soc.,* **53,** 3053 (1931).

(74) Kharasch, M. S., Seyler, R. C., and Mayo, F. R., *J. Am. Chem. Soc.,* **60,** 882 (1938).

(75) Klement, R., and Köddermann-Gros, E., *Z. anorg. Chem.,* **254,** 201 (1947).

(76) Krause, E., and Schmitz, M., *Ber.,* **52,** 2159 (1919).

(77) Krause, E., and Wendt, B., *Ber.,* **56,** 2064 (1923).

(78) Lichtenwalter, M., *Iowa State Coll. J. Sci.,* **14,** 57 (1939).

(79) Malatesta, L., and Cariello, C., *J. Chem. Soc.,* 2323 (1958).

(80) Mathews, J. A., and Watters, L. L., *J. Am. Chem. Soc.,* **22,** 108 (1900).

(81) Menzies, R. C., *J. Chem. Soc.,* 565 (1928).

(82) Menzies, R. C., Chatterjee, A. K., Steel, J. R., and Youdale, F. N., *J. Chem. Soc.,* 1706 (1958).

(83) Menzies, R. C., and Lile, W. J., *J. Chem. Soc.,* 1168 (1949).

(84) Menzies, R. C., and Wiltshire, E. R., *J. Chem. Soc.,* 21 (1933).

(85) Nast, R., and Griesshammer, H., *Chem. Ber.,* **90,** 1315 (1957).

(86) Nast, R., and Kasperl, H., *Chem. Ber.,* **92,** 2135 (1959).

(87) Nast, R., and Lewinsky, H., *Z. anorg. Chem.,* **282,** 210 (1955).

(88) Nast, R., and Pfab, W., *Chem. Ber.,* **89,** 415 (1956).

(89) Nast, R., and Pfab, W., *Z. anorg. Chem.,* **292,** 287 (1957).

(90) Nast, R., and Sirtl, E., *Chem. Ber.,* **88,** 1723 (1955).

(91) Nast, R., and Urban, F., *Z. anorg. Chem.,* **287,** 17 (1956).

(92) Nast, R., and Vester, K., *Z. anorg. Chem.,* **279,** 146 (1955).

(92a) Orgel, L. E., The Chemistry of Transition-Metal Compounds, London, 1960.

(93) Owston, P. G., Alderman, P. R. H., and Rowe, J. M., *Acta Cryst.,* **13,** 149 (1960).

(94) Pope, W. J., and Peachey, S. J., *Proc. Roy. Soc.,* **23,** 86 (1907).

(95) Pope, W. J., and Peachey, S. J., *J. Chem. Soc.,* **97,** 571 (1909).

(96) Powell, H. M., and Phillips, R. F., *Proc. Roy. Soc.,* **173,** 147 (1939).

(97) Reich, R., *Compt. rend.,* **177,** 322 (1923).

(98) Rochow, E. G., and Hurd, D. T., *J. Am. Chem. Soc.,* **67,** 1057 (1945).

(99) Rundle, R. E., and Illuminati, G., *J. Am. Chem. Soc.,* **71,** 3575 (1949).

(100) Rundle, R. E., and Lewis, P. H., *J. Chem. Phys.,* **21,** 986 (1953).

(101) Rundle, R. E., and Snow, A. I., *Acta Cryst.,* **4,** 348 (1951).

(102) Rundle, R. E., and Sturdivant, J. H., *J. Am. Chem. Soc.,* **69,** 1561 (1947).

(103) Scheiber, J., and Reckleben, H., *Ber.,* **44,** 210 (1911).

(104) Semerano, G., and Riccoboni, L., *Ber.,* **74,** 1089 (1941).

(105) Skinner, H. A., and Pilcher, G., *J. Inorg. and Nucl. Chem.,* **7,** 8 (1958).

(106) Smidt, J., *Angew. Chem.,* **71,** 176 (1959).

(107) Smidt, J., and Hafner, W., *Angew. Chem.,* **71,** 284 (1959).

(108) Smidt, J., and Jira, R., *Angew. Chem.,* **71,** 651 (1959).

(109) Summers, L., Uloth, R. H., and Holmes, A., *J. Am. Chem. Soc.,* **77,** 3604 (1955).

(110) Truter, M. R., and Swallow, A. G., *Proc. Roy. Soc.,* **252A,** 205 (1960); Truter, M. R., and Hazell, A. C., *Proc. Roy. Soc.,* **252A,** 218 (1960).

(111) Vestin, R., and Ralf, E., *Acta Chem. Scand.,* **3,** 101 (1949).

(111a) Wilkinson, G., and Bennett, M. A., *Chemistry and Industry,* 1516 (1959).

(111b) Wilkinson, G., Bennett, M. A., and Abel, E. W., *J. Chem. Soc.,* 3178 (1959).

(112) Wilkinson, G., and Birmingham, J. M., *J. Am. Chem. Soc.,* **76,** 6210 (1954); **78,** 42 (1956).

(113) Wilkinson, G., and Griffith, W. P., *J. Chem. Soc.,* 1629 (1959).

(114) Wilkinson, G., and Piper, T. S., *J. Inorg. and Nucl. Chem.,* **2,** 38 (1956).

(115) Wilkinson, G., and Piper, T. S., *J. Inorg. and Nucl. Chem.,* **3,** 104 (1956).

(116) Wollensak, J. C., and Filbey, A. H., personal communication.

(117) Wunderlich, J. A., and Mellor, D. P., *Acta Cryst.,* **7,** 130 (1954); **8,** 57 (1955).

(118) Zeise, W. C., *Pogg. Ann.,* **9,** 632 (1827).

(119) Zeiss, H., and Herwig, W., *J. Am. Chem. Soc.,* **79,** 6561 (1957).

(120) Zeiss, H., and Herwig, W., *J. Am. Chem. Soc.,* **81,** 4798 (1959).

(121) Zeiss, H., and Schrauzer, G. N., *Chemistry and Industry,* 540 (1959).

(122) Zeiss, H., and Tsutsui, M., *J. Am. Chem. Soc.,* **81,** 1367 (1959).

(122a) Zeiss, H., Herwig, W., and Metlesics, W., *J. Am. Chem. Soc.,* **81,** 6203 (1959).

10. METAL CARBONYLS AND RELATED COMPOUNDS

J. Chatt, P. L. Pauson and L. M. Venanzi

Imperial Chemical Industries, Ltd.
Royal College of Science and Technology, Glasgow, Scotland, and
Oxford University, England

STRUCTURE

With the development of our knowledge of hydrocarbon complexes of transition metals, carbon monoxide has lost much of its uniqueness as a ligand for these elements. It can now take its place along with other unsaturated carbon compounds; and thus the metal carbonyls* may very properly be included in a text on *organo*metallic compounds. The outstanding feature of carbon monoxide—its tendency to form stable complexes only with the lowest oxidation states of these metals—is shared in varying degree by the hydrocarbon ligands as well as by phosphines, arsines etc. This may be linked both to the relatively electropositive nature of the donor atom in these ligands, and to the possibility of overlap of the π-orbitals of the ligand with suitable (d) orbitals of the metal. It contrasts with the behavior of very electronegative donors, e.g., fluorine, which brings out the highest oxidation state of which the metal is capable.

It is also recognized that there is no sharp division in properties between complexes with carbon ligands and the purely inorganic coördination compounds. The compounds formed by the related ligands, carbon monoxide, isonitriles, acetylides and cyanide, reveal a gradation of types and bridge such apparent extremes as $[C_6H_6]_2Cr$ and $Cr(H_2O)_6^{+++}$. The isonitrile complexes are sufficiently like those of carbon monoxide to be included in this chapter.

Considerations Governing the Constitution of Metal Carbonyls

Carbon monoxide commonly acts as either a monodentate ligand or a bivalent bridging group. In both capacities it provides two electrons for bond formation, and an example of apparently intermediate type is discussed later (p. 496). Several compounds are known in which carbon monoxide is linked simultaneously to three metal atoms. This is firmly established (206) in tricyclopentadienyl-trinickel dicarbonyl (*cf.* p. 475) (77),

*For earlier reviews see references 7,23,33.

and by analogy may be assumed for the tribenzene-tricobalt dicarbonyl cation (66) (cf. Chapter 8). More speculatively the structure (I) appears possible (206) for the trimeric iron carbonylate ion, $Fe_3(CO)_{11}^{--}$.

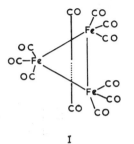

I

In the metal carbonyls the metal atom normally attains the effective atomic number (E.A.N.) of the next inert gas. This rule is invariably obeyed in the pure carbonyls which are listed in Table 10.1.*

Thus, nickel in the first transition series has atomic number 28 and so attains the E.A.N. of krypton, 36, by combining with four molecules of carbon monoxide to give $Ni(CO)_4$. Clearly elements with odd atomic number cannot form monomeric carbonyls on this basis and hence we find that the simplest carbonyls formed by cobalt, manganese and vanadium (216a,244) are, respectively, $Co_2(CO)_8$, $Mn_2(CO)_{10}$ and $V_2(CO)_{12}$.*

The E.A.N. rule implies of course that all such compounds are inner orbital complexes. It further appears that the inner d-orbitals are always completely filled or used in σ-bonding, but the outer d-orbitals are never utilized. If this is correct, it enables us to deduce which orbitals are utilized in bonding and hence to assign probable structures. Thus $Ni(CO)_4$ must use sp^3 hybrid orbitals and hence be tetrahedral, in agreement with experimental results. It is also clear that we are more likely to find carbonyl derivatives with vacant p orbitals than compounds exceeding the E.A.N. of the next inert gas.

Exceptions to the E.A.N. rule are found among the carbonyl halides, but our structural knowledge of this group is very incomplete. A few are also found among other carbonyl derivatives. Replacement of one carbonyl group per metal atom in dimanganese decacarbonyl by phosphines leads to monomeric products or equilibrium mixtures (119,148), e.g.,

$$Mn(CO)_4(P[C_6H_{11}]_3) \rightleftarrows Mn_2(CO)_8(P[C_6H_{11}]_3)_2.$$

The monomeric species can only have 35 electrons about the manganese atom and in accordance with this has been found to show paramagnetism,

*But see references 33a and 216a.

TABLE 10.1. THE METAL CARBONYLS

Group V	Group VI	Group VII	Group VIII
$V(CO)_6$ green-black or blue dec. 70° sublimes 45–60°/10 mm	$Cr(CO)_6$ colorless sublimes		$Fe(CO)_5$ yellow m.p. −20° b.p. 103°
$V_2(CO)_{12}$ yellow-orange (solution)		$[Mn(CO)_5]_2$ golden-yellow m.p. 154–155° sublimes	$Fe_2(CO)_9$ golden-yellow dec. 100°
			$[Fe(CO)_4]_3$ green dec. 140°
			$[Co(CO)_4]_2$ orange-red m.p. 51°
			$[Co(CO)_3]_4$ black dec. 60° crystalline
			$Ni(CO)_4$ colorless m.p. −25° b.p. 43°

$Mo(CO)_6$
colorless
sublimes

$W(CO)_6$
colorless
sublimes

$[Re(CO)_5]_2$
colorless
m.p. 177°
sublimes

$Ru(CO)_5$
colorless
m.p. −22°

$Ru_2(CO)_9$
orange
sublimes

$[Ru(CO)_4]_3$
green
crystalline

$Os(CO)_5$
colorless
m.p. ca. −15°

$Os_2(CO)_9$
yellow
m.p. 224°
sublimes

$[Rh(CO)_4]_2$
orange
m.p. 76° (dec.)

$[Rh(CO)_3]_n$
red
sublimes

$[Rh_4(CO)_{11}]_n$
(dec. ca. 200°)

$[Ir(CO)_4]_2$
yellow-green
sublimes

$[Ir(CO)_3]_n$
canary-yellow
dec. 210°

corresponding to one unpaired electron. $Fe(CO)_3SC_6H_5$ may be a similar example if its monomeric nature (146) is confirmed.

A paramagnetic (?) azulene dimolybdenum hexacarbonyl has been reported (32). The above mentioned tricyclopentadienyltrinickel dicarbonyl also possesses one unpaired electron (76,77), which may be regarded as being in excess of the E.A.N. and as resonating among the three nickel atoms. Another compound which appears to exceed the E.A.N. is $Fe(CO)_5I_2$, but this may well prove to be ionic, viz., $[Fe(CO)_5I]^+I^-$, and thus fit the rule.

Structures

The structures of the monomeric carbonyls are all known from electron diffraction studies (64). The symmetrical tetrahedral structure of $Ni(CO)_4$ (sp^3 hybridization) and octahedral structures of Cr—, Mo—, and W—$(CO)_6(d^2sp^3$ hybrids) are in accord with expectation and the former has also been confirmed by X-ray methods (175). In the case of the dsp^3 hybridization for iron pentacarbonyl both square pyramidal and trigonal bipyramidal configurations have been considered. The latter structure is favored (50,51,236,275) by electron diffraction, Raman and infrared spectroscopic results, and the apparently contradictory dipole moment of 0.7 D may be attributed to atom polarization (151). The structures of the carbonyls of Ru and Os can at present only be assumed to be analogous to those of Fe. No experimental confirmation exists.

In the polynuclear carbonyls the metal atoms may be held together by metal-metal bonds with or without bridging carbonyl groups. Presence of the latter can generally be recognized by absorption below $1900 \, cm^{-1}$ in the infrared region. Terminal carbonyl groups absorb at higher frequency, but the presence of certain other ligands, especially amines, may shift these bands into the "bridging CO region." That this criterion may fail even in pure carbonyls is shown by the case of tri-iron dodecacarbonyl. Bulk samples of this substance show only very weak absorption at 1858 and 1826 cm^{-1}, but single crystals show a strong maximum at $1875 \, cm^{-1}$ when examined in a polarized infrared beam (60). Unfortunately the molecules appear to be disordered in the crystal (59,203). This interpretation of the X-ray data leads to a triangular arrangement of the Fe atoms with Fe—Fe bonds of approximately 2.8 Å. It has not yet been found possible to locate the attached carbonyl groups.

Fortunately, no such difficulties have been met in determining the structures of the dimeric carbonyls. $Mn_2(CO)_{10}$ and its Re analog are composed of metal atoms having nearly regular octahedral coördination (58); five of the six positions are occupied by CO groups and the sixth by the second metal atom at distances of 2.93 and 3.02 Å in the Mn and Re compounds respectively. Thus there are no bridging groups in agreement with the absence of strong absorption below 1900 cm^{-1}. Iron enneacarbonyl, $Fe_2(CO)_9$, (II), has three bridging groups and the presence of a metal-metal bond evident from its diamagnetism is reflected in an Fe—Fe distance (241) of 2.46 Å, a value also found in several other iron carbonyl derivatives. In

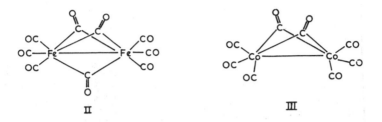

II   III

dicobalt octacarbonyl, the presence of two bridging and six terminal CO groups was deduced from spectroscopic results. X-ray data (36), while confirming this arrangement, are insufficiently complete to allow exact assignment of the geometry. But a convincing body of indirect evidence suggests formulation as shown in (III) (similar to $Fe_2(CO)_9$ with one bridging group removed), i.e., with two bridging groups lying in intersecting planes (207). Such a structure has been demonstrated (206,207) for the complex (IV) derived from this carbonyl by reaction with an acetylene and carbon monoxide. It accounts for the splitting of the absorption band near 1859 cm^{-1} in $Co_2(CO)_8$, and the presence of a vacant coördination site provides a ready explanation for the facile exchange (12) with radioactive carbon monoxide,* the ability to add one mole of carbon monoxide (202), the

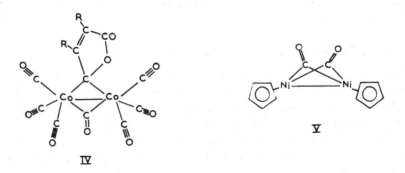

IV   V

*In general, exchange rates vary widely. $Ni(CO)_4$ also exchanges rapidly, but $Cr(CO)_6$, $Mn_2(CO)_{10}$ and $Fe(CO)_5$ do so very slowly. In the latter case metallic Pt and Ni have been shown to be effective catalysts (297).

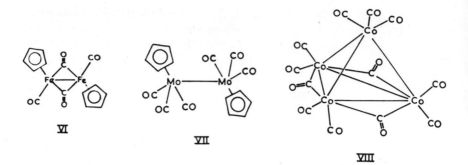

addition of aluminium bromide (*40*), the ease of reaction with acetylenes (*278*) and related "catalytic" properties. For the same reason, a folded structure (V) has been suggested (*286*) for dicyclopentadienyldinickel dicarbonyl (*77*), in contrast to the coplanar arrangement of the bridging groups established (*204*) for dicyclopentadienyldi-iron tetracarbonyl (VI). The remaining dimeric cyclopentadienyl-metal carbonyls, those of Cr, Mo and W, resemble manganese carbonyl in being held together only by metal-metal bonds. Only the Mo compound (VII) has been examined in detail (*311*). Its Mo—Mo bond is 3.22 Å in length. Change to this type of bonding also occurs when two of the carbonyl groups in $Co_2(CO)_8$ are replaced by phosphines as in $[Co(CO)_3PPh_3]_2$ which lacks absorption below 1900 cm^{-1} (*294*).

Tetracobalt dodecacarbonyl has recently been assigned the structure (VIII) (*48,49*). This is unfortunately another disordered crystal structure and the proposed formulation is therefore based largely on symmetry arguments. An interesting mixed cobalt-iron hydrocarbonyl, $HFeCo(CO)_{12}$ may be derived (*39*) from this by replacing the top $Co(CO)_3$ group by $HFe(CO)_3$.

Nature of the Metal–Carbon and Carbon–Oxygen Bonds

The molecular orbital description of the bonding in metal carbonyls has been considered in Chapter 1 and it is the purpose of this section to fill in the experimental background by summarizing information regarding molecular shapes, polarity, bond orders etc.

All structure determinations suggest that the M—C—O grouping is accurately linear when the carbonyl group is terminal and that the bridging groups

$$\underset{M \qquad M}{\overset{\overset{\textstyle O}{\|}}{C}}$$

are symmetrical. Typical bond lengths for both types are given in Table 10.2 for a varied selection of carbonyl derivatives.

TABLE 10.2. BOND LENGTHS

Compound	Type of Carbonyl Group*	C-O (Å)	M-C (Å)	Method†	Ref.
$Ni(CO)_4$	T	1.15 ± 0.02	1.82 ± 0.03	E	64
$Fe(CO)_5$	T	1.15 ± 0.03	1.84 ± 0.03	X	175
$Fe(CO)_5$ (II)	T	1.15 ± 0.04	1.84 ± 0.03	E	64
$Fe(CO)_9$	T	1.15 ± 0.05	1.9 ± 0.05	X	241
	B	1.3 ± 0.05	1.8 ± 0.05		
$Cr(CO)_6$	T	1.15 ± 0.05	1.92 ± 0.04	E	29,64
$Mo(CO)_6$	T	1.15 ± 0.05	2.08 ± 0.04	E	29
$W(CO)_6$	T	1.15 ± 0.05	2.06 ± 0.04	E	29
$Fe_2(CO)_4(C_5H_5)_2$ (VI)	T	1.12 ± 0.04	1.75 ± 0.03	X	204
	B	1.21 ± 0.04	1.85 ± 0.03		
$Fe_2(CO)_6[CMeC(OH)C(OH)CMe]$ (XXXI)	T	1.15 (average of five)	1.775 (average of five)	X	205
$Co_2(CO)_6[C_2(C_6H_5)_2]$ (XXVII)	T	1.16 (average of six)	1.78 (average of six)	X	273
$Co_2(CO)_7\left(> C {\overset{CH=CH}{\underset{O}{\diagdown}}} CO \right)$ (XXVIII)	T	1.15 (average of six)	1.81 (average of six)	X	206
$Ni_3(CO)_2(C_5H_5)_3$	B	1.19	1.98	X	206
	B‡	1.19	1.94		

*T = terminal; B = bridging
†E = electron diffraction; X = X-ray diffraction
‡bridging three metal atoms.

There is little variation in the bond lengths for each type, although more data are desirable particularly concerning the influence of other ligands on these distances. If the metal-carbon distances for bridging groups are taken to represent normal single bonds (more suitable standards should be obtainable by study of the metal alkyls, but measurements on these are not yet available)* it can be seen that there is considerable shortening in the case of terminal CO. This must imply an increased bond order for the metal-carbon bond in the latter type, in harmony with the simple valence bond representation of such carbonyls as resonance hybrids with

$\overset{-}{M}-C\equiv\overset{+}{O}$ and $M=C=O$ as the principal canonical forms. The form $\overset{+}{M}\equiv C-\overset{-}{O}$ must also be seriously considered as a possible contributor, especially in view of the low dipole moment (*151*) associated with this grouping (the relative electro-negativities leading to inductive polarization $\overset{\delta+}{M}=\overset{\delta-}{C}=\overset{\delta-}{O}$ also help to balance the opposite dipole suggested by the first resonance form). Although all the simple carbonyls are too symmetrical, so that the individual M—C—O dipoles cancel out, a reasonable estimate can be made by study of such unsymmetrical derivatives as those listed in Table 10.3. This leads to an upper limit of 0.6D per carbonyl group (*151*). This table also includes a value for an isonitrile complex. These are seen to be much more polar and the resonance form $\overset{-}{M}-C\equiv\overset{+}{N}-R$ must be relatively more important in agreement with the greater basicity of Nitrogen compared to Oxygen.

TABLE 10.3. DIPOLE MOMENTS

Compound	Moment (D)	Ref.
$Mn(CO)_5H$	0.70 ± 0.05	*149*
$Mn(CO)_5CH_3$	0.79 ± 0.05	*150*
$Mn(CO)_3C_5H_5$	3.26	*85*
$Fe(CO)_4I_2$	3.60 ± 0.05	*151*
$Fe(CO)_2(NO)_2$	0.72 ± 0.07	*151*
$Fe(CO)_4CNCH_3$	5.02 ± 0.03	*151*
$Co(CO)_3NO$	0.43 ± 0.05	*151*
$Co_2(CO)_4(1,3,6-C_8H_{10})_2$	3.02	*79*
$Ni_2(CO)_2(C_5H_5)_2$	0 ± 0.38	*81*
$Cr(CO)_3C_6H_6$	4.92 ± 0.05	*81*
	5.08 ± 0.05	*245*
$Cr(CO)_3C_7H_8$	4.52 ± 0.05	*245*
$Cr(CO)_3C_{10}H_8$	6.33 ± 0.03	*81*
$Mo(CO)_3C_{10}H_8$	4.15	*85*
$Re(CO)_2(C_5H_5)(C_5H_6)$	3.85 ± 0.09	*81*

*In compound (XXXI), the Fe—C(OH) distance is 1.945 Å, i.e., 0.17 Å greater than the Fe—C($\equiv$O) distances (*205*).

The same difference is reflected in the preferred oxidation states of the carbonyl and isonitrile complexes. The stabilization of the lower oxidation states in both cases is intimately connected with the utilization of the d-electrons in π-bond formation. Hence simple carbonyls form only from the lowest (zero for the carbonyls themselves and -1 or -2 for the hydrocarbonyls) oxidation states which possess the maximum number of d-electrons and hence permit considerable double bonding. By contrast the simplest known isonitrile complexes range from oxidation number zero to two:

$$Cr(CNR)_6, [Mn(CNR)_6]^+, [Mn(CNR)_6]^{++}, [Fe(CNR)_4 \text{ or }_6]^{++},$$

$$[Co(CNR)_5]^+, [Co(CNR)_5]^{++}, Ni(CNR)_4.$$

A more sensitive criterion of bond order exists in the infrared absorption maxima. A rather large body of experimental data are now available from which selected examples are quoted in Table 10.4. These values show con-

TABLE 10.4. MAXIMA IN THE CARBONYL STRETCHING REGION OF THE INFRARED

Compound	Maxima[g]				Ref.
$[Fe(CNMe)_6](NO_3)_2$	2315				*231*
CO	2168				*176*
$Fe(CO)_3(C_2F_4)_2$	2160	2120	2100		*296*
$Pt_2(CO)_2Cl_4$	2152				*163*
$[Pt(CO)dipy\ Br]^{+(a)}$	2132				*165*
$Fe(CO)_4I_2$	2140	2095	2087		*97*
$[Fe(CO)_3C_7H_7]^+$	2128	2068	(1980)		*211*
	2110	2049	1970		*85*
$Mn(CO)_5COCH_3$	2105	2041	1992		*45*
$Rh_2(CO)_4Cl_2$	2104	2088	2033	(2002)	*312*
$Fe(CO)_3(PPh_3)I_2$	2095	2050	2035		*97*
$Co_2(CO)_6(C_2Ph_2)$	2088	2054	2026		*293*
$Fe_2(CO)_9$	2087	2023	$1831^{(f)}$		*97*
$Mn(CO)_5CH_3$	2083	2000	1960		*44*
$Fe(CO)_2diars.\ I^{(b)}$	2083	2024	(1976)		*223*
$Co_2(CO)_8$	2077	2054	2034	$1859^{(f)}$	*33*
$[Cr(CO)_3C_7H_7]^+$	2070	2030	2010		*211*
$Mn_2(CO)_{10}$	2063	2028	1997		*56*
$Ni(CO)_4$	2050	2043			*33*
$Co_3Fe(CO)_{12}H$	2053	$1887^{(f)}$			*39*
$Fe(CO)_2(C_5H_5)Cl$	2053	1994			*97*
$Fe_2(CO)_4(C_5H_5)_2$	2054	2005	1958	$1786^{(f)}$	*55*
$Fe(CO)_3C_4H_6$	2051	1978			*96*
$Fe(CO)_3C_7H_8$	2050	1995			*211*
$[Ru(CO)_2I_2]_n$	2050	1995			*162*
$Re(CO)_3(PPh_3)_2I$	2049	1966	1904		*5*
$Ni(CNC_6H_4Br\text{-}p)_4$	2045	2010			*231*

TABLE 10.4. (*continued*)

Compound	Maxima[g]				Ref.
$Mo(CO)_3(PCl_3)_3$	2041	1989	1960		*3*
$Fe(CO)_5$	2028	1994			*271*
$Mn(CO)_3C_5H_5$	2023	1939			*55 (cf. 243)*
$Mo(CO)_3(PPhCl_2)_3$	2016	1943			*3*
$[Fe(CO)_6]^{++}$ (?)	2016				*277*
$W_3(CO)_9(OH)_2(H_2O)H_4$	2010	1928			*111*
$Fe(CO)_3diars.$[b]	2009	1916	1880		*223*
$Cr(CO)_6$	2000				*272*
$[Fe_2(CO)_8H]^-$ (?)	1996	1972	1897[f]		*35,279*
$Ni(CO)_2 diars.$[b]	1996	1940			*225*
$Cr(CO)_3C_6H_6$ (in C_6H_{12})	1987	1917			*85*
(in CS_2)	1981	1907			
	1980	1895			*221*
$Mo(CO)_3(PPh_2Cl)_3$	1977	1885			*3*
$Re(CO)_2(C_5H_5)(C_5H_6)$	1971	1890			*92 (cf. 243)*
$Ti(CO)_2(C_5H_5)_2$	1964	1883			*212*
$[Fe_4(CO)_{13}]^{--}$	1960–1935[e]				*126*
$Fe(CO)(diars.)_2$[b]	1953				*223*
$Ni(CO)_2dipy.$[a]	1950	1861			–
$Mo(CO)_3(PPh_3)_3$	1949	1908	1891	1835	*3*
$Mn_2(CO)_6(diars.)_2$[b]	1944	1937	1885		*227*
$[Co(CO)_4]^-$	1916–1878[e]				*293,294*
$Mo(CO)_4(PPh_3)_2$	1902[h]				*132*
$[Fe(CO)_4]^{--}$ (?)	1898				*277*
	1780				*85*
$Mo(CO)_3dien.$[c]	1883	1723			*3*
$[Cr(CO)_3C_5H_5]^-[(C_5H_5)_2Cr]^+$	1880	1760	(1727 sh)		*85*
$[Cr(CO)_3C_5H_5]^-$ Na$^+$	1876	1695			*85*
$Fe(CO)_3(PPh_3)_2$	1880				*97,197*
$[Ni(CO)(P[CH_2CH_2CN]_3)]_n$	(1875)	1815[f]			*201*
$[Fe_2(CO)_8][Ni(phen)_3]$[d]	1847				*127*
$[V(CO)_3C_5H_5]^{--}$	1748	1645			*85*

[a] dipy = 2,2′-dipyridyl
[b] diars = *o*-phenylene-bis-dimethylarsine
[c] dien = diethylenetriamine
[d] phen = *o*-phenanthroline
[e] single maxima are observed; frequencies vary with the cation.
[f] peaks attributable to bridging carbonyl groups.
[g] very weak peaks are given in parentheses.
[h] *trans*-isomer; for *cis*-isomer see reference *240a*.

siderable variations. Most noticeable is the shift towards lower frequency, corresponding to lower bond order for the C—O bond when strongly electron-donating ligands, e.g., phosphines and amines, are introduced. These would of course be expected to favor stronger back-donation of electrons from the metal to carbon monoxide, hence lowering the carbon-oxygen bond order to a value nearer that of normal "ketonic" carbonyls.

Indeed, the lowest values in Table 10.4 correspond to the typical "ketonic" C=O stretching region.

Until recently values below *ca.* 1900 cm^{-1} were regarded as characteristic of bridging carbonyl groups, and although this is seen to be no longer strictly true, it still affords a useful guide in the absence of electron-donating groups. Structures such as $\overset{+}{M}\equiv C$—$\overset{-}{O}$ for terminal and similarly

$\overset{+}{M}=C$—M with $\overset{O^-}{|}$ above C for bridging carbonyl groups suggest that even when the C—O bond order becomes comparable to that in a ketone, there is little if any positive charge on the carbon atom in a metal carbonyl. Hence we should not expect these to undergo typical "ketonic" reactions; this is in. accordance with experimental observation.

In all the unsubstituted metal carbonyls the CO frequencies are closely similar. There is a slight gradual drop from Ni to Cr indicating increasing metal-carbon double bonding. Since there are only three unshared electron pairs available in Cr for six CO groups giving a maximum bond order of $1\frac{1}{2}$, and since theoretical predictions suggest that compounds with d^2sp^3 hybridization can form three strong π-bonds (but those with dsp^3 or sp^3 hybridization only two) it appears reasonable to assume that this bond order is very nearly attained. It cannot be attained in divanadium dodecacarbonyl (*216u,244*) which only has two unshared pairs of electrons per metal atom. The low resultant bond order (maximum $1\frac{1}{3}$) may be the chief source of its instability. No other metal carbonyls appear to be known in

TABLE 10.5. HEATS OF FORMATION

Carbonyl	State	(1) Standard Enthalpy(*a*) of formation (ΔHf°_{298}), kcal.	(2) ΔH°_{298} per metal carbon bond(*b*) kcal.	(3) as (2), but corrected[54] for $\Delta H_{M^*;}$(*c*) kcal.	Ref.
Mn$_2$(CO)$_{10}$	solid	-400.9			*89a*
Cr(CO)$_6$	solid	-257.57 ± 0.51	27.1	87	*53,272*
Mo(CO)$_6$	solid	-234.79 ± 0.27	35.9	—	*53,272*
W(CO)$_6$	solid	-227.34 ± 0.29	42.1	—	*53,272*
Fe(CO)$_5$	gas	-182.6 ± 1.7	27.7	89(*d*)	*54*
Ni(CO)$_4$	liquid	-39.1 ± 0.5	35.2	77	*65 (cf. 285)*
		-40.8	—	—	*229*

(*a*)Calculated for $M(s) + nC$ (graphite) $+ \dfrac{n}{2}O_2$ (g) $= M(CO)_n$ (in state specified)

(*b*)Calculated for $\dfrac{1}{n}M(CO)_n$ (g) $= \dfrac{1}{n}M(g) + CO(g)$

(*c*)Energy necessary to promote the gaseous metal from its ground state to the excited state formed by pairing all electrons in the lowest available d orbitals.

(*d*)This value is a mean for five bonds which are not equivalent.

which sufficient unshared electrons are not available for the bond order $1\frac{1}{2}$ to be reached, although the higher frequencies of nickel carbonyl and others suggest it is not a minimum bond-order for stability.

Bond energies: The heats of combustion of several metal carbonyls have been measured. The best available values are collected in Table 10.5.

PREPARATION

Simple Carbonyls

The simplest method is reaction of carbon monoxide with the free metal, the method by which Mond (*209*) discovered nickel carbonyl in 1888 and which was extended to iron (*210*) in 1891 and cobalt (*208*) in 1908. Other transition metals do not appear to react directly with carbon monoxide,* although their compounds may do so.

All other methods involve reduction of a suitable salt or complex of the metal in presence of carbon monoxide. The choice of metal derivatives and reductant may however be quite critical.

Cobalt salts, especially the sulfide (*14,15*), hydrosulfite (*116*) or complex cyanide (*89*) react in cold alkaline solution at atmospheric pressure giving the anion $Co(CO)_4{}^-$. Here carbon monoxide itself behaves as reducing agent being oxidized to carbonate. Nickel, as the cyanide or preferably complexed with sulfur compounds, reacts under similar conditions (*14,15, 110,115*). In the latter case it has been shown that disproportionation of Ni^{II} to $Ni^O + Ni^{IV}$ is involved, e.g.,

$$Ni\left(\underset{S}{\overset{S}{<}}C{-}Ph\right)_2 + CO + SH^- \longrightarrow Ni(CO)_4 + \frac{1}{2}\left[SNi\underset{S}{\overset{S}{<}}C{-}Ph\right]_2$$

Depending on the stability of the Ni^{IV} complex, this may either accumulate together with the carbonyl, or it may react further after reduction back to Ni^{II} by CO, e.g., according to the scheme:

$$2\,Ni^{II}(SR)_2 + 2\,OH^- + 4\,CO \longrightarrow Ni^O(CO)_4 + \frac{1}{2}\underset{RS}{\overset{RS}{>}}Ni^{IV}\underset{O}{\overset{O}{<}}Ni^{IV}\underset{SR}{\overset{SR}{<}}$$

$$+\ 2\,SR + H_2O$$

$$[(RS)_2Ni^{IV}O]_2 + 2\,CO \longrightarrow 2\,Ni^{II}(SR)_2 + 2\,CO_2.$$

---

*The successful preparation (*208*) of molybdenum hexacarbonyl and of traces of unidentified ruthenium carbonyls by Mond may have been due to the presence of sulfur or other catalytically active impurities.

Under pressure of carbon monoxide, cobaltous oxide (*10*) or a mixture of cobaltous carbonate and hydrogen (*301,302*) have given useful results. The oxides and halides of Re, Ru, Os, Ir and Au react with CO directly to give the corresponding carbonyls or carbonyl halides (*7,23,139,172*). In this case CO again acts as reducing agent and is oxidized to CO_2, viz. $COCl_2$ or $COBr_2$. The oxide and sulfide of molybdenum behave similarly. But the halides of Mo, W, Rh all require the use of a separate reducing agent, such as $LiAlH_4$ or the metals, Li, Na, Mg, Al, Cu etc.; $Fe(CO)_5$ acts both as reducing agent and source of carbon monoxide (*219*). The same method was used in the first preparation (*28*), albeit in only 1 per cent yield, of manganese carbonyl from MnI_2. Use of pyridine as solvent makes it applicable to the chloride (*218,220*) or the acetylacetone complex (*217*) of chromium. The carbonyl of the latter element was first prepared by Job by the "Grignard" method (*230*). Here treatment of chromic chloride with carbon monoxide and phenylmagnesium bromide affords chromium carbonyl directly and we may regard triphenylchromium as the probable intermediate (see Chapter 8). Related methods have been applied to manganese, e.g., by treatment of its salts with triethylaluminum (*239,240*), undoubtedly to give initially dialkyl manganese as an intermediate. Since such alkyl and aryl derivatives of transition metals are unstable and may decompose to lower valence states of the metal plus the corresponding hydrocarbon radicals, no separate reducing agents are required. A further variant of the same principle is represented by the very successful use (*43*) of the benzophenone-ketyls of the same metals: e.g.,

$$CrCl_3 + 3\,Ph_2\dot{C}ONa \longrightarrow 3\,NaCl + Cr(OCPh_2)_3 \xrightarrow{6\,CO} 3\,Ph_2CO + Cr(CO)_6.$$

The highest yields (90%) reported for chromium carbonyl have been obtained by Fischer and co-workers (*72*) from chromic chloride. The reaction, which occurs at 140°C/300 atmospheres pressure proceeds according to the equation:

$$CrCl_3 + Al + 6\,CO \xrightarrow[AlCl_3]{C_6H_6} Cr(CO)_6 + AlCl_3.$$

This formulation demonstrates the experimental simplicity of a reaction which undoubtedly involves initial formation of the bis-benzene-chromium cation, $(C_6H_6)_2Cr^+$, followed by stepwise replacement of benzene by carbon monoxide *via* the mixed carbonyl $C_6H_6Cr(CO)_3$. Such displacement of hydrocarbon ligands by carbon monoxide is a general reaction which provides a valuable route to mixed hydrocarbon metal carbonyls. In the cyclopentadienyl series it has been employed for the conversion of the corresponding dicyclopentadienyl derivatives of cobalt (*75,233*), manganese (*74,233*), rhenium (*84,92,243*), and vanadium (*70*) to the mixed carbonyls discussed in Chapter 7. In the case of titanium (212), carbon monoxide adds to $(C_5H_5)_2Ti$ to give the only known carbonyl complex, $(C_5H_5)_2Ti(CO)_2$ of this metal.

The Polynuclear Carbonyls

These are all derivable from the simpler carbonyls by loss of carbon monoxide. This loss is usually effected by heat or light (7,23). Thus, $Os(CO)_5$ decomposes reversibly to the enneacarbonyl even at room temperature:

$$Os(CO)_5 \longrightarrow Os_2(CO)_9 + CO.$$

The corresponding decomposition of iron carbonyl is accomplished photochemically. It may be thought of (228) as proceeding via an initially formed radical-like $Fe(CO)_4$:

$$Fe(CO)_5 \xrightarrow{h\nu} CO + [Fe(CO)_4] \xrightarrow{+\ Fe(CO)_5} Fe_2(CO)_9$$

The enneacarbonyl so produced decomposes further at 95°:

$$6\ Fe_2(CO)_9 \longrightarrow 2\ Fe_3(CO)_{12} + 6\ Fe(CO)_5,$$

a reaction which may be regarded as a reversal of the second stage of its formation. The iron dodecacarbonyl so formed is obtained more conveniently via the carbonyl hydride.

$$3\ Fe(CO)_4H_2 + 3\ MnO_2 + 6\ H^+ \longrightarrow Fe_3(CO)_{12} + 6\ H_2O + 3\ Mn^{++}$$

Tetracobalt dodecacarbonyl is prepared most efficiently by interaction of cobaltous or cobaltic salts with hydrogen and dicobalt octacarbonyl (62).

SUBSTITUTION REACTIONS IN METAL CARBONYLS

Most known reactions of metal carbonyls are of this type. A wide variety of other ligands can displace carbon monoxide with or without change in oxidation state of the metal. Only in a few isolated cases do these reactions lead to complete displacement of all the carbon monoxide.

Cyclopentadiene is the only ligand which has been shown (308,310) to be able to displace CO completely from the carbonyls of Cr, Fe, and Co as well as Ni, yielding in each case the dicyclopentadienyl derivative of the metal in oxidation state two, $(C_5H_5)_2M$. Even here, intermediate monocyclopentadienyl metal carbonyls are readily obtained as intermediates showing that partial is easier than complete replacement. In addition, all the CO groups have been displaced from $Ni(CO)_4$ without change of oxidation state by cyclopentadiene (83), by isonitriles (179), by phosphorus halides (161,306) or phosphines (37) by an arsine (224) and by acrylonitrile (*268*). The apparently unique position of nickel in this respect must be attributed to the relatively low strength of the Ni—C bonds in nickel carbonyl compared to the others. In all cases the presence of other ligands may stabilize (*85,226*) the metal-carbon bond and the degree of substitution will be determined by this stabilization together with the affinity of the metal for the entering ligand. Illustrative examples are given in the following section.

The stabilization results from an intrinsic difference in the nature of carbon monoxide and the other groups concerned as ligands. Whereas the strength of the M—CO bond depends to a large degree on back-donation, i.e., on the electron acceptor properties of the carbonyl group, the other ligands are primarily electron donors, so that charged resonance forms, e.g., of the type $R_3\overset{+}{P}$—M≡C—O, become increasingly important in the mixed complexes.

Displacement without Change in Oxidation State

Displacement of Carbon Monoxide by Isonitriles. Bearing the closest formal analogy to CO, the isonitriles should be ideally suited for such reactions. The types of compounds which have been obtained in this manner are $Cr(CO)_5(CNR)$ (*135*); $Mn(CO)_3(CNR)_2Br$ (*138*); $Fe(CO)_4(CNR)$ (*133,134*); $Fe(CO)_3(CNR)_2$ (*133,134*); $Ni(CO)(CNR)_3$ (*104*) and $Ni(CNR)_4$ (*104*). Even with nickel, complete replacement occurs only with aryl isocyanides whereas with ethyl isocyanide for example, reaction stops at the $Ni(CO)(CNR)_3$ stage (*104*). This incompleteness of reaction is not due to instability of the ultimate product. The hexa-isocyanide complexes, $M(CNR)_6$, of Cr, Mo and W can be obtained quite readily directly from the metal halides or acetates with isocyanides in presence of reducing agents (*187,189,190*). That increasing strength of the metal-carbon bond is one of the factors involved is clearly illustrated by the higher temperature required before the second isonitrile group may be introduced in the iron series (*134*). Most of the work has been done with aryl isocyanides which are both easier to handle and form the more stable complexes. It has been shown in the case of iron, that successive replacement of two carbonyl groups by one molecule of methyl isocyanide and one of ethyl isocyanide yields the same product, regardless of the order in which these two are used (*134*). Hence the two groups must be attached in equivalent positions and the most probable structure is (IX).

IX

This type of structure can be deduced (*50*) for a whole series of complexes, $Fe(CO)_3L_2$, from the single infrared active vibration in the carbonyl region.

Displacement of Carbon Monoxide by Phosphines, Arsines and Stibines. These displace carbon monoxide to about the same extent as do isocyanides. Thus with triphenyl-phosphines (*108,118,119,132,149,200,247, 250,252,259,260*) we get $Cr(CO)_5PPh_3$; $Cr(CO)_4(PPh_3)_2$; $Mn(CO)_4PPh_3$; $Fe(CO)_4PPh_3$; $Fe(CO)_3(PPh_3)_2$; $[Co(CO)_3PPh_3]_2$; $Ni(CO)_3PPh_3$; $Ni(CO)_2$-$(PPh_3)_2$. This and triphenylphosphite (*255*) are the only neutral non-hydrocarbon ligands which have been shown to displace CO from dicobalt octacarbonyl without disproportionation, and even in these cases only under carefully controlled conditions (*118,259,260*). Whereas the above product is formed in inert solvents at 0°, the ionic product, $[Co(CO)_3$-$(PPh_3)_2][Co(CO)_4]$, results when the reaction is carried out in dioxan at 30°. The decomposition of the latter into the former occurs on standing in air.

More highly substituted products may be obtained by indirect methods. Thus the product formed from chromium carbonyl with aqueous base, $K_2[Cr_2(CO)_6(OH)_3H]$, reacts with isocyanides to give $Cr(CO)_3(CNR)_3$ (*101*), and the cycloheptatriene and benzene metal tricarbonyls of the chromium group yield $Cr(CO)_3(PPh_3)_3$, $Mo(CO)_3(PPh_3)_3$ etc. by displacement of the hydrocarbon ligand (*1,3,197,200*). Similarly $C_7H_8Fe(CO)_2$ and even $C_4H_6Fe(CO)_3$ yield $Fe(CO)_2(PPh_3)_3$ whereas both $C_8H_8Fe(CO)_3$ and $[C_5H_5Fe(CO)_2]_2$ afford only the bisphosphine complex $Fe(CO)_3(PPh_3)_2$ (*95,197*).

The reactivity towards carbonyls decreases in the order (*38,161,188,200, 307*) $PCl_3 > PF_3 > P(OR)_3 > PR_3 > AsR_3 > SbR_3$. Diphosphines (*37*) and diarsines capable of forming chelates are much more effective than the monodentate analogs. Thus the diarsine o-$C_6H_4(AsMe_2)_2$ has yielded (*222–227*) all the products in Table 10.6. This Table also illustrated the fact that carbonyl halides may react in the same manner as the carbonyls proper, but the halide ligand as well as carbon monoxide may be displaced by the entering ligand, thus giving an ionic complex (*5,138,141*), e.g.,

$$ClMn(CO)_5 + 2 C_5H_5N \longrightarrow ClMn(CO)_3(C_5H_5N)_2$$

$$ClMn(CO)_5 + 2 Ph_3As \longrightarrow ClMn(CO)_3(Ph_3As)_2$$

$$ClMn(CO)_5 + 2 NH_3 \longrightarrow [Mn(CO)_4(NH_3)_2]Cl$$

$$ClMn(CO)_5 + (NH_2CH_2CH_2)_2NH \longrightarrow [Mn(CO)_3(trien)]Cl.$$

By the reverse displacement of triphenylphosphine from $Pt(PPh_3)_3$ or

TABLE 10.6. COMPLEXES FORMED BY REACTIONS OF METAL CARBONYLS WITH o-PHENYLENEBISDIMETHYLARSINE (D)

(1) Initial Carbonyl	(2) Diarsine Complex Obtained	(3) Products Obtained from (2) by Treatment with Halogen
$Ni(CO)_4$	$Ni(CO)_2D$	$NiDBr_2$
	NiD_2	NiD_2Br_2
$Fe(CO)_5$	$Fe(CO)_3D$	$Fe(CO)_2DI$
		$Fe(CO)_2DBr_2$, $Fe(CO)_2DI_2$
	$Fe(CO)D_2$	FeD_2I_2
$Fe(CO)_4I_2$	$Fe(CO)_2DI_2$	
$Mn_2(CO)_{10}$	$[Mn(CO)_3D]_2$	
	$Mn(CO)_3D.$	
$Cr(CO)_6$	$Cr(CO)_4D$	
	$Cr(CO)_2D_2$	
$Mo(CO)_6$	$Mo(CO)_4D$	$Mo(CO)_3DBr_2$
	$Mo(CO)_2D_2$	
$W(CO)_6$	$W(CO)_4D$	$W(CO)_3DBr_2$
		$[W(CO)_3DBr_2]$ Br
	$W(CO)_2D_2$	

$Pt(PPh_3)_4$ by carbon monoxide, platinum has yielded $Pt(PPh_3)_3CO$ and probably also $Pt(PPh_3)_2(CO)_2$ (*184*).

Displacement of Carbon Monoxide by Amines. Ammonia, pyridine and a variety of other amines have been shown to displace up to three CO groups stepwise from chromium, molybdenum and tungsten carbonyls (*19,101,177*). Nickel behaves similarly, with displacement of up to at least two CO groups, e.g., by o-phenanthroline, to give $Ni(CO)_2(C_{12}H_8N_2)$ (*130*). Little is known about manganese;* iron and cobalt invariably react with disproportionation (see below).

Displacement of Carbon Monoxide by Cyanide. Nickel carbonyl reacts (*30*) according to

$$KCN + Ni(CO)_4 \longrightarrow K[Ni(CO)_3CN] + CO.$$

Further reaction yields $K_2Ni(CN)_2(CO)_2$ and possibly even $K_3Ni(CN)_3CO$, but not the complete displacement product $K_4Ni(CN)_4$, although this cyanide analog of nickel carbonyl has been obtained by reduction of the Ni^{II} cyanide with potassium in liquid ammonia (*61*).

$$K_2[Ni(CN)_4] + 2K \longrightarrow K_4Ni(CN)_4$$

*Hieber and Schropp (*138a*) have now shown that manganese reacts by simple displacement or with disproportionation depending on the amine used.

Similarly the cobalt nitrosocarbonyl, $Co(CO)_3NO$, affords $K[Co(CO)_2-(CN)(NO)]$ on treatment with potassium cyanide in methanol. Dicobalt octacarbonyl is said to give a mixture of $K_2[Co_2(CO)_6(CN)_2]$ and $K_3-[Co_2(CO)_5(CN)_3]$ (103). Cyclopentadienyl-iron dicarbonyl chloride reacts (233) by simple replacement of chlorine only, giving $C_5H_5Fe(CO)_2CN$. Both manganese (138) and rhenium (141) carbonyl chlorides react by displacement of chlorine and carbon monoxide: e.g.,

$$Re(CO)_5Cl + 2 KCN \longrightarrow KCl + K[Re(CO)_4(CN)_2] + CO,$$

while the polymeric $[Ru(CO)_2I_2]_x$ adds potassium cyanide (122) yielding $K_2[Ru(CO)_2(CN)_2I_2]$.

Other cyano-carbonyls have been obtained by the inverse procedure of treating the corresponding complex cyanides with carbon monoxide. In this way $K_3[Fe^{II}(CN)_5CO]$; $K_2[Co^I(CN)_3CO]$; $K_4[Ni^I(CN)_3CO]_2$ and $K_2-[Ni^O(CN)_2(CO)_2]$ have been obtained from $K_3[Fe^{II}(CN)_5H_2O]$ (131); $Co^{++} + CN^- + CO + OH^-$ (102); $K_4[Ni^I_2(CN)_6]$ (215,216) and $K_4[Ni^O(CN)_4]$ (216) respectively. The ferrous complex is also formed from potassium ferrocyanide and carbon monoxide at $130-150°$. Its remarkable stability is emphasized by its formation as a result of oxidation of one cyano group on heating potassium ferricyanide in air. The nickel(I) complex is regarded by Nast and Kasperl (214) as having bridging carbonyl groups (infrared max. at 1895 cm^{-1} in KBr), but Griffith et al.(94) have drawn the opposite conclusion from the infrared evidence (max. at 1905 cm^{-1} in Nujol). In the case of chromium the series of related carbonyl cyanide anions, $[Cr(CO)_5CN]^-$; $[Cr(CO)_4(CN)_2]^{2-}$ and $[Cr(CO)_3(CN)_3]^{3-}$ have been obtained (101) from $[Cr(CO)_5]^{--}$; $Cr(CO)_5NH_3$; and $Cr(CO)_3(NH_3)_3$ respectively by treatment with solutions of potassium cyanide in water or liquid ammonia. The formation (18) of the monocyanide complex from $[Cr(CO)_5]^{--}$ is an oxidative process, hydrogen being liberated. Alternatively it may be accomplished with cyanogen or cyanogen iodide:

$$[Cr(CO)_5]^{--} + ICN \longrightarrow [Cr(CO)_5CN]^- + I^-$$

Displacement of Carbon Monoxide by Hydrocarbon Ligands. The first such reaction, that of butadiene with iron pentacarbonyl, was described by Reihlen in 1930 (249). The general examination of such reaction is however of very recent date and our knowledge of such reactions is therefore necessarily incomplete. Only a single example (295), the reaction of tetrafluoroethylene with iron carbonyl to give $(CF_2 = CF_2)_2Fe(CO)_3$, is known in which the hydrocarbon ligand is a simple olefin. Acrylonitrile also appears to act as a simple olefin ligand in its reaction with iron pentacarbonyl to form the complex $Fe(CO)_4CH_2 = CHCN$ (171), but its behavior with nickel carbonyl (268) is more complex. Numerous reactions with acetylenes have been studied, but in nearly all of these the reaction involves modification of the hydrocarbon. These cases are deferred to pp. 492–498.

The remaining reactions all involve dienes, polyenes and aromatic systems. Even acetylenes, in the few cases where they displace CO without further change, act as bidentate ligands. Thus no reactions with hydrocarbons are known, in which only a single CO is displaced. The above mentioned reaction of butadiene yields butadiene iron tricarbonyl, $C_4H_6Fe(CO)_3$, and many other conjugated dienes behave similarly (90,96, 197,249,267,295), but conjugation is not essential, as shown by the formation of the complex (X) from bicyclo[2:2:1]heptadiene (31,232).

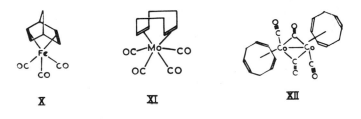

X XI XII

The latter diolefin (232) as well as 1,5-cyclooctadiene (24,69,196), have been shown to react with the Group VI carbonyls to give complexes such as (XI).

1,3,6-Cyclooctatriene is a *conjugated* diene which appears to be particularly reactive towards metal carbonyls. It has been shown (79) to react with cobalt carbonyl to yield (XII), and it can displace up to four molecules of carbon monoxide from molybdenum carbonyl, yielding a complex (78,80) formulated as (XIV) presumably *via* the intermediate (XIII). The fully conjugated isomer, 1,3,5-cyclooctatriene, displaces (78,80) three CO groups from molybdenum carbonyl, as does cycloheptatriene (1,2). The latter does likewise with iron pentacarbonyl (31,197) yielding the dicarbonyl (XV),* but cyclooctatetraene only displaces two CO groups to afford

XIII XIV

*Since this chapter was written, evidence has accumulated (211) to suggest that this is a tri-carbonyl like the tropone complex (XVIII).

(XVI) (*195,197,213,246*). This would not be unexpected if the 8-membered ring retained its usual tub-shape. However the single proton resonance peak observable by nuclear spin resonance spectroscopy and the failure of the complex to add bromine or hydrogen strongly suggest that the ring becomes planar and symmetrical—and hence possibly even aromatic in this complex and in the accompanying di-iron complex (XVII). Iron can also form the tricarbonyl complex (XVIII) with tropone (*160*). Here, as in the cycloöctatetraene complex, there can only be partial donation to the

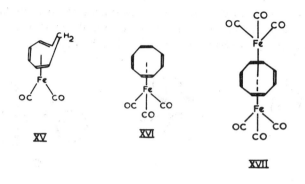

metal of the π-electrons available in the ring. This contrasts with the cyclopentadienone complexes of the type (XIX) which can reversibly lose carbon monoxide (at least in the case of the unsubstituted compound) despite the fact that the endocyclic double bonds can supply only four elec-

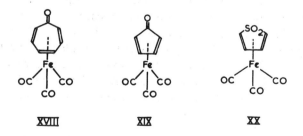

trons to iron (*90a,298a,309*). Although both (XVIII) and (XIX) were first obtained (*157,158,168,265,266,267,298*) by reactions of iron carbonyls with acetylenes, they have also been obtained from these carbonyls with tropone (*160*) and cyclopentadienones (*267,298*) respectively. Similarly, thiophene dioxides (*298*) yield the sulphone analogs (XX) of (XIX) and related compounds have been obtained from pentaphenylphosphole (XXXVI) and its oxide (*27*). The reactions of tetracyclone with carbonyls may lead to either partial or complete displacement of CO as in the examples (*298*):

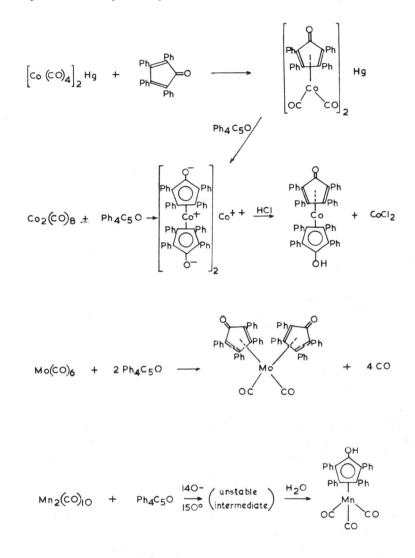

Aromatic substances appear always to utilize all six π-electrons for donation to the metal atom, and hence to displace three carbonyl groups. Their complexes (discussed more fully in Chapter 8) thus bear a strong formal resemblance to those formed by the conjugated trienes discussed above. This is brought out by the following illustrative formulae:

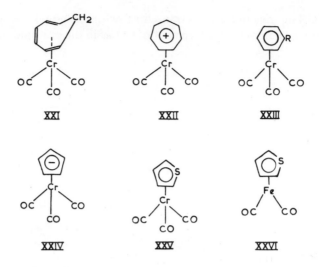

The red cycloheptatrienechromium tricarbonyl (XXI) is converted into the similarly colored tropylium derivative (XXII) by hydride abstraction. The greater symmetry of the latter is reflected in the possession of only two carbonyl stretching maxima in the infrared, compared to three in the triene complex. The symmetry of the π-electron system which interacts with the metal atom in these complexes is involved here—not the overall symmetry of the molecule, as shown by the fact that not only benzene-chromium-tricarbonyl (XXIII; R = H), but all its numerous substitution products (XXIII; R = CH_3, C_6H_5, OMe, COOMe, NH_2 etc.,) show only two maxima. The cyclopentadienyl group, which likewise behaves as a symmetrical aromatic system in these complexes is discussed more fully in Chapter 7. The formation of cyclopentadienyl derivatives from metal carbonyls and cyclopentadiene involves loss of hydrogen from the hydrocarbon. Only nickel has been shown (*83*) to react by simple displacement of carbon monoxide, cyclopentadiene acting like other conjugated diolefins:

$$Ni(CO)_4 + C_5H_6 \longrightarrow (C_5H_6)_2Ni + 4\,CO.$$

But even this reaction is accompanied by formation of $(C_5H_5)_2Ni$ which becomes predominant at higher temperature.

The reactions of all the other carbonyls are exemplified by cobalt and iron:

$$Co_2(CO)_8 + 3\,C_5H_6 \longrightarrow 2\,C_5H_5Co(CO)_2 + 4\,CO + C_5H_8$$

$$2\,Fe(CO)_5 + 3\,C_5H_6 \longrightarrow [C_5H_5Fe(CO)_2]_2 + 6\,CO + C_5H_8.$$

(VI)

As indicated in these equations the hydrogen liberated is not set free as such, but reduces another molecule of cyclopentadiene to cyclopentene (*282*).

A plausible suggestion (*282*) concerning the mechanism of this reaction involves initial formation of a hydride, e.g., $C_5H_5Fe(CO)_2H$, by displacement of CO followed by hydride shift. The ready oxidation of this type of molecule to the dimeric type (*cf.* p. 501) would complete the process. Carbonyl hydrides are known to be good reducing agents, and it is interesting to note that even the protonated form of (VI) has been shown (*282*) to transfer hydrogen atoms to unsaturated molecules, e.g., azobenzene:

$$[C_5H_5Fe(CO)_2H]_2{}^{++} + PhN{=}NPh \longrightarrow 2[C_5H_5Fe(CO)_2]^+ + NH_2C_6H_4{\cdot}C_6H_4NH_2.$$

In the case of cobalt, the suggested first step is

$$2\,C_5H_6 + Co_2(CO)_8 \longrightarrow (C_5H_5)Co(CO)_2 + C_5H_6Co(CO)_2H$$

followed by hydrogen transfer from the latter product to a further molecule of cyclopentadiene.

Further displacement of CO from such complexes (as XXI-XXVI) does not usually occur readily, and other ligands frequently displace the hydrocarbon residue preferentially. This is true both of displacement by other hydrocarbon ligands (e.g., one benzene derivative by another in XXIII) and by phosphines, arsines, amines etc. Thus all the above chromium compounds would react with pyridine, or triphenylphosphine to give $(C_5H_5N)_3$-$Cr(CO)_3$, viz. $(Ph_3P)_3Cr(CO)_3$. For exceptions see Chapter 7.

Displacement with Disproportionation

The general pattern of this type of reaction may be expressed by the equation $2\,M(CO)_n + 6\,L \longrightarrow [ML_6]^{++}[M(CO)_{n-1}]^{--} + (n + 1)CO$ or minor variants thereof, e.g., (*114,303,254*).

$$3\,Fe(CO)_5 + 6\,NH_3 \longrightarrow [Fe(NH_3)_6]^{++}\,[Fe(CO)_4H]_2^- + 7\,CO$$

$$Co_2(CO)_8 + 5\,CNR \longrightarrow [Co(CNR)_5]^+\,[Co(CO)_4]^- + 4\,CO$$

$$3\,Co_2(CO)_8 + 12\,NH_3 \longrightarrow 2[Co(NH_3)_6]^{++}\,[Co(CO)_4^-]_2 + 8\,CO$$

Although this is the commonest mode of reaction of both cobalt (*108, 143,144,154,155,284,303*) and iron carbonyls (*106,107,114,117,126,127, 128,129,145,152,153*) (and probably occurs with other metals in the same groups), it does not appear to have been observed with Cr, Mn or Ni except with aqueous caustic alkalis. It has been studied in most detail with iron, where, depending on the base used, any of the four carbonylate ions

$Fe(CO)_4^{--}$, $Fe_2(CO)_8^{--}$, $Fe_3(CO)_{11}^{--}$ and $Fe_4(CO)_{13}^{--}$ can result. These variations are discussed more fully on pp. 503–505. With piperidine, for example, as the base it has been shown that an intermediate having infrared maxima at 1898 and 2016 cm^{-1} is formed in the cold without evolution of carbon monoxide. The first maximum is attributed to the ion $Fe(CO)_4^{--}$ and although the species responsible for the other peak has not been identified conclusively, it is suggested (*277*) that iron carbonyl may ionize in this solvent according to the equation:

$$2\,Fe(CO)_5 \longrightarrow Fe(CO)_6^{++} + Fe(CO)_4^{--}.$$

The cation would then react further with pyridine at higher temperature,

$$Fe(CO)_6^{++} + 6\,C_5H_5N \longrightarrow Fe(C_5H_5N)_6^{++} + 6\,CO.$$

Cations such as $Fe(CO)_6^{++}$ have not been isolated, but closely related species may be intermediate in the conversion of the carbonyls to carbonyl halides (*cf.* p. 472). The analogous ion $Co(CO)_5^+$ has been postulated (*202*) as resulting from the reaction of dicobalt octacarbonyl with carbon monoxide, and the isosteric isonitrile complexes, e.g., $Fe(CNMe)_6^{++}$, are of course well known (*cf.* p. 518). In the further reaction, stepwise displacement of CO must occur. The simultaneous linkage of CO and amine to the metal at some intermediate stage receives support from the formation of amides which occurs (*284*) with some amines in place of carbon monoxide evolution: e.g.,

$$3[Co(CO)_4]_2 + 20\,Me_2NH \longrightarrow 2[Co(Me_2NH)_6][Co(CO)_4]_2 + 8\,Me_2NCHO$$

With cobalt the reaction has been formulated as going through an initial stage:

$$B + Co_2(CO)_8 \longrightarrow [BCo(CO)_4]^+[Co(CO)_4]^-$$

When piperidine is used as the base, an oil possibly containing this complex may be isolated (*303*) and evidence for formation of a similar salt with dimethylamine has been presented (*284*).

Reactions with Acetylenes

Dicobalt octacarbonyl (*93,278*) and dicyclopentadienyl dinickel dicarbonyl (V) (*286*) are the only cases where simple displacement of carbon monoxide by acetylenes has been established.* In both cases two bridging carbonyl groups are replaced by one acetylene: e.g.,

*The recently reported $Co_4(CO)_{10}(C_2R_2)$ (*173*) may be similarly related to $Co_4(CO)_{12}$.

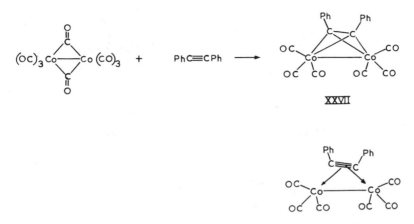

XXVII

XXVIIa

In all other reactions of this type, changes involving the acetylene as well as the carbonyl functions occur. The structure of (XXVII) has been demonstrated by X-ray methods (*273*). The molecule has a cobalt-cobalt bond of 2.48 Å and the acetylene is considerably modified, for the C—C bond is lengthened to 1.37 Å and the C-phenyl bonds make angles of *ca* 140° with it. We can regard the molecule as formed by means of two π-bonds (roughly at right angles) from the acetylene to the two cobalt atoms (structure XXVIIa) or by σ-bonds as suggested in structure (XXVII), but these structures are merely extreme pictorial representations. Analogs of (XXVII) have been obtained with acetylene itself and many substituted acetylenes. The mercury salt of cobalt hydrocarbonyl may serve as starting material (*108*) in place of the neutral carbonyl. This type of acetylene derivative can absorb three molecules of carbon monoxide under pressure (*281*) to yield (XXVIII) which is also formed directly from $Co_2(CO)_8$ with acetylenes under pressure of carbon monoxide. The interesting structure of this product was deduced both from X-ray data (*207*), and, independently, from its chemical transformation (*281*) to the dilactone (XXIX) (*262*, *263*). Another remarkable compound is obtained by treating (XXVII) with hydrochloric acid in methanol (*199*) when it is converted to a trimeric compound, $Co_3(CO)_9C_2H_3$, whose exact structure is still uncertain, but which probably has a triangular arrangement of the metal atoms, possibly as in (XXX). Several metal carbonyls, especially $(Ph_3P)_2Ni(CO)_2$, $[(PhO)_3-P]_2Fe(CO)_3$ and related compounds, but also similar carbonyl-free transition metal derivatives were employed by Reppe (*250*) to induce polymerization of acetylenes to benzene derivatives. More recent work (*159*, *252*) has shown that most metal carbonyls may be employed; e.g.,

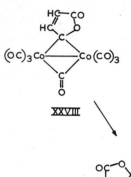

XXVIII

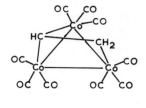

XXX

XXIX

$Co_2(CO)_8$, $Fe_3(CO)_{12}$, $Mn_2(CO)_{10}$ and $Mo(CO)_6$ all proved effective.* The best results appear to be obtained with $Hg[Co(CO)_4]_2$ in refluxing dioxan as solvent. As byproducts or possibly intermediates of these reactions numerous hydrocarbon metal carbonyl complexes may be isolated under appropriate conditions.

Reppe (*251*), who heated iron carbonyl with acetylene in aqueous alcohol under pressure, obtained a product, $C_{11}H_7O_5Fe$, of unknown structure. On hydrolysis with water at 80° this affords hydroquinone and $C_8H_4O_4Fe$, now known (*90a,298,298a*) to be the cyclopentadienone complex (XIX). He also described the reaction of the alkaline solutions—(now known (*35*) to involve $[Fe_2(CO)_8]^{=}$) with acetylene to give $C_{10}H_4O_8Fe_2$. This reaction

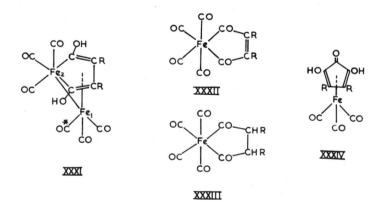

XXXI

XXXII

XXXIII

XXXIV

*Benzonitrile may similarly be polymerized to triphenyltriazine by iron carbonyls (*170*).

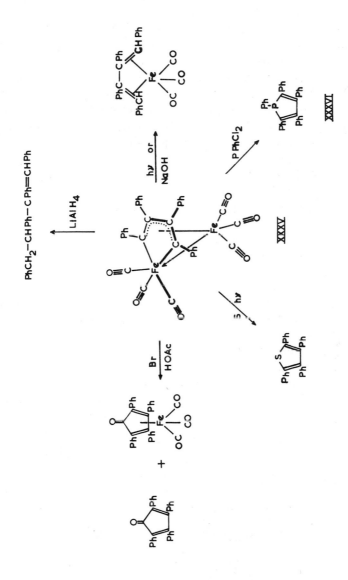

has been further studied by Wender *et al.* (*276,299*) and by Jones *et al.* (*34,42*) who modified the conditions to make the reaction applicable to other acetylenes and demonstrated the presence of the fragment

$$\overset{\displaystyle HO \qquad\qquad OH}{-C-CR-CR-C-}$$ in the products. Finally X-ray analysis (*156*) led to the complete structure (XXXI). Mild oxidation (*34*) leads to (XXXII), which may be regarded as an acyl derivative of iron hydrocarbonyl, $H_2Fe(CO)_4$. Reduction with zinc and acetic acid converts the maleyl derivative (XXXII) to the corresponding succinyl derivative (XXXIII) and/or the dihydroxycyclopentadienone complex (XXXIV) depending on the nature of R (*34,305*). The carbonyl group asterisked in formula (XXXI) is bent and may be regarded as "partially bridging" (Fe^1—C^*—O = 168°; Fe^1—C^* = 1.736 Å.; Fe^2—C^* = 2.484 Å.; C^*—O = 1.171 Å.) (*205,206*). This effect would tend to counteract to some extent the charge distribution implied by the formally coördinate Fe—Fe bond.

In their extensive investigation of the reactions of the three iron carbonyls with a variety of acetylenes, but especially with phenylacetylene and tolane, Hübel and his co-workers (*157–160,298*) have observed the formation of compounds of the types (XVIII) and (XIX), as well as many additional types, depending both on the acetylene and the reaction conditions. A group of products (XXXV) with the general formula $(C_2R_2)_2Fe_2(CO)_6$ are regarded (*157,267*) as related to (XXXI) with R in place of OH. On this basis the reactions of the product (XXXV) from tolane shown on p. 495 receive a ready explanation.

The products corresponding to (XXXV), obtained from unsymmetrical acetylenes RC≡CR', have the symmetrical structure (XXXVII). The specific formation of complexes similar to (XXXVII) is regarded as a likely intermediate stage in the trimerization of acetylenes (*159*) using metal carbonyl catalysts, in which the unsymmetrical 1,2,4-trisubstituted benzenes are formed selectively from monosubstituted acetylenes, or more generally products of the type (XXXVIII) from unsymmetrical acetylenes.

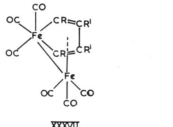

XXXVII

XXXVIII

By analogy, the series $(C_2R_2)_2Fe_2(CO)_7$ containing one additional carbonyl group are formulated (157,267) as (XXXIX) accounting *inter al.* for the ketonic carbonyl absorption at 1665 cm^{-1}. The similarity of the reactions of these two classes is illustrated. The complex (XXXIX) is regarded by Schrauzer (267) as intermediate in·the formation of (XIX). Another type

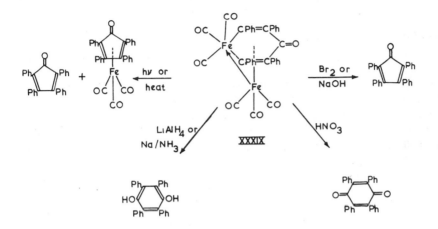

XXXIX

of complex, the duroquinone iron tricarbonyl (XL) is formed (280) by irradiating iron pentacarbonyl with butyne-2. It decomposes to duroquinone on standing in air and may be hydrolyzed quantitatively to durohydroquinone by acid. HMn(CO)$_5$ yields durohydroquinone directly under the irradiation conditions (198) and Reppe's (251) hydroquinone synthesis from iron carbonyl must proceed similarly.

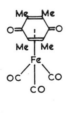

XL

Not all reactions of metal carbonyls with acetylenes yield isolable metal carbonyl acetylene complexes, although such products may be intermediates. This applies to the Reppe carbonylation processes (6,41,167,251):

$$C_2H_2 + CO + ROH \xrightarrow{Ni(CO)_4} CH_2{=}CH{-}COOR \text{ (where R = H, alkyl or acyl)}$$

$$C_2H_2 + CO + RNH_2 \xrightarrow{Ni(CO)_4} CH_2{=}CH{-}CONHR$$

$$C_2H_2 + CO + RSH \xrightarrow{Ni(CO)_4} CH_2{=}CH{-}COSR$$

Apart from the catalytic method in which $Co_2(CO)_8$ or $Fe(CO)_5$ can replace $Ni(CO)_4$, but as less efficient catalysts, the reaction can be carried out stoichiometrically according to the equation:

$$H_2O + C_2H_2 + {}^1/_4\,Ni(CO)_4 + {}^1/_2\,HCl \longrightarrow$$

$$CH_2{=}CHCOOH + {}^1/_4\,NiCl_2 + {}^1/_4\,H_2$$

It proceeds at room temperature and atmospheric pressure and has been studied intensively by Jones, Whiting and their co-workers (*11,167,169*). Unsymmetrical acetylenes may yield (*6*) single products (e.g., PhC$\equiv$CH $\longrightarrow$ ROOC$\cdot$CPh$=$CH$_2$) or mixtures (e.g., PhC$\equiv$CMe $\longrightarrow$ ROOC$\cdot$CPh$=$CHMe + PhCH$=$CMeCOOR). A synthetically useful variant is offered by the α-hydroxy or chloro substituted acetylenes which afford allenic acids (*169*) according to

$$R_2CCl\cdot C{\equiv}CR + CO + R'OH \longrightarrow R_2C{=}C{=}CR\cdot COOR' + HCl$$

in buffered solution or the corresponding unsaturated lactones $R_2C{-}CH{=}CR$ in acidic medium. The formation (*11*) of products of the

$$\underset{O\text{------------}CO}{R_2C{-}CH{=}CR}$$

type (XLI) from RC$\equiv$C$-$CH$_2$Br may be more revealing as to the nature of the intermediate nickel complex.

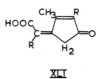

XLI

THE CARBONYL HYDRIDES AND RELATED COMPOUNDS

Introduction

The carbonyl hydrides or hydrocarbonyls are compounds in which both hydrogen and carbon monoxide may be regarded as directly attached to the metal. Only three simple compounds of this type, $HMn(CO)_5$, $H_2Fe(CO)_4$ and $HCo(CO)_4$, are readily accessible and have been studied in some detail. In general, reduction of metal carbonyls leads to cleavage of the metal-metal bond (of dimeric carbonyls), or loss of one molecule of carbon monoxide with formation of a singly or doubly charged negative ion respectively:

$$(CO)_n M—M(CO)_n + 2\ e \longrightarrow 2\ M(CO)_n^-$$

$$M(CO)_n + 2\ e \longrightarrow CO + M(CO)_{n-1}^{--}$$

The hydrocarbonyls are the conjugate acids of these anions. As they are generally of low stability, the number of known hydrocarbonyls is much smaller than that of their anions. The latter are included in the present section even when the free acids are unknown.

Preparation of Carbonyl Hydrides

The free hydrides are most generally obtained by acidification of solutions of their salts. A few have also been obtained by direct reduction of metal carbonyls with hydrogen. Thus dimanganese decacarbonyl reacts with hydrogen (*149*) at 200° under pressure:

$$Mn_2(CO)_{10} + H_2 \longrightarrow 2\ HMn(CO)_5$$

and the dimeric cyclopentadienylchromium carbonyl, $(C_5H_5)_2Cr_2(CO)_6$, has been converted to the corresponding hydride, $C_5H_5Cr(CO)_3H$, at 70° and 150 atmospheres pressure. However, its molybdenum and tungsten analogs are less reactive (*73*).

Cobalt hydrocarbonyl has been obtained (*7,23*) in one step by reaction of cobaltous sulfide, (or cobalt metal and sulfur) with carbon monoxide under pressure and either hydrogen or water, in presence of copper at 100–150°.

$$2\ CoS + 8\ CO + H_2 + 4\ Cu \longrightarrow 2\ HCo(CO)_4 + 2\ Cu_2S$$

$$2\ CoS + 9\ CO + H_2O + 4\ Cu \longrightarrow 2\ HCo(CO)_4 + 2\ CuS + CO_2$$

Properties

The known hydrocarbonyls are listed in Table 10.7 together with their melting or boiling points. The simple iron and cobalt hydrocarbonyls are highly poisonous, evil-smelling liquids of remarkable volatility. They decompose even at –20° with evolution of hydrogen. The manganese and rhenium compounds are considerably more stable, undergoing similar decomposition only near or above 100° C. The cyclopentadienyl derivatives of Fe (*91*), Cr (*71,73*) and Mo (*73*) decompose rapidly at their melting points, but the tungsten compound is stable to at least 180° (*73*). In keeping with their volatility the hydrocarbonyls behave generally as covalent compounds, being sparingly soluble in water and soluble in organic solvents. However they readily redissolve in alkalis to give back their salts. Indeed the dissociation constants included in the table show that their acidities increase steadily from the manganese to the cobalt compound which is too strong to be measured and is comparable with strong mineral

TABLE 10.7. METAL CARBONYL HYDRIDES

$[HCr(CO)_5]^-$ (17,100) $[HCr_2(CO)_{10}]^-$ (17) $[HCr_2(CO)_6(OH)_3]^{2-}$ (136) $C_5H_5Cr(CO)_3H$ (71,73) m.p. 57–58° (dec.)	$HMn(CO)_5$ (148,149) m.p. ~ –20° pK = 7.1	$H_2Fe(CO)_4$ $pK_1 = 4.4$ (124,174) $[HFe(CO)_4]^-$ (114) $pK \sim 14$ (124,174) $[HFe_2(CO)_8]^-$ (106) $[HFe_3(CO)_{11}]^-$ (106) $H_2Fe_4(CO)_{13}$ (152) $HFeCo_3(CO)_{12}$ (39) $C_5H_5Fe\,(CO)_2H$ (91) m.p. ~ –5° (dec.)	$HCo(CO)_4$	$H_2Ni_2(CO)_6$ (20)
$[HMo_2(CO)_{10}]^-$ (16) $H_3[Mo_2(CO)_6(OH)_3]$ (112) $C_5H_5Mo(CO)_3H$ (73) m.p. 50–52° (dec.)	—	$H_2Ru(CO)_4$	$HRh\,(CO)_4$	
$H_4W_4(CO)_{12}(H_2O)_4$ (111,113) $H_4W_3(CO)_9(OH)_2(H_2O)$ (111) $pK_1 \sim 10^{-2}$ $C_5H_5W(CO)_3H$ (73) m.p. 66–67°	$HRe(CO)_5$ (105)	$H_2Os(CO)_4$	$HIr(CO)_4$	

acids (*124,283*). The dimeric nickel hydrocarbonyl however is reported to be nonacidic (*20*). The second dissociation constants of the dihydrides are presumably all much smaller so that "acid" salts of these are commonly isolated more readily than their "neutral" salts. The redox potentials in Table 10.8 have been reported. Detailed studies of infrared spectra have not led to useful correlations of bands due to hydrogen vibrations, but the very large chemical shifts associated with hydrogen atoms directly linked to metals make their nuclear magnetic resonance spectra a powerful tool for detecting carbonyl hydrides (*25,52,57,88*). Richards and his coworkers (*25*) have assigned an interproton distance of 1.88 $\pm$ 0.05 Å. and a probable Fe—H separation of 1.1 Å. to $H_2Fe(CO)_4$ on the basis of a study of its broad-line proton resonance spectrum.

TABLE 10.8.   REDOX POTENTIALS OF CARBONYL HYDRIDES IN
AQUEOUS ALKALINE SOLUTION

Reaction	E_0 volts (20°)	Ref.
$2\,[Co(CO)_4]^- \longrightarrow Co_2(CO)_8 + 2\,e$	-0.4	*125*
$3\,[Fe(CO)_4]^= \longrightarrow [Fe(CO)_4]_3 + 6\,e$	-0.74	*125*
$3\,[HFe(CO)_4]^- \longrightarrow [Fe(CO)_4]_3 + 3\,H^+ + 6\,e$	-0.35	*125*
$2\,[Mn(CO)_5]^- \longrightarrow Mn_2(CO)_{10} + 2\,e$	-0.68	*149*

The decomposition which cobalt hydrocarbonyl suffers on warming (*283*):

$$2\,HCo(CO)_4 \longrightarrow Co_2(CO)_8 + H_2$$

is the basis of all the solution methods for preparing cobalt carbonyl. Iron hydrocarbonyl reacts with carbon monoxide to regenerate the pentacarbonyl and hydrogen. But its thermal decomposition gives a mixture of iron pentacarbonyl and unidentified lower carbonyls (*6,142*). Oxidative methods lead smoothly to the expected tetracarbonyl:

$$3\,H_2Fe(CO)_4 + 3\,O \longrightarrow [Fe(CO)_4]_3 + 3\,H_2O$$

The commonly used oxidizing agents are $KMnO_4$ and MnO_2. It is however by no means necessary to use such powerful oxidants. Indeed the hydrocarbonyls, especially $HCo(CO)_4$, are excellent reducing agents. This has already been discussed in relation to the behavior of metal carbonyls with cyclopentadiene (p. 491). Other examples are (*282,304*):

$$CH{\equiv}CH + 2\,HFe(CO)_4^- \longrightarrow CH_2{=}CH_2$$

$$Me_2CO + H_2Fe(CO)_4 \longrightarrow Me_2CHOH$$

$$PhCMe{=}CH_2 + 2\,HCo(CO)_4 \longrightarrow PhCHMe_2$$

Reductions which have been carried out with a mixture of cobalt carbonyl and hydrogen include reductions (*63,282,304*) of thiophene to tetrahydrothiophene, of benzhydrol to diphenylmethane, and of acylfurans to the corresponding alkylfurans.

The production of alcohols (*251*) from olefins, carbon monoxide, hydrogen and iron carbonyl may reasonably be assumed to involve reduction of the corresponding aldehyde by iron hydrocarbonyl or its anion $HFe(CO)_4^-$ as the last step. The formation of the aldehyde itself occurs with cobalt hydrocarbonyl as the effective catalyst in what is known as the hydroformylation or oxo reaction. This has recently been formulated (*282*) as

$$CH_2{=}CH_2 + HCo(CO)_4 \longrightarrow CH_3CH_2Co(CO)_4$$
$$(XLIII)$$

$$CH_3CH_2Co(CO)_4 + CO \longrightarrow CH_3CH_2COCo(CO)_4$$
$$(XLIV)$$

$$CH_3CH_2COCo(CO)_4 + H_2 \longrightarrow HCo(CO)_4 + CH_3CH_2CHO$$

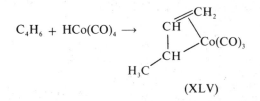

$$(XLII)$$

with the first stage probably proceeding *via* an intermediate such as (XLII) in which the olefin has replaced CO and is π-bonded to the metal. The following step is then the transfer of hydrogen from metal to carbon and thus another example of reduction by the hydrocarbonyl. It finds a close parallel in the addition of the hydrocarbonyl to butadiene (*6a,166,242,274*) to give a stable product formulated as (XLV):

$$C_4H_6 + HCo(CO)_4 \longrightarrow$$

(XLV)

The suggested intermediates (XLIII) and (XLIV) are alkyl and acylcobalt tetracarbonyls of the type discussed on pp. 506–508. The addition of the hydrocarbonyl to olefins is believed to be reversible and hence can account (*282*) for the isomerization of olefins by hydrocarbonyl catalysts by a mechanism of successive addition and elimination:

$$RCH_2CH{=}CH_2 + HM(CO)_n \longrightarrow RCH_2CH{-}CH_3 \longrightarrow$$
$$\underset{\displaystyle M(CO)_n}{|}$$

$$RCH{=}CHCH_3 + HM(CO)_n, \text{ etc.}$$

Salts of the Hydrocarbonyls

As moderately strong acids the hydrocarbonyls give true ionic, water-soluble salts with alkali metals whereas mercury and various other heavy metals form essentially covalent derivatives. As the sodium and potassium salts are intermediates not only in the preparation of these heavy metal derivatives, but of the hydrocarbonyls themselves, their preparation is of importance.

(i) Direct preparation from metal salts and carbon monoxide is important only in the case of cobalt.

(ii) Reduction of the corresponding metal carbonyl is the only method available in many cases, including the preparations of the chromium carbonyl anion $Cr(CO)_5^{--}$ (16,17,18,22) and the cyclopentadienyl iron carbonyl anion $C_5H_5Fe(CO)_2$ (68). The reducing agent employed is metallic sodium either as amalgam or in liquid ammonia. The former is more convenient, but the latter is more generally applicable. By using sodium borohydride in liquid ammonia Behrens (16) has obtained the dimeric salts $Na_2[M_2(CO)_{10}]$ from the hexacarbonyls of Cr, Mo and W. The reactions follow the typical equations (13,16,21,22,82).

$$(a) \quad M(CO)_n + 2\,Na \longrightarrow Na_2[M(CO)_{n-1}] + CO$$

or

$$(b) \quad M_2(CO)_{2n} + 2\,Na \longrightarrow 2\,NaM(CO)_n$$

The polymeric carbonyls behave similarly, e.g. (13,21),

$$Fe_3(CO)_{12} + 6\,Na \longrightarrow 3\,Na_2Fe(CO)_4$$

$$Fe_2(CO)_9 + 2\,Na \longrightarrow Na_2[Fe_2(CO)_8] + CO$$

The preparation of nickel hydrocarbonyl (20) is analogous, but the anion which may be assumed to be an intermediate, is converted directly into the hydride owing to the low acidity of the latter:

$$2\,Ni(CO)_4 + 2\,Na \xrightarrow{NH_3} 2\,CO + Na_2[Ni_2(CO)_6]$$

$$Na_2[Ni_2(CO)_6] + 4\,NH_3 \longrightarrow 2\,NaNH_2 + H_2Ni_2(CO)_6 \cdot 2\,NH_3$$

(iii) By alkaline disproportionation of metal carbonyls. This includes all the reactions discussed on pp. 491–492. Whereas in the case of organic bases reduction of the metal carbonyl usually occurs at the expense of partial oxidation of the metal to the $+2$ state, with aqueous alkalis it more commonly involves oxidation of the liberated carbon monoxide:

e.g., $4\,NaOH + Fe_2(CO)_9 \longrightarrow Na_2[Fe_2(CO)_8] + Na_2CO_3 + 2\,H_2O$ (106).

$$3\,KOH + Cr(CO)_6 \longrightarrow K[HCr(CO)_5] + K_2CO_3 + H_2O$$

The latter reaction is followed rapidly by

$$4\,KOH + 2\,K[HCr(CO)_5] + 3\,H_2O \longrightarrow$$
$$K_2[Cr_2(CO)_6(OH)_3H] + 2\,H_2 + 4\,HCOOK$$
$$(XLVI)$$

and only the resultant dimeric salt (XLVI) is isolated (100,101,136). However the monomeric hydrocarbonyl anion may be isolated by adding the disodium salt [obtained as described in paragraph (ii)] to strong NaOH (17):

$$Na_2Cr(CO)_5 + H_2O \longrightarrow NaOH + NaHCr(CO)_5;$$

with water, the reaction proceeds further:

$$2\,NaHCr(CO)_5 + H_2O \longrightarrow Na[Cr_2(CO)_{10}H] + NaOH + H_2.$$
$$(XLVII)$$

The product (XLVII) should be another intermediate in the formation of (XLVI), but their relationship has not been established experimentally. Molybdenum and tungsten carbonyls behave similarly to the chromium compound (22,111,112,113). Since the conversion of $Co_2(CO)_8$ to $Co(CO)_4^-$ (144,154,155) and $Mn_2(CO)_{10}$ to $Mn(CO)_5^-$ (148) does not involve loss of carbon monoxide, some of the metal must necessarily become oxidized, and the carbon monoxide which is then liberated may also be oxidized, leading to a rather complex reaction. In the case of cobalt, Hieber has shown that strong alkali favors formation of carbonate, whereas at lower pH more of the cobalt becomes oxidized with concomitant liberation of CO.

$Fe(CO)_5$ and $Fe_3(CO)_{12}$ behave (106) like the enneacarbonyl, above, in yielding $NaHFe(CO)_4$ and $Na_2Fe_3(CO)_{11}$* respectively. The relationship between the iron carbonyl anions of different complexities has been studied under a variety of conditions and since they are interconvertible the exact result will depend on the pH and temperature (35).

*This or $NaHFe_3(CO)_{11}$ is formed with mild alkalis [e.g. Na_2CO_3], but reaction with KOH is more complex and yields $Fe_2(CO)_8^{==}$, apparently not *via* the trimeric salt.

Thus, on standing, solutions containing the monomeric ion undergo oxidation (35,279) in presence of air or other oxidizing agents or decompose on irradiation:

$$2\ HFe(CO)_4^- \longrightarrow H_2 + Fe_2(CO)_8^{--}.$$

Acids convert the dimeric ion (stable above pH 10) reversibly to the trimeric ion (stable at $\sim pH$ 5–pH 10):

$$Fe_2(CO)_8^{--} \underset{OH^-}{\overset{H^+}{\rightleftarrows}} Fe_3(CO)_{11}^{--}.$$

The effect of temperature (117) has best been illustrated in the reaction of ethylenediamine with the dodecacarbonyl. As the temperature is raised, increasing amounts of this base react, thus (145):

$$4\ Fe_3(CO)_{12} + 9\ en \xrightarrow{40°} 3\ [Fe(en)_3]^{++}[Fe_3(CO)_{11}]^{--} + 15\ CO$$

$$Fe_3(CO)_{12} + 3\ en \xrightarrow{90°} [Fe(en)_3]^{++}[Fe_2(CO)_8]^{--}* + 4\ CO$$

$$2\ Fe_3(CO)_{12} + 9\ en \xrightarrow{145°} 3\ [Fe(en)_3]^{++}[Fe(CO)_4]^{--} + 12\ CO$$

Other factors, e.g., base strength and the structure of the base, influence the course of the reaction. Thus, the monomeric ion is formed with benzidine (127), whereas under comparable conditions the dimeric ion is favored by (117,127,128,129,153): α and γ-picoline, o-phenanthroline, triphenylphosphine oxide etc. The trimeric ion is favored by (107,128): dipyridyl, methanol, etc., and the tetrameric ion $Fe_4(CO)_{13}^{--}$ is favored by (126,129, 152): pyridine, piperidine, dimethylformamide, dimethylsulfoxide etc.

Heavy metal salts of a few of the hydrocarbonyls have been described, especially of the divalent metals Zn, Cd, Hg, and Sn, but also of monovalent Ag and Tl, of trivalent Tl, In, As, Sb and Bi, as well as of Sb^{5+}. The very stable mercury compounds are best known and the following exemplify the chief types; $Hg[Fe(CO)_4]$ (14); $Hg[HFe(CO)_4]_2$; $Hg[Co-(CO)_4]_2$ (108,109,116); $Hg[Co(CO)_3PPh_3]_2$ (108); $Hg[C_5H_5Cr(CO)_3]_2$ (71, 73); $Hg[C_5H_5Fe(CO)_2]_2$ (68). In addition, related covalent compounds derivable from the carbonylate anions and the alkylmetal cations: R_3Pb^+, R_3Sn^+, R_2Tl^+, RHg^+, R_2Pb^{++}, R_2Sn^{++}, are known (109,121). The formulation of $Bu_2Sn[Co(CO)_3PPh_3]_2$ for example, as (XLVIII) has been suggested (109), but no structural evidence is available. Metal-metal

*Case and Whiting (35) have recently suggested that this salt is in reality $[Fe(en)_3][HFe(CO)_4]_2$.

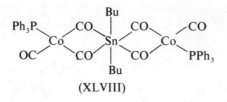

(XLVIII)

bonding must be considered as equally probable and such structures have been suggested (*121*) at least for some of the compounds, e.g., (XLIX) for $Pb[Fe_3(CO)_{12}](!)$

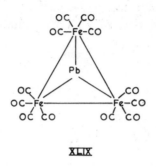

XLIX

There is no sharp dividing line between these covalent derivatives and the salt like derivatives formed by the alkali metals or by such complex ions as $[Ni(o\text{-phen})_3]^{++}$. Ammoniacal solutions of copper, zinc and cadmium yield (*114*) with $Fe(CO)_4^{--}$ precipitates of the types, $Cu_2(NH_3)_2Fe(CO)_4$, $Zn(NH_3)_3Fe(CO)_4$ and $Cd(NH_3)_2Fe(CO)_4$, belonging to an intermediate type as shown e.g., by the conductivities:

$(ClHg)_2[Fe(CO)_4]_2$	$Zn(NH_3)_3Fe(CO)_4$	$[Ni(o\text{-phen})_3][HFe(CO)_4]_2$
too small to be measured (20°/acetone)	25.4 mhos (20°/methanol)	129.7 mhos (20°/methanol) 114 mhos (18°/acetone)

Alkyl Metal Carbonyls

As acids the metal hydrocarbonyls yield "esters" on treatment with diazomethane. These must have alkyl groups directly attached to the metal, i.e., they are true metal alkyls, and their comparatively high stability must be attributed to the effect of the carbonyl group on the alkyl ligands. The simplest examples are the alkyl manganese pentacarbonyls (*44,148,150*):

$$HMn(CO)_5 + CH_2N_2 \rightarrow CH_3Mn(CO)_5 + N_2$$

The same product is obtained (44) from sodio-manganese pentacarbonyl and methyl iodide:

$$NaMn(CO)_5 + CH_3I \rightarrow CH_3Mn(CO)_5 + NaI$$

The latter method is more readily applicable, not only to a large variety of alkyl groups, but also to the preparation of acyl derivatives (45):

$$NaMn(CO)_5 + CH_3COCl \rightarrow CH_3COMn(CO)_5 + NaCl$$

A third method, the reaction of the carbonyl halides with Grignard reagents, organo-lithium or -sodium compounds proved successful in only one recorded example with bromomanganese pentacarbonyl (150), but has been used for the preparation of the cyclopentadienyl derivatives $C_5H_5Fe(CO)_2R$ (95,236,237) and the related $C_5H_5Cr(NO)_2R$ (235), e.g.,

$$C_5H_5Fe(CO)_2Br + PhMgBr \rightarrow C_5H_5Fe(CO)_2Ph + MgBr_2$$

Although this method has not been used to prepare the aryl manganese pentacarbonyls, these are accessible as a result of the interconversion (45,46) of the alkyl or aryl and acyl derivatives:

e.g., $$PhCOMn(CO)_5 \underset{CO}{\overset{heat}{\rightleftharpoons}} PhMn(CO)_5 + CO$$

It has been demonstrated (46), that the carbon monoxide evolved in this decomposition is *not* the group originally attached to the alkyl or aryl group and conversely, that in the reverse reaction the entering carbon monoxide does *not* become attached to the alkyl or aryl group. The reaction is therefore a concerted process and may be written as in (L) and (LI). Only the insertion of CO has been reported (46) in the cyclopentadienyl iron series, $C_5H_5Fe(CO)_2R$. The acyl derivatives of this type are better

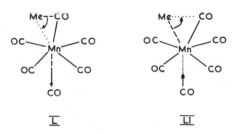

L   LI

obtained from $C_5H_5Fe(CO)_2Na + RCOCl$ and apparently decompose more extensively on heating, than to the corresponding alkyls. The only other known acyls of this type are the diacyl-iron tetracarbonyls (XXXII) and (XXXIII) (see p. 496) obtained from acetylenes. Alkyls have also been made (*234,237*) from $C_5H_5Cr(CO)_3Na$ and $C_5H_5Mo(CO)_3Na$ by the second method (above). All the above alkyl and acyl derivatives are fairly stable to air and cold water. By contrast, methylcobalt tetracarbonyl $CH_3Co(CO)_4$ decomposes above $-35°$ (*147*). Despite this instability, alkylcobalt tetra-carbonyls are believed to be important intermediates in reactions "cata-lyzed" by cobalt hydrocarbonyl—indeed the effectiveness of this catalyst may be attributed to the high reactivity of these alkyls. Their probable formation in the hydroformylation process, where they arise by addition of the hydrocarbonyl to olefins, has been referred to. Very similar mechanisms may be postulated for the carbonylation of alcohols and ethers, for which Reppe (*251*) suggested, in the case of methanol, the steps:

$$MeOH + HCo(CO)_4 \longrightarrow MeCo(CO)_4 \xrightarrow[H_2]{CO} MeCHO + HCo(CO)_4$$

This mechanism may now be expanded by postulating acetylcobalt tetra-carbonyl as a second intermediate (*282*). Further, if similar carbonylation of cobalt hydrocarbonyl can occur, then the sequence

$$HCo(CO)_4 + CO \longrightarrow HCOCo(CO)_4 \xrightarrow{MeOH} HCOOMe$$

explains (*282*) a major byproduct. Esters (or lactones) become the prin-cipal products when the reaction is applied to ethers. When nickel car-bonyl replaces the cobalt compound as catalyst in these carbonylation reac-tions the addition of halide ions becomes necessary. The reactions are therefore believed (*251*) to involve alkyl halides under these conditions and allylic halides have been shown (*41*) to be particularly effective, but the structure of the intermediate nickel complexes is unknown.

The coupling (*296*) of allylic halides ($2 RCl \longrightarrow R-R$) and various ad-dition reactions, e.g., of HCN (*10*), $HSiR_3$, (*87*) and CCl_4, (*86*) to olefins are catalyzed by metal carbonyls, but it is not clear whether these form intermediate alkyls as in the carbon monoxide additions, or merely act as radical initiators. Strong evidence for intermediate formation of acyl- and alkylcobalt carbonyls in the reactions of acid anhydrides, amides etc. with cobalt octacarbonyl has been presented (*300*). As shown in the following reaction scheme, phthalic anhydride treated with labelled carbonyl gives an intermediate which may be converted to labelled anhydride ("carbon monoxide exchange") with (inactive) carbon monoxide, but which affords unlabelled benzoic acid on treatment with hydrogen:

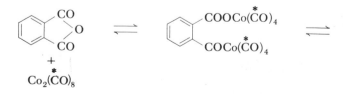

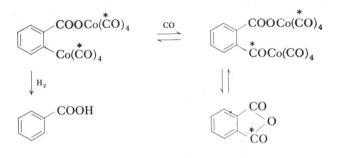

METAL CARBONYL HALIDES AND RELATED COMPOUNDS

Compounds containing halogen and carbon monoxide but no other ligands attached to a metal extend over a different range of the periodic table than the pure carbonyls as shown in Tables 10.9 and 10.10. Thus,

TABLE 10.9. METALS WHICH FORM CARBONYLS AND CARBONYL HALIDES

Ti*	V	Cr	Mn	Fe	Co	Ni	Cu	Zn
Zr	Nb	Mo	–	Ru	Rh	Pd	Ag	Cd
Hf	Ta	W	Re	Os	Ir	Pt	Au	Hg

———— encloses metals of which metal carbonyls are known.
encloses metals of which metal carbonyl halides are known.

*See p. 482.

although neither the chromium group nor nickel has been shown to give compounds of this type, Pd, Pt, the copper group and possibly Hg (*264*) do so. The oxidation number of the metal in these compounds is ordinarily one or two and they are thus more akin to the usual metal complexes. The metal atom is covalently bonded to the halogens although ionic complexes may be intermediate in the reactions of metal carbonyls with halogens and the unstable $Fe(CO)_5X_2$ may be of this type. As fully covalent molecules they are frequently volatile. Heating usually results in stepwise loss of carbon monoxide leading to complexes with progressively lower CO content. These are generally di- or polymeric, the metal atoms being linked by halide (rather than CO) bridges,

e.g. (*5*) $Mn_2(CO)_{10} + X_2 \longrightarrow 2\,XMn(CO)_5 \xrightarrow{\text{heat}}$

$$2\,CO + (CO)_4Mn \underset{X}{\overset{X}{\rightleftarrows}} Mn(CO)_4$$

TABLE 10.10. METAL CARBONYL HALIDES (7, 23) (X = Cl, Br, OR I)

$Mn(CO)_5X$ (5, 138, 148)	$Fe(CO)_5X_2$	$Co(CO)X_2$		$Cu(CO)X$
$[Mn(CO)_4X]_2$ (5)	$Fe(CO)_4X_2$			
	$[Fe(CO)_3X_2]_8$			
	$Fe(CO)_2X_2$			
	$Fe(CO)_2X$			
—	$[Ru(CO)_2X_2]_n$ (122, 162)	$[Rh(CO)_2X]_2$ (123, 250, 312)	$[Pd(CO)X_2]_n$	—
	$Ru(CO)X$	$[Rh(CO)_2X_2]^-$ (252)	$[Pd(CO)X_3]^-$	
		$[Rh_2(CO)_2X_4]^{--}$ (252)		
$Re(CO)_5X$ (139, 141)	$[Os(CO)_4X]_2$	$Ir(CO)_3X$ (193)	$Pt(CO)_2X_2$ (98)	$Au(CO)X$ (172)
$[Re(CO)_4X]_2$ (4)	$Os(CO)_4X_2$	$Ir(CO)_3X_3$ (193)	$Pt_2(CO)_3X_4$ (98)	
	$Os(CO)_3X_2$	$Ir(CO)_2X_2$	$[Pt(CO)X_2]_2$ (163, 164)	
	$Os(CO)_2X_2$	$Ir(CO)_2X_3$ (193)	$[Pt(CO)X_3]^-$ (98, 178)	
		$[Ir(CO)_2X_2]^-$ (9)		
		$[Ir_2(CO)_4X_3]^-$ (9)		
		$[Ir(CO)_2X_4]^-$ (193)		
		$[Ir_2(CO)_4X_5]^{--}$ (9)		
		$[Ir_2(CO)_2X_2]^{--}$ (182)		
		$[Ir_2(CO)_2X_3]^{--}$ (182)		
		$[Ir_2(CO)_2X_5]^-$ (8, 9)		
		$[Ir(CO)X_5]^{--}$ (193)		
		$[Ir_2(CO)X_4]^-$ (182)		

Preparation of the Noble Metal Derivatives (7,23)

Most of the halocarbonyls of Mn and Fe have only been obtained from the corresponding carbonyls, but others can be formed directly from the metal halides and carbon monoxide with a reducing agent where necessary (7,23,139),

e.g., $$2 RuI_3 + 4 CO \longrightarrow 2 Ru(CO)_2I_2 + I_2,$$

occurs at atmospheric pressure in absence of other reactants; the further step

$$Ru(CO)_2I_2 + CO \longrightarrow Ru(CO)_5$$

requires a halogen acceptor, e.g., Cu metal. Rhodium appears to require copper to form the halocarbonyls:

$$RhX_3 + 2 CO + 2 Cu \longrightarrow Rh(CO)_2X + 2 Cu_2X_2$$

The halogen may be liberated as carbonyl halide, e.g.,

$$2 IrBr_3 + 5 CO \longrightarrow 2 Ir(CO)_2Br_2 + COBr_2$$

$$2 Ir(CO)_2Br_2 + 3 CO \longrightarrow 2 Ir(CO)_3Br + COBr_2$$

The platinum derivatives have been prepared by allowing a mixture of chlorine and carbon monoxide to react with the free metal at 240–250°. This results in a mixture of the complexes, $Pt(CO)_2Cl_2$, $Pt(CO)Cl_2$, $Pt_2(CO)_3Cl_4$, $Pt(CO)_2Cl_6$. They decrease in volatility in that order and may be separated by sublimation. The structure of the last mentioned $Pt(CO)_2Cl_6$ is not obvious and it may prove not to be a true carbonyl. $Pt(CO)_2Cl_2$ is known from its dipole moment to have the *cis* structure (LII) and $Pt(CO)Cl_2$ is dimeric and formulated as (LIII). The structure of $Pt_2(CO)_3Cl_4$ is not known. All these three carbonyls are unstable to water

LII   LIII

and react with hydrochloric acid to yield the anion $[COPtCl_3]^-$. This may also be obtained directly by the action of CO on K_2PtCl_4 or Na_2PtCl_6. It forms sparingly soluble salts with such large cations as the quinolinium ion. The corresponding bromides and iodides are also known. Stability to hydrolysis of the complexes $Pt_2(CO)_2X_4$ increases in the order Cl, Br, I but stability to heat follows the reverse order. Palladium forms the analogous but much less stable palladous complexes, $Pd_2(CO)_2Cl_4$ and $[Pd(CO)Cl_3]^-$.

Anhydrous cuprous halides absorb carbon monoxide under pressure (100–150 atm.) to yield the complexes $Cu(CO)X$, but from aqueous cuprous solutions, which so readily absorb carbon monoxide, only solvated complexes, e.g., $Cu(CO)Cl \cdot 2H_2O$, have been isolated. Gold yields $Au(CO)Cl$ (*172*), but silver has not yielded any analogs, although solutions of silver sulfate in fuming sulfuric acid absorb one molecule of carbon monoxide reversibly.

Mercuric acetate absorbs carbon monoxide in aqueous or alcoholic solution yielding $Hg(CO)(OR)(OCOCH_3)$ which is converted by KCl to $Hg(CO)(OR)Cl$ (where R = H or alkyl). These however cannot be regarded as true carbonyls (*264*) for, although hydrochloric acid liberates carbon monoxide:

$$Hg(CO)(OR)Cl + HCl \longrightarrow HgCl_2 + ROH + CO,$$

other reactions suggest that they are formic acid derivatives,

e.g., $$Hg(COOR)Cl + I_2 \longrightarrow HgI_2 + ClCOOR$$

The Manganese, Iron and Cobalt Carbonyl Halides (*7,23*)

In contrast to the Cu and Pt compounds the iron carbonyl halides increase in stability to heat in the order: Cl, Br, I, the halides $Fe(CO)_5X_2$ decomposing to $Fe(CO)_4X_2$ at $-35°$, $-10°$ and $0°$ respectively. The same order is displayed in the heats of formation of the latter type from FeX_2 and CO which are 17.9(Cl), 28.3(Br) and 38.9(I) kcals/mole. The lower carbonyl halides $Fe(CO)_2X_2$ and $Fe(CO)_2X$ are obtained on heating the tetracarbonyl halides or directly, e.g., by reaction of iron pentacarbonyl with iodine in boiling benzene in the case of $Fe(CO)_2I_2$. The monoiodide, $Fe(CO)_2I$, is unstable, losing carbon monoxide to yield the likewise unstable bright red FeI. The existence of the intermediate tricarbonyl halides, $Fe(CO)_3X_2$, is somewhat doubtful. The ruthenium and osmium compounds are broadly similar to those of iron but more stable and do not follow a general rule regarding the effect of halogen on stability. The bromides and iodides of the types, $Os(CO)_4X_2$, $Os(CO)_3X_2$ and $[Os(CO)_4X]_2$, all exist in two forms, possibly geometrical isomers, whereas all the other carbonyl halides mentioned are known only in one form. In most cases the structures are unknown, but $Fe(CO)_4I_2$ has been shown (*151*) to have a dipole moment of $3.60 \pm 0.05D$ and must thus be the *cis*-form (LIV). The polymeric structure (LV) has been proposed (*162*) for $[Ru(CO)_2I_2]$

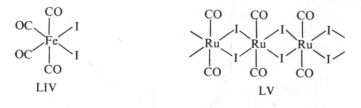

LIV   LV

Nickel and cobalt (*130*) carbonyls are decomposed completely by halogen but the dark brown, unstable $Co(CO)I_2$ has been obtained from cobaltous iodide and carbon monoxide at room temperature and 100 atmospheres pressure.

Displacement Reactions of Carbonyl Halides.

Displacements of carbon monoxides by amines, phosphines and iso-nitriles follow the general paths described on pp. 483–485. Halogen or CO or both may be displaced, but in the case of halogen-bridged complexes the first step is usually the breaking of such bridges without any displacement,

e.g., (*163*) $$[Pt(CO)X_2]_2 + 2 L \longrightarrow 2 Pt(CO)LX_2.$$

The *trans* directing influence of carbon monoxide is demonstrated in this reaction, since the product, e.g., $Pt(CO)(pyridine)Cl_2$, has been shown to have the *trans*-structure, whereas a member of the *cis*-series may be obtained by the reaction:

$$[NH_3PtCl_3]^- + CO \xrightarrow{12°} cis\text{-}[Pt(CO)(NH_3)Cl_2].$$

The principal types of complexes obtainable in these ways are summarized in Table 10.11. where L represents any of the amine, phosphine or isonitrile ligands. Preferential displacement of carbon monoxide (rather than isonitrile) has been demonstrated in the reactions of (p-MeOC$_6$H$_4$-NC)$_2$Rh(CO)Cl with ligands like phosphines to give (*288*), e.g., (p-MeOC$_6$-H$_4$NC)$_2$Rh(PPh$_3$)$_2$Cl. Displacement of both carbon monoxide and halide from $Mn(CO)_5X$ or $C_5H_5Fe(CO)_2X$ by aromatic compounds under Friedel-Crafts conditions (*47*) is discussed in Chapter 8.

Carbonyl Sulfides and Related Compounds

Substitution reactions with such negative ions as CN^-, SR^- etc. may likewise cause replacement of halogen and carbon monoxide or may lead to addition products in the case of polymeric carbonyl halides. The reactions with cyanide have been exemplified on p. 486. Sulfides can act as bridging groups. Thus the product (LVI) is analogous to $Re_2(CO)_8Cl_2$, with sulfide

$$2 Re(CO)_5Cl + 2 PhSNa \longrightarrow 2 NaCl + CO + Re_2(CO)_8(SPh)_2$$

LVI

in place of halide bridges. In the case of rhenium an analogous oxide complex (LVII) is also known (*140*), being obtained from $Re(CO)_5Cl$ or $Re_2(CO)_{10}$ with caustic potash. Related carbonyl sulfides of iron and

TABLE 10-11. KNOWN TYPES OF CARBONYL HALIDE COMPLEXES WITH A THIRD LIGAND L; (X = Cl, Br OR I)

(VI)	(VII)	(VIII)	(VIII)	(VIII)
—	$[Mn(CO)_4L_2]X$ (138) $Mn(CO)_3L_2X$ (5,138)	$Fe(CO)_3LX_2$ (247) $Fe(CO)_2L_2X$ (223) $Fe(CO)_2L_2X_2$ (134,223) $Fe(CO)L_2X_2$ $Fe(CO)L_3X_2$ (134)	$[Co(CO)_3L_2]X$ (260)	—
$Mo(CO)_3L_2X_2$ (224) $Mo(CO)_2L_3X_2$	—	$Ru(CO)_2L_2X_2$ (122,162)	$[Rh(CO)_2L_2X]_2$ (123) $Rh(CO)_2L_3X$ (123) $Rh(CO)L_2X$ (123,287, 288,289, 290,291) $Rh(CO)L_2X_3$ (288)	—
$W(CO)_3L_2X_2$ (224) $[W(CO)_3L_2X_2]X$ (224)	$Re(CO)_4LX$ (141) $[Re(CO)_4L_2]X$ (141) $Re(CO)_3L_2X$ (141)	—	$Ir(CO)_2LX$ (8,9) $Ir(CO)_2L_2X$ (8) $Ir(CO)L_2X$ (8,9)	$Pt(CO)_2L_2X_2$ (98) $[Pt(CO)L_2X]^+$ (163,164) $Pt(CO)LX_2$ (98,163,164) $Pt(CO)L_2X_2$ (98)

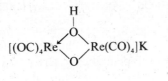

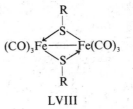

LVII   LVIII

cobalt have been obtained directly from metal(II) salts (*248*) and carbon monoxide or from the neutral carbonyls (*137*) with the appropriate mercaptan, RSH, the corresponding disulfide, RSSR, or even the thioether R_2S. The ethyl and β-naphthylthio compounds have been shown to be dimeric and may be formulated satisfactorily with sulfide bridges as in (LVIII). The cobalt analog (*146*) $[Co(CO)_3SEt]_2$ could be formulated similarly without metal-metal bond, but the monomeric C_6H_5-$SFe(CO)_3$ (*137,146*) and $C_6H_5SCo(CO)_3$ (*146*) are more difficult to understand. Likewise unknown is the structure of "$Fe_3(CO)_{10}(SCH_2S)$" obtained from iron dodecacarbonyl and parathioformaldehyde (*137*). Further replacement of CO from the ethyl- or phenylthio-iron tricarbonyl with *o*-phenanthroline has yielded products of the empirical formula, $Fe(CO)$-$(C_{12}H_8N_2)SR$, and a similar type of mixed amine-sulfide complex of molybdenum, $PhSMo(CO)_2(C_5H_5N)$, has been obtained by the action of thiophenol on the tripyridomolybdenum tricarbonyl, $Mo(CO)_3(C_5H_5N)_3$ (*137*).

Such carbonyl sulfides must be of importance as intermediates in the formation of metal carbonyls in the presence of sulfur compounds and the complexes $[RSFe(CO)_3]_n$ have in fact been obtained directly from ferrous ion and carbon monoxide in presence of mercaptide. The reaction of metallic iron, carbon monoxide and sulfur, hydrogen sulfide or selenium affords $Fe_3X_2(CO)_9$ where X = S or Se, and these as well as their tellurium analog may also be obtained (*120*) from the carbonylate anions [Fe-$(CO)_4^{--}$, $Fe_2(CO)_8^{--}$ or $Fe_3(CO)_{11}^{--}$] and sulfite, selenite or tellurite according to reactions formulated thus:

$$3\ Fe(CO)_4^{--} + 2\ XO_3^{--} + 10\ H^+ \longrightarrow Fe_3X_2(CO)_9 + CO_2 + 2\ CO + 5\ H_2O$$

The products are highly colored, diamagnetic solids and show only terminal type carbonyl stretching frequencies in the infrared. They may perhaps be formulated as in (LIX).

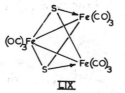

LIX

METAL NITROSOCARBONYL AND NITROSOISONITRILE COMPLEXES

As a three-electron donor the nitrosyl group can form a somewhat unique range of mixed carbonyl derivatives. The two chief examples are $Co(CO)_3NO$ and $Fe(CO)_2(NO)_2$. In the cyclopentadienyl series the compounds $C_5H_5M(CO)_2NO$ where M = Cr, Mo or W, and salts of the cation $[C_5H_5Mn(CO)_2NO]^+$ have been obtained (67,233,234). The chromium (67) and cobalt (99) compounds may be obtained from the corresponding dimeric carbonyls with nitric oxide, which both cleaves the metal-metal bond and displaces one molecule of carbon monoxide per metal atom,

e.g., $$Co_2(CO)_8 + 2 NO \longrightarrow 2 Co(CO)_3NO + 2 CO$$

The iron compound is formed similarly from $Fe_2(CO)_9$ or $Fe_3(CO)_{12}$ (99) and may be regarded as derived from $Fe(CO)_5$ by replacement of three carbonyl by two nitrosyl groups. Ruthenium enneacarbonyl reacts with complete replacement of all the carbon monoxide and a mixed complex, e.g., $Ru(CO)_2(NO)_2$, is not yet known. Various other preparative techniques have been employed. The most convenient method is the action of nitric oxide or sodium nitrite on aqueous or acetic acid solutions of $NaCo(CO)_4$ (26,269), viz. $NaHFe(CO)_4$ (269). Both nitric oxide and N-methyl-N-nitroso-p-toluene-sulphonamide have been used to convert cyclopentadienylmolybdenum tricarbonyl hydride, $C_5H_5Mo(CO)_3H$, to the nitrosyl, $C_5H_5Mo(CO)_2NO$. Both the latter compounds may be regarded as isosteric with $C_5H_5Mn(CO)_3$ and the nitrosocarbonyls as well as the carbonyl hydrides of iron and cobalt form closely isosteric series with nickel carbonyl, all having similar tetrahedral structures:

$Fe(CO)_4H_2$	$Co(CO)_4H$	$Ni(CO)_4$
$Fe(CO)_2(NO)_2$	$Co(CO)_3NO$	$Ni(CO)_4$
$Fe(CNR)_2(NO)_2$	$Co(CNR)_3NO$	$Ni(CNR)_4$

To these may be added the analogous isonitrile-nitrosyl complexes (186), $Fe(CNR)_2(NO)_2$ and $Co(CNR)_3NO$ which bear the same relationship to nickel isonitrile or mixed carbonyl-isonitrile derivatives. Both $Fe(CNR)_2$-$(NO)_2$ and the mixed cobalt complexes, $Co(CNR)_2(CO)NO$, may be obtained from the corresponding nitrosocarbonyls by direct replacement of CO. The iron compound has also been obtained (186) by the action of iso-cyanides on Roussin's red, $K_2Fe_2(NO)_4S_2$, or of hydroxylamine on tetra-isonitrilo ferrous salts:

$$Fe(CNR)_4X_2 + 4 NH_2OH \longrightarrow Fe(CNR)_2(NO)_2 + 2 NH_4X + 2 H_2O + 2 CNR$$

The cobalt tri-isonitrile compound is formed similarly from the nitrosyl ammine complex, $[Co(NO)(NH_3)_5]Cl_2$, or the isonitrile complex, $[Co(CNR)_5]^+$, respectively.

Other ligands also replace $(23,99,183,247)$ carbon monoxide (rather than NO) from the nitroso-carbonyls as illustrated by the equations:

$$Fe(NO)_2(CO)_2 + C_{12}H_8N_2 \longrightarrow Fe(NO)C_{12}H_8N_2 + 2\ CO$$
$$o\text{-phenanthroline}$$

$$Co(NO)(CO)_3 + C_{12}H_8N_2 \longrightarrow Co(NO)(CO)(C_{12}H_8N_2) + 2\ CO$$

$$Fe(NO)_2(CO)_2 + \tfrac{1}{2}I_2 \longrightarrow Fe(NO)_2I + 2\ CO$$

CATIONIC ISONITRILE COMPLEXES

Apart from the complexes in low valency states referred to on p. 483, isonitriles can also yield cationic complexes of the more usual $+2$ or even higher oxidation states of the metal. As these are more akin to the ordinary coördination complexes of these metallic ions, and as an extensive recent review (179) is available, only some salient features will be mentioned here.

Two general methods of preparation have been used. The first is simple treatment of metal salts in appropriate valency states with isonitrile. In this way Fe^{++} yields initially $Fe(CNR)_4^{++}$ $(192,258)$ while Co^{++} yields $Co(CNR)_2X_2$, $Co(CNR)_4X_2$ $(191,258)$, or $[Co(CNR)_5]^{++}$ $(256,261)$ depending on the anion used. These may be converted to higher (253) or lower $(185,253,256,261)$ oxidation states. The halide complexes, e.g., $Co(CNR)_4Cl_2$ and $Fe(CNR)_4Cl_2$ (192), are probably largely covalent, but the $[Co(CNR)_5]^{++}$ and $[Fe(CNR)_4]^{++}$ ions have been isolated in the form of perchlorates. Mn^{++}, Cr^{++}, Ru^{+++} and Rh^{+++} all form complexes with disproportionation to lower oxidation states, the isolated products being $Mn(CNR)_6^+$, $Cr(CNR)_6$, $Ru(CNR)_4X_2$ and $Rh(CNR)_4X$ (194) respectively. In the case of Mn, only the iodide has been successfully used (257) and reduction occurs at the expense of the anion so that the overall reaction may be formulated as

$$2\ MnI_2 + 12\ CNR \longrightarrow [Mn(CNR)_6]I + [Mn(CNR)_6]I_3.$$

The divalent complex, $Mn(CNR)_6^{++}$, which may be intermediate in this reaction, can however be obtained by oxidation of the monovalent ion, e.g., with nitric acid, to give $[Mn(CNR)_6](NO_3)_2$.

In the chromium case (190) the acetate, $Cr(OAc)_2$, reacts in the absence of added reducing agents, and although the Cr^{III} complex has not been isolated, the stoichiometry of the reaction is regarded as suggesting disproportionation according to the equation:

$$3\ Cr^{++} + 18\ CNR \longrightarrow Cr(CNR)_6 + 2\ [Cr(CNR)_6]^{+++}.$$

Palladium and platinum in the divalent state both yield compounds $M(CNR)_2X_2$ and although palladium does not form a neutral carbonyl, it affords $Pd(CNAr)_2$ by disproportionation of $Pd(CNAr)_2X_2$ in strongly alkaline medium and in presence of excess isocyanide (*180*). The latter is thought to be oxidized, so that the change may be formulated as:

$$Pd(CNAr)_2(OH)_2 + CNAr \longrightarrow Pd(CNAr)_2 + ArNCO + H_2O.$$

A complex richer in isocyanide may be intermediate in this and can in fact be shown to form from the di-isocyanide complex on dissolution in excess isocyanide; but it is unstable in the absence of the latter. Oxidation back to the divalent complex is readily effected by treatment of $Pd(CNAr)_2$ with iodine. Addition as well as replacement of isocyanide occurs (*181*) on reaction with phosphines or phosphites to yield $(p\text{-}MeOC_6H_4NC)Pd\text{-}[P(OPh)_3]_3$ for example.

The second general preparative method is the alkylation of complex cyanides. Methylation may be effected by treating the silver salts with methyl iodide, the sodium or potassium salts with methyl sulfate or the free acid, e.g., $H_4Fe(CN)_6$, with diazomethane in ether. Although such methylation or similar ethylation methods have been applied extensively to complex cyanides of Cr, Mo, W, Fe and Co, the results are complicated by incompleteness of reaction and hydrolysis, and characterization of pure compounds has not always been achieved.

Cobalt affords chiefly the "trimethyl" derivative, $Co(CN)_3(CNMe)_3$, and under mild conditions iron similarly yields $Fe(CN)_2(CNMe)_4$. Both these compounds are obtained in two stereoisomeric modifications and for the iron case the structures (LX) and (LXI) have been secured by X-ray diffraction studies.

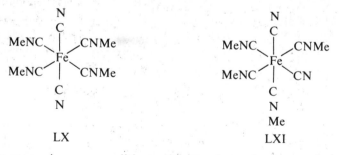

Under more vigorous conditions, these undergo further methylation to give $Fe(CNMe)_6^{++}$, isolated, e.g., as the nitrate or chloride. On heating, the latter loses methyl chloride to give back the covalent cyanide:

$$Fe(CNMe)_6Cl_2 \longrightarrow 2\ MeCl + Fe(CNMe)_4(CN)_2$$

References

(1) Abel, E. W., Bennett, M. A., Burton, R., and Wilkinson, G., *J. Chem. Soc.*, 4559 (1958).

(2) Abel, E. W., Bennett, M. A., and Wilkinson, G., *Proc. Chem. Soc.*, 152 (1958).

(3) Abel, E. W., Bennett, M. A., and Wilkinson, G., *J. Chem. Soc.*, 2323 (1959).

(4) Abel, E. W., Hargreaves, G. B., and Wilkinson, G., *J. Chem. Soc.*, 3149 (1958).

(5) Abel, E. W., and Wilkinson, G., *J. Chem. Soc.*, 1501 (1959).

(6) Adkins, H., and Kresk, G., *J. Am. Chem. Soc.*, **70**, 383 (1948); *J. Am. Chem. Soc.*, **71**, 3051 (1949).

(6a) Aldridge, C. L., Jonassen, H. B., and Pulkkinen, E., *Chemistry and Industry*, 374 (1960).

(7) Anderson, J. S., *Quart. Reviews*, **1**, 331 (1947).

(8) Angoletta, M., Special Publ. No. 13, p. 121, London, The Chemical Society, 1959. (Int. Conf. Coörd. Chem.)

(9) Angoletta, M., *Gazz. chim. ital.*, **89**, 2359 (1959).

(10) Arthur, P., England, D. C., Pratt, B. C., and Whitman, G. M., *J. Am. Chem. Soc.*, **76**, 5364 (1955).

(11) Ashworth, P. J., Whitham, G. H., and Whiting, M. C., *J. Chem. Soc.*, 4633 (1957).

(12) Basolo, F., and Wojcicki, A., Abstr. A, XVIIth International Congress of Pure and Applied Chemistry, p. 139, Munich, 1959.

(13) Behrens, H., *Z. Naturforsch.*, **7b**, 321 (1952); C.A., **46**, 8562 (1952).

(14) Behrens, H., and Eisenmann, E., *Z. anorg. Chem.*, **278**, 155 (1955).

(15) Behrens, H., and Eisenmann, E., *Z. anorg. Chem.*, **278**, 166 (1955).

(16) Behrens, H., and Haag, W., *Z. Naturforsch.*, **14b**, 600 (1959).

(17) Behrens, H., and Klek, W., *Z. anorg. Chem.*, **292**, 151 (1957).

(18) Behrens, H., and Köhler, J., *Z. Naturforsch.*, **14b**, 463 (1959).

(19) Behrens, H., and Köhler, J., *Z. anorg. Chem.*, **300**, 51 (1959); C.A., **53**, 17746 (1959).

(20) Behrens, H., and Lohöfer, F., *Z. Naturforsch.*, **8b**, 691 (1953); C.A., **48**, 5012 (1954).

(21) Behrens, H., and Weber, R., *Z. anorg. Chem.*, **281**, 190 (1955).

(22) Behrens, H., and Weber, R., *Z. anorg. Chem.*, **291**, 122 (1957).

(23) Belozersky, N. A., "Karbonily Metallov," Moscow, 1958.

(24) Bennett, M. A., and Wilkinson, G., *Chemistry and Industry*, 151 (1959).

(25) Bishop, E. O., Down, J. L., Emtage, P. R., Richards, R. E., and Wilkinson, G., *J. Chem. Soc.*, 2484 (1959).

(26) Bor, G., and Mohai, B., *Acta Chim. Acad. Sci. Hungary*, **12**, 57 (1957); C.A., **52**, 5192 (1958).

(27) Braye, E. H., and Hübel, W., *Chemistry and Industry*, 1250 (1959).

(28) Brimm, E. O., Lynch, H. A., and Sesny, W. S., *J. Am. Chem. Soc.*, **76**, 3831 (1954).

(29) Brockway, L. O., Ewens, R. V. G., and Listér, M. W., *Trans. Faraday Soc.*, **34**, 1350 (1938).

(30) Burg, A. B., and Dayton, J. C., *J. Am. Chem. Soc.*, **71**, 3233 (1949).

(31) Burton, R., Green, M. L. H., Abel, E. W., and Wilkinson G., *Chemistry and Industry*, 1592 (1958).

(32) Burton, R., and Wilkinson, G., *Chemistry and Industry*, 1205 (1958).

(33) Cable, J. W., and Sheline, R. K., *Chem. Reviews*, **56**, 1 (1956).

(33a) Calderazzo, F., Cini, R., Corradini, P., Ercoli, R., and Natta, G., *Chemistry and Industry,* 500 (1960).
(34) Case, J. R., Clarkson, R., Jones, E. R. H., and Whiting, M. C., *Proc. Chem. Soc.*, 150 (1959).
(35) Case, J. R., and Whiting, M. C., *J. Chem. Soc.*, in press.
(36) Cavalca, L., and Bassi, I. W., *Ricerca sci.*, **23**, 1377 (1953).
(37) Chatt, J., and Hart, F. A., *Chemistry and Industry*, 1474 (1958).
(38) Chatt, J., and Williams, A. A., *J. Chem. Soc.*, 3061 (1951).
(39) Chini, P., Abstr. A, XVIIth International Congress of Pure and Applied Chemistry, p. 135, Munich, 1959.
(40) Chini, P., and Ercoli, R., *Gazz. chim. ital.*, **88**, 1170 (1958).
(41) Chiusoli, G. P., *Gazz. chim. ital.*, **89**, 1332 (1959); *Angew. Chem.*, **72**, 74 (1960).
(42) Clarkson, R., Jones, E. R. H., Wailes, P. C. and Whiting, M. C., *J. Am. Chem. Soc.*, **78**, 6206 (1956).
(43) Closson, R. D., Buzbee, L. R. and Ecke, G. C., *J. Am. Chem. Soc.*, **80**, 6167 (1958).
(44) Closson, R. D., Kozikowski, J., and Coffield, T. H., *J. Org. Chem.*, **22**, 598 (1957).
(45) Coffield, T. H., Kozikowski, J., and Closson, R. D., *J. Org. Chem.*, **22**, 598 (1957).
(46) Coffield, T. H., Kozikowski, J., and Closson, R. D., Special Publ. No. 13, p. 126, London, The Chemical Society, 1959. (Int. Conf. Coörd. Chem.)
(47) Coffield, T. H., Sandel, V., and Closson, R. D., *J. Am. Chem. Soc.*, **79**, 5826 (1957).
(48) Corradini, P., *J. Chem. Phys.*, **31**, 1676 (1959).
(49) Corradini, P., and Ercoli, R., Abstr. A, XVIIth International Congress of Pure and Applied Chemistry, p. 138, Munich, 1959.
(50) Cotton, F. A., Abstr. A, XVIIth International Congress of Pure and Applied Chemistry, p. 140, Munich, 1959.
(51) Cotton, F. A., Danti, A., Waugh, J. S., and Fessenden, R. W., *J. Chem. Phys.*, **29**, 1427 (1958).
(52) Cotton, F. A., Down, J. L., and Wilkinson, G., *J. Chem. Soc.*, 833 (1959).
(53) Cotton, F. A., Fischer, A. K., and Wilkinson, G., *J. Am. Chem. Soc.*, **78**, 5168 (1956).
(54) Cotton, F. A., Fischer, A. K., and Wilkinson, G., *J. Am. Chem. Soc.*, **81**, 800 (1959).
(55) Cotton, F. A., Liehr, A. D., and Wilkinson, G., *J. Inorg. and Nucl. Chem.*, **1**, 175 (1955).
(56) Cotton, F. A., Liehr, A. D., and Wilkinson, G., *J. Inorg. and Nucl. Chem.*, **2**, 141 (1956).
(57) Cotton, F. A. and Wilkinson, G., *Chemistry and Industry*, 1305 (1956).
(58) Dahl, L. F., Ishishi, E., and Rundle, R. E., *J. Chem. Phys.*, **26**, 1750 (1957).
(59) Dahl, L. F., and Rundle, R. E., *J. Chem. Phys.*, **26**, 1751 (1957).
(60) Dahl, L. F., and Rundle, R. E., *J. Chem. Phys.*, **27**, 323 (1957).
(61) Eastes, J. W., and Burgess, W. M., *J. Am. Chem. Soc.*, **64**, 1187 (1942).
(62) Ercoli, R., Chini, P., and Massi-Mauri, M., *Chim. e ind.*, **41**, 132 (1959).

(63) Ercoli, R., and Torregrosa, R. E., *Chim. e ind.,* **40**, 552 (1958); C.A., **53**, 3186 (1959).
(64) Ewens, R. V. G., and Lister, M. W., *Trans. Faraday Soc.,* **35**, 681 (1939).
(65) Fischer, A. K., Cotton, F. A., and Wilkinson, G., *J. Am. Chem. Soc.,* **79**, 2044 (1957).
(66) Fischer, E. O., and Beckert, O., *Angew. Chem.,* **70**, 744 (1958).
(67) Fischer, E. O., Beckert, O., Hafner, W., and Stahl, H.-O., *Z. Naturforsch.,* **10b**, 598 (1955).
(68) Fischer, E. O., and Böttcher, R., *Z. Naturforsch.,* **10b**, 600 (1955).
(69) Fischer, E. O., and Fröhlich, W., *Chem. Ber.,* **92**, 2995 (1959).
(70) Fischer, E. O., and Hafner, W., *Z. Naturforsch.,* **9b**, 503 (1954).
(71) Fischer, E. O., and Hafner, W., *Z. Naturforsch.,* **10b**, 140 (1955).
(72) Fischer, E. O., Hafner, W., and Öfele, K., *Chem. Ber.,* **92**, 3050 (1959).
(73) Fischer, E. O., Hafner, W., and Stahl, H.-O., *Z. anorg. Chem.,* **282**, 47 (1955).
(74) Fischer, E. O., and Jira, R., *Z. Naturforsch.,* **9b**, 618 (1954).
(75) Fischer, E. O., and Jira, R., *Z. Naturforsch.,* **10b**, 355 (1955).
(76) Fischer, E. O., Joos, G., and Meer, W., *Z. Naturforsch.,* **13b**, 456 (1958).
(77) Fischer, E. O., and Palm, C., *Chem. Ber.,* **91**, 1725 (1958).
(78) Fischer, E. O., and Palm, C., *Z. Naturforsch.,* **14b**, 347 (1959).
(79) Fischer, E. O., and Palm, C., *Z. Naturforsch.,* **14b**, 598 (1959).
(80) Fischer, E. O., Palm, C., and Fritz, H. P., *Chem. Ber.,* **92**, 2645 (1959).
(81) Fischer, E. O., and Schreiner, S., *Chem. Ber.,* **92**, 938 (1959).
(82) Fischer, E. O., and Vigoureux, S., *Chem. Ber.,* **91**, 2205 (1958).
(83) Fischer, E. O., and Werner, H., *Chem. Ber.,* **92**, 1423 (1959).
(84) Fischer, E. O., and Wirzmüller, A., *Z. Naturforsch.,* **12b**, 737 (1957).
(85) Fischer, R. D., *Chem. Ber.,* **93**, 165 (1960).
(86) Freidlina, R. Kh., and Beliavsky, A. B., *Doklady Akad. Nauk. S.S.S.R.,* **127**, 1027 (1959).
(87) Freidlina, R. Kh., Chukovskaia, E. Ts., and Tsao, I., *Doklady Akad. Nauk, S.S.S.R.,* **127**, 352 (1959).
(88) Friedel, R. A., Wender, I., Shufler, S. L., and Sternberg, H. W., *J. Am. Chem. Soc.,* **77**, 3951 (1955).
(89) Gilmont, P., and Blanchard, A. A., *Inorganic Syntheses,* **2**, 238 (1946).
(89a) Good, W. D., Fairbrother, D. M., and Waddington, G., *J. Phys. Chem.,* **62**, 853 (1958).
(90) Green, M. L. H., Pratt, L., and Wilkinson, G., *J. Chem. Soc.,* 3753 (1959).
(90a) Green, M. L. H., Pratt, L., and Wilkinson, G., *J. Chem. Soc.,* 989 (1960).
(91) Green, M. L. H., Street, C. N., and Wilkinson, G., *Z. Naturforsch.,* **14b**, 738 (1959).
(92) Green, M. L. H., and Wilkinson, G., *J. Chem. Soc.,* 4314 (1958).
(93) Greenfield, H., Sternberg, H. W., Friedel, R. A., Wotiz, J. H., Markby, R., and Wender, I., *J. Am. Chem. Soc.,* **78**, 120 (1956).
(94) Griffith, W. P., Cotton, F. A., and Wilkinson, G., *J. Inorg. and Nucl. Chem.,* **10**, 23 (1959).
(95) Hallam, B. F., and Pauson, P. L., *J. Chem. Soc.,* 3030 (1956).
(96) Hallam, B. F., and Pauson, P. L., *J. Chem. Soc.,* 642 (1958).

(97) Hallam, B. F., and Pauson, P. L., unpublished results.
(98) Hel'man, A. D., and Bauman, M., *Compt. rend. acad. sci. S.S.S.R.*, **18**, 645 (1938). C.A., **32**, 5718 (1938).
(99) Hieber, W., and Anderson, J. S., *Z. anorg. Chem.*, **208**, 238 (1932); **211**, 132 (1933).
(100) Hieber, W., Abeck, W., and Platzer, H. K., *Z. anorg. Chem.*, **280, 241 (1955)**.
(101) Hieber, W., Abeck, W., and Platzer, H. K., *Z. anorg. Chem.*, **280**, 252 (1955).
(102) Hieber, W., and Bartenstein, C., *Z. anorg. Chem.*, **276**, 1 (1954).
(103) Hieber, W., and Bartenstein, C., *Z. anorg. Chem.*, **276**, 12 (1954).
(104) Hieber, W., and Böckly, E., *Z. anorg. Chem.*, **262**, 344 (1950).
(105) Hieber, W., and Braun, G., *Z. Naturforsch*, **14b**, 132 (1959).
(106) Hieber, W., and Brendel, G., *Z. anorg. Chem.*, **289**, 324 (1957).
(107) Hieber, W., and Brendel, G., *Z. anorg. Chem.*, **289**, 338 (1957).
(108) Hieber, W., and Breu, R., *Chem. Ber.*, **90**, 1259 (1957).
(109) Hieber, W., and Breu, R., *Chem. Ber.*, **90**, 1270 (1957).
(110) Hieber, W., and Brück, R., *Z. anorg. Chem.*, **269**, 28 (1952).
(111) Hieber, W., and Englert, K., *Z. anorg. Chem.*, **300**, 311 (1959).
(112) Hieber, W., Englert, K., and Rieger, K., *Z. anorg. Chem.*, **300**, 295 (1959).
(113) Hieber, W., Englert, K., and Rieger, K., *Z. anorg. Chem.*, **300**, 304 (1959).
(114) Hieber, W., and Fack, E., *Z. anorg. Chem.*, **236**, 84 (1938).
(115) Hieber, W., and Fischer, E. O., *Z. anorg. Chem.*, **269**, 292 (1952).
(116) Hieber, W., Fischer, E. O., and Böckly, E., *Z. anorg. Chem.*, **269**, 308 (1952).
(117) Hieber, W., and Floss, J. G., *Chem. Ber.*, **90**, 1617 (1957).
(118) Hieber, W., and Freyer, W., *Chem. Ber.*, **91**, 1230 (1958).
(119) Hieber, W., and Freyer, W., *Chem. Ber.*, **92**, 1765 (1959).
(120) Hieber, W., and Gruber, J., *Z. anorg. Chem.*, **296**, 91 (1958), C.A., **53**, 961 (1959).
(121) Hieber, W., Gruber, J., Lux, F., *Z. anorg. Chem.*, **300**, 275 (1959).
(122) Hieber, W., and Heusinger, H., *J. Inorg. and Nucl. Chem.*, **4**, 179 (1957).
(123) Hieber, W., Heusinger, H., and Vohler, O., *Chem. Ber.*, **90**, 2425 (1957).
(124) Hieber, W., and Hübel, W., *Z. Elektrochem.*, **57**, 235 (1953).
(125) Hieber, W., and Hübel, W., *Z. Elektrochem.*, **57**, 331 (1953).
(126) Hieber, W., and Kahlen, N., *Chem. Ber.*, **91**, 2223 (1958).
(127) Hieber, W., and Kahlen, N., *Chem. Ber.*, **91**, 2234 (1958).
(128) Hieber, W., and Lipp, A., *Chem. Ber.*, **92**, 2075 (1959).
(129) Hieber, W., and Lipp, A., *Chem. Ber.*, **92**, 2085 (1959).
(130) Hieber, W., Mühlbauer, F., and Ehmann, E. A., *Ber.*, **65**, 1090 (1932).
(131) Hieber, W., Nast, R., and Bartenstein, C., *Z. anorg. Chem.*, **272**, 32 (1953).
(132) Hieber, W., and Peterhans, J., *Z. Naturforsch.*, **14b**, 462 (1959).
(133) Hieber, W., and Pigenot, D., *Chem. Ber.*, **89**, 193 (1956).
(134) Hieber, W., and Pigenot, D., *Chem. Ber.*, **89**, 610 (1956).
(135) Hieber, W., and Pigenot, D., *Chem. Ber.*, **89**, 616 (1956).
(136) Hieber, W., and Rieger, K., *Z. anorg. Chem.*, **300**, 288 (1959).
(137) Hieber, W., and Scharfenberg, C., *Ber.*, **73**, 1012 (1940).
(138) Hieber, W., and Schropp, W., Jr., *Z. Naturforsch*, **14b**, 460 (1959).

(138a) Hieber, W., and Schropp, W., Jr., Z. Naturforsch., 15b, 271 (1960).
(139) Hieber, W., Schuh, R., and Fuchs, H., Z. anorg. Chem., 248, 243 (1941).
(140) Hieber, W., and Schuster, L., Z. anorg. Chem., 285, 205 (1956).
(141) Hieber, W., and Schuster, L., Z. anorg. Chem., 287, 214 (1956).
(142) Hieber, W., and Sedlmeier, J., Angew. Chem., 65, 534 (1953).
(143) Hieber, W., and Sedlmeier, J., Chem. Ber., 87, 25 (1954).
(144) Hieber, W., Sedlmeier, J., and Abeck, W., Chem. Ber., 86, 700 (1953).
(145) Hieber, W., Sedlmeier, J., and Werner, R., Chem. Ber., 90, 278 (1957).
(146) Hieber, W., and Spacu, P., Z. anorg. Chem., 233, 359 (1937).
(147) Hieber, W., Vohler, O., and Braun, G., Z. Naturforsch., 13b, 192 (1958).
(148) Hieber, W., and Wagner, G., Z. Naturforsch., 12b, 478 (1957).
(149) Hieber, W., and Wagner, G., Z. Naturforsch., 13b, 339 (1958).
(150) Hieber, W., and Wagner, G., Ann., 618, 24 (1958).
(151) Hieber, W., and Weiss, E., Z. anorg. Chem., 287, 223 (1956).
(152) Hieber, W., and Werner, R., Chem. Ber., 90, 286 (1957).
(153) Hieber, W., and Werner, R., Chem. Ber., 90, 1116 (1957).
(154) Hieber, W., and Wiesboeck, R., Chem. Ber., 91, 1146 (1958).
(155) Hieber, W., and Wiesboeck, R., Chem. Ber., 91, 1156 (1958).
(156) Hock, A. A., and Mills, O. S., Proc. Chem. Soc., 233 (1958).
(157) Hübel, W., and Braye, E. H., J. Inorg. and Nucl. Chem., 10, 250 (1959).
(158) Hübel, W., Braye, E., Clauss, A., Weiss, E., Krüerke, U., Brown, D. A., King, G. S. D., and Hoogzand, C., J. Inorg. and Nucl. Chem., 9, 204 (1959).
(159) Hübel, W., and Hoogzand, C., Chem. Ber., 93, 103 (1960).
(160) Hübel, W., and Weiss, E., Chemistry and Industry, 703 (1959).
(161) Irvine, J. W. Jun., and Wilkinson, G., Science, 113, 742 (1951).
(162) Irving, R. J., J. Chem. Soc., 2879 (1956).
(163) Irving, R. J., and Magnusson, E. A., J. Chem. Soc., 1860 (1956).
(164) Irving, R. J., and Magnusson, E. A., J. Chem. Soc., 2018 (1957).
(165) Irving, R. J., and Magnusson, E. A., J. Chem. Soc., 2283 (1958).
(166) Jonassen, H. B., Stearns, R. I., Kenttamaa, J., Moore, D. W., and Whittaker, A. G., J. Am. Chem. Soc., 80, 2586 (1958).
(167) Jones, E. R. H., Shen, T. Y., and Whiting, M. C., J. Chem. Soc., 230 (1950); ibid., 48, 763, 766 (1951).
(168) Jones, E. R. H., Wailes, P. C., and Whiting, M. C., J. Chem. Soc., 4021 (1955).
(169) Jones, E. R. H., Whitham, G. H., and Whiting, M. C., J. Chem. Soc., 4628 (1957).
(170) Kettle, S. F. A., and Orgel, L. E., Proc. Chem. Soc., 307 (1959).
(171) Kettle, S. F. A., and Orgel, L. E., Chemistry and Industry, 49 (1960).
(172) Kharasch, M. S., and Isbell, H. S., J. Am. Chem. Soc., 52, 2919 (1930).
(173) Krüerke, U., and Hübel, W., Abstr. A, XVIIth International Congress of Pure and Applied Chemistry, p. 163, Munich, 1959.
(174) Krumholz, P., and Stettiner, H. M. A., J. Am. Chem. Soc., 71, 3035 (1949).
(175) Ladell, J., Post, B., and Fankuchen, I., Acta Cryst., 5, 795 (1952).
(176) Lagemann, R. T., and Dickey, F. P., Phys. Rev., 72, 284 (1947).

(177) Lüttringhaus, A., and Kullick, W., *Tetrahedron Letters,* No. 10, 13 (1959).
(178) Malatesta, L., Abstr. A, XVIIth International Congress of Pure and Applied Chemistry, p. 136, Munich, 1959.
(179) Malatesta, L., "Progress in Inorganic Chemistry," Vol. 1, Ed. by F. A. Cotton, New York, Interscience, 1959.
(180) Malatesta, L., *J. Chem. Soc.,* 3924 (1955).
(181) Malatesta, L., and Angoletta, M., *J. Chem. Soc.,* 1186 (1957).
(182) Malatesta, L., and Angoletta, M., Coördination Conference, Rome (1957); *J. Inorg. and Nucl. Chem.,* **8,** 273 (1958).
(183) Malatesta, L., and Aràneo, A., *J. Chem. Soc.,* 3803 (1957).
(184) Malatesta, L., and Cariello, C., *J. Chem. Soc.,* 2323 (1958).
(185) Malatesta, L., and Sacco, A., *Accad. Naz. Lincei Roma* [VIII], **15,** 93 (1953); C.A., **48,** 8108 (1954).
(186) Malatesta, L., and Sacco, A., *Z. anorg. Chem.,* **273,** 247 (1953); C.A., **48,** 2704 (1954).
(187) Malatesta, L., and Sacco, A., *Ann. chim. (Rome),* **43,** 622 (1953); C.A., **48,** 7477 (1954).
(188) Malatesta, L., and Sacco, A., *Ann. chim. (Rome),* **44,** 134 (1954).
(189) Malatesta, L., Sacco, A., and Gabaglio, M., *Gazz. chim. ital.,* **82,** 548 (1952); C.A., **48,** 5131 (1954).
(190) Malatesta, L., Sacco, A., and Ghielmi, S., *Gazz. chim. ital.,* **82,** 516 (1952); C.A., **48,** 5130 (1954).
(191) Malatesta, L., Sacco, A., and Matiello, L., *Gazz. chim. ital.,* **83,** 499 (1953); C.A., **48,** 7475 (1954).
(192) Malatesta, L., Sacco, A., and Padoa, G., *Ann. chim. (Rome),* **43,** 617 (1953).
(193) Malatesta, L., and Sandroni, S., Special Publ. No. 13, p. 122, London, The Chemical Society, 1959. (Int. Conf. Coörd. Chem.)
(194) Malatesta, L., and Vallarino, L., *J. Chem. Soc.,* 1876 (1956).
(195) Manuel, T. A., and Stone, F. G. A., *Proc. Chem. Soc.,* 90 (1959).
(196) Manuel, T. A., and Stone, F. G. A., *Chemistry and Industry,* 1349 (1959).
(197) Manuel, T. A. and Stone, F. G. A., *J. Am. Chem. Soc.,* **82,** 366 (1960).
(198) Markby, R., Sternberg, H. W., and Wender, I., *Chemistry and Industry,* 1381 (1959).
(199) Markby, R., Wender, I., Friedel, R. A., Cotton, F. A., and Sternberg, H. W., *J. Am. Chem. Soc.,* **80,** 6525 (1958).
(200) Matthews, C. N., Magee, T. A., and Wotiz, J. H., *J. Am. Chem. Soc.,* **81,** 2273 (1959).
(201) Meriwether, L. S., Colthup, E. C., Fiene, M. L., and Cotton, F. A., *J. Inorg. and Nucl. Chem.,* **11,** 181 (1959).
(202) Metlin, S., Wender, I., and Sternberg, H. W., *Nature,* **183,** 457 (1959).
(203) Mills, O. S., *Chemistry and Industry,* 73 (1957).
(204) Mills, O. S., *Acta Cryst.,* **11,** 620 (1958).
(205) Mills, O. S., personal communication.
(206) Mills, O. S., Hock, A. A., and Robinson, G., Abstr. A, XVIIth International Congress of Pure and Applied Chemistry, p. 143, Munich, 1959.
(207) Mills, O. S., and Robinson, G., *Proc. Chem. Soc.,* 156 (1959).

(208) Mond, L., Hirtz, H., and Cowap, M. D., *J. Chem. Soc.*, **97**, 798 (1910).
(209) Mond, L., Langer, C., and Quincke, F., *J. Chem. Soc.*, **57**, 749 (1890).
(210) Mond, L., and Quincke, F., *J. Chem. Soc.*, **59**, 604 (1891).
(211) Munro, J. D., and Pauson, P. L., unpublished results.
(212) Murray, J. G., *J. Am. Chem. Soc.*, **81**, 752 (1959).
(213) Nakamura, A., and Hagihara, N., *Bull. Chem. Soc. Japan*, **32**, 880 (1959).
(214) Nast, R., and Kasperl, H., *Chem. Ber.*, **92**, 2135 (1959).
(215) Nast, R., and Krakkay, T. von., *Z. anorg. Chem.*, **272**, 232 (1953).
(216) Nast, R., and Roos, H., *Z. anorg. Chem.*, **272**, 242 (1953).
(216a) Natta, G., Ercoli, R., Calderazzo, F., Alberola, A., Corradini, P., and Allegra, G., *Atti Acad. naz. Lincei, Rend. Classe Sci. fis. mat. nat.*, **27**, 107 (1959).
(217) Natta, G., Ercoli, R., Calderazzo, F., and Rabizzoni, A., *J. Am. Chem. Soc.*, **79**, 3611 (1957).
(218) Nesmeyanov, A. N., Anisimov, K. N., Volkov, V. L., Fridenberg, A. E., Mikheev, E. P., and Medvedeva, A. V., *Zhur. Neorg. Khim.*, **4**, 1827 (1959).
(219) Nesmeyanov, A. N., Mikheev, E. P., Anisimov, K. N., Volkov, V. L., and Valueva, Z. P., *Zhur. Neorg. Khim.*, **4**, 503 (1959); *Zhur. Neorg. Khim.*, **4**, 249 (1959).
(220) Nesmeyanov, A. N., Mikheev, E. P., Anisimov, K. N., and Filimonova, N. P., *Zhur. Neorg. Khim.*, **4**, 1958 (1959).
(221) Nicholls, B., and Whiting, M. C., *Proc. Chem. Soc.*, 152 (1958).
(222) Nigam, H. L., and Nyholm, R. S., *Proc. Chem. Soc.*, 321 (1957).
(223) Nigam, H. L., Nyholm, R. S., and Rao, D. V. R., *J. Chem. Soc.*, 1397 (1959).
(224) Nigam, H. L., Nyholm, R. S., and Rao, D. V. R., Special Publ. No. 13, p. 120, London, The Chemical Society, 1959. (Int. Conf. Coord Chem.)
(225) Nyholm, R. S., *J. Chem. Soc.*, 2906 (1952).
(226) Nyholm, R. S., *Chem. Reviews*, **53**, 263 (1953).
(227) Nyholm, R. S., and Rao, D. V. R., *Proc. Chem. Soc.*, 130 (1959).
(228) Orgel, L. E., Special Publ. No. 13, p. 93, London, The Chemical Society, (1959). (Int. Conf. Coord. Chem.)
(229) Ormont, B. F., and Smagina, E. I., *J. Gen. Chem. U.S.S.R.* (*Eng. Transl.*), **28**, 281 (1958).
(230) Owen, B. B., English, J., Cassidy, H. G., and Dundon, C. V., *Inorg. Syntheses*, **3**, 156 (1950).
(231) Pauson, P. L., and Stubbs, W. H., unpublished results.
(232) Pettit, R., *J. Am. Chem. Soc.*, **81**, 1266 (1959).
(233) Piper, T. S., Cotton, F. A., and Wilkinson, G., *J. Inorg. and Nucl. Chem.*, **1**, 165 (1955).
(234) Piper, T. S., and Wilkinson, G., *Naturwissenschaften*, **42**, 625 (1955).
(235) Piper, T. S., and Wilkinson, G., *Chemistry and Industry*, 1296 (1955).
(236) Piper, T. S., and Wilkinson, G., *Naturwissenschaften*, **43**, 15 (1956).
(237) Piper, T. S., and Wilkinson, G., *J. Inorg. and Nucl. Chem.*, **3**, 104 (1956).
(238) Pistorius, C. W. F. T., and Haarhoff, P. C., *J. Chem. Phys.*, **31**, 1439 (1959).
(239) Podall, H. E., *J. Am. Chem. Soc.*, **80**, 5573 (1958).
(240) Podall, H. E., and Shapiro, H., Abstr., 136th Meeting, Am. Chem. Soc.,

p. 51N, Atlantic City, Sept., 1959.

(240a) Poilblanc, R., and Bigorgne, M., *Compt. rend.,* **250,** 1064 (1960).

(241) Powell, H. M., and Ewens, R. V. G., *J. Chem. Soc.,* 286 (1939).

(242) Prichard, W. W., U. S. Patent 2,600,571 (June 17, 1952); C.A., **46,** 10188 (1952).

(243) Pruett, R. L., and Morehouse, E. L., *Chemistry and Industry,* 980 (1958).

(244) Pruett, R. L., and Wyman, J. E., *Chemistry and Industry,* 119 (1960).

(245) Randall, E. W., and Sutton, L. E., *Proc. Chem. Soc.,* 93 (1959).

(246) Rausch, M. D., and Schrauzer, G. N., *Chemistry and Industry,* 957 (1959).

(247) Reed, H. W. B., *J. Chem. Soc.,* 1931 (1954).

(248) Reihlen, H., Friedolsheim, A. v., and Oswald, W., *Ann.,* **465,** 72 (1928).

(249) Reihlen, H., Gruhl, A., v. Hessling, G., and Pfrengle, O., *Ann.,* **482,** 161 (1930).

(250) Reppe, W., and Schweckendiek, W. J., *Ann.,* **560,** 1, 93, 104 (1948).

(251) Reppe, W., and Vetter, H., *Ann.,* **582,** 1, 38, 72, 87, 133 (1953).

(252) Rose, J. D., and Statham, F. S., *J. Chem. Soc.,* 69 (1950).

(253) Sacco, A., *Accad. Naz. Lincei Roma,* **15,** 82 (1953); C.A., **48,** 8109 (1954).

(254) Sacco, A., *Gazz. chim. ital.,* **83,** 632 (1953).

(255) Sacco, A., *Ann. chim. (Rome),* **43,** 495 (1953).

(256) Sacco, A., *Gazz. chim. ital.,* **84,** 370 (1954).

(257) Sacco, A., *Rec. trav. chim.,* **75,** 646 (1956).

(258) Sacco, A., and Coletti, O., *Accad. Naz. Lincei Roma,* **15,** 89 (1953); C.A., **48,** 8108 (1954).

(259) Sacco, A., and Freni, M., *Ann. chim. (Rome),* **48,** 218 (1958); *C.A.,* **52,** 19656 (1958).

(260) Sacco, A., and Freni, M., *J. Inorg. and Nucl. Chem.,* **8,** 566 (1958).

(261) Sacco, A., and Freni, M., *Gazz. chim. ital.,* **89,** 1800 (1959).

(262) Sauer, J. C. (to E. I. du Pont de Nemours & Co.), U. S. Patent 2,840,570 (June 24, 1958); (to E. I. du Pont de Nemours & Co.) British Patent 811, 498 (April 8, 1959).

(263) Sauer, J. C., Cramer, R. D., Engelhardt, V. A., Ford, T. A., Holmquist, H. E., and Howk, B. W., Abstr., 135th Meeting, Am. Chem. Soc., p. 55-O, Boston, April, 1959.

(264) Schoeller, W., *Ber.,* **53,** 2144 (1920).

(265) Schrauzer, G. N., *Chemistry and Industry,* 1403 (1958).

(266) Schrauzer, G. N., *Chemistry and Industry,* 1404 (1958).

(267) Schrauzer, G. N., *J. Am. Chem. Soc.,* **81,** 5307 (1959).

(268) Schrauzer, G. N., *J. Am. Chem. Soc.,* **81,** 5310 (1959).

(269) Seel, F., *Z. anorg. Chem.,* **269,** 40 (1952).

(270) Sharafov, K. A., and Rezukhina, T. N., *C.A.,* **49,** 2173 (1955).

(271) Sheline, R. K., *J. Am. Chem. Soc.,* **72,** 5761 (1950).

(272) Shufler, S. L., Sternberg, H. W., and Friedel, R. A., *J. Am. Chem. Soc.,* **78,** 2678 (1956).

(273) Sly, W. G., *J. Am. Chem. Soc.,* **81,** 18 (1959).

(274) Smidt, J., and Hafner, W., *Angew. Chem.,* **71,** 284 (1959).

(275) Stammreich, H., Sala, O., and Tavares, Y., *J. Chem. Phys.,* **30,** 856 (1959).

(276) Sternberg, H. W., Friedel, R. A., Markby, R., and Wender, I., *J. Am. Chem. Soc.*, **78**, 3621 (1956).

(277) Sternberg, H. W., Friedel, R. A., Shufler, S. L., and Wender, I., *J. Am. Chem. Soc.*, **77**, 2675 (1955).

(278) Sternberg, H. W., Greenfield, H,, Friedel, R. A., Wotiz, J., Markby, R., and Wender, I., *J. Am. Chem. Soc.*, **76**, 1457 (1954).

(279) Sternberg, H. W., Markby, R., and Wender, I., *J. Am. Chem. Soc.*, **79**, 6116 (1957).

(280) Sternberg, H. W., Markby, R., and Wender, I., *J. Am. Chem. Soc.*, **80**, 1009 (1958).

(281) Sternberg, H. W., Shukys, J. G., Donne, C. D., Markby, R., Friedel, R. A., and Wender, I., *J. Am. Chem. Soc.*, **81**, 2339 (1959).

(282) Sternberg, H. W., and Wender, I., Special Publ. No. 13, p. 35, London, The Chemical Society, 1959. (Int. Conf. Coörd. Chem.)

(283) Sternberg, H. W., Wender, I., Friedel, R. A., and Orchin, M., *J. Am. Chem. Soc.*, **75**, 2717 (1953).

(284) Sternberg, H. W., Wender, I., Friedel, R. A., and Orchin, M., *J. Am. Chem. Soc.*, **75**, 3148 (1953).

(285) Sykes, K. W., *J. Chem. Soc.*, 2053 (1958).

(286) Tilney-Bassett, J. F., and Mills, O. S., *J. Am. Chem. Soc.*, **81**, 4757 (1959).

(287) Vallarino, L., *J. Chem. Soc.*, 2287 (1957).

(288) Vallarino, L., *Rend. ist. lombardo sci.* Pt. I, **91**, 397 (1957); *C.A.*, **52**, 18064 (1958).

(289) Vallarino, L., *Rend. ist. lombardo sci.* Pt. I. **91**, 399 (1957); *C.A.*, **52**, 18065 (1958).

(290) Vallarino, L., *J. Chem. Soc.*, 2473 (1957).

(291) Vallarino, L., *Gazz. chim. ital.*, **89**, 1632 (1959).

(292) Vallerino, L., Special Publ. No. 13, p. 123, London, The Chemical Society, 1959. (Int. Conf. Coörd. Chem.)

(293) Vohler, O., *Chem. Ber.*, **91**, 1161 (1958).

(294) Vohler, O., *Chem. Ber.*, **91**, 1235 (1958).

(295) Watterson, K. F., and Wilkinson, G., *Chemistry and Industry*, 991 (1959).

(296) Webb, I. D., and Borcherdt, G. T., *J. Am. Chem. Soc.*, **73**, 2654 (1951).

(297) Webb, A. N., and Mitchell, J. J., *J. Phys. Chem.*, **63**, 1878 (1959).

(298) Weiss, E., and Hübel, W., *J. Inorg. and Nucl. Chem.*, **11**, 42 (1959).

(298a) Weiss, E., Merényi, R. G., and Hübel, W., *Chemistry and Industry*, 407 (1960).

(299) Wender, I., Friedel, R. A., Markby, R., and Sternberg, H. W., *J. Am. Chem. Soc.*, **77**, 4946 (1955).

(300) Wender, I., Friedman, S., Steiner, W. A., and Anderson, R. B., *Chemistry and Industry*, 1694 (1958).

(301) Wender, I., Greenfield, H., and Orchin, M., *J. Am. Chem. Soc.*, **73**, 2656 (1951).

(302) Wender, I., Sternberg, H. W., Metlin, S., and Orchin, M., *Inorg. Syntheses*, **5**, 190 (1957).

(303) Wender, I., Sternberg, H. W., and Orchin, M., *J. Am. Chem. Soc.*, **74**, 1216

(1952).

(304) Wender, I., Sternberg, H. Ẇ., and Orchin, M., *J. Am. Chem. Soc.,* **75,** 3041 (1953).

(305) Whiting, M. C., Abstr. A, XVIIth International Congress of Pure and Applied Chemistry, p. 161, Munich, 1959.

(306) Wilkinson, G., *J. Am. Chem. Soc.,* **73,** 5501 (1951).

(307) Wilkinson, G., *J. Am. Chem. Soc.,* **73,** 5502 (1951).

(308) Wilkinson, G., *J. Am. Chem. Soc.,* **76,** 209 (1954).

(309) Wilkinson, G., and Cotton, F. A., "Progress in Inorganic Chemistry," Vol. 1, Ed. by F. A. Cotton, New York, Interscience, 1959.

(310) Wilkinson, G., Pauson, P. L., and Cotton, F. A., *J. Am. Chem. Soc.,* **76,** 1970 (1954).

(311) Wilson, F. C., and Shoemaker, D. P., *J. Chem. Phys.,* **27,** 809 (1957).

(312) Yang, A. C., and Garland, C. W., *J. Phys. Chem.,* **61,** 1506 (1957).

AUTHOR INDEX

Chapter, page (*reference*)

530 AUTHOR INDEX

SUBJECT INDEX